Roads and Traffic in Urban Areas

Produced by
The Institution of Highways and Transportation
with
The Department of Transport

ISBN 0 11 550818 X

STRUCTURE OF CONTENTS

Foreword

By Peter Bottomley MP, Parliamentary Under Secretary of State, Minister for Roads and Traffic.

Our towns and cities have grown up over the centuries around the means of communication of the time—rivers, Roman roads, turnpikes, canals, railways, seaports and airports. Urban areas have been shaped by the structure of industry and the pattern of trade and employment. These in turn depend on the available transport because industry and commerce rely on good access to markets.

Today over 90 per cent of passenger miles and 60 per cent of goods tonne miles go by road. Over half the adult population can drive. Motor transport has opened up new opportunities and with increasing affluence there has been a revolution in leisure activity. It has also brought problems of congestion and accidents. The shift of new enterprise, attractive housing, and shopping to the edges of our towns and cities has left behind social and environmental problems in the inner areas to which we give high priority.

We must also remember that a large proportion of all journeys are made on foot. Cycling plays an important part too, especially for the young. We have to provide means of access for people with disabilities. Proper priority must be given to essential services.

The road system must be managed so as to reduce transport costs, improve the environment and enhance safety. The art of traffic management and of road building is to get the right balance. This manual contains a wide range of information that will help to achieve that. It should prove of great value to all those involved in looking after the future of towns and cities and planning ahead for future needs.

I welcome the initiative shown by the Institution of Highways and Transportation in conceiving this manual and the co-operative efforts of the many people who have contributed to it.

Peter Bottomley

Introduction

By the President of the Institution of Highways and Transportation.

In 1965 and 1966 the Ministry of Transport published two documents entitled, 'Urban Traffic Engineering Techniques' and 'Roads in Urban Areas', respectively, which have for many years been used as standard reference works by traffic engineers and road designers in the United Kingdom. But times change and bring with them new attitudes and expectations of freedom of choice and movement. We are experiencing a growth in 'out of town' residential and commercial developments as more people are prepared to travel longer distances to work or to shop. Nevertheless, the focus of commerce and industry remains in our urban centres. A steady growth in car ownership has brought about a gradual drift away from public to private transport and the provision of adequate parking facilities and the control of traffic in city and town centres has become increasingly difficult. We have seen an increase in the size and weight of heavy goods vehicles on the roads and the general growth in traffic has increased vehicle/pedestrian conflict, emphasising the need for a fresh look at ways to improve the efficiency of our existing urban road systems and other transportation modes in terms of accessibility, environmental quality and safety.

Against this background the Institution of Highways and Transportation decided on an initiative to review the two existing manuals and produce a more comprehensive publication which would be of value to both newly qualified and experienced practitioners and would draw upon experiences of transport policies and practices from elsewhere in the world. Support for this project was offered by the Department of Transport and other major bodies.

It was clear from the outset that a project of this importance and magnitude required a high quality research capability and substantial professional and technical input. The initial finance for the project was provided by the Science and Engineering Research Council in the form of a research grant to the Transport Operations Research Group at the University of Newcastle Upon Tyne, led by Professor Peter Hills and Mr Tony Rhodes, in association with Professor Richard Allsop of University College London. Thanks go to Dr John Latchford, Chairman of the SERC Environment Committee, for his valuable assistance in this respect.

The Department of Transport have also played a major role and their cooperation and technical input was vital. Particular references have also been made to variations in legislation and standards adopted in Northern Ireland, Scotland and Wales, contributed by the appropriate Departments.

'Roads and Traffic in Urban Areas', is intended as a guide to good practice but it does not attempt to offer detailed solutions to every situation. The authors were also aware that the United Kingdom does not have a monopoly on the best ideas or all of the problems and the text provides many references to other sources of information which should be used when further detail is required.

Times will no doubt continue to change and different modes of transport may receive different emphases in the future bringing with them the need for new approaches and techniques. I have no doubt that a revision of this publication will be required in the years ahead. Nevertheless, I am sure that 'Roads and Traffic in Urban Areas' will provide good, sound advice to the problems of today and can perhaps act as a catalyst to generate solutions to tomorrow's problems.

No technical work like 'Roads and Traffic in Urban Areas' comes to fruition without a lot of hard work and commitment. The Chairman of the Working Party of the Transportation Board, who has seen this work through to completion with skill and dedication, was Mr T W Thompson, Chief Engineer, Leicestershire County Council, and I would like to record the Institution's appreciation for his efforts in carrying out this difficult task over the last 4 years. I would also like to thank Mr A J Lovell of the Department of Transport for the work he undertook as Technical Editor.

V S PAYNE
President

June 1987

Acknowledgements and main Contributors

The basic drafting of this manual was undertaken by a team of University researchers working on a project, under the auspices of the Institution of Highways and Transportation (IHT), financed by a grant from the Science and Engineering Research Council (SERC). The grant was awarded to the Transport Operations Research Group at the University of Newcastle Upon Tyne in association with the Transport Studies Group at University College London. The project ran for 30 months, from November 1983 to June 1986.

During this period, the Working Team consisted of:

Project Directors

Professor Peter Hills (University of Newcastle upon Tyne)
Mr Tony Rhodes (University of Newcastle upon Tyne)
Professor Richard Allsop (University College London)

Project Manager

Mr Alastair Dick (Consultant)

Project Team

Mr Stephen Sexton (Newcastle)
Miss Gladys Morton (UCL)
Mr Tony Wood (Newcastle)
Dr Stephen Gallivan (UCL)

Substantial contributions and comments were also made by a large number of people acting both as individuals and as representatives of their organisations. The list is too long to produce in full but included immediate colleagues, academic reseachers, the Department of Transport and its Transport and Road Research Laboratory, the Department of Environment, members of IHT and many Local Authorities, independent consultants and representative groups.

Special thanks are, however, due to:

Mr T W Thompson (Chief Engineer, Leicestershire County Council);

Mrs J Bridgeman, Mr T Rochester, Mr A J Lovell (Technical Editor) and other staff at the Department of Transport;

Mr M Callery (County Surveyor and Bridgemaster, Lancashire County Council);

Mr G S R Hunter (Consultant, Pell Frischmann and Partners);

and staff of the West Yorkshire Highways Engineering and Technical Services group (HETS).

Preface: A guide to the scope and use of the manual

Purpose and scope

The purpose of this manual is to set down the principles of current good practice for planning and developing highways and traffic schemes within the context of wider transportation planning issues. It deals with the various stages of scheme development from transportation policy considerations and integration with land use planning; to transport demand forecasting; to the assessment and evaluation of problems and potential solutions; and to the selection and design of measures for various purposes.

Parts 1 and 2 provide an informative background to responsibilities, legislation and policy issues, all of which are essential to the consideration of road and traffic schemes. However, although the policy context necessarily covers all land based transport modes, the consideration of solutions in Parts 3–5 deals primarily with road and traffic solutions since this is the main objective of the manual.

Currency of the advice given

The material included in this manual was assembled between 1984 and 1987 and every attempt has been made to reflect the latest position in terms of legislation, practice and research. Inevitably, the passage of time will see changes to legislation and the development and adoption of new techniques, but this is a gradual and sometimes slow process. To avoid confusion, the legislative position and references provided should be taken as current at April 1987.

Structure and content

This is arranged as follows:

Part 1 urban transportation planning issues, trends, statutory basis, the planning framework and the bodies involved;

Part 2 the context of alternative transportation policies, the need for data, the estimation of future travel demand, economic and environmental appraisal techniques and involvement of the public;

Part 3 the objectives of traffic management, the statutory basis and procedures involved and the use of many different techniques for particular purposes;

Part 4 the highway and traffic considerations arising from new developments of various kinds;

Part 5 the procedures and design considerations for the development of major highway schemes; and

Part 6 the variations in legislation, procedures and standards which are appropriate for Northern Ireland, Scotland and Wales.

Limitations

In view of its wide subject coverage this manual cannot provide the level of detailed advice required for design purposes for all of the subject it deals with or provides a reference to (e.g. street lighting, drainage systems, road maintenance etc.). This is recognised by the inclusion at the end of each chapter, of a broad range of references and sources from which further information can be sought.

Use of the advice given

Various chapters provide advice and information on the responsibilities of particular authorities, enabling legislation and procedures. Whilst every attempt has been made to ensure that these are accurate, they are not intended to be, or should be treated as being, legal advice and it is the responsibility of each body and individual to satisfy themselves as to the correct procedures and legislated powers for particular circumstances.

Department of Transport's policies and standards

The Department of Transport has cooperated fully in the production of this manual and its particularly relevant technical standards and advice notes are listed as references at the end of each chapter. The manual does not, however, purport to set out Government policy. Moreover, the use of the Department's standards is only mandatory for trunk roads and although the Department commends their use to other highway authorities in England it is for these authorities to use their own judgement on whether to follow the Department's recommendations at all times. The manual does not, therefore, confine itself solely to the Department's practices and sometimes describes alternatives or additional techniques or approaches. Where it is necessary to determine the Department's current policy or position on a particular subject, this must be obtained from current Government publications or directly from the Department itself.

Use of design standards

Transportation policies and objectives will vary in different urban areas reflecting both the various factors which affect transport needs and provisions and the inclinations of the decision makers. Thus the weight given to different factors in the design and assessment process will vary from time to time and place to place. In addition, the urban environment is continually changing and designers should be prepared to be flexible and seize opportunities where they occur. The design of highways in urban areas will therefore require care and judgement to strike an appropriate balance between costs, impact on the environment and land availability, but road safety will always be a major consideration.

Application in Northern Ireland, Scotland and Wales

The responsibilities, procedures and legislation referred to in this manual are mainly those appropriate to English practice and certain differences exist in other parts of the United Kingdom. In order to extend the application of the information given, Part 6 provides an explanation of these differences for Northern Ireland, Wales and Scotland, referenced so that they can be easily related back to the appropriate annotation in the main text.

Sources of further information

The publications referred to in the text of the manual are listed with bibliographic details at the end of each chapter. A list of sources of further information is also given. Many of the publications have been produced by the Department of Transport and unpriced **Departmental publications** are available from the sponsoring division. Initial enquiries can be directed to:

DoE/DTp Library Enquiries
Rm C3/01
DoE/DTp Headquarters
2 Marsham Street
London SW1P 3EB
Tel: 01–212 4847

Priced DTp publications can be obtained from:

DoE/DTp Publication Sales Unit
Building One
Victoria Road
South Ruislip
Middlesex HA4 0NZ
Tel: 01–845 1200 Ext 200

Transport and Road Research Laboratory publications are available from:

Publication Division
Transport and Road Research Laboratory
Old Wokingham Road
Crowthorne
Berks RG11 6AU
Tel: 0344–773131

HMSO publications (including published legislation) can be obtained from:

HMSO Books
Mail Order
POB 276
London SW8 5DT
Tel: 01–622 3316

or from HMSO bookshops and approved agents.

Orders for **IHT publications** should be addressed to:

Institution of Highways and Transportation
3 Lygon Place
London SW1W 0JS
Tel: 01-730 5245

Further information or publications for **Northern Ireland** may be obtained from:

Department of the Environment for Northern Ireland
Roads Service Headquarters
Commonwealth House
35 Castle Street
Belfast BT1 1GU
Tel: Belfast 221212

Further information and unpriced memoranda for **Scotland** may be obtained from:

The Chief Road Engineer
Scottish Development Department
New St Andrew's House
Edinburgh EH1 3SZ
Tel: 031-244 4286 (SH series) or 031-244 4367 (SB series)

Requests for copies of **priced Scottish memoranda** may be obtained from:

The Scottish Office Library
Official Publications Section (Sales)
Room 2/65
New St Andrew's House
Edinburgh EH1 3SZ
Tel: 031-244 4806

Welsh Office Circulars and further information may be obtained from:

Welsh Office
Highways Directorate
Phase 1
Government Buildings
Ty Glas Road
Llanishen
Cardiff CF4 5PL
Tel: 0222-753271

Detailed list of contents

PART 2   TRANSPORTATION PLANNING, POLICY DEVELOPMENT AND SCHEME APPRAISAL

PART 3 TRAFFIC MANAGEMENT OBJECTIVES, TECHNIQUES AND PROCEDURES

PART 4   HIGHWAY AND TRAFFIC CONSIDERATIONS FOR NEW DEVELOPMENT

PART 5   THE DEVELOPMENT AND DESIGN OF MAJOR HIGHWAYS SCHEMES

PART 6 APPLICATION IN NORTHERN IRELAND, SCOTLAND AND WALES

List of Figures, Tables and Plates

PART 1 URBAN TRANSPORTATION ISSUES, RESPONSIBILITIES AND PRINCIPLES

1   Urban Traffic Conditions in Britain

The 'Buchanan Report', entitled 'Traffic in Towns' (Ref. 1), published by the Ministry of Transport in 1963, achieved wide acceptance and continues to provide the basis for many traffic management policies in use in the 1980s.

The report demonstrated that whilst there are absolute limits to the amount of traffic that can be accepted in towns, if urban areas are to function efficiently and provide an acceptable living and working environment, then land use, transport, highway and traffic developments have to be planned and managed together as part of the same process. This philosophy is as true today as it was then, especially as car ownership continues to rise.

1.1 Traffic Growth

During the period since the 'Traffic in Towns' report appeared, the pattern of growth in car ownership which it forecast has indeed materialised, though not always in a smoothly incremental way, despite successive rises in oil prices in 1974 and 1979. Further growth in car ownership is still being predicted for future decades (see Figure 2.7) bringing with it the expectation of, and potential for, increased mobility for those who own or have access to privately owned vehicles and increased traffic in every town and city.

The effects of steadily increasing demand for unrestricted use of private vehicles and increasing volumes of heavy commercial traffic are apparent for all to see (see Plate 1.1) and many urban areas of Britain, in common with other built-up areas around the world, have to cope with large volumes of traffic seeking to use local road systems which in many cases owe their origins to street patterns laid down long before the motor vehicle was thought of.

1.2 Effects on Public Transport

Other potential problems also exist. Car ownership often brings with it an understandable reluctance to make use of public transport facilities which may be perceived to be less convenient or comfortable. This trend has led to difficulties in maintaining adequate levels of public transport services for those in the community without the option of private transport and a number of alternative transport policies have been tried to reverse or at least halt this trend.

Plate 1.1 Typical urban traffic congestion in the 1970s

Source: British Road Federation

1.3 Environmental Considerations

Increased use of motor vehicles and particularly the growth in heavy commercial traffic, has put great pressure on the environmental fabric of our cities and towns; the impacts of congestion, noise and air pollution being familiar to all who live in, work in, or visit urban areas (see Plate 1.2).

Yet progress has been made. Major new roads have been constructed not only to link major urban centres but also to by-pass smaller built up areas. Within cities too, major new routes have provided the road capacity to allow traffic management measures to protect environmentally sensitive areas from the worst, or at least some, of the adverse effects of traffic.

The concept of an environmental area was defined in the Buchanan Report which advocated that control of access from a carefully planned hierarchy of roads could limit overall traffic levels within an environmental area to that consistent with predefined standards of safety and amenity.

Plate 1.2 The impact of goods vehicles in towns

Source: Leicestershire County Council

The policy of diverting through traffic on to a defined network of roads more suited to the role of traffic arteries is now widely accepted and pursued. In some areas existing roads may have provided a suitable basis for this approach; elsewhere, new roads have been required to provide the traffic carrying capacity necessary to allow the transport demands of commerce and individuals to be met whilst enabling protective measures to be implemented in sensitive areas.

- improve access for industry and commerce;

- protect and enhance the safety of all road users;

- improve conditions for pedestrians, cyclists, public transport and disabled people;

- improve the conditions and appearance of roads, particularly those in or near residential areas which are carrying heavier traffic than that for which they were designed or are suitable.

1.4 Criteria for New Schemes

There is still much to be done and many areas continue to suffer from intolerable burdens from traffic. This situation will ensure that many new road and traffic schemes will be necessary in the foreseeable future to deal effectively with traffic-related problems. Of particular importance will be the need to:

- ease congestion and reduce delays, especially where this would enable public transport to operate more effectively;

- protect or improve the environment (eg. by taking heavy through traffic out of residential and shopping areas);

1.5 Priority for Public Transport

The main criteria for road and traffic schemes may be supported by others reflecting the particular policy inclinations of the authorities responsible for highway and traffic matters. Typical of such policies are those which give priority to certain classes of vehicle and perhaps foremost amongst these are the priorities given to public transport vehicles in order to maintain or improve levels of service by improving the efficiency and effectiveness of the services provided and hence their attractiveness to the travelling public. The passenger carrying capability of buses is effectively demonstrated in Plate 1.3.

These vehicles
are carrying...

69 people
who could all...

be on this
one bus ➡

⊖

Plate 1.3 An illustration of the passenger carrying capacity of
public transport

Source: London Regional Transport

1.6 Pedestrians, Cyclists and the Disabled

Priority or special treatment is also frequently provided
for the more vulnerable road users like pedestrians,
cyclists and disabled people. Schemes which provide
varying degrees of exclusivity and assistance for these
groups have been implemented in many areas, each
responding to the particular environmental, safety and
economic factors appropriate to local conditions.

1.7 Road Safety

The safety of all road users is vital to the consideration
of all urban road or traffic matters. Anything that is
perceived to have an adverse effect on safety has
become, and will remain, an issue of public concern.
As a consequence much attention is given to the
treatment of accident sites and to public awareness of
road safety matters. This must continue and be
complemented by a high standard of design for any

new measures to ensure that they do not produce new
hazards which might have been avoided with more care
at the design stage.

1.8 A Balanced Approach

A thoughtful and balanced approach towards urban
transportation planning and design can make vast
improvements to safety and amenity whilst also
contributing to the more efficient passage of people
and their goods. A combination of traffic management
techniques and new urban roads (where these are
appropriate) can, when designed to appropriate
standards and provisions, reduce the effects of noise,
vibration, pollution and visual intrusion on the areas
through which they pass. These different objectives
need to be carefully considered to achieve the desired
balance and must take account of the level of resources
available to achieve them.

In every situation professional practitioners and
decision makers alike will be faced with competing
demands from different sections of the community and
difficult choices will have to be made. The various
chapters in this manual give a guide to current British
practice and what can be achieved within the
framework of social, economic and legal constraints
using techniques which have been developed over many
years and are now widely accepted.

What is clear is that no one policy or technique should
be slavishly applied to every situation. All problems
need careful individual attention and a range of
alternative solutions should be examined before
deciding upon a particular course of action which might
involve a variety of complementary measures.

1.9 References

*Text
References*

1. Ministry of Transport—'*Traffic in Towns—
   A study of the long term problems of traffic
   in urban areas*' (Buchanan Report), Reports
   of the Steering Group and Working Group
   appointed by the Minister of Transport,
   HMSO (1963).   (1.1)

1.10 Further Information

2. DTp—Cmnd. 9059 '*Policy for Roads in England*',
   HMSO (1983). [Sco.1]

2 Road Traffic Trends in Urban Areas

2.1 Definition of an Urban Area

Local Authority Boundaries

The definition of what constitutes an urban area has traditionally been related to local government boundaries. This is not entirely satisfactory since these boundaries may often extend well beyond built-up areas and are amended at irregular intervals to take account of changes in development and for other reasons. In major conurbations, individual administrative authorities may be only a part of a larger homogenous urban area which may contain many urban authorities. These authorities share, to a greater or lesser extent, a need to develop strategic policies jointly so that the policies of each authority avoid major conflict with those of the others.

Built-up Areas

A more useful definition of an urban area has been developed by the Office of Population Censuses and Surveys (OPCS). Under this definition an urban area is an area of land that is irreversibly urban in character and has a minimum population of approximately 1000 persons. Urban land should extend for 20 hectares or more (linking together areas less than 50 metres apart), and may comprise permanent buildings, transportation corridors with built-up sites (or features such as railway yards, motorway service areas, or car parks), mineral workings and quarries and any open space completely surrounded by built-up sites. Urban areas less than 200 metres apart are considered to form a continuous urban area.

Using this definition, Figure 2.1 shows the proportion of the urban population living in different sizes of urban area in Britain. It is notable that almost 90% of the population live in urban areas, whilst 52% live in the sixty largest urban areas having individual populations of more than 100,000. Nearly 33% of the population live in urban areas with populations greater than 500,000 [Sco. 2].

Self-Contained Functional Regions

Other definitions of urban areas have been based on functional regions. A functional region is an area which can be considered to be self contained for the purpose of commuting, work, shopping, education and recreation. This concept recognises that built-up areas which are physically separate may be an integral part of a larger urban area if considered in terms of the functions which they fulfill together.

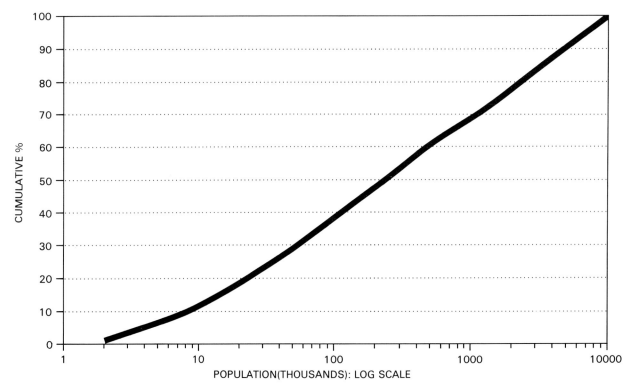

Figure 2.1 Cumulative proportion of urban population living in different sizes of urban area

Source: OPCS (1981)

Speed Limits

The Department of Transport uses speed limits as a basis for distinguishing between 'built-up' and 'non-built-up' roads for their annual publications of transport and accident statistics.

Built-up roads are those with a speed limit not greater than 40 mph. The term 'built-up' when used in this sense includes a number of roads which are outside what might normally be considered to be urban areas. Conversely, some roads in urban areas have speed limits greater than 40 mph [Sco.3]. A more satisfactory definition for an urban road might be obtained by relating it to the functions it is expected to serve (see also Chapter 5 which explains a roads hierarchy).

2.2 Trends in Urbanisation

Over any period of time changes occur in the distribution of population which create differing pressures for development and therefore have notable consequences for the design of roads and traffic in urban areas. As an example of this, Figure 2.2 shows changes in population in local labour market areas in Great Britain (see Ref. 1), between 1971 and 1981 and Table 2.1 indicates the places showing the most extreme rates of change during this period (again using local labour market areas).

In the census period from 1971 to 1981, two-thirds of the 225 functional regions identified experienced some decentralisation. The remaining one-third, experiencing the reverse effect of centralisation, were mainly new towns or those towns affected by overspill from the major cities. Figure 2.3 confirms this trend by showing the population change by category of district in Britain over the same period.

Generally then, there is a noticeable drift away from the centres of large urban areas to the smaller towns and villages in the outer suburbs. This trend has generated a demand for housing development in the suburbs, redevelopment in city centres (often concentrating on commercial development because of high land values) and a greater demand for commuter travel from home to place of work.

2.3 Car Ownership and Travel to Work

A considerable variation exists in the average number of cars per household owned in areas of different population size in England and Wales; ownership rates in rural areas being almost twice those of large cities. Car ownership levels tend to reflect the importance of cars for journeys to work. Figures 2.4 and 2.5 show how this diminishes for larger urban areas, while conversely, public transport becomes more important, especially in the nine largest conurbations (over 0.5 million population).

Car ownership levels also vary with time and will continue to grow in the future to reflect increasing levels of affluence and the demands for travel that it brings. Figure 2.6 shows the steady growth of car ownership patterns in Great Britain between 1960 and 1985 and Figure 2.7 provides the Department of Transport's high and low option forecasts up to 2015 (Ref. 2).

By way of comparison it is interesting to examine Figure 2.8 which demonstrates that car ownership levels in the United Kingdom in 1980 were only about half those of the United States of America and were also well below ownership levels in many other European countries such as France, Switzerland and Germany. This illustration serves to demonstrate the potential that still exists for car ownership to increase in Britain even though present levels may already appear quite high [Sco.4].

2.4 Public Transport

The trend in public transport patronage in the United Kingdom between 1974 and 1984 has, by way of contrast to car ownership, declined markedly as illustrated in Figure 2.9; the total number of passengers per annum having fallen by 25% until 1982, since when it has shown a slight increase. There is, however, a wide variation in this trend and as an example, Tyne and Wear Passenger Transport Executive recorded an increase of 10% in passengers per annum during the same period (Ref. 3). Other examples of changes in patronage against the trend have also been recorded in different areas of the UK and the more consistent levels of patronage recorded in recent years may reflect the positive efforts made by many authorities to improve services and hold down fare levels [Sco.5].

It should also be noted that the trend in the United Kingdom differs from many other European countries where only Greece has shown a similar decline and countries such as Italy, Denmark, Spain, Portugal, Belgium and Germany have all shown a marked increase. However, comparisons between different countries should be treated with care as there are many social, economic, demographic and geographical functions which affect public transport patronage to the extent that the situation which exists in any individual country may be unique to that country and not necessarily transportable elsewhere.

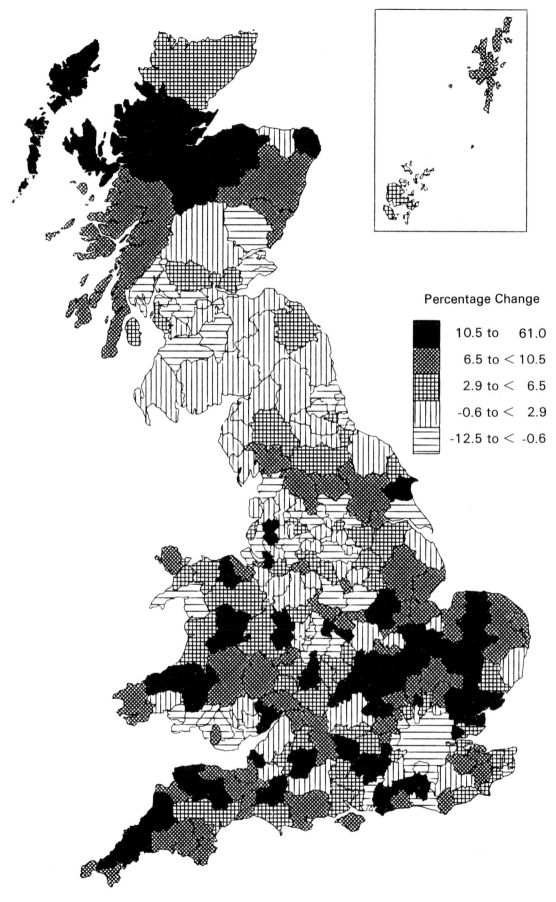

Figure 2.2 Population change by local labour market area—Great Britain (1971–1981)

Source: Champion et al 'A new definition of cities' Town and Country Planning (November 1983)

A. IN PERCENTAGE TERMS

Fifteen Fastest Growing	(% increase)	Fifteen Fastest Declining	(% decrease)
Milton Keynes	60.8	Liverpool	−12.5
Redditch	49.9	Glasgow	−12.1
Tamworth	37.4	Manchester	−11.1
Dingwell & Invergordon	34.0	South Shields	−9.4
Thetford	30.4	Sunderland	−8.8
Bracknell	28.1	London	−8.6
Basingstoke	25.7	Greenock	−7.2
Huntingdon	24.7	Peterlee	−6.5
Widnes & Runcorn	23.6	West Bromwich	−5.4
Peterborough	23.4	Consett	−5.1
Telford	22.5	Dundee	−4.6
Horsham	19.2	Hartlepool	−4.6
Newmarket & Ely	18.0	Birmingham	−4.2
Northampton	18.0	Bradford	−4.1
Banbury	18.0	Birkenhead & Wallasey	−4.0

B. IN ABSOLUTE TERMS

Fifteen Fastest Growing	(increase)	Fifteen Fastest Declining	(decrease)
Milton Keynes	+60,995	London	−740,781
Peterborough	+37,752	Glasgow	−166,193
Aldershot & Farnborough	+37,487	Manchester	−145,375
Northampton	+36,910	Liverpool	−134,371
Bournemouth & Poole	+36,461	Birmingham	−63,799
Norwich	+34,377	Leeds	−27,374
Chelmsford	+31,792	Sunderland	−26,532
Luton & Dunstable	+30,795	Sheffield	−18,047
Telford	+30,106	South Shields	−16,694
Wigan	+28,658	Coventry	−16,509
Aberdeen	+27,687	Bradford	−15,193
Redditch	+27,361	Birkenhead & Wallasey	−14,760
Widnes	+26,615	Dundee	−11,850
Colchester	+25,772	Brighton	−10,739
Tamworth	+25,794	Greenock	−9,689

Table 2.1 Local labour market areas recording the most extreme rates of population change in Great Britain between 1971 and 1981

N.B. These areas differ from the OPCS areas used by
government departments (see para 2.1 & 2.2)

Source: Champion et al 'A new definition of cities' Town and Country Planning (November 1983)

10

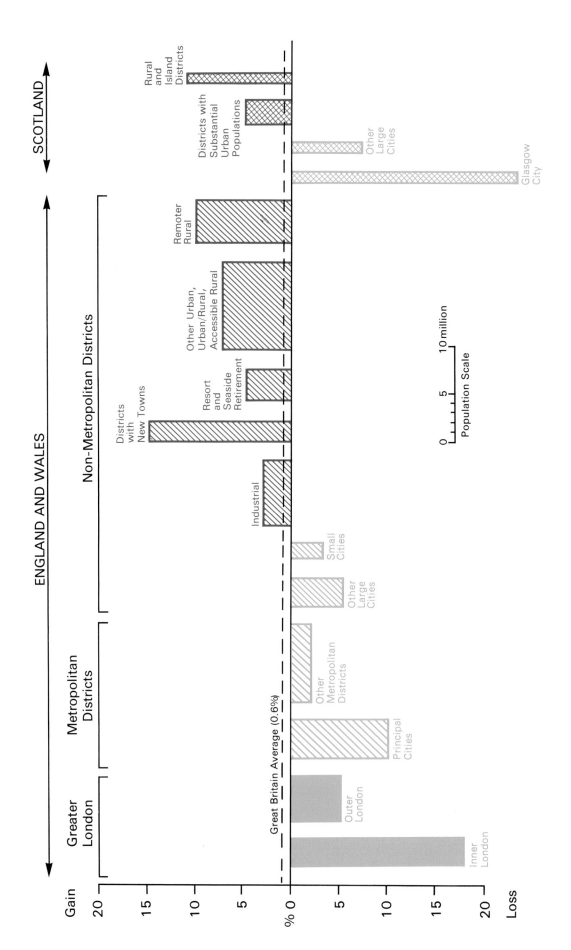

Figure 2.3 Percentage population change by category of district—Great Britain (1971–1981)

Source: OPCS (1981)

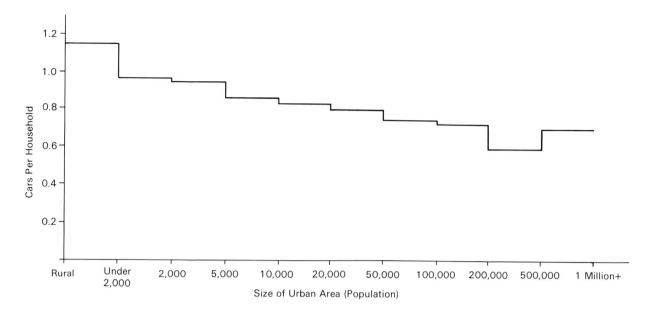

Figure 2.4 Relationship between car ownership and size of urban area—England and Wales (1981)

Source: OPCS (1981)

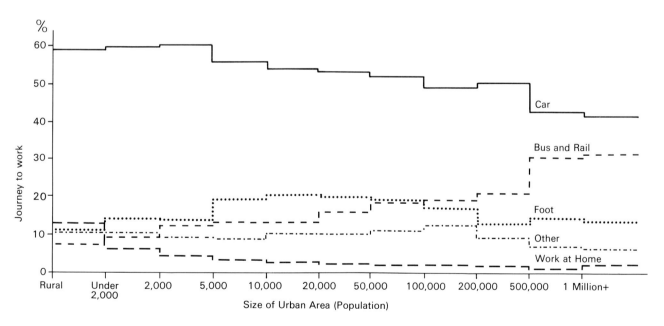

Figure 2.5 Mode of transport used for journey to work in urban areas of different sizes—England and Wales (1981)

Source: OPCS (1981)

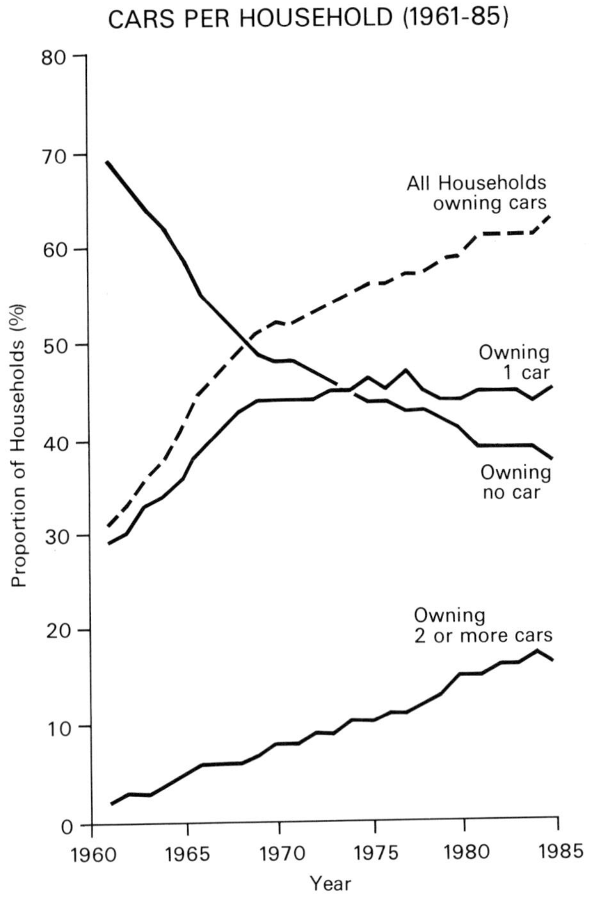

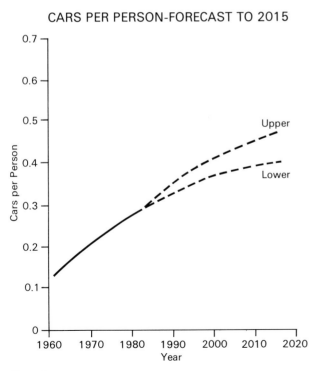

CARS PER HOUSEHOLD (1961-85)

Figure 2.6 Pattern of car ownership in Great Britain (1961–1985)

Source: Transport Statistics Great Britain (published annually), HMSO

CARS PER PERSON-FORECAST TO 2015

Figure 2.7 Forecast of car ownership in Great Britain to 2015

Source: National Road Traffic Forecasts (Great Britain—1984), HMSO

2.5 Freight Transport

The proportion of freight transport carried by road has also shown an inexorable rise to the extent that 96% of the expenditure on freight transport in 1983 was on goods moved by road. This is not really surprising since most freight movements have to commence or finish their journeys by road and the use of containers together with improvements in lorry construction and carrying capacity, have increased their attraction. There have also been increases in the permitted size and weight of goods vehicles. The amount of lorry traffic produces particular problems in urban areas where the adverse aspects of their size, noise and exhaust emissions are most noticeable [Sco.6].

2.6 Cyclists and Pedestrians

No suitable statistics are available to portray trends in behaviour below national level although situations vary substantially from area to area and district to district. Topography, land-use characteristics and other local factors all affect the extent to which people are inclined to walk or cycle rather than use public or privately owned motorised transport. Although nationally there has been a decline in cycling there has undoubtedly been a noticeable rise in its popularity in certain areas both as a means of basic transport and as a source of recreation. Both pedestrians and cyclists are, however, at particular risk in urban traffic conditions where they compete, often unequally, with motor vehicles for the use of road space.

2.7 Road Safety

In 1985, over 75% of all road accidents in Britain occurred on built-up roads (Ref. 4).

Tables 2.2, 2.3 and 2.4 together with Figures 2.10, 2.11 and 2.12 provide some useful background information from which it can be seen that:

- a greater proportion of accidents occur in urban areas than would be expected based upon road length or amount of traffic;

- within urban areas it is apparent that more accidents occur in the main shopping streets than in residential areas;

- motorways are, in terms of accident rate, much the safest type of road;

- more than two thirds of all accidents on built-up roads occur at junctions;

- 95 per cent of all pedestrian casualties occur on built-up roads; and

- 89 per cent of all cyclist casualties occur on built-up roads.

For more detailed information see list of references and also Chapter 10.4 [Sco.7].

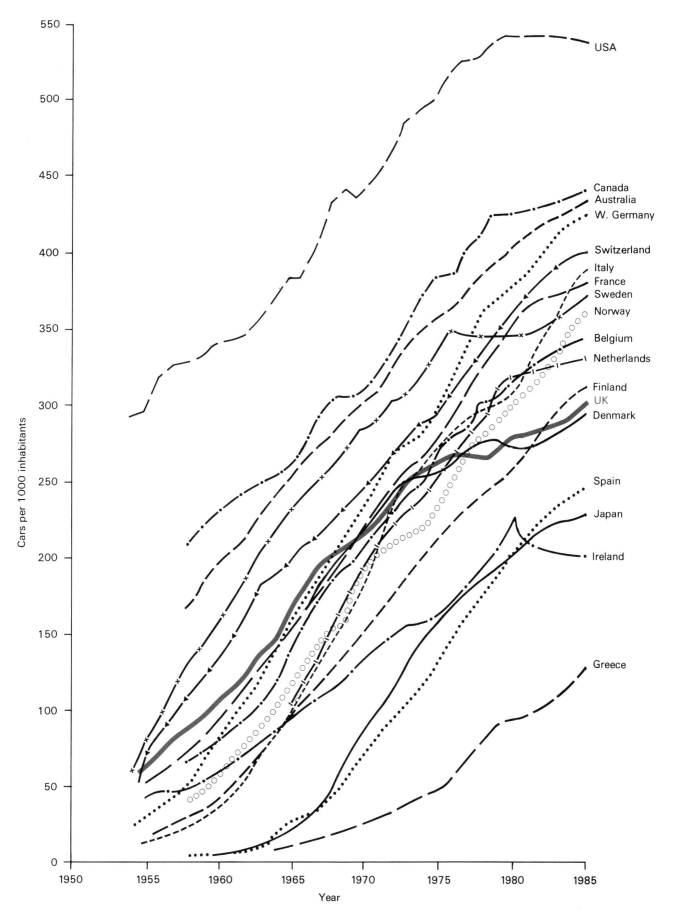

Figure 2.8 Growth in car ownership in a number of countries

Source: International Road Federation Statistics

13

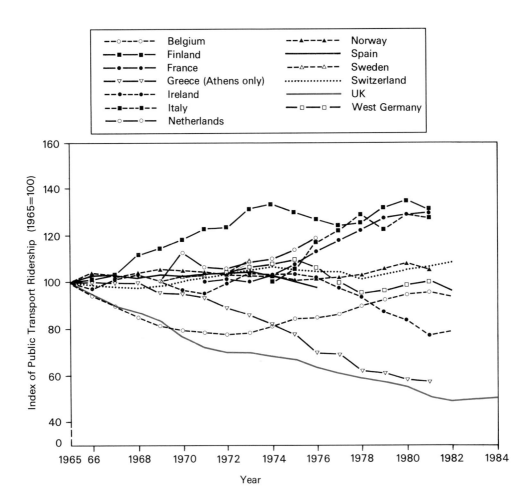

Legend:

--o--o--	Belgium	--▲--▲--	Norway
--■--■--	Finland	————	Spain
--•--•--	France	--△--△--	Sweden
--▽--▽--	Greece (Athens only)	··········	Switzerland
--•--•--	Ireland	————	UK
--■--■--	Italy	--□--□--	West Germany
--o--o--	Netherlands		

Figure 2.9 Trends in public transport ridership in a number of European countries (1965–1982)

Source: Based on 'Changing Patterns of Urban Travel' Transport Reviews Vol 6 No 2 (1986)

Road class (built-up roads)	Accident rate (per 100 million vehicle kms)	Proportion of all accidents (%)				Proportion (%)	
		Fatal	Serious	Slight	All severities	Road length	Total traffic
A Roads	129	28.8%	31.8%	36.1%	34.9%	N/A	23.6%
B Roads	144	6.9%	9.3%	9.7%	9.5%	N/A	58.0%
Other Roads	172	18.3%	29.6%	33.2%	32.1%	N/A	15.8%
All Built-up Roads	not available	54.0%	70.6%	79.0%	76.5%	41.0%	45.2%
Motorways	12	4.0%	1.6%	1.9%	1.9%	0.8%	13.4%
All Roads	86	100.0%	100.0%	100.0%	100.0%	100.0%	100.0%

Table 2.2 Accident rates by road class in Great Britain (1985)

Source: DTp Road Accidents Great Britain (1985)

	Proportion at junction	Proportion of junction accidents (%)							
		Round-about	T or staggered	Y junction	Cross-roads	Multiple junction	Private drive or entrance	Other junction	All junctions
Built-up Roads									
Fatal	56.8%	2.9%	63.6%	2.9%	21.6%	2.9%	2.8%	3.4%	100.0%
Serious	63.5%	5.2%	60.8%	2.6%	20.3%	2.1%	6.1%	3.1%	100.0%
Slight	69.4%	7.7%	56.8%	2.4%	21.2%	2.2%	6.4%	3.4%	100.0%
All Severities	67.9%	7.1%	57.7%	2.5%	21.0%	2.1%	6.2%	3.3%	100.0%
Non built-up roads									
Fatal	25.9%	3.9%	43.7%	6.5%	17.2%	1.1%	14.4%	13.2%	100.0%
Serious	31.8%	8.3%	45.6%	5.8%	15.7%	1.1%	14.9%	8.7%	100.0%
Slight	36.2%	15.7%	42.0%	4.9%	13.6%	1.1%	13.5%	9.2%	100.0%
All Severities	34.5%	13.3%	43.1%	5.2%	14.3%	1.1%	14.1%	9.2%	100.0%

Table 2.3 Accidents at junctions in Great Britain (1985)

Source: DTp Road Accidents Great Britain (1985)

Type of road user	Fatal	Serious	All severities
Pedestrian: Child	80.3%	95.6%	97.1%
Adult	80.6%	92.1%	93.9%
All ages	80.6%	93.3%	95.2%
Pedal Cyclist: Child	60.6%	85.1%	91.2%
Adult	57.3%	80.4%	88.1%
All ages	58.0%	82.1%	89.2%
Mopeds	60.0%	78.2%	83.6%
Motor scooters (riders & passengers)	57.1%	78.8%	80.8%
Motor cyclists (riders & passengers)	52.7%	70.2%	77.0%
Car occupants	28.6%	43.4%	57.2%
Bus & Coach occupants	59.4%	78.3%	87.5%
LGV occupants	27.4%	42.5%	55.3%
HGV occupants	14.9%	26.6%	29.9%
All casualties	52.1%	66.0%	71.7%

Table 2.4 Proportion of all casualties on built-up roads by road user type—Great Britain (1985)

Source: DTp Road Accidents Great Britain (1985)

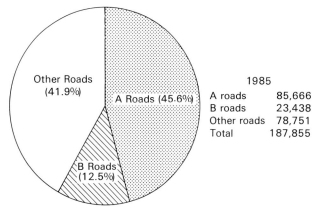

Figure 2.11 Accidents on built-up roads by class of road in Great Britain (1985)

Source: DTp Transport Statistics

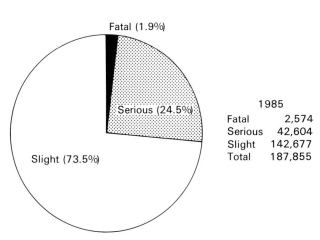

Figure 2.10 Severity of accidents on built-up roads in Great Britain (1985)

Source: DTp Transport Statistics

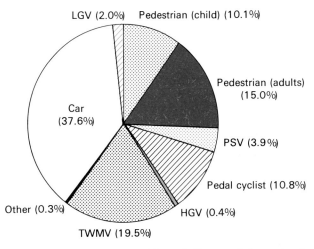

Figure 2.12 Road accident casualties on built-up roads by mode of transport in Great Britain (1985)

Source: DTp Annual Statistics (1986)

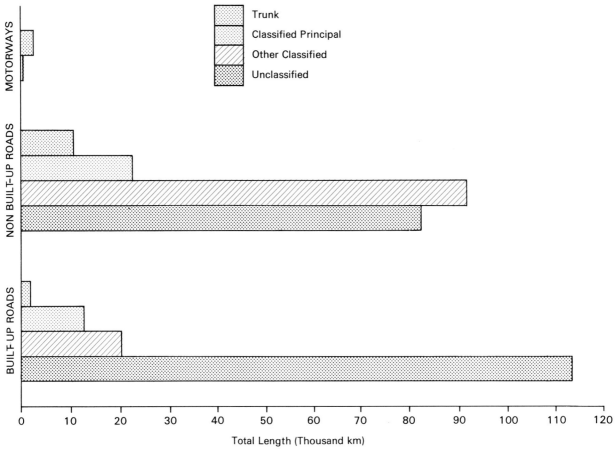

Figure 2.13 Length of surfaced road—Great Britain (1986)

Source: DTp Transport Statistics

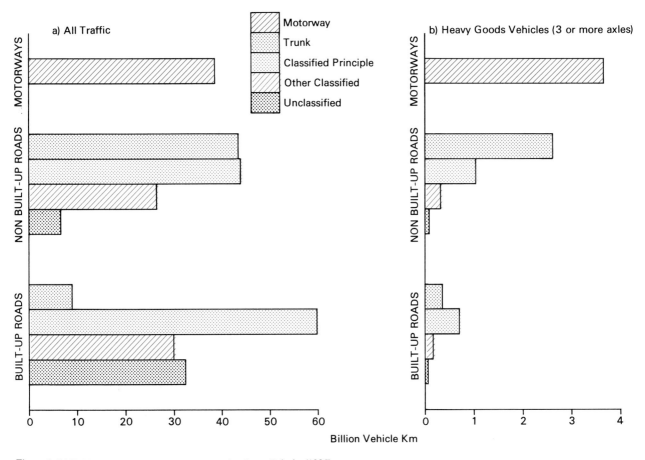

Figure 2.14 Vehicle movements by class of road—Great Britain (1985)

Source: DTp Annual Statistics (1986)

2.8 Road Traffic Trends

The total lengths of road in Britain by class for built-up and non built-up roads, are shown in Figure 2.13 (see also Chapter 5 for Statutory Definitions). The volume of traffic occuring on different classes of road is given in Figure 2.14. Trunk and Principal Roads (ie. those that form the national network and act as primary distributors) constitute approximately 10 per cent of the total length of built-up roads yet carry more than half of the total traffic and over 80 per cent of the very heavy goods vehicles (those with three axles or more) within built-up areas. However, unclassified roads (which contribute over three quarters of the total length of built-up roads) carry only a quarter of the total traffic and less than 10 per cent of heavy goods vehicle traffic.

The trend in the amount of road traffic in Britain is shown in Figure 2.15, which demonstrates the intermittent nature of the increases that have occurred during the last twenty years. The figure also indicates the Department of Transport's forecasts for traffic growth (high and low) made in 1984 demonstrating the considerable uncertainty which exists by the range of the lowest and highest forecasts. Forecasts of heavy goods vehicle traffic exhibit a similar variation. These forecasts are based on relatively modest annual growths for per capita real income.

Figure 2.16 shows the changes in the index of the length of different classes of road since 1973. Although some of these changes result from the re-classification of existing roads, (hence the reduction in the length of built-up trunk road), most will be due to new construction. It is apparent that unclassified roads account for the most significant proportion of new road construction, especially built-up roads [Sco.8].

2.9 References

Text References

1. Champion, A et al—'*A new Definition of Cities*', Town & Country Planning, November (1983).   (2.2)

2. DTp—'*National Road Traffic Forecasts (Great Britain): December 1984*', DTp/HMSO (1985). [Sco.9]   (2.3)

3. Tyne and Wear PTE et al—'*Tyne and Wear Study: Metro Monitoring and Development Study Report*', Tyne & Wear PTE (1986).   (2.4)

4. DTp—'*Road Accident Statistics Great Britain 1985*', HMSO (1986). [Sco.7]   (2.7)

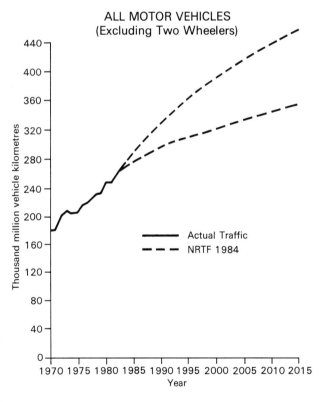

HEAVY GOODS VEHICLES

The forecasts give a range of figures for high and low growth rates.

ALL MOTOR VEHICLES
(Excluding Two Wheelers)

Figure 2.15 Actual and forecast growth in road traffic—Great Britain (1970-2015)

Source: DTp National Road Traffic Forecasts Great Britain 1984

17

Motorway

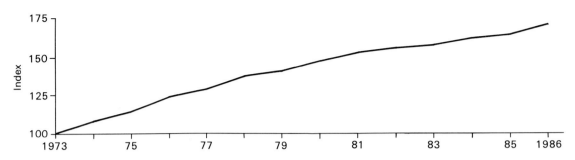

Built-Up

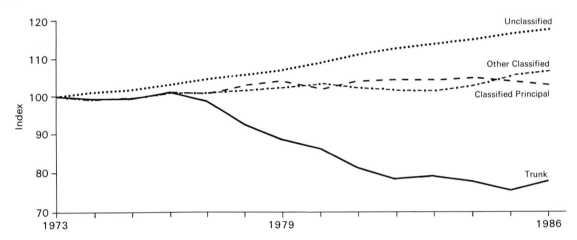

Non Built-Up

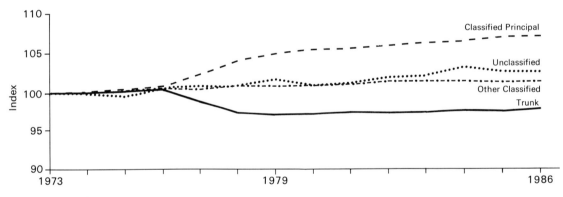

Figure 2.16 Indices of changes in length of surfaced road—Great Britain (1973–1986) (1973 = 100)

Source: DTp Annual Statistics (1986)

2.10 Further Information

5. DTp—'*Transport Statistics Great Britain
   1975–1985*', HMSO (1986).

6. DTp—'*Annual Transport Statistics—Great Britain*',
   HMSO. [Sco.10]

7. OPCS—*National Census 1981*, HMSO. [Sco.11]

3 The Statutory Basis for Road Planning

3.1 The Legislative Background

The planning and management of highways and traffic in Britain is determined by or under Acts of Parliament which confer powers and duties on central and local government. These Acts provide the statutory framework for Secretaries of State and local authorities to promote and control the use of land and to build, maintain and regulate traffic on the public highway (see Chapter 4 for details).

Under the Acts secondary legislation is issued from time to time relating to specific matters. In addition, central government issues guidance in the form of Circulars, Advice Notes and Design Standards.

The legislation which controls and/or affects planning, highways and traffic matters is subject to a continuous process of scrutiny and, when appropriate, change. Changes may be required either to the primary legislation itself or to the secondary legislation (eg. Statutory Instruments). Thus it can be seen that at any point in time, it is only possible to provide a view of current legislation and procedures [NI.1].

3.2 Current Legislation

Whilst there are many Acts of Parliament that have some bearing on highways and traffic matters the following are of major importance, and a brief explanation of their purpose is included:

The Local Government Act 1972 (as amended) and *the Local Government Act 1985,* [NI.2, Sco.12] established local authorities and the legal and administrative framework within which they must work and also nominated the authorities to be responsibile for different functions. The 1985 Act provides for the preparation of Unitary Development Plans by District planning authorities in Metropolitan Areas (see also 3.3 below) [Sco.13].

The Town and Country Planning Act 1971 (as amended), [NI.3, NI.4, Sco.14] provides the basis for land use planning, the preparation of development plans and the system of development control whereby, with certain exceptions, no development of land should take place without the prior consent of the local authority.

The Highways Act 1980, [NI.5, NI.6, Sco.15] provides, inter alia, for highway authorities to construct, maintain and improve highways, for the stopping-up of highways, interference with them, the making up of private streets and the acquisition of land.

The Road Traffic Regulation Act 1984, [NI.7] provides for the regulation and control of the speed, movement and parking of vehicles on the highway.

The Road Traffic Act 1972, [NI.7] deals with driving offences, the licensing of vehicles and drivers and the construction and use of vehicles.

The Transport Act 1985, [NI.2] established a competitive market situation for the provision of local bus services and provided for the re-organisation and privatisation of the National Bus Company. It also established a new system of registration in place of road service licensing (outside London), see also Chapter 26.1.

Lists of these and other relevant but generally subordinate Acts and Regulations are provided in Table 3.1 [Sco.16]. This table serves only as an introductory guide. Other statutes are referred to at the appropriate points in the text and in references throughout the document, but it will always remain the responsibility of authorities to make sure that they are acting within their legislated powers. Ultimately, decisions on these matters rest with the courts but lawyers can provide advice and guidance on interpretation of particular statutes.

3.3 The Statutory Planning Framework

The statutory planning framework for the planning and management of the highways and traffic in Britain is provided by Structure Plans, Local Plans and Unitary Development Plans [NI.8, Sco.13].

Structure and Local Plans were introduced by the Town and the Country Planning Act 1968 (now consolidated in Part II of the Town and Country Planning Act 1971) to replace the old development plans established intially by the Town and Country Planning Act 1947 and continued by the Town and Country Planning Act 1962 [Sco.17].

Following the abolition of the Greater London Council and the Metropolitan County Councils by the Local Government Act 1985 a system of Unitary Development Plans was introduced for these areas. Structure and Local Plans continue in force there until replaced by Unitary Development Plans [Sco.18].

Each of the systems of development plans is described briefly below together with their relationship to the non-statutory system of Transport Policies and Pro-grammes. Advice on the procedures for, and content

ACTS OF PARLIAMENT	MOST IMPORTANT ASPECTS IN RELATION TO ROADS AND TRAFFIC IN URBAN AREAS
COMPULSORY PURCHASE ACT 1965	Provides the acquisition code applied by CPO made under the Highways Act 1980 for acquiring land for highway purposes.
ACQUISITION OF LAND ACT 1981	Provides the procedures for making CPO under the Highways Act 1980 for acquiring land for highway purposes.
TOWN AND COUNTRY PLANNING ACT 1971 (as amended)	Provides the basis for land use planning, the preparation of development plans and the system of development control whereby, with certain exceptions, no development of land should take place without the prior consent of the local authority.
ROAD TRAFFIC ACT 1972	Provides for the licensing of vehicles and drivers, the construction and use of vehicles and penalties for driving offences.
LOCAL GOVERNMENT ACTS 1972 AND LOCAL GOVERNMENT ACT 1985	Established local authorities and the legal and administrative framework within which they must work and also nominated the authorities to be responsible for different functions. The 1985 Act also provided for the preparation of Unitary Plans by District Planning Authorities, and London Boroughs.
LAND COMPENSATION ACT 1973	Provides for the compensation of owner-occupiers of land adversely affected by public works including new or alterations to an existing highway. Also provides for the making of regulations (currently the Noise Insulation Regulations 1975) for the soundproofing of buildings affected by such works.
ROAD TRAFFIC ACT 1974	Imposes a duty on local authorities to promote road safety, to carry out investigations into road accidents and to take remedial measures.
INNER URBAN AREAS ACT 1978	Gives additional powers and responsibilities (and provides for additional finance) to those authorities with problems of urban decay in inner cities.
LOCAL GOVERNMENT PLANNING AND LAND ACT 1980	Established Urban Development Corporations (to regenerate urban areas) and Enterprise Zones (with reduced planning controls on development).
THE HIGHWAYS ACT 1980	Provides inter alia for highway authorities to construct, maintain and improve highways and for the stopping up of highways, interference with them, the making up of private streets and the acquisition of land.
THE ROAD TRAFFIC REGULATION ACT 1984	Provides for the regulation and control of the speed, movement and parking of vehicles on the highway.
NEW TOWNS ACT 1985	Empowers the appropriate Secretary of State to designate areas as New Towns and provides for the establishment of Development Corporations with wide powers to secure their layout and development. Established the Commission For New Towns to take over and manage those aspects not transferred to local authorities when a development corporation's work is complete.
TRANSPORT ACT 1985	Significantly amended the regulations applying to bus operation by the abolition of road service licensing. Requires bus operators outside London to register a service with the Traffic Commissioners, within London to obtain a local service licence or, in the case of non-profit making services, to obtain a permit. Requires authorities to invite tenders for services it intends to subsidise.

REGULATIONS AND ORDERS	MOST IMPORTANT ASPECTS IN RELATION TO ROADS AND TRAFFIC IN URBAN AREAS
TOWN AND COUNTRY PLANNING (USE CLASSES) ORDER 1972 SI 1972 No. 1385	Specified the different classes of use of land or buildings and provides that changes of use within the same class do not require planning permission.
TOWN AND COUNTRY PLANNING GENERAL DEVELOPMENT ORDER 1977 (SI 1977 No. 289)	Specified the types of development requiring planning permission, the procedures to be followed in determining a planning application (notably with regard to developments affecting existing and proposed highways) and the making of an appeal to the Secretary of State.
TRAFFIC SIGNS REGULATIONS AND GENERAL DIRECTIONS 1981 (SI 1981 No. 859)	Prescribes the traffic signs and the circumstances and conditions which apply to their use on the public highway.
TRAFFIC SIGNS (WELSH AND ENGLISH LANGUAGE PROVISIONS) REGULATIONS AND GENERAL DIRECTIONS 1985 (SI 1985 No. 13)	Prescribes bilingual warning and regulatory signs which may be used in Wales in place of the monolingual signs prescribed in TSRGD 1981.
TOWN AND COUNTRY PLANNING GENERAL DEVELOPMENT (AMENDMENT) (No. 2) ORDER 1985 (SI 1985 No. 1981)	Articles 11 to 15 set down the relevant highway and traffic requirements for dealing with planning applications.
LOCAL AUTHORITIES TRAFFIC ORDERS (PROCEDURE) (ENGLAND AND WALES) REGULATIONS 1986 (SI 1986 No. 179)	Sets out the procedures to be followed by a local authority when making an order to control the speed, movement or parking of vehicles on the highway.
also THE SECRETARY OF STATE'S TRAFFIC ORDERS (PROCEDURE) (ENGLAND AND WALES) REGULATIONS 1986 (SI 1986 No. 180)	Sets out the procedures to be followed by the Secretaries of State in exercising their powers under the RTRA 1984.
THE LONDON AUTHORITIES' TRAFFIC ORDERS (PROCEDURE) REGULATIONS 1986 (SI 1986 No. 259)	Sets out the procedures to be followed by London authorities when using their powers under the RTRA 1984.
	N.B. There are also other regulations for use in specific circumstances (e.g. exemptions for disabled persons, parking in goods vehicle loading areas).

Table 3.1 The more important Acts of Parliament, regulations and orders with considerations for roads and traffic in urban areas in England and Wales [See also Sco.16 and NI.9]

of, Structure and Local Plans is currently given in the memorandum accompanying the Department of Environment's Circular 22/84 (Ref. 1) [NI.4, Sco.19]. It is always advisable to check the latest position on statutory development plans by referring to the Encyclopedia of Planning, Law and Practice (Ref. 2) [Sco.20].

Information on the statutory procedures required to implement a traffic management scheme is given in Chapter 15 and for a highway construction scheme in Chapter 35.

Structure Plans

Structure plans are prepared by County Planning Authorities in England and Wales [Sco.21]. The structure plan for an area sets out the policies and general proposals for the development and other use of land in the area including measures for improving the physical environment and the management of traffic. It should be limited to policies and general proposals of structural importance. The procedure for the preparation and approval of a Structure Plan is illustrated in Figure 3.1.

A Structure Plan provides an overall strategy for the development of an area, including the full integration of land use and transport. Transport problems should be treated in a comprehensive way through the medium of the structure plan, taking account of the interaction of public passenger transport, freight transport, highways and control of access to them, parking and traffic management.

Structure plans deal with road proposals at the highest level of the hierachy, ie. the structure plan primary road network. This should not be confused with the primary route network (PRN) of 'green backed' signed roads (see also Chapter 43) although in some areas the two networks may be similar. Trunk roads are normally included as part of the structure plan primary network and all road schemes listed in the Department of Transport's most recent annual Roads White Paper will normally be included as proposals in structure plans [Sco.22]. However, in order to avoid unnecessary blight structure plans should only include proposed road schemes which the relevant highway authority intends to commence within about 10 years.

Structure plans also include, where appropriate, policies and proposals for the management of traffic. For example, policies for the co-ordination of public transport services, the movement of freight on road, rail and by canal, the provision of lorry routes and parks and criteria for the location of major freight generating activities. A broad indication of the criteria to be applied in determining standards of car parking provision may also be included in structure plans.

Local Plans

Local plans are generally prepared by District Councils or London Borough Councils [Sco.23]. They are intended to:

● develop the policies and general proposals of the structure plan and to relate them to precise areas of land defined on a proposal map;

● provide a detailed basis for development control;

● provide a detailed basis for co-ordinating and directing development and other use of land—both public and private; and

● bring local planning issues before the public.

Local plans must conform generally to the approved structure plan and cannot be used to alter the policies and general proposals of the structure plan.

The procedure for the preparation and approval of a Local Plan is illustrated in Figure 3.2. Specialized types of Local Plan are:

Action Area Plans: these are appropriate for areas intended for comprehensive development, redevelopment or improvement by public authorities or private enterprise, and where the implementation is to be given priority over a comparatively short period of time (see also Chapter 4.2).

Subject Plans: these are for a particular description or descriptions of development and concentrate on the preparation of proposals for one or two issues across what may be an extensive area (see also Chapter 4.2).

Local plans should elaborate the proposals for the improvement of the structure plan primary road network and indicate other proposed new roads and improvements. Like structure plans they should only include proposed road schemes on which the highway authority intends to commence work within about 10 years so as to avoid unnecessary blight. Local plans may also include proposals related to the management of traffic; for example, measures to help control traffic in areas of congestion, to improve the safety of cyclists and pedestrians or the detailed car parking standards to be applied within the area of the plan (see Chapter 30).

Unitary Development Plans

The Local Government Act 1985 (Section 4) (Ref. 3) provides for a system of Unitary Development Plans (UDPs) to be brought into operation in the area of each London Borough and Metropolitan District [Sco.13] when the Secretary of State for the Environment issues a commencement order for that

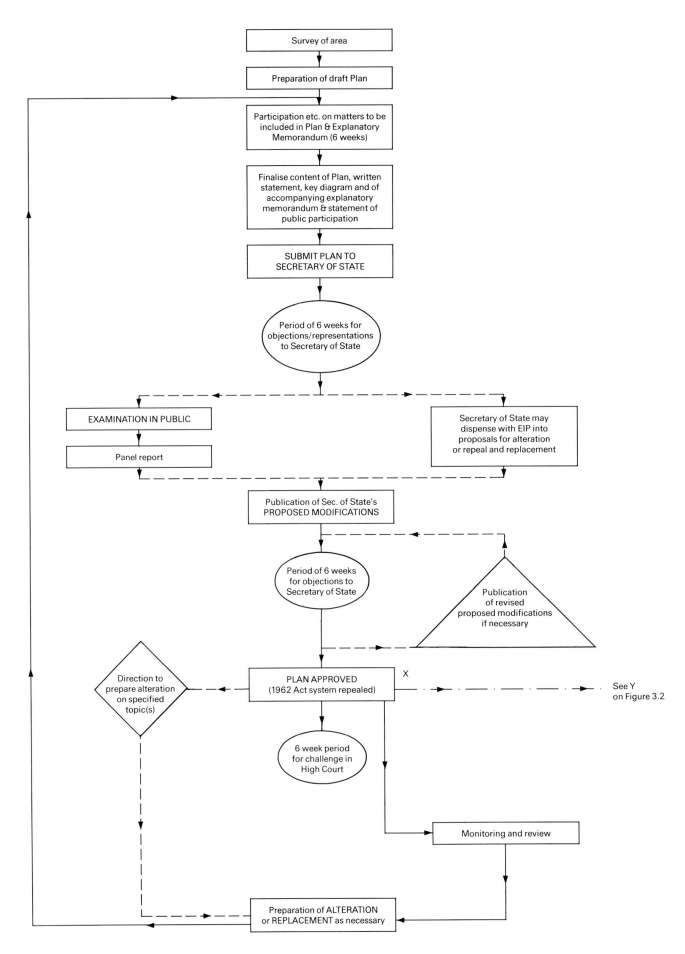

Figure 3.1 The structure plan process [Sco.24]

22

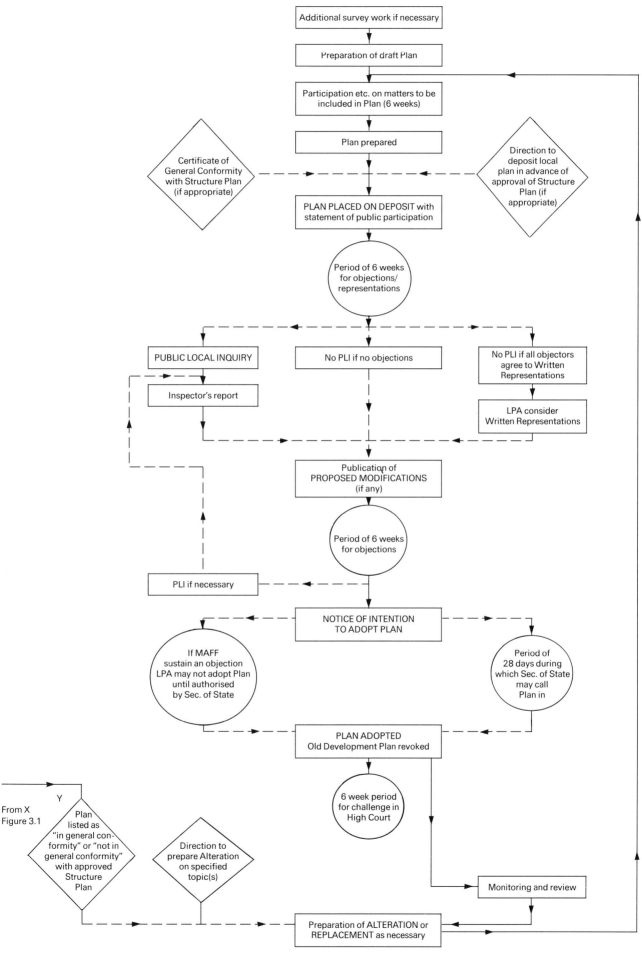

Figure 3.2 The local plan process [Sco.24]

area. UDPs are intended to replace all structure plans, local plans and old development plans in these areas. They will cover the whole area of a Borough or District and will have to be prepared having regard to any strategic guidance which the Secretary of State may issue. They will contain two parts; Part I will contain general policies similar to a structure plan, and Part II site specific proposals similar to a local plan.

Approved structure plans remain in force until replaced by Part I of a UDP, but London Boroughs and Metropolitan Districts have no power to carry out work on structure plans and, therefore, approved structure plans for these areas cannot be altered, repealed or otherwise replaced. Local plans continue in force until a UDP for an area becomes operative. They will then become part of Part II of the UDP subject to any alterations included in the UDP. London Boroughs and Metropolitan Districts may continue to make, alter, repeal or replace local plans until a commencement order for the new UDP powers has been issued.

Strategic guidance (including guidance on transport) for the preparation of UDPs will be issued by the Department of the Environment. Before this guidance is issued the advice of the London Planning Advisory Committee in Greater London and Planning Conferences of the Local Planning Authorities in the Metropolitan District areas will be taken into account.

The procedure for the preparation and approval of a UDP is illustrated in Figure 3.3.

3.4 Transport Policies and Programmes

Local highway authorities in England (County Councils, Metropolitan District Councils, London Boroughs and the Common Council of the City of London) are asked to submit an annual Transport Policies and Programme (TPP) to the Department of Transport [NI.2, Sco.25, Wa.1]. The TPP contains estimates of capital expenditure which are used for distributing Transport Supplementary Grant (TSG) [Sco.26] and setting capital allocations for roads each year (see Chapter 4.2).

Information that local authorities are asked to provide is set out in an annual circular and typically includes:

- a statement of the policies for improving the highway network designed to meet the needs of the areas within the likely resources available;

- details of the highways capital expenditure programme for the coming year (including those parts intended to help more important local roads) which constitute the bid for TSG;

- a progress report on the implementation of the previous year's highways programme particularly those elements accepted for TSG;

- an outline of the highways programme for future years;

- information on road maintenance policies.

The TPP is a non-statutory plan and a local authority document. For many authorities it also provides an important management tool for overall interests in transport and may therefore contain other information relevant to that goal.

Relationship with Statutory Development Plans

Department of Environment Circular 104/73 [Wa.2] on Local Transport Grants (Annex, paragraphs 13–15) (Ref. 4) sets out the relationship between TPPs and statutory development plans [Sco.27]. It advises that, as far as possible, there should be a single planning process which expresses itself on the one hand in TPPs (for the purposes of grant and resource decisions) and on the other hand in development plans.
Because development plans set transport policies in their wider context, go through public participation procedures and receive formal statutory approval, they will form a framework for TPPs. The development plan system provides a statutory framework for publicity and participation which enables transport policies to be set in their wider context; but, local authorities may also find it appropriate to consult the public from time to time on particular aspects of their transport proposals.

3.5 Private Parliamentary Bills

Where a local authority (or other transport undertaking) wishes to proceed with a project which is outside its existing statutory powers (eg. a light rapid transit system or changes to railways or navigable waterways), it may seek the necessary powers by promoting a Private Parliamentary Bill [NI.2].

3.6 Agreements Between Developers and Local Authorities

Since 1975, statutory planning agreements [NI.2] have been used to overcome some of the limitations inherent in the development control system. By this means, agreements are secured through negotiation between the applicant and the local authority, often to secure financial contributions from private developers towards the costs of infrastructure works. These agreements may involve highway improvements to assist access to the development site, the adoption of on-site roads and provision of non-operational car parking outside the site (see also Chapter 28.3 and Chapter 31).

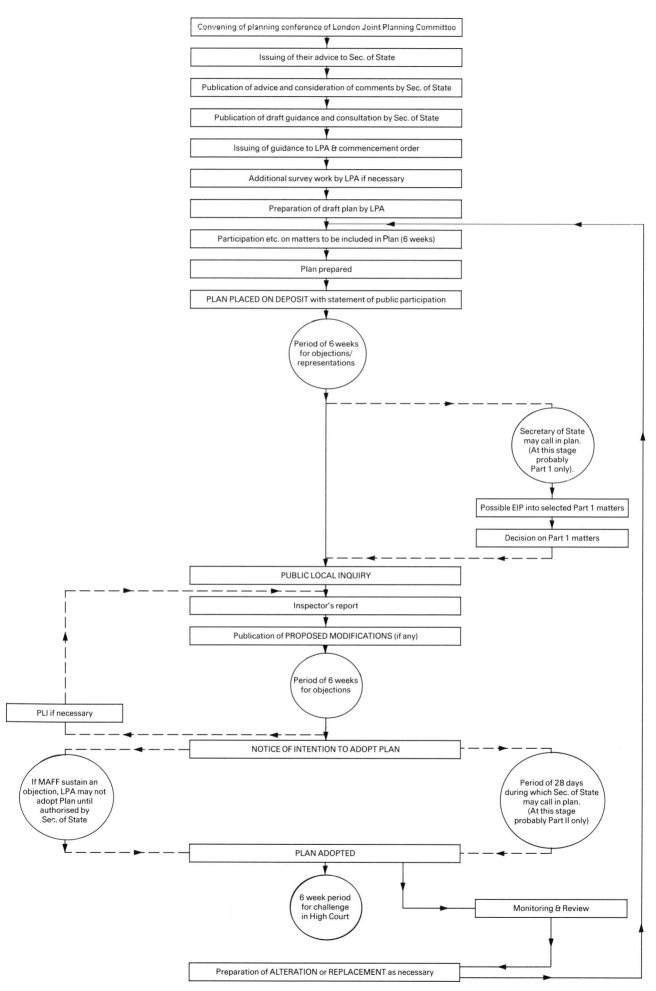

Figure 3.3 The unitary development plan process

25

3.7 References

1. DoE—Circular 22/84, '*Memorandum on Structure and Local Plans: The Town and Country Planning Act, 1971, Part II (as amended by the Town and Country Planning (Amendment) Act 1972, the Local Government Act 1972, and the Local Government, Planning and Land Act 1980)*', DoE (1984). [Sco.28, Wa.3] (3.3)

2. Grant, M (Ed)—'*Encyclopedia of Planning Law and Practice*', Sweet and Maxwell, (1986) (amended). [Sco.29] (3.3)

3. *Local Government Act 1985,* HMSO (1985). (3.3)

4. DoE—Circular 104/73 '*Local Transport Grants*', DoE (1973). [Wa.4] (3.4)

3.8 Further Information

The procedures described in this Chapter relate to the Acts shown in Table 3.1 and associated Statutory Instruments and Circulars, all of which are subject to change by subsequent legislation. It is always advisable to check the latest situation by referring to the appropriate Encyclopedia of Planning, Highway or Traffic Law (eg. Sweet and Maxwell) (Ref. 2).

5. DTp—Circular 2/86 '*Transport Policies and Programme Submission for 1987/88*', HMSO (1986). [Sco.30, Wa.5]

6. HMSO—'*Town and Country Planning (Structure and Local Plans) Regulations 1982*', HMSO (1982). [Sco.31]

7. Ministry of Housing and Local Government/Welsh Office—'*Development Plans: a manual of form and content*', HMSO (1970).

N.B. Information on the statutory procedures required to implement a traffic management scheme are given in Chapter 15 and those for a highway construction scheme in Chapter 35.

4 Powers and Responsibilities of the Agencies Involved

4.1 Statutory Basis

Chapter 3 has described how, in Britain [NI.1], Parliament establishes (and from time to time modifies) the statutory framework for the administration and control of land use planning and transport related matters by enacting legislation.

The various Acts vest a wide range of powers and responsibilities in the various Secretaries of State on matters of national significance such as airport policy, responsibility for trunk roads and vehicle safety and licensing; and in local councils for a wide range of other matters of a more regional or local nature. A guide to the powers and responsibilities of the agencies involved is set out in Table 4.1 [Sco.32] but precise details should be obtained from the Acts themselves.

Local Authority Responsibilities

Outside of Metropolitan Areas (see Ref. 1) there is a two tier system of local government [NI.2] whereby County Councils deal with strategic matters, such as highways (other than trunk roads) and transport and the preparation of Structure Plans; whilst District or Borough Councils are responsible for local matters such as development control and the preparation of Local Plans. Many County Councils delegate, by mutual agreement, some of their powers and responsibilities to the appropriate District or Borough Councils, who then act as their agents. County Councils may also act as agents for the Secretaries of State, most notably with regard to the maintenance of trunk roads. In some areas there may also be a parish or community council but their highways and traffic powers and responsibilities are of only minor importance.

In the metropolitan areas of England, there is a single tier of local government where District Councils (or London Borough Councils including the City of London) are responsible for all local authority matters including planning and highways (other than for trunk roads) [Sco.33].

County Councils in England and Wales also have a duty under Section 63(1) of the Transport Act 1985 to secure the provision of public transport services which would not otherwise be met. Both County Councils and non-metropolitan district councils have powers to enter into service subsidy agreements (Section 63(4) and (5)) and must have regard to the needs of the elderly and disabled persons (Section 63(8)). In Metropolitan County areas (ie. excluding London) public transport policy is the responsibility of Passenger Transport Authorities (PTAs) comprised of members nominated by Metropolitan District Authorities. PTAs appoint Passenger Transport Executives (PTEs) to carry out the executive and administrative tasks.

In addition under Section 122 of the Road Traffic Regulations Act 1984 local authorities using their powers under the Act have a duty to secure the expeditious, convenient and safe movement of vehicular and other traffic (including pedestrians) and to provide suitable and adequate parking facilities on and off the highway having regard to:

- the desirability of securing and maintaining reasonable access to premises;

- the effect on the amenities of any locality (particularly in respect of the passage of heavy commercial vehicles);

- the importance of facilitating the passage of public service vehicles and of securing the safety of the people who use them;

- and any other matter that the local authority considers relevant.

In areas designated by the appropriate Secretary of State, Urban Development Corporations have wide powers to promote and influence development [Sco.34].

Influence of Central Government

Central government exerts a considerable influence on the way in which local councils discharge their responsibilities. This is achieved by promoting legislation to alter the statutory framework within which local authorities operate, by issuing policy directives through its Circulars and Advice Notes and by regulating the finance available for spending on different projects or areas [NI.2].

4.2 Funding for Roads in Urban Areas

The availability of funding is important to decisions on the scale and timing of a project. Sources of finance for highway and traffic schemes vary according to the type of scheme and the category (see Chapter 5) of roads affected [NI.10]. Trunk roads receive 100% funding from central government. Non-trunk roads are the responsibility of local highway authorities but the funding of schemes depends upon both the capital allocation and the availability of grant support.

Capital Allocation

Authorities receive an annual capital allocation to cover the entire expenditure accepted for Transport

AUTHORITY	LAND USE PLANNING	HIGHWAYS AND TRAFFIC	PUBLIC TRANSPORT
CENTRAL GOVERNMENT			
SECRETARY OF STATE FOR THE ENVIRONMENT	1. Promote legislation and determine policy on national and regional issues. 2. Approve Structure and Unitary Development Plans for his own approval. 3. May "call-in" Local Development Plans. 4. Appoint Inspectors to conduct public inquiries or determine planning appeals (SoS may retain the right to determine a planning appeal).	1. Promotes legislation and determines policy on national and regional issues. 2. Highway Authority for Trunk Roads with reserve powers for all roads (and approval of speed limits on Principal Roads).	
SECRETARY OF STATE FOR TRANSPORT		3. Issues design standards for Trunk Road design and assessment to be used as guidance by other highway authorities. 4. Payment of Transport Supplementary Grant to assist capital expenditure on highway and regulation of traffic on roads of more than local importance. 5. May issue guidance on how London and Metropolitan authorities should exercise their (traffic management) powers. 6. London Boroughs must obtain SoS's approval when their proposals affect traffic or parking on "designated" roads. 7. Must determine disputes between authorities in London and in Metropolitan Counties.	1. Promotes legislation and determines policies. 2. Appoints Traffic Commissioners responsible for licensing. 3. Administration of Rural Transport and Innovation Grants through Development Commission in England, (these may be applicable to some urban areas). 4. Appoints members of London Regional Transport Board. 5. Appoints members of British Railways Board and is generally responsible for control of finance and policy on railway matters. 6. Imposes obligations on BRB to provide a public passenger service and pays compensation under relevant EEC legislation.
LOCAL GOVERNMENT			
COUNTY COUNCILS IN ENGLAND AND WALES	1. County Planning Authority (CPA). 2. Responsible for preparing the Structure Plan. 3. Responsible for development control relating to: a) Mineral exploration and mining. b) Waste disposal (except Wales). c) Developments on National Park boundaries.	1. Highway Authority for all non-trunk roads in their area. 2. May act as agent of SoS for maintenance and lighting of trunk roads.	1. Determines level of subsidy. 2. Identify socially desirable services and enter into contracts with operators for provision. 3. Co-ordinate school transport services. 4. Administer concessionary fares schemes. 5. Licence taxis and hire cars
DISTRICT COUNCILS IN ENGLAND AND WALES (excluding Metropolitan areas)	1. District Planning Authority (DPA). 2. Generally responsible for preparation of Local Plans (subject to agreement on highway and traffic input with highway authority). 3. Development control except 3a, b and c above.	1. May act as agent of County Council for some highway functions. 2. As of right can carry out maintenance of unclassified roads. 3. May provide off-street car parking subject to consultation with the highway authority.	1. Identify socially desirable services and enter contracts with operators for provision. 2. Administer concessionary fares scheme.
DISTRICT AND BOROUGH COUNCILS IN METROPOLITAN AREAS	1. Planning Authority. 2. Responsible for preparation of Unitary Plan. 3. Responsible for development control.	1. Highway Authority for all non-trunk roads in their area. 2. May act as agent of S. of S. for maintenance of Trunk Roads.	1. Nominate members of Passenger Transport Authorities which are responsible for the same functions as County Councils above. 2. Taxi and Private Hire licensing (excluding London). 3. PTA/PTE have powers to enter agreements with BRB for the provision of passenger services.
PARISH COUNCILS (in England)		1. May carry out certain minor functions such as: a) the provision and maintenance of footpaths and verges and footways and lighting on unclassified roads. b) the provision of amenities such as bus shelters, seating and off-street car parks.	

Table 4.1 Main powers and responsibilities of the agencies involved in England and Wales [See also Sco.32 and NI.2]

Supplementary Grant (TSG) plus an amount for other roads spending [Wa.2]. Capital allocations convey permission to spend the specified amounts, with permission to borrow the same amount less TSG used to defray capital spending. Authorities can supplement allocations with the prescribed proportion of capital receipts generated within a year and accumulated from previous years. They can vire between different service blocks within their overall capital allocation for all services; and they can carry forward unused allocations from previous years and anticipate the next year's, to a ceiling of 10% of the current year's allocation [Sco.35].

Sources of funding

Within the constraints of the capital allocation funding for non-trunk roads comes from a variety of sources as follows:

Transport Supplementary Grant (TSG): is a grant (currently paid at 50% of accepted expenditure) towards that part of the local authority's programme of capital expenditure on highways and regulation of traffic on roads of more than local importance. These roads include the primary route network (PRN) (and designated roads, in London); by-passes and relief roads relieving communities of the effects of through traffic; and other roads carrying flows similar to the PRN such as links to it and major urban roads [Sco.36].

Rate Support Grant (RSG): general support is provided from the Exchequer for local authorities to carry out their range of responsibilities. Grant is established by a series of formulae; those bearing on highways include support for current maintenance spending which takes into account, inter alia, road length and classification and support for borrowing to finance capital spending based on capital allocations. Capital allocations for roads determine borrowing power for the authority and include expenditure accepted for TSG [Sco.35].

Revenue from central government and the European Economic Community (EEC) for specific regional, industrial and urban development projects: specific funds may be established from time to time to promote schemes with particular attributes such as those currently being funded by the Urban Programme to assist regeneration in some inner city areas.

Grants under Section 272 of the Highways Act 1980 (Ref. 2): to local authorities for road construction and improvement in exceptional cases conditional upon the government considering it inequitable for the local authority to bear the expenditure [Sco.38].

Developers who construct new residential and industrial estate roads and/or agree to finance highway related

works on roads outside their development but adversely affected by it.

Other highway authority revenue: such as income from parking charges and tolls.

These provisions and the rules governing them are subject to change from time to time, to reflect Government policies.

Area Improvement Schemes

Area improvements, including '**Housing Action Areas**' and '**General Improvement Areas**' can be carried out under powers provided in the Housing Acts and the Inner Urban Areas Act 1978 (Ref. 3).

Schemes of this kind seek to improve the land, buildings, environment and infrastructure of older areas and may include highways or traffic measures for resolving the conflict between traffic, parked vehicles and pedestrians.

The Department of the Environment have published a series of Area Improvement Notes (Ref. 4) giving advice on traffic management, design of roads, footpaths, play space and pedestrian areas and Circular 68/78 (Ref. 5) [Sco.37, Wa.6] explaining the 1978 Act.

Broadly speaking:

● **Housing Improvement Areas and General Improvement Areas** [Sco.39] seek to manage traffic in existing residential streets by making better use of limited highway land;

● **Industrial Improvement Areas and Commercial Improvement Areas** seek to improve access, parking and loading facilities and could include the provision of new access points or roads.

4.3 Capital and Revenue Expenditure

All major schemes are funded by raising capital, usually by borrowing from the Public Works Loan Board or on commercial money markets [NI.2]. Repayment periods are geared to the assumed useful life of the asset but are usually between twenty and forty years for highway schemes and rather longer for major structures (eg. bridges).

Smaller schemes, usually those valued below an arbitrary limit (eg. perhaps £20,000) and highway maintenance on non-trunk roads are funded from revenue, meaning that they are paid for from the local authorities' annual income from rates and other sources. Revenue income also pays the debt charges and capital repayment costs incurred from capital expenditure [Sco.40].

4.4 References

Text Reference

1. *Local Government Act 1985*, HMSO (1985).   (4.1)

2. *The Highways Act 1980*, HMSO (1980).   (4.2)

3. *Inner Urban Areas Act 1978*, HMSO (1978). [Sco.37]   (4.2)

4. DoE, *Area Improvement Notes— Environmental Design*, HMSO (1972).
   The Design of Streets and other Spaces in General Improvement Areas, HMSO (1973).
   Parking and Garaging in General Improvement Areas HMSO (1973).
   Traffic in General Improvement Areas, HMSO (1974).
   Good Practice in Improvement Areas, HMSO (1984).   (4.2)

5. DoE—Circular 68/78, '*Inner Urban Areas Act 1978*' HMSO (1978). [Wa.7]   (4.2)

4.5 Further Information

6. DTp—'*National Roads—England*', HMSO (1985).

7. DTp—Circular 2/86, '*Transport Policies and Programme Submission for 1987/88*', HMSO (1986). [Sco.41, Wa.8]

5 The Principles of a Functional Hierarchy of Roads

5.1 Problems Arising from Mixed Use of Urban Roads

Most urban roads perform many functions besides those of providing passage for moving vehicles and pedestrians. These functions may be broadly categorised as environmental, access, local traffic and through traffic. An illustration of typical mixed activity is shown in Plate 5.1. Not all of these will need to be accommodated in any particular road but for the purposes of planning and design, the functions that a road should cater for need to be identified and relevant priorities assigned to them.

Design Standards

Assessing the major roles a road should fulfill and the standard of provision which should be made will often be a matter for judgement since there is a range of design standards available to suit different levels of performance criteria. In other words judgement of what is 'acceptable' involves striking a balance between traffic capacity, the environment, speed, safety and road user comfort for the road in question.

Selecting Priorities

Typically, conflicts arise when a road cannot accommodate the competing demands made upon it. Sometimes it is simply a lack of capacity at certain times of the day. As the periods of congestion lengthen the problems are seen to worsen. Sometimes the problems are related to particular activities, like lorry traffic at night, but often they are caused by a whole range of conflicting uses and the impacts which they have on one another.

Whenever these situations occur it is important to determine which of the various demands should be given priority, taking account of the most appropriate role for the road in question and its relationship with other roads in the area.

5.2 Alternative Solutions

Achieving priorities for certain kinds of traffic (or types of use) can be done in a variety of ways depending

Plate 5.1 Mixed use of an urban street

Source: Plessey Controls Ltd

upon the required timescale. Traffic management measures (see Part 3) can be effective and relatively cheap to install, but will not bring about major infrastructure changes. These will only be achieved by longer term programmes involving investment in new transport facilities or through land-use planning and development control. In practice a combination of both short term and longer term measures may be desirable.

5.3 The Benefits of Establishing a Road Hierarchy

The benefits which can be obtained by categorising and managing existing road systems in the form of a hierachy of roads are similar to those obtained from purpose designed road networks, namely:

● activities most closely related to frontage buildings can be given more space when environmental and access functions are allowed to predominate;

● activities which are incompatible with traffic flow can be restricted on designated routes where traffic movement should predominate;

● the capacity of designated traffic routes can be increased by segregating different forms of traffic and by restricting vehicular access to frontages;

● the risk of accidents can be reduced and junction capacities increased by reducing the number of intersections and vehicular conflicts on the designated traffic routes;

● the overall environmental impact of traffic can be reduced by concentrating flows onto fewer routes; and

● the rate of return on new investment designed to improve traffic flow, save accidents and reduce environmental intrusion can be increased by concentrating traffic onto a few selected corridors.

5.4 Road Categories Within a Hierarchy

The main distinction to be made is between **primary** and **district** distributor roads (whose primary objective is the efficient movement of vehicular traffic) and **local** distributor and **access** roads (all of which are described in more detail in Parts 3 and 4) (see also 5.7 below).

Table 5.1 describes a five level hierarchy typical of a major urban area. The number of levels required in a hierarchy is usually related to the size of the urban area and also to population densities and levels of vehicle ownership.

Having decided upon an appropriate hierarchical set of descriptions, all existing roads should be identified with them. It is important to ensure that roads are assigned to the appropriate level in the hierarchy on the basis of their proposed (or desired) functions rather than on their existing use since as noted above, most existing highways will not be performing a single function (eg. a major shopping street may also be acting as a through road).

Network Capacity

It may be possible to make a theoretical assessment of whether the traffic flow capacity of the designed road hierarchy is sufficient, recognising that it will almost certainly be less than is achieved by the network in its unrestricted form.

Figure 5.1 provides a guide for this type of assessment (supplied by University of Newcastle Upon Tyne—Transport Operations Research Group) which requires data on the distribution of trip lengths within the area under study (obtained from a transport survey) and a number of threshold levels for journey distances designed to relate to the suitability of using different levels of road in the hierarchy (eg. long distance trips should use primary distributors, only local traffic should use local distributors, etc.).

The total capacity provided by all of the roads in the network for a given level in the hierarchy would be the sum of their lengths multiplied by their traffic flow capacities taken on a lane capacity basis appropriate to the road type (eg. residential roads would have a lower value of throughput per traffic lane than primary distributors).

If network capacity, calculated in this way, was found to be deficient for one level in the hierarchy and in surplus for another, the balance of capacity could be adjusted by altering the threshold values between the two distance scales of operation.

An adjustment of this kind would require great care as, if a threshold value were altered upwards, it would imply that journeys of somewhat greater distance were being accommodated on the lower level in the hierarchy; whereas if a threshold value were lowered, it would imply that some of the shorter trips might transfer to the main traffic arteries. There will be limits to the extent to which this is desirable and a certain amount of physical control can be exercised to influence patterns of movement by having (for example) a minimum spacing between interchanges on district and/or primary distributors.

5.5 Implications for Planning and Development Control

One of the benefits of defining a hierarchy of roads is that it can help clarify policies concerning the highway aspects of individual planning decisions on properties

	Pedestrian Streets	Access Roads	Local Distributors	District Distributors	Primary Distributors
Predominant Activities	Walking Meeting Trading	Walking Vehicle access Delivery of goods and servicing of premises Slow moving vehicles	Vehicle movements near beginning or end of all journeys Bus stops	Medium distance traffic to Primary Network Public transport services All through traffic with respect to environmental areas	Fast moving long distance traffic No pedestrians or frontage access
Pedestrian Movement	Complete freedom Predominant activity	Considerable freedom with crossing at random	Controlled with channelised (e.g. zebra) crossings	Minimum pedestrian activity with positive measures for their safety	Nil-vertical segregation between vehicles and pedestrians
Stationary Vehicles	Nil except for servicing and emergency	Some, depending on safety considerations	Considerable if off highway facilities not provided	Some depending on traffic flow conditions	Nil
Heavy Goods Vehicle Activity	Essential servicing and frontage deliveries only	Residential: related activities only Other areas: delivery of goods and services	Minimum through trips	Minimum through trips	Suitable for all HGV movements especially through trips
Vehicle Access To Individual Properties	Nil [except for emergency vehicles and may include limited access for servicing – see Chapter 24.11]	Predominant activity	Some to more significant activity centre	Nil apart from major centres i.e. equivalent to local distributor level of vehicle flow	Nil apart from sites of national traffic importance
Local Traffic Movements	Nil [but may include public transport – see Chapter 24.11]	Nil	Predominant activity	Some – only a few localities may be severed, junction spacing important	Very little – junction spacing will preclude local movements
Through Traffic Movements	Nil	Nil	Nil	Predominant role for medium distance traffic	Predominant role for long distance traffic
Vehicle Operating Speeds/Speed Limits	Less than 5 miles/h (vehicles enter on sufferance)	Less than 20 miles/h with speed control devices	Subject to 30 miles/h limit but layout should discourage speed	Subject to 30 or 40 miles/h limit within the built-up area	More than 40 miles/h depending on geometric constraints

Table 5.1 Hierarchical classification system for urban roads, based on function

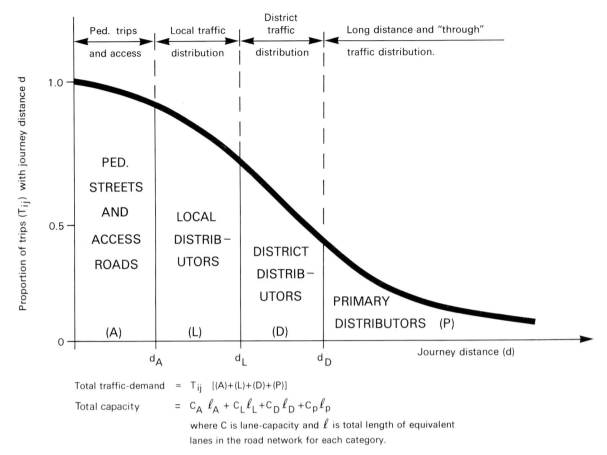

Total traffic-demand $= T_{ij} \ [(A)+(L)+(D)+(P)]$

Total capacity $= C_A \, \ell_A + C_L \ell_L + C_D \, \ell_D + C_p \ell_p$

where C is lane-capacity and ℓ is total length of equivalent
lanes in the road network for each category.

Figure 5.1 Balance of capacity in hierarchy on urban roads

Source: University of Newcastle upon Tyne—Transport Operations Research Group

EXAMPLE VEHICLE TYPE	PEDESTRIAN STREET	ACCESS ROAD	LOCAL DISTRIBUTOR	DISTRICT DISTRIBUTOR	PRIMARY DISTRIBUTOR
Goods vehicles	Total ban, except for special deliveries	Limited time for loading/ unloading	Limited to specific places for loading/ unloading	Essential loading and unloading permitted only where no forecourts or rear access available	N
Cars	Total ban	Severely limited to allow access for goods	Limited to groups of parking spaces away from junctions	Severely limited to mid block designated bays (metered)	A B L
Light vans	Limited to loading/unloading	Minimum control	Severely limited essential loading/ unloading only	Total ban except at designated goods inter-change places	A T
Taxis	Limited to designated ranks	Limited to designated ranks	Minimum control	Total ban except where reserved areas can be provided	O T

Table 5.2 Parking control policies in relation to the urban roads hierarchy

DEFINITION	ADDITIONAL INFORMATION
A Highway is a way over which the public have the right to pass and repass.	On some highways this right of passage may only be exercised on foot, on horseback or by specific classes of vehicles (as described by any order which may be applicable). Public highway refers to those highways which are maintained at public expense (i.e. by the highway authority). Highways not maintainable at public expense are none the less highways. A highway may also be a waterway, a navigable river or road ferry. The term highway maintainable at public expense roughly corresponds to roads maintained by the road authority in Scotland.
A Carriageway is a highway or part of a highway over which the public have right of way for vehicles.	These rights may be restricted by the implementation of a traffic regulation, speed limit or other orders such as one giving special road status (see Table 5.2). The right of way for vehicles does not detract from the established right of pedestrians to cross the carriageway.
A Footway is that part of a highway which also comprises a carriageway, over which the public have right of way on foot only.	——
A Footpath is a highway over which the public have right of way on foot only, not being a footway.	The essential difference between a footway and a footpath is that the former is adjacent to a carriageway. A way which is exclusively for passage on foot is a footpath.
A Bridleway is a highway over which the public have right of way on foot and on horseback.	The right of way may also apply to leading horses or driving animals in which case it may be known as a driftway.
A Cycle Track is a way which is part of a highway over which the public have right of way on pedal cycles, other than pedal cycles which are motor vehicles, with or without the right of way on foot.	——
A Street includes any highway and any road, lane, footpath square, alley or passage whether thoroughfare or not. A general prerequisite for a street is that there should be a succession of houses or buildings on at least one side.	A street need not be a highway.
A Road in England and Wales is any length of highway or any other road to which the public have access and includes bridges over which a road passes. [NI. 11]	However a highway may be designated as a 'Special Road' and 'Trunk Road' or a 'Principal Road' (see Table 5.2).

Table 5.3 Statutory definitions for terminology (England and Wales) [Sco.42]

served by the roads concerned. Furthermore, specific planning criteria could be developed and applied according to a road's designation in the hierarchy; for example design speed, width of carriageway, control over pedestrian movements, on-street parking (see Table 5.2 which provides a guide to levels of parking appropriate to a road hierarchy) and frontage access for vehicles. In this way the planning objectives would be clear for each level of road in the hierarchy and policies on development control and traffic management would reinforce one another.

5.6 Statutory Definitions

Many terms and expressions used in highway and traffic planning have precise meanings when used in a legal or administrative context and some of the more common of these are set out in Table 5.3 [Sco.42].

Classification	Additional Information
A Trunk Road is a highway which constitutes part of the national system of routes for through traffic and for which the Secretaries of State for Transport, Wales and Scotland respectively are the highway authority. [NI. 11]	——
A Principal Road is a non-trunk road which is classified as such by the appropriate Secretary of State as being sufficiently important in the national highway system to justify principal road status.	Principal road status is currently less important than it once was. It is still used as one element in the determination of the level of grant to local highway authorities and is important in some legal procedures such as the making of or alteration to, a speed limit order and is used by some highway authorities to specify and delegate functions to agency authorities.
A Classified Road is a highway which is agreed by the Secretary of State and where appropriate the local highway authority as being of importance to the movement of traffic. [NI. 11]	Classified Roads may be either Class I, II or III. All Class I and II roads and some Class III roads are given numbers. Class I, II and III generally coincide with the prefix A, B or C although there are some exceptions to this. Numbers are allocated according to the relationship between the origin of the road and the sectors of the country created by the main routes from London (A1-A6) and Edinburgh (A7-A9).
A Primary Route is a route that is designated by the appropriate Secretary of State as the most satisfactory all-purpose route for through traffic between two or more places of traffic importance.	Primary routes have green background direction signs for non-local destinations. A list of primary destinations is given in the Traffic Signs Manual Chapter 2. Motorways are not primary routes because they are 'special roads' and therefore not available for use by all traffic. A trunk road need not necessarily be a primary route.
A Special Road is a road designated by an Order made by the appropriate Secretary of State, which restricts its use to certain classes of traffic. [NI. 11]	The most common type of special road is a motorway whereby pedestrians, animals, pedal cycles etc. are prohibited. Roads other than motorways may be designated a 'special road'. Another important feature of special roads is that public utilities do not have a statutory right to place their apparatus within a special road.
A Motorway is a particular type of special road where motorway regulations apply.	All motorways are special roads but not necessarily trunk roads.
An All Purpose Road is any road other than a special road i.e. a road which is not restricted by a Special Road Order.	——
A Designated Road (within London) is a non-trunk road designated by the Secretary of State because of its importance as a traffic route.	All highway and traffic proposals on or affecting these roads have to be cleared by the Secretary of State.

Table 5.4 Classification of highways according to their status as traffic routes

As with many other matters covered in this document, there are differences between England and Wales, and Scotland reflecting the two separate and independent legal systems in use.

The status or classification of a highway is important to many of the matters dealt with in this document including who owns it and is responsible for maintaining it and regulating its use and who has powers to control adjacent development. The terms currently in use to classify highways according to their status as traffic routes are set out in Table 5.4.

5.7 The Relationship Between Hierarchy And Statutory Road Classification

The hierarchy proposed in the Buchanan Report (Ref. 1), and adopted in the Department of Transport's 'Roads in Urban Areas' (Ref. 2) in 1966 continues to

(a) Pedestrianised Streets

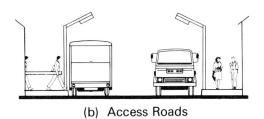

(b) Access Roads

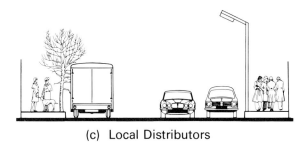

(c) Local Distributors

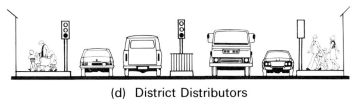

(d) District Distributors

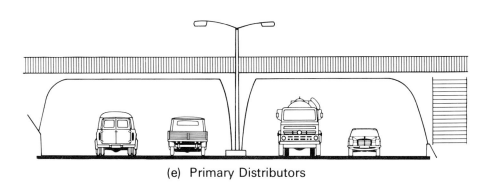

(e) Primary Distributors

Figure 5.2 Illustrations of the use of different types of road within a hierarchy

37

be appropriate with the addition of a level for pedestrianised streets. This hierarchy is as follows:

Primary distributors

These roads form the primary network for the urban centre as a whole and will normally comprise trunk roads and important classified roads (see Table 5.4) and link up with the national trunk road system. All longer distance traffic movements to, from and within urban areas should be channelised onto the primary distributors.

District distributors

These roads distribute traffic within the principal residential and industrial districts. They would include the remainder of the principal road category (see Table 5.4) and form the link between the primary network and the roads within environmental areas (ie. areas free from extraneous traffic in which considerations of environment predominate over the use of vehicles).

Local distributors

These roads distribute traffic within environmental areas. They form the links between district distributors and access roads and may include a few minor classified roads but should generally be unclassified.

Access roads

These roads give direct access to buildings and land within environmental areas and will be unclassified roads (often culs-de-sac).

Pedestrian streets

These roads are primarily for the passage of pedestrians and sometimes for cyclists, but may permit vehicles to enter at specified times of the day to service frontage property or to provide public transport services. (See also Chapter 23.)

In small towns, the distinctions between primary and district distributors for the town's own network may be unnecessary but there may also be inter-urban roads which provide for movements between the towns and generally by-pass them.

Some typical examples of the use of different roads in a hierarchy are shown in Figure 5.2.

It should be emphasised that no absolute correlation is required between the hierarchical level defined for an urban road based upon its function and its statutory classification, though a relationship will usually exist.

5.8 References

Text Reference

1. Ministry of Transport—'*Traffic in Towns—A study of the long term problems of traffic in urban areas*' (Buchanan Report), Reports of the Steering Group and Working Group appointed by the Minister of Transport, HMSO (1963). (5.7)

2. Ministry of Transport—'*Roads in Urban Areas*', HMSO (1966). (5.7)

6 Alternative Concepts of Road Capacity

6.1 Traffic Capacity

The capacity of a road is usually taken to mean the maximum rate at which traffic can pass along it within a particular set of conditions and is useful as a yardstick in assessing present day traffic conditions or the impact of proposed new developments.

The capacity of a road is, in practice, usually determined by the vehicle throughput capability of the junctions along it. Road capacity is not, however, a fixed quantity as it can vary in a number of ways and its maximum value is dependent upon other factors such as road user comfort and safety.

A highway network is composed of junctions and links, and each of these components has its own physical characteristics which influence the maximum traffic flows that can be achieved. Traffic flows also depend upon patterns of movement of vehicles and pedestrians in the network as a whole, as well as on the geometric layout and amount of road space available. The values of road capacity used for route or junction design purposes must reflect the various conditions outlined above and should result in the use of traffic flows which are appropriate to the roads in question (see also Parts 4 and 5 which deal with Traffic Management and Highway Design).

Factors Affecting Traffic Capacity

Several different concepts have been used to describe the maximum volume of vehicular traffic that can, or should, be accommodated by a section of road or by a road junction. It has long been recognised that this maximum volume of traffic (ie. capacity) depends upon prevailing conditions, which include:

- physical characteristics of the road (eg. width, number and type of intersections, alignment, road surface, etc.);

- composition of traffic and vehicle capabilities (eg. proportion of different types of vehicle and their performance capabilities);

- environmental and operating conditions (eg. weather, level of pedestrian activity, number of parked vehicles, frontage activity etc.).

In addition, traffic flows can be affected by driver's familiarity with the road in question and there can be significant differences between traffic flows achieved on, for example, holiday routes, from those on commuter routes of a similar standard where drivers will generally know the road very well.

Traffic Speeds and Flows and Quality of Service

The relationship between traffic speed and volume is such that, for free-flowing traffic, as speeds rise the distance between vehicles increases and the volume of traffic carried falls (see Table 36.1). Thus, the objective of achieving a high vehicle operating speed in safety on a primary distributor road may be desirable, but the maximum volume of traffic passing along the link at this speed would be relatively low. Conversely, if lower operating speeds are acceptable, correspondingly higher traffic volumes will pass along the link assuming that the same prevailing conditions exist. Some countries (eg. the USA—see Ref. 1) recommend a range of maximum traffic volumes for a road link depending on the desired level of service. A high level of service corresponds to a high operating speed and low concentrations of traffic with a corresponding inverse relationship with capacity.

Summary

There is no unique figure for the maximum acceptable traffic flow for an urban highway, as it depends upon the circumstances that are being considered. Later chapters provide details about characteristics of movements and delays, and environmental conditions (eg. speed/flow relationships for urban roads and delay/flow relationships for junctions are given in Part 5). These can then be used to derive the relevant information on the affects on traffic flows of frontage access, pedestrians and other factors so that the necessary judgements on design flows can be made.

6.2 Economic Capacity

The economic capacity of a road is the traffic flow at which the investment cost of providing new road capacity is just equal to the present value of the net benefits to traffic that the investment would achieve. The concept of economic capacity is discussed in 'The Traffic Capacity of Major Routes' (Ref. 2).

The concept is one of a trade-off between the resource cost of an improvement and the benefits which would be lost if the investment was not made. In practice a number of different improvements may be possible. For example, one improvement might be adequate to deal with long term traffic growth and exceptional peaks in traffic demand while another, lower cost, improvement might give rise to congestion sooner and more frequently in peak periods. The economic capacity of the existing road in relation to the two improvements will necessarily be different.

As future traffic flows tend to be higher than present day ones and the value of traffic benefits also tends to increase (as real incomes rise), economic capacity will tend to increase over time. This situation supports the strategy of phased construction exemplified by building (say) a single carriageway with at-grade intersections, in the first instance, and adding a second carriageway or extra lanes or grade-separation at later stages as the calculated value for economic capacity rises (see also Chapter 12).

6.3 Environmental Capacity

The concept of environmental capacity was advanced by the 'Traffic in Towns' report (Ref. 3), where it was defined as:

> 'The capacity of a street or area to accommodate moving and stationary vehicles having regard to the need to maintain the (chosen) environmental standards.'

In other words, environmental considerations could be used to determine the upper limit of traffic flow and the proportion of heavy vehicles consistent with a maximum acceptable level of (say) pedestrian delay and noise nuisance previously established as the minimum environmental standards for a particular street. The minimum standard and the most significant environmental factor (eg. noise, safety, etc.) might vary from street to street and at different times of day, according to the type of activities taking place and their sensitivity to intrusion by traffic. Thus, a street with wide footways and predominantly commercial frontages would have a higher figure for environmental capacity (ie. a lower environmental standard) than a street with narrow footways fronted by terraced housing. Likewise, the environmental capacity for a residential street based upon noise nuisance would be higher during the day than during the night.

Buchanan suggested that the environmental capacity for an access road or local distributor lies, typically, in the range 300–600 vehicles per hour, demonstrating that the environmental capacity will be substantially lower than the traffic capacity determined merely by the width and alignment of the carriageway or the intersections along it. Thus, to ensure that the environmental capacity of a street or network is not exceeded, design features or traffic management measures are often required to restrict traffic flow and to control the type and speed of vehicles permitted to use certain streets. There are many ways in which this can be achieved and a variety of techniques are explained in Part 3.

Advice on the relevant components of environmental capacity and their various acceptable levels in situations is scarce. Some guidance in this difficult area is provided in Chapter 12 but each scheme should be considered in the light of the wishes of the people whose environment will be affected.

6.4 References

Text Reference

1. Transportation Research Board—Special Report 209, '*Highway Capacity Manual*', Transportation Research Board (1985). (6.1)

2. Organisation for Economic Cooperation and Development—'*The Traffic Capacity of Major Routes*', OECD (1983). (6.2)

3. Ministry of Transport—'*Traffic in Towns— A study of the long term problems of traffic in urban areas*' [Buchanan Report], Reports of the Steering Group and Working Group appointed by the Minister of Transport, HMSO (1963). (6.3)

7   The Need for a Balance of Transport Modes

7.1 Alternative Policies

In some of the world's cities (notably in North America), attempts have been made to design urban areas to accommodate the needs of car users in a totally unrestrained way. This has involved the construction of massive urban motorway networks with their consequent need for high levels of capital expenditure and an abundant suply of land (see Plate 7.1).

The result of this policy has been that up to one-third of urban land area has been given over to roads, parking lots, service areas and other transport infrastructure creating an enormous impact on the environment.

Yet, despite the massive provision, congestion can still be experienced during peak periods, at critical points on the road network. Furthermore, accidents and pollution are now endemic social problems with serious economic consequences. It has been argued that the general quality of life in these areas has been sacrificed to meet the demands of traffic.

At the other end of the policy spectrum some Scandanavian cities have restrained traffic, to minimise the impact of private cars on the urban environment. This type of policy brings with it its own risks such as a threat to the economic prosperity of the area because both car users and businesses may transfer to alternative areas, where restraints on traffic movement are less severe. Thus, a perceived need for 'traffic restraint' (or the management of demand) will always be tempered by the requirements of sufficient access to sustain business activity.

7.2 Managing Demand for Traffic Movement

Many different methods of managing the demand for traffic movement have been attempted, with varying degrees of success. These have included controlling the provision and price of car parking, physically constraining the way in which traffic uses the road network and introducing some form of permit system or direct pricing mechanism to produce a system of priority for certain road users (see Plate 7.2).

Plate 7.1 Major US highway construction in an urban area

Source: G Jacobs (TRRL)

Plate 7.2 A gateway to the Singapore area licencing scheme

Source: JMP Consultants

A variety of arguments can and have been used to support particular restraint schemes reflecting the different conditions and objectives found in different areas. They may be to maximise the economic activity of the urban area; or perhaps to influence a more desirable modal split between private and public transport; or to limit air pollution or accidents. A description of the techniques which might be used to achieve these goals can be found in Chapter 23.

What has become clear is that traffic restraint techniques should not be resorted to as a result of a failure to plan or provide adequate transport services but should rather be seen as a positive measure which can make a valuable contribution to integrated transport policies.

An important, and in some circumstances essential, complementary policy measure involves the encouragement and continued support for efficient public transport services. Adequate provision of public transport is essential to provide reasonable mobility for the large minority who will never own their own car. It should also provide a realistic and attractive alternative choice of transport for car users and assist in limiting the amount of congestion and consequent pressure for major road building.

In summary, the future health and vitality of urban areas relies to a considerable extent on maintaining an appropriate balance between public and private modes of transport.

7.3 Further Information

1. Webster F V et al—'*Changing Patterns of Urban Travel*',—Transport Reviews, Vol 6 No 2, April—June 1986.

PART 2 TRANSPORTATION PLANNING, POLICY DEVELOPMENT AND SCHEME APPRAISAL

8   Transportation Policy

8.1 Transportation Policy Objectives

The term transportation comprises:

the movement of people:

- as pedestrians (sometimes using lifts, escalators or travelators);

- in vehicles available for their private use (mainly pedal cycles, motor cycles and cars); or

- in vehicles available for public use (mainly taxis, buses of various types, trains, ferries and aeroplanes); and

the movement of goods:

- by hand (often with the help of barrows or trolleys);

- by conveyor (such as hoist, belt or pipeline);

- by vehicles provided by organisations offering freight transport services (van, lorry, railway wagon, barge, ship or aeroplane); or

- by a similar range of vehicles provided by the owners of the goods.

These activities are carried out within a framework of economic, social and personal activities of people and organisations located in various places and taking place at various times.

A comprehensive transportation policy should cover all (or at least most) of these modes of transport. Each mode has particular infrastructure requirements (eg. road construction, bus stations, railway tracks and terminals) and operational characteristics. Transportation policies may aim to emphasise different modes of transport and result in proposals for investment in specific types of infrastructure, or include financial arrangements to encourage the use of specific transport services or particular uses of the transport system [NI.12].

The Characteristics of Travel

People seldom travel without a specific reason for the trip (eg. to go to work, or to visit). Commerce requires that goods be moved from their point of manufacture to points of sale. The need for transport and the patterns of movements that result, are influenced by the relative locations of homes, shops, workplaces and recreational facilities. For this reason, effective transportation policies must take full account of land use patterns, economic and social activity. It follows that the transportation policies appropriate for a particular town or city will depend on the physical,

social and economic characteristics of that area. However, local transportation policies must take account of the regional and national transport framework within which they must operate since trip making in any area will include a proportion of longer distance journeys and the infrastructure provided for these trips will be the responsibility of other authorities.

Defining Policy Objectives

When formulating a transportation policy, it is necessary to define objectives which should be realistic and attainable. These objectives should also relate closely to objectives set for other policy areas such as those concerned with housing, industry, commerce and recreation.

All policy objectives will have both economic and financial implications. In 1985 the total expenditure in the UK on road and rail (by users) was £58 billion of which £13 billion was levied in taxes. In comparison capital and current expenditure in this area by national and local government amounted to £6 billion. At the personal level, over 15 per cent of household expenditure is concerned with transport. These figures demonstrate that transport issues are very important to the national economy and it is vital to ensure that transport systems are as efficient as possible within the practical constraints under which they operate.

The Pursuit of Efficiency

Precise criteria for efficiency are difficult to establish and will differ with the viewpoint of the observer. For example, a policy involving a reduction of national resources devoted to transport might result in less travel, which some might consider desirable, but this could adversely affect economic output and individual perceptions of quality of life. The demands for transport by different sections of the community often compete with each other. For example, if the times of journeys could be staggered throughout the day, peak hour congestion would diminish but this would involve a wider spread of working hours and cause additional costs and difficulties for industry and commerce. Similarly, if vehicle users on uncongested roads were compelled to travel at speeds which minimised fuel consumption, many drivers would be very frustrated and might even feel that their personal liberty had been infringed.

As individuals and as a community there is evidence of a willingness to pay substantial amounts for the benefits of personal travel at increasingly high levels of resource consumption. The quest for efficiency in the consumption of resources might be pursued by weighing the benefits to vehicle users and to society against the social and economic cost consequences of achieving them. The scope for saving is considerable as, for example, the Transport and Road Research Laboratory have estimated that the nation wastes as much as £2000m each year (at 1983 prices) through traffic delays at intersections, quite apart from other losses due to excess mileage travelled and from accidents.

8.2 Urban Transportation Policies

Typical policy objectives for urban transportation include:

- improving accessibility for work, leisure, shopping, business, education and welfare services;

- enhancing travel opportunities for the less mobile (including children, the elderly and disabled people);

- stimulating economic activity and employment opportunities;

- reducing the incurred costs of maintenance, wear and tear, fuel and depreciation for vehicle owners;

- improving road safety; and

- improving the environment.

The general objective of most transportation policies will be to improve the quality of life for the community but there are a wide range of quite different measures which might be used to achieve this. The choices made will depend upon local circumstances and on the political predisposition of decision makers. For instance, some policies may require more centralised planning or regulation, whereas others will rely more upon market forces. Some policies may be relatively straightforward to implement whilst others may be attainable only at high financial or social cost. It is therefore important that proposed policy objectives can be achieved within available resources and within a reasonable timescale.

The interaction between transportation policies and other social, economic and land use factors is especially strong in urban areas. This needs to be fully appreciated when determining whether objectives are feasible. For these reasons, the long term effects of alternative policies need to be carefully assessed and considered before substantial public expenditure is committed and an urban area changed, perhaps irrevocably. Thus, for practical reasons, it may be preferable to favour policies which do not depend for their success on major land use or social change and are largely consistent with changes already seen to be taking place.

Policy Statements

The strategic aims for transportation in an urban area should be explicitly stated and widely known. They will usually be contained within:

- national transport policies or guidelines (issued from time to time by Central Government, often in the form of 'White Papers' or by specific policy statements);

- development plans (structure plans, local plans and unitary development plans) and Transport Policy and Programme Statements;

- and in Metropolitan County areas, policy statements by Passenger Transport Authorities.

These policies will be reflected in:

- policy decisions on local issues by highway or planning authorities; and

- decisions by officers acting under powers delegated to them by local authorities.

Since expenditure on transport and transportation is funded by private individuals and organisations as well as by public authorities, it is important that the policies adopted are compatible with the desires and needs of the private sector, although there will inevitably be those who lose as well as those who gain from the effects of any transportation policy or specific scheme. It is also desirable that transportation policies be broadly in harmony with the objectives of other organisations and with the wider aspirations of the community at large. Where capital investment is planned by a public authority, private sector gains and social net benefits have to be assessed against public costs.

Formulating Transportation Policy

Because transportation policies are presented in structure plans, local plans, unitary development plans and transport policies and programmes (TPP's), it is essential that they stem from a common planning process so that the decisions that are appropriate to each are wholly compatible. No generally accepted method exists for deriving an overall urban transportation strategy and each situation has to be considered on its merits, taking account of the particular characteristics of the locality. The main transport related policy options which could form part of an overall strategy include:

- land use planning and the control of development;

- traffic management and control measures;

- new road construction and improvements to existing highways;

- public transport subsidies; and

- new railway construction and improvements to existing services.

These options are discussed in more detail in Chapter 9.

8.3 Problems and Opportunities

Even after the broad policy objectives have been established, specific problems cannot be tackled without first identifying what they are. It is often found that there are more problems than there are resources available to solve them and so some way of assessing their relative importance is needed. The same is true where opportunities for improvement exist. Problems or opportunities are usually identified by:

- assessing the performance of existing facilities, in terms of:
  the incidence of accidents;
  environmental conditions;
  traffic conditions (eg. congestion, delays, queues, operating costs);
  particular conflicts which may exist (eg. in shopping streets between pedestrians, service-access and through traffic);

- the occurrence of proposals for development or other changes in land use; and by

- receiving public complaints and concerns expressed either individually or through elected representatives, lobbies or interest-groups.

Heavy traffic flows on inappropriate roads are often associated with high accident rates, severe environmental intrusion and traffic delays. Those areas with the worst traffic problems are generally well known and the range of possible solutions will often be well rehearsed. Changes in policy may, however, change the priority afforded to finding a solution as well as the values used in the assessment of possible options.

The part which political priorities can play in determining the relative importance of problems and opportunities has to be recognised by professional transportation planners and traffic engineers. The professional's role should be to establish a sufficiency of data on the transport system and the characteristics of travel demands, to enable the effects of proposed policies and their likely impact upon the community concerned to be assessed by the decision makers before they are implemented.

National policies on these issues may be promoted by new legislation or regulations or by the production of new technical advice and the application of standard criteria when awarding grants. The initiative for local schemes will, however, invariably be generated at the local level. Local councillors and the local government officers who advise them should be well equipped to take decisions concerning the types of development to be encouraged or the ways in which conflicts between traffic, safety and the environment might be resolved; taking account of the views of the public through consultation when appropriate (see also Chapter 13).

Forecasting the Effects of Transportation Policies

It is, in principle, feasible to estimate future travel demand and traffic trends within an area prior to developing policies which will maximise overall benefits to the community for a given level of capital investment. It was this concept that lay behind the land use/transportation studies carried out for most major cities and conurbations in Britain in the 1960s and early 1970s. However, this approach lost favour because of:

- the uncertainties inherent in estimating long term changes in population, employment, housing needs, social structure and economic outlook;

- the difficulties in maintaining long term programmes of public capital investment; and

- the difficulties in ensuring continuity of political commitment to an initially agreed set of policies.

During the 1970s policies in urban areas began to reflect the desire to achieve immediate or short term action rather than longer term programmes. However, this trend should not be allowed to obscure the need for measures to conform with longer term transportation strategies. Such long term vision will always be a vital ingredient in planning for a better future.

It is always desirable that transportation policies should permit advantage to be taken of any opportunities for change which present themselves. These can occur in the following ways:

- by central government actions which can provide the legal or administrative mechanism to permit a policy to be implemented;

- by public or private sector initiatives to develop an area, which might provide the impetus to undertake new projects;

- by changes to the infrastructure which may permit actions that could not otherwise have taken place (eg. construction of a bypass could provide opportunities to improve the environment and service access of existing streets relieved of through traffic).

All these possibilities require a continuous process of evaluation and decision taking. The evaluation of emerging problems or opportunities may not be as formal or rigorous as that undertaken for firm proposals but should, nevertheless, be systematic and clearly defined. The values and standards adopted in determining the relative importance of such problems should also be consistent with those used in the subsequent evaluation of schemes designed to solve them.

8.4 The Role of Lobbies and Interest Groups

In a democratic society, particular issues are bound to be raised from time to time by individuals or groups from within the community. These may occur at national level through parliamentary lobbies and the national press, television and radio; or at local level through ad hoc groups and societies using the local press and publicity media. Interest groups can often be highly effective in raising public awareness of a particular problem, although they often express narrow sectional views. Such lobbies and interest groups can identify problems and opportunities in urban transport and, as the scope for public participation in planning has widened, advantage has been gained by extending the ways in which opinions and attitudes can be obtained. Early consultation is important, particularly where large and potentially controversial schemes are being considered, both to speed the process and improve the prospects of progress. It can also help to minimise the points of conflict which might otherwise need to be dealt with at Public Inquiry (these issues are covered more fully in Chapter 13).

8.5 Informed Public Debate

Informed public debate is a good thing and can lead to fuller consideration of and enhancements to scheme proposals. Exhibitions and presentations all assist in informing the public leading to a better understanding of proposals, thereby facilitating improved debate which may involve lobbies and interested groups.

For the future, more freedom of access to information on local authority affairs could influence the way in which urban transportation problems and opportunities are identified and given priority and might include the use of local television networks to widen the opportunities for public participation in planning matters (see also Chapter 13).

8.6 Further Information

1. Standing Advisory Committee on Trunk Road Assessment—'*Urban Road Appraisal*', HMSO (1986).

2. '*The Government Response to the SACTRA Report on Urban Appraisal*', HMSO (1986).

3. Advisory Committee on Trunk Road Assessment (Chairman, G Leitch)—'*Report of the Advisory Committee on Trunk Road Assessment*', HMSO (1978).

9 Transport Policy Options

9.1 Introduction

There are many optional policies and individual measures which may be employed to deal with urban traffic problems. In practice it is invariably found necessary to develop a package of complementary measures to achieve an outcome which reflects the range of objectives being sought [NI.12].

The value of a number of these options is discussed briefly below and developed in more detail in subsequent chapters, but the main policy options are:

- at the broadest level, constructing new transport infrastructure (eg. roads and/or tracked transport systems) and applying planning regulations to influence the location of new developments;

- making the current transport networks more efficient in terms of capacity, safety and accessibility and by improving the environment (eg. by applying traffic engineering measures); and

- improving or subsidising some transport modes and applying measures to restrain or discourage journeys by other modes in certain places at certain times, in order to change the balance of use between alternative modes of transport.

9.2 The Use of Planning Powers and Development Control

Public authorities have control over significant amounts of land in urban areas and have some powers to initiate development. This is especially so in areas administered by urban or new town development corporations or where special local initiatives apply (see also Chapter 4). However, whilst some authorities (eg. central government departments) are not subject to the usual planning controls, most are constrained by competing demands on resources. Pressure for land-use change often comes from the private sector. Since the purpose of structure plans is to encourage development to take place in locations preferred by the planning authorities, they will reject proposals that conflict with their policy objectives. It is therefore desirable that planning authorities take full account of market trends and needs when preparing or amending their structure plans. The current trend is towards decentralisation of urban activities with a consequent increase in the use of cars (see also Chapters 2.2 and 2.3).

Purely local attempts to inhibit development may result in some employment and population migrating to other places with less restrictive policies or with fewer constraints on central area development. Hence, planning control is mainly effective in a negative sense; it is less able to exert a strong positive influence on well established trends governed by the market forces in private development. Whilst this is true of location it is less true of the intensity of development. Planning controls can have an important influence in keeping down the traffic generating potential of new development in congested areas by controlling its density and design.

9.3 New Railway Systems

Many cities in the world have, for a variety of reasons, emabarked on or are planning new urban and suburban railway systems (see Table 9.1). The newest railway in Britain is the Docklands Light Rail due to open in July 1987 (see Plate 9.1). It is an automatic, driverless system which partly uses previously abandoned British Rail routes. Built at low cost; it has been designed and constructed in only 3 years. The metro in Newcastle upon Tyne is another completely new light railway and other systems in London, Glasgow and Liverpool have improved their central penetration by substantial new construction.

Many of the operational factors concerning new railways are equally true of light rapid transit systems which can take many forms but are usually track or rail based and may be suspended from an overhead rail or located at, or below, ground level. Some forms of light rapid transit can allow more flexibility in geometric layout than is possible with conventional rail systems which can make them easier to integrate within existing urban areas. This together with their initial cost advantages has resulted in their use in a variety of urban locations throughout the world, but they are generally less well suited to continuous and intensive mass haulage requirements over longer distances.

New railway systems require major capital investment, particularly where they are built in tunnels or as new alignments. Although it may be possible to meet operating costs from revenue (if this is a chosen objective of fares policy), experience has shown that it is extremely difficult to repay capital cost from revenue. Despite these drawbacks, new urban railways can greatly improve the level of access and mobility offered by urban public transport and can provide a viable alternative investment to major urban road construction, especially where the objective is to distribute the benefits more equitably amongst the population.

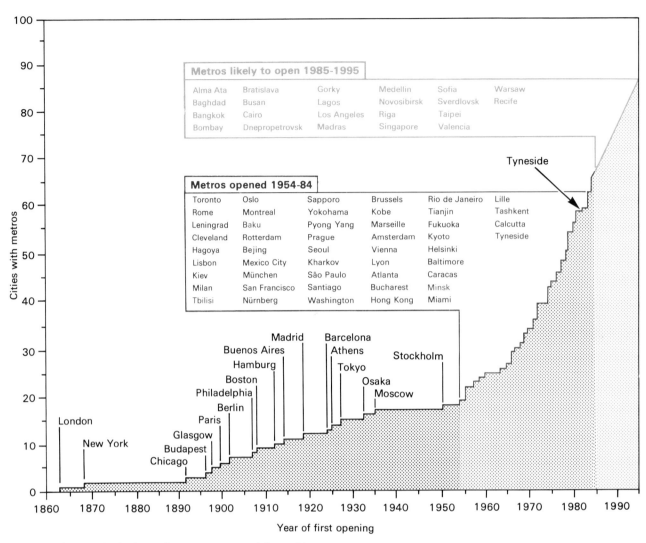

Table 9.1 The growth of urban railway systems around the world

Source: The Metro in Industrial and Developing Countries—Railway Gazette International (1985)

Plate 9.1 A new driverless light railway system under test in London's Docklands

Source: London Docklands Light Railway

Construction costs and environmental intrusion can be reduced by making use of existing or previously abandoned rights of way and structures where these are suitably located to meet future travel demand. Circumstances which may favour a rail system are high density centres of urban activity to which it is difficult to provide uncongested access by road at acceptable cost, combined with high density residential areas which can benefit from short walking distances to railway stations.

Except where there is a high intensity of common trip destinations, any new fixed track system would need to be integrated with other forms of urban transport to extend its catchment area more widely (see Plate 9.2). This would be true for medium and low density residential areas and other suburban developments.

Examples of such integration are effective feeder bus services to suburban stations and suitably located car parks for 'park and ride'. Integration is important if the full benefits of rail investment are to be realised, not only for those who travel by the new system but also to achieve improved road traffic conditions and economies in bus operation. The deregulation of bus services makes it especially important for local authorities to have regard for this requirement in seeking tenders from operators for such feeder services for which subsidies can be provided.

Whatever objectives the railway system is aiming to achieve, evaluation of costs and benefits must be wide enough to cover all possible effects whilst recognising that the distribution of both benefits and disbenefits are likely to be different for users from different

Plate 9.2 Integration of bus and rail systems

Source: G Crow Esq

geographical locations. Whilst grants are available for major public transport investment under Section 56 of the Transport Act 1968 (Ref. 1), all possible sources of funding from both public and private sectors should be explored, together with opportunities for joint financing and operation, with the aim of avoiding an excessive burden on local funding which cannot be supported from revenue. This approach is particularly appropriate where new railway systems can assist urban regeneration and enhance land values and has been successfully pursued in London's docklands redevelopment.

9.4 New Urban Road Construction

Major controversy at public inquiries and elsewhere has in recent years demonstrated the difficulties of determining the effects of new road construction within an existing congested urban area. One reason for this is that existing methods of analysis (transportation models) offer insufficient understanding of the underlying rationale for, and mechanism of trip making. Consequently, they may be incapable of taking full account of all the many effects of new road construction (see also Chapter 11).

The creation of a new road within a complex urban network will result in many changes to trip making including choice of destination, time of travel and route taken, as well as changes concerning access and servicing over a wide area. The longer term consequence of providing more highway capacity within an urban area may be to stimulate more vehicle trips, to lengthen journey distances (still, perhaps, within the same overall journey time) and possibly to encourage diversion from other modes of transport.

There is, therfore, a possibility that the same level of congestion might be recreated over a larger network of roads than before, albeit with more vehicle kilometres being travelled by more people than previously. This extra amount of travel is made because of benefits perceived by the users, but the additional traffic may generate extra costs to other transport users and could be detrimental to the environment. Another effect recognised in recent years is that the impact of major urban road development is different for different social groups, raising difficulties for equity in evaluation (eg. it generally favours car owners).

Nevertheless, it should be recognised that new roads can provide access to new developments and replacement traffic capacity can facilitate improvements in pedestrians' safety and to the environment.

Purpose designed roads on a new alignment often have a crucial role to play in the development of a hierarchy of roads (see Plate 9.3). In this sense, the overall

improvement can be a qualitative one with the capacity equivalent to that of the new road being transferred to some other function, elsewhere in the network (eg. pedestrianised areas, or the provision of kerbside parking).

In view of the difficulties of evaluating the longer term consequences of new road construction in urban areas, some authorities assess proposed highway schemes against objectives such as:

● the ability to divert industrial and commercial traffic away from environmentally sensitive areas and town centres;

● the ability to open up access to industrial and commercial areas by direct connection to the primary distributor network;

● assistance to major inner city renewal programmes by creating a new road hierarchy; and

● improved access to public transport interchanges and provision of additional capacity to assist public transport.

These objectives demonstrate clearly that new roads can help to provide much more than just an increase in the overall traffic capacity of a road network. Indeed, in some situations there may be good reasons for not increasing the network capacity at all but securing these other improvements instead, by replacement of old roads with new. (Detailed design of new highways is covered in Part 5.)

9.5 Improvements to Existing Infrastructure

Up-grading of an existing road or railway is sometimes seen as an alternative to investment in a new route on a separate alignment. For example, the dualling of an existing main road, the replacement of a single level junction by a grade-separated one and the re-equipping of an old suburban railway with electric traction and refurbished or relocated stations, can provide improvements in capacity, safety and journey time which compare favourably with those of completely new infrastructure. The main advantage is often that no new right of way is needed thus avoiding the possibility of new severance in residential areas.

The main drawbacks are:

● the net gain in capacity is likely to be less than that associated with an entirely new facility (assuming that the right of way being improved is in active use);

● that only limited potential exists for development of a route hierarchy by merely replacing one artery by another;

Plate 9.3 Major road construction on a primary distributor in an urban area

Source: British Road Federation

● that the capital works are disruptive due to existing traffic having to be accommodated throughout the construction period;

● the delays to existing traffic are often considerable, even if they are not quantified; and

● that existing geometric and operating standards are often lower than those achievable on a new alignment.

These drawbacks are more serious in the case of an up-graded road than for a railway. This is because the railway already has an exclusive right of way and existing traffic is usually tightly scheduled and controlled. Even so, the capital cost of a comparable scheme can be substantially higher than that for a new track alignment. Major highway improvements may qualify for Transport Supplementary Grants (TSG) (see also Chapters 3.3 and 4.2 and Sco.43). Grants may also be available for urban railway schemes involving 'substantial innovation' under Section 56 of the Transport Act 1968 (Ref. 1).

9.6 Traffic Engineering Measures

Traffic engineering techniques may be employed to:

● improve road safety;

● protect the environment;

● reduce delays by careful and comprehensive design and operation of road junctions;

● provide facilities for pedestrians, cyclists and dis-abled people;

● give priority to public transport; and

● control parking.

They can also provide relatively low cost and effective solutions to many urban traffic problems. Widespread application of such measures has produced significant safety and environmental benefits and savings in travel costs that greatly exceeded the capital cost of the schemes and the disbenefits to other road users.

Traffic engineering techniques include:

● physical modifications to highway links, junctions and the road environment (eg. the re-allocation of space amongst different categories of road user, changes in junction layout, signing and road marking, landscaping);

● regulating the use of the highway—see Plates 9.4 and 9.5 (eg. introducing speed limits, traffic signal control and limiting waiting and loading);

● providing information for the road user (eg. traffic signs, road markings, street name plates, fixed and variable message signing and traffic broadcasting); and

● differential charging for the use of the road system (eg. parking charges, tolls and road use pricing).

Traffic management measures are seldom employed on a large enough scale to have a major effect on strategic issues like choice of mode of travel, but they can be designed to be complementary to new investment in road or rail infrastructure.

(The design and implementation of traffic management measures are dealt with in detail in Part 3.)

Plate 9.4 Regulating the use of the carriageway in Bangkok, before . . . .

Plate 9.5 . . . and after

Source: G Jacobs (TRRL)

9.7 Public Transport Subsidies

Public transport subsidies may be used to lower fare levels, improve services, or both. In either case the aim will be to increase patronage or, at least, halt its decline. Internal cross-subsidies within the fare structure can also allow simpler ticketing systems and fares structures to be employed, perhaps by means of travel cards and zonal or flat fares.

People with particular transport difficulties (eg. the poor, the elderly, the disabled, people in remote areas, children) can sometimes be helped through concessionary fare schemes, which subsidise the user directly, rather than by subsidising the operator.

Influence of Subsidy on Modal Choice

It is generally accepted that the net benefit from a subsidy tends to fall as the level of subsidy increases (Ref. 2). Subsidies, like any other form of public expenditure, have a high opportunity cost (ie. the unrealised value of the next best alternative way of using the money). Thus a point is reached when the extra benefit gained is insufficient to justify the extra costs incurred.

It has been found that existing car users are often reluctant to use public transport (especially buses) even when fare levels are reduced, so that most of the benefits of subsidy go to those who are already using the public transport system rather than to new passengers. For the same reason, the effect of fare reductions on traffic congestion is generally relatively small, except perhaps in central areas at peak periods. It has therefore been held that the scope for increasing patronage of road based public transport in urban areas, solely by fare reductions is limited (Refs. 3 and 4).

Even if services were offered free of charge, it has been estimated that only about 50 per cent more passengers would be attracted relative to the number carried when break-even fares are charged. However, improved or subsidised fixed track systems in high density corridors tend to be viewed differently by car owners who are prepared to park and ride or even to switch mode entirely, especially if this is part of an integrated system of public transport facilities. The introduction of the Tyne and Wear Metro system exemplified such a change.

Whilst network-wide subsidy of public transport may produce net benefits in terms of social cost-benefits and level of use (ref. 3), it would be inconsistent with policies designed to foster competition between public transport operators, or to limit the amount of revenue support provided from public funds for unremunerative but perhaps socially desirable services.

The Transport Act 1985 (see Chapter 26.1 and Ref. 5) which came into general effect in Great Britain in October 1986 (largely outside Greater London) exemplifies the influence of a national policy aimed at encouraging the provision of public transport in a free market situation intended to allow interplay of supply and demand to produce an appropriate mix of services and fare levels. However, it is also contained provisions which require local authorities to subsidise particular bus services where a need exists which was not provided for by commercial operators. The longer term effects of the policy remain to be seen but the route-by-route approach to subsidised services, when allied with public expenditure constraints does limit the ability of local authorities to provide widespread public transport subsidies as the major thrust of their transport policies.

9.8 Traffic Restraint (or Management of Demand)

One of the arguments advanced by those favouring policies of public transport subsidy is that it can provide a positive restraint on the growth in private car traffic. The provision of cheap and convenient public transport can help to encourage car owners to use buses and trains instead of personal transport. In recognition of present car ownership levels, it may delay the time at which car owning households acquire a second or third car. Car ownership has been rising steadily (see Figure 2.6). In 1985, 62 per cent of households had regular use of one or more cars compared with 31% in 1961. 17% of households now have regular use of 2 or more cars. The ability to forecast future traffic demand will require a better understanding of why people choose to buy cars and when and where they use them. As overall levels of car ownership rise the number of people to whom a discretionary choice of trip making by car is available will also increase. This situation must be taken into account when plans to deal with traffic congestion are being prepared.

Apart from the positive inducements to use an alternative mode already discussed, almost all other forms of traffic restraint are negative in that they set out to deter use of private cars and unnecessary goods vehicles in congested areas at peak times by some form of discriminatory measure.

'Out of Town' Development

The development of out of town facilities, such as hypermarkets and leisure centres is worthy of mention here since it represents a planning option which aims to encourage traffic away from existing congested centres. Such development may, however, also encourage the trend towards multi-car ownership in households, as well as affecting the economics of traditional centralised shopping areas and, in consequence, the accessibility of facilities for those without cars. Thus, although it may ease congestion in central areas in the short term, land use changes may stimulate additional car ownership and traffic growth over a longer period.

Restrictive Restraint Measures

The most commonly used method of traffic restraint involves exerting control over the amount and price of car parking in central areas. Restrictions on time, location and price of parking are now widely accepted in the interests of maintaining efficient traffic flow, of ensuring adequate access for goods and service vehicles and of providing pedestrians with sufficient visibility to cross the road safely. In 1986 wheel clamping was introduced in Central London as an aid to enforcement to combat illegal on-street parking, but it is not appropriate where vehicles are causing a hazard or obstruction.

Rationing time at the kerbspace is usually achieved by pricing mechanisms but it is related only indirectly to parking demand. An alternative, and arguably fairer, system would be to price the use of road space directly (whether it is used for movement or for parking) at rates which reflect the marginal social costs of congestion prevailing at the time. Electronic sensing and communications technology have been developed to the point where automatic road use pricing systems are feasible, with a very high potential for economic return on equipment in major urban areas.

Although a variety of road or area pricing systems have been considered for use in many of the world's cities there are very few examples of such systems being implemented as a permanent measure. One of the reasons most commonly put forward to explain this is that road pricing allocates road space, not on the basis of demand or need but simply on the ability of some road users to pay the going price. It is therefore open to the criticism that it does not make the most effective use of road space and is also socially inequitable.

Until systems are devised which overcome the drawbacks associated with current approaches it seems likely that localised traffic restraint will continue to rely on conventional traffic management and control measures. These include selective area-wide bans on

particular vehicle types at particular times of day, purpose designed width, weight and speed controls on roads within environmental areas, special signing and signal settings to encourage use of certain routes rather than others and the effective control of parking. (All of these techniques are discussed in more detail in Part 3 in which Chapter 21 deals with On-Street Parking and Chapter 23 deals with Measures for Limiting the Amount of Road Traffic).

9.9 References

		Text Reference
1.	*Transport Act 1968*, HMSO (1968).	(9.3, 9.5)
2.	Glaister, S et al—'*Estimating Economic Benefits from Public Transport Subsidy*', 11th Summer Annual Meeting, PTRC Education and Research Services (1983).	(9.7)
3.	Webster, F V et al—'*Changing the Cost of Travel*'. Paper D35, World Conference on Transport Research (1980).	(9.7)
4.	Webster, F V et al—'*Changing Patterns of Urban Travel*' in Transport Reviews, Vol 6, Nos 1 and 2, (Jan—June 1986).	(9.7)
5.	*Transport Act 1985*, HMSO (1985).	(9.7)

9.10 Further Information

6. Tyne and Wear PTE et al—'*Tyne and Wear Study: Metro Monitoring and Development Study Report*', Tyne & Wear PTE (1986).

7. Bäckstrom, I—'*The Metro in Industrial and Developing Countries*', Developing Metros 85, Railway Gazette International (1985).

8. Dawson, J et al,—'*Electronic Road Pricing in Hong Kong*', Traffic Engineering and Control, Vol 26, No 11 (November 1985).

9. Walters, A A—'*Cost Scale of Bus Services*', World Bank working paper 325, World Bank (1979).

10. Smeed, R J—'*Road Pricing, the economic and technical possibilities*', HMSO (1964).

10 Traffic Data Collection and Monitoring

10.1 Introduction

Throughout the design process from the initial identification of a problem to the final selection of the most appropriate scheme to remedy it, data are required to assist the judgements being made at every stage. This process will require:

● information about the current state of the traffic system and how it has, and is, changing over time (for problem identification);

● specification of any alternative design standards and their implications, for application to scheme proposals;

● forecasts of the effects that each proposed scheme is likely to have, considered against its objectives as well as any side effects that are foreseen; and

● the values (and any priorities or weightings) to be used in assessing the overall impact of each scheme on different sections of the community.

Some of these data will be specific to the particular areas in which problems are occurring and to the alternative schemes being considered. This will require up to date local data which will need to be obtained from purpose designed surveys and from any regular monitoring data which is relevant.

Consideration of alternative design standards and evaluation procedures should, however, involve the adoption of national (or sometimes international) standards. This is particularly important where schemes are competing for scarce resources and will be considered against other projects. Where locally determined values or standards are adopted, this should be made clear. In dense urban areas it is sometimes necessary to adopt standards which depart from the norm because of physical constraints or because of the disproportionate economic effects of adhering to the best possible standards.

Survey Techniques

A range of survey types and possible sources of data for different purposes is set out in Table 10.1. This covers the assessment of:

● traffic characteristics and manoeuvres, including pedestrians (ie. the components of traffic);

● demands for movement, journey times and costs, including accidents (ie. demand for the service offered by the transport network); and

● the various impacts of traffic on the users of the system and on the environment (ie. the consumers' response to prevailing traffic conditions).

The table classifies various methods of data collection into those which rely on observation or routine census taking, those which require individuals to be questioned and those which require active participation by representative groups within the community. The techniques differ widely according to the type of survey to be undertaken. The needs of traffic component assessment can usually be met by observational techniques, those of network assessment and travel demand by interview surveys and those requiring consumers' response and involving environmental impact, by interactive techniques of attitude measurement akin to market research.

Monitoring Data

Although the majority of data needed to design an urban traffic scheme will be derived from specific sample surveys, the need for continuous monitoring should not be overlooked. The main objectives of a monitoring programme are to have readily available, the relevant data to allow periodic assessment of the transport related issues that are likely to be raised within an area and to monitor the performance of existing networks. It is therefore advisable to commit resources to a regular programme that provides this information and enables trends to be established, including analysis of the consequences of applying particular policies.

Ad hoc sample surveys provide useful data for specific problems but their output may be difficult to integrate within a comprehensive time series data bank. Thus, regular monitoring surveys can provide the means to relate various ad hoc surveys to a more substantial base (eg. using factors to convert to average annual flows with an appreciation of the confidence levels of the estimates).

The Department of Transport's Traffic Appraisal Manual (TAM) 1985 (Ref. 1) [Sco.44] gives details of all the data sources provided from national surveys and of the appropriate methods for converting sample counts into equivalent traffic flow estimates for design purposes. These data are derived mainly from the core (170 sites) and rotating censuses of traffic carried out on the national road system. Comparatively few of these sites are located in urban areas.

Travel Data

There are a number of other sources of travel data which are often relevant to urban traffic studies. Examples are the national population census, which gives information on journeys to work; the National

	Types of Survey	Volume	Classification	Speed	Saturation flows	Turning flows	Parking	Goods access	Pedestrians' crossing and delay	Pedestrian and cycle movements	Goods movements O-D	Person trips O-D (by mode)	Journey times/operating costs	Accidents	Impacts on environment	Attitudes and choice criteria	Impacts on travel behaviour and activities
		Traffic assessment								*Network assessment*					*Community impact assessment*		
Observational	Inventory records	Core and rotating census data									Planning data/household census/NTS, etc.			Police stats 19 records			
Observational	Continuous monitoring	Automatic sensors – loop-detectors, radar, microwave, infra-red etc.											Network data NIS, TARA, etc.				
Observational	Sample surveys	Video recording image processing				Manual counts, portable event-recorders, etc.			Patrol surveys cordon counts; Video recordings	"Floating" observer	Number-plate matching		"Floating" observer methods	Conflict measurement	Noise and pollution measurement		
Interview	Postal questionnaires							Delivery records		Travel diary	Vehicle logs	Travel diary	Vehicle logs				Travel and activity diary
Interview	Roadside/on-board questionnaires											Specific trip data using portable data capture devices, etc.				Subjective response measurements – attribute-scaling semantic differential, etc.	
Interview	Home interviews									Travel diary	Delivery records	Travel diary; HATS gaming-simulation					HATS gaming-simulation
Interactive	Group discussions														Public meetings	Repertory grid/Delphi techniques	Household role and decision models

Table 10.1 Types and purposes of surveys

Travel Survey (NTS) which provides information on household travel patterns; accident data bases (compiled from the 'STATS 19' record forms completed by Police authorities) (Ref. 2) and a wide range of planning data bases held at both local and national level and essential for transport modelling.

Many local highway authorities have established road network information systems for monitoring conditions and assessing priorities for the management of urban road networks. Developments in information technology are helping improve the range and accessibility of the information held and the Department of Transport is developing a Network Information System (NIS) to provide a wide range of basic data and video-taped records of the entire trunk road network.

It is fundamental to all information systems and to any kind of continually updated record of conditions, that they must include an accurate basis of referencing. This should include locations and times at which items of data are collected or events of interest occur. Some locational referencing systems are described below.

10.2 Locational Referencing for Road Based Information Systems

Locational referencing can be achieved on a geographical area basis or in relation to fixed points on the highway network. The location of traffic data can be specified in terms of:

● administrative areas (eg. local authority areas or electoral wards);

● the ordnance survey grid reference (OSGR) system (which covers Britain and is thus capable of giving a unique reference to any location or area, in hectometre or kilometre squares);

● postal codes (as the Post Office have allocated unique codes to each major property or small group of residential properties throughout the UK);

● an ad hoc zoning system (eg. for a traffic survey where the zoning system is determined by the transport networks, usually based on enumeration districts); or

● by known fixed points on the highway network (eg. A1 at 100 metres north of junction with the B100).

Ordnance Survey Grid References

Various procedures have been developed to establish gazetteers (ie. lists of addresses that relate to any given zoning system). A particular example of this is the file which has been created so that every post code has been allocated an Ordnance Survey Grid Reference (OSGR). The various boundaries of administrative areas in Britain have also been digitised to OSGR. This facility allows any address, given by a post code, to be converted into a digitised code for any specified zoning system. These zones can be used for referencing information on journeys (eg. the origin and destination of a trip).

Road Networks

It is common for traffic related data to be referenced to the road network which can be specified as links (ie. sections of a highway with reasonably constant characteristics) and nodes (ie. junctions or points where changes in link characteristics occur). In most systems the nodes are given a reference number, frequently the OSGR location, and links are then specified by the numbers of the nodes at either end. These network codes can then be used to store information relating to highway characteristics, traffic flows, accidents, maintenance records and so on. A summary of the more generally available road network information systems is given in Table 10.2.

10.3 Sources of National Inventory Data

In 1976 the Department of Transport sponsored a large number of coordinated traffic counts, roadside interviews and household interview surveys. These data, now largely out of date, are held at SIA and in the Economic and Social Research Council's archives and in the absence of other data could be used for traffic appraisal.

More up to date data are held by the Department of Transport; these consist of:

● Network Information System (NIS) (held by HCSL Division) [Sco.45] and

● Core and Rotating traffic census data (TRACDAS) (held by STC Division) [Sco.46].

The NIS road network describes the motorway and major road network as a series of digitised links as described above. Certain items of interest are recorded for motorways and trunk roads. These include the speed limit, single/dual carriageway, hilliness, bendiness, road class and whether or not a primary or an E route. Further more detailed information is to be added, and the roads are linked to video recordings.

Traffic counts are taken on each of the links held in the NIS network and the information held in the NIS database and by the Department's Statistics Division C. Data from the rotating census has yielded traffic flow (annual average daily flow) estimates for every link on the motorway, trunk and principal road network (see para 10.5 below).

Systems	Main Area of Application (Originators)
TARA – Technical Appraisal Route Analysis.	Initially applied traffic and accident information but wider applications being developed (County Surveyor's Society).
NIS – Network Information Systems.	Highway management – general inventory of traffic and accident information for Trunk Roads (Department of Transport).
TRAMS – Transport Referencing and Mapping Systems.	Network description and storage of general information (Transport and Road Research Laboratory).
CHIPS – Computerised Highway Information and Planning System.	General purpose highway database (Scottish Development Department).
WHIS – Welsh Highway Information System	Under Development (Welsh Office).

*Note: Systems specially developed for recording maintenance-related data or for highway design purposes have been excluded.

Table 10.2 Examples of road network information systems

10.4 Recording of Accidents

Details of all injury accidents reported to the Police are transcribed onto coding sheets in accordance with the STATS 19 form specified by the Department of Transport. This form is divided into three sections:

attendant circumstances: giving details of the site (eg. location, date, road conditions, weather);

vehicle record: giving details of each vehicle involved;

casualty record: giving details of each casualty involved.

Full details of the contents of the form are given in the booklet STATS 20 (Ref. 3). The data are held by the appropriate Local Processing Authority (LPA), which may be the Police force or County Council [Sco.47] and are also transferred to the Department of Transport where they are held for Britain as a whole in a central data bank maintained by the Transport and Road Research Laboratory (TRRL) [Sco.48]. Some police authorities maintain limited records of 'damage only' accidents, but many of these go unreported. The STATS 19 data are restricted to reported accidents that involve personal injury. Records are considered to be virtually complete for accidents involving fatal injury, but are known to be far less complete where only slight injury is involved. Reported accidents are defined and classified as slight, serious or fatal according to the most severe casualty in the accident. Definitions of these categories are as follows:

slight injury: injuries of a minor nature such as sprains, bruises or cuts not judged to be severe, or slight shock requiring only roadside attention;

serious injury: injuries for which a person is detained in hospital as an in-patient; or any of the following injuries, whether or not the injured person is detained in hospital; fractures, concussion, internal injuries, crushing, severe cuts and lacerations, severe general shock requiring medical treatment, injuries which result in death more than 30 days after the accident. The serious category, therefore, covers a very broad range of injuries;

fatal injury: injuries which cause death at any time up to 30 days after the accident.

Accident Severity Ratio

Public concern about the occurrence of fatal accidents is understandably high and is partly reflected in the high monetary cost attributed to them. However, in any particular locality fatal accidents may occur in numbers that are too small and variable to give a reliable indication of road safety on a localised basis. For this reason the number of serious or fatal accidents is often used as the indicator and should usually be analysed in terms of the involvement of different classes of road user (eg. pedestrians, pedal cyclists). Numbers of slight accidents, though subject to greater uncertainty in reporting, can provide an indicator of the relative severity of accidents by means of the Severity Ratio (SR), where:

$$SR = \frac{\text{Number of Fatal or Serious Accidents}}{\text{Total no of Injury Accidents}}$$

But, the uncertainties of under reporting and the difficulties in distinguishing serious from slight accidents throw some doubt on its value. It should also be noted that because of the different vulnerabilities to injury of road users in different classes, values of this ratio are only comparable between sets of accidents in which the proportions of various classes of road user involved are similar. If this is not the case, the ratio should be calculated separately for accidents involving each class of road user.

Accident Rates

The frequency of accidents at a particular location (number of injury accidents per year) is not necessarily an appropriate indicator of risk, as it takes no account of the degree of exposure to risk. For example, a large number of accidents may simply reflect a large volume of traffic. For this reason accident reporting is often expressed in terms of accident rates (ie. injury accidents per unit of vehicle movement or total distance travelled). Rates are normally expressed in accidents per 100 million vehicle kilometres. In practice it is sometimes found that accident rates can bias investigations towards low traffic flow sites. In some circumstances it may be better to use the Potential for Accident Reduction (PAR) approach. PAR is designed to estimate, from data at similar sites, the number of accidents expected at the particular site in question, according to its layout and traffic conditions prevailing (Ref. 4). However, accident causation factors are not always related to the limited number of physical features which are recorded and so this method also must be used with care and the perception afforded by experienced practitioners.

Accident data are normally stored on computer file for analysis purposes. Most local authorities use a similar file structure whereby accidents are individually numbered and recorded in the order in which they occurred. Each record contains the accident number, date and time, location and other principal details, as recorded on the STATS 19 form. It is sensible to include two separate entries for 'location' which allow checking of one against the other (eg. the grid reference and a verbal description). Processing the raw data usually follows straightforward computing procedures which perform four basic functions:

assignment of each accident to a node, link, cell or road section as defined within the authority's representation of the road system for the purposes of accident location. Manual editing is usually required at this stage due to errors arising from the raw data;

extractions of standard tables showing trends in accidents for the area as a whole, trends for specific categories of accident or accidents at specific site categories;

plotting of the spatial distribution of accidents over the network. This usually reveals clusters of accidents at blackspots, and on routes where systematic treatment may be desirable; and

blackspot (or cluster) analysis in which the individual links, nodes, cells and road sections can be examined further.

Lists of links, nodes and road sections are usually compiled in descending order of accident frequency so that clusters can easily be identified (Ref. 5). Care must be taken to allow for the fact that sites having the largest numbers of accidents in a given period will usually include a number of sites where the occurrence of accidents has been above average in that period as a result of random fluctuation. Proper use of the PAR technique or other methods of identifying sites for application of safety measures should take this into account.

Accident Analysis

The design of appropriate remedial measures normally involves a detailed analysis of each candidate site, in the form of a 'grid' or 'stick' diagram (see Chapter 18). These show the characteristics of individual accidents in successive columns together with a diagram indicating the nature of the conflict. This process is usually done by hand although much of the work can now be done using computer programs. A further advantage of a graphics oriented computer system is that it allows for the plotting of accident data to a relatively fine degree of detail, which is often helpful in planning remedial work. However, it should be borne in mind that there is little point in trying to plot to a level of detail which is finer than that attained in the Police reporting system.

10.5 Continuous Monitoring

Transport policies contained within Structure Plans (and following the Local Govt. Act 1985 (Ref. 6), Unitary Development Plans [Sco.49]) are necessarily expressed in broad terms, mainly because they deal with long term aims, and broad approaches to meeting them. In practice, policies are continually interpreted and translated into specific programmes of shorter term action. Both of these activities rely on monitoring the state of the transport system. Monitoring may also reveal that changes either taking place or in prospect, justify reconsideration of the basic policies themselves.

A system for monitoring the components of traffic (eg. flow, speed, classification) requires a structured sample to be taken from within the study area. To achieve this the road network may be divided into short sections (sometimes only 100 metres long), each section being identified by its type (eg. motorway, primary distributor, district or local distributor). The required number of census points for a representative sample are then chosen for each of the road type sections or for the cordon or screenline. Traffic counting is carried out either continuously at a site, or by establishing a rota for a programme of counts. The data from randomly selected count locations not only provides information on the amount of traffic demand (vehicle km/day) within the area, but may also be used to provide factors to convert sample short period traffic flows (vehicles/hour) on any link in the network to standard measures. For example, sample counts may be expanded to produce annual average daily traffic flows (vehicles/day) to be used for assessment purposes.

National Traffic Data

Most highway authorities have their own systems for monitoring traffic but the Department of Transport performs this task on a national basis [Sco.50] with its core and rotating (link based) traffic censuses. The core census, at present using manual enumerators, produces continuous classified counts at 170 randomly selected sites in Great Britain representing all road classes and subdividing traffic flow into vehicle types (see Figure 10.1). The counts start at 06.00 hours and are taken for 16 hours a day, three days per month (one week day and a Saturday and a Sunday), throughout the year. (An automatic traffic counting and classification system is in prospect for installation at 120 of the 170 locations.) From these data day to month and seasonal patterns are derived. In particular, expansion factors can be calculated for input into the Department's program ROTAN (Ref. 7) to convert short period counts (12 or 16 hours) to Annual Average Daily Flow (AADF) for assessment purposes. The rotating census (RTC) or link based traffic census (LBTC) provides a comprehensive set of short period counts which have been converted to AADF for the whole of the major road network. Counting is undertaken for one 12-hour day on every link of the major road network once every 6 years to an annual cyclical programme. The first cycle started in 1979 and was completed in 1984. Thus from 1984 the Department holds AADF traffic flow estimates for every link of the major road network in Britain [Sco.51]. (See Figure 10.2 as an example of the output.)

The Department also provides data on traffic flows in the form of maps and diagrams. Annual average daily flow estimates are provided for a 12 hour, 16 hour and 24 hour weekday, and for a 24 hour average day. The information is available on computer printout, on microfiche, or can be provided on computer magnetic tape or floppy disc. Aperture cards, which show details of the flows on ordnance survey maps, are also available as are the overlay maps from which the aperture cards are made. (All of this data can be obtained from DTp/STC [Sco.52].)

10.6 Inaccuracy and Variability in Traffic Surveys

Little definitive work has been published about the accuracy of traffic counts by automatic traffic counters. Practical experience suggests that errors arise from both machine failures and poor installation. For longer term counts, the frequency and diligence of survey station monitoring and servicing will be crucial to reliability. Permanently installed inductive loops should be more reliable than pneumatic tubes. Using the limited information available, the best working estimate of the accuracy of measurement of the number of vehicles that pass an automatic traffic counter is that the 95% confidence interval of a count of longer than 12 hours duration is of the order of plus or minus 5% of the total count obtained.

All counters should be installed and maintained to the standards laid down in the Manual of Practice on Automatic Traffic Counting (Ref. 8). When a short term automatic count is used to predict the average traffic flow for a longer period than the counter was on station, the estimated traffic flow will be subject to sampling error. (This aspect of sampling error is more fully covered in 10.7 below.)

A statistical study of the reliability of manual classified counts has been carried out by the Department of Transport and is reported in a paper entitled 'Accuracy of Manual Road Traffic Counts' (Ref. 9). The conclusion reached was that the true 16 hour flow of all motor vehicles at a given site lies, with 95% confidence, within an interval of about plus or minus 10% of the manual count.

The 95% confidence intervals for some individual vehicle classes were:

All vehicles including cars and taxis	±10%
Light Goods Vehicles	±24%
Other Goods Vehicles	±28%
All (light plus other) Goods Vehicles	±18%

The relatively wider confidence intervals for individual goods vehicle classes results largely from mis-classification between them. The accuracy of the total number of goods vehicles will be better than that for an individual class. The confidence intervals for individual hours are likely to be larger, but the 16 hour figures shown above can be taken as a guide. To assist

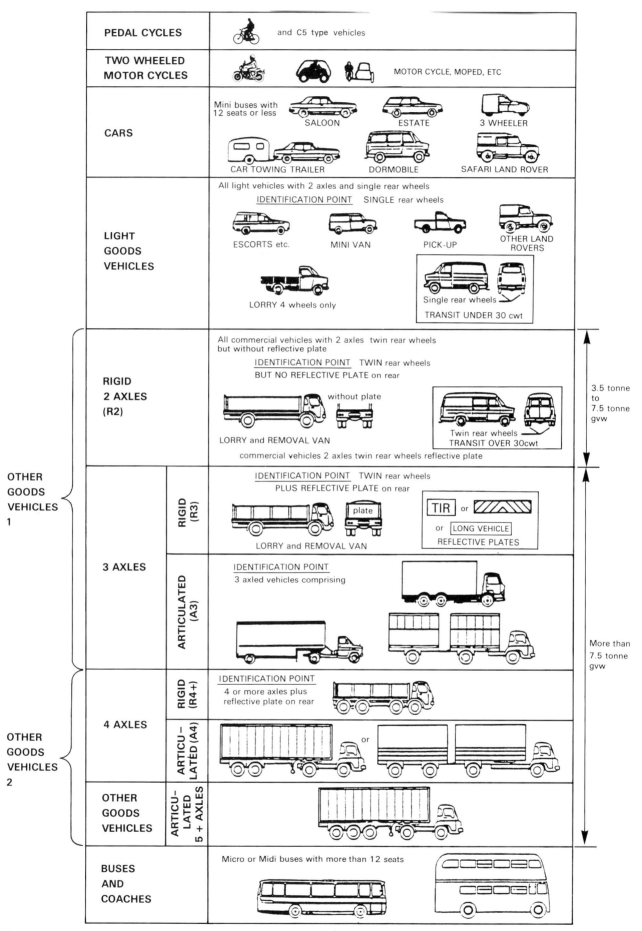

Figure 10.1 Vehicle categories used for survey purposes (and in COBA 9)

Source: DTp (STC) 1986

DEPARTMENT OF TRANSPORT

ROTATING TRAFFIC CENSUS

REGION: GREATER LONDON **LOCAL AUTHORITY: LAMBETH**

ROAD No: A23	CLASS: PRINCIPAL	LOCATION OF COUNT (8 FIG GRID REF): 5311755	LOCATION OF NODES: 5311757 53101753	POINT No: 36269
	SPEED LIMIT: 30 MPH	CARRIAGEWAYS: 2	CARRIAGEWAY WIDTH: 20.0M	LANES: 4	DAY OF COUNT: WEDNESDAY 26/5/82

	Pedal Cycle	Motor Cycle	Cars + Taxis	Bus + Coach	Light Goods	Other Goods Vehicles	Rigid 2 AX	Rigid 3 Ax	Rigid 4+ Ax	Artic 3 Ax	Artic 4 Ax	Artic 5+ Ax	All Motor Vehicles	OG %
Observed 12 hour flow (7am–7pm)	1650	2529	24728	1998	4182	1673	1206	113	58	71	213	12	35110	4.
Estimated annual average flow 1982 Average weekday(5) 12 hour flow (7–7) Coefficient of variation	1430 30%	2350 26%	24600 16%	1775 28%	3925 16%	1660 19%	1110 21%	210 178%	70 90%	80 70%	190 49%	10 49%	34300 16%	4.
Average weekday (5) 24 hour flow Coefficient of variation	1910 37%	3250 26%	32300 17%	2225 30%	4475 16%	1860 19%	1220 22%	230 176%	70 93%	90 69%	230 49%	10 49%	44100 16%	4.
Average daily (7) 24 hour flow Coefficient of variation	1630 30%	2750 24%	32200 10%	2050 29%	3800 16%	1410 19%	940 21%	160 151%	60 89%	70 72%	180 50%	10 50%	42200 17%	3.
Estimated annual average flow 1984 Average weekday (5) 12 hour flow (7–7) Coefficient of variation	1280 34%	2125 28%	25800 17%	1850 29%	4250 17%	1660 24%	1180 22%	200 179%	60 92%	60 72%	150 50%	9 58%	35700 16%	4.
Average weekday (5) 24 hour flow Coefficient of variation	1710 39%	2950 28%	33900 17%	2325 31%	4850 17%	1850 24%	1300 23%	220 177%	60 95%	70 71%	190 50%	10 58%	45900 17%	4.
Average daily (7) 24 hour flow Coefficient of variation	1460 34%	2500 26%	33800 11%	2150 30%	4100 17%	1400 24%	1000 22%	150 152%	50 91%	60 75%	140 51%	8 58%	44000 18%	3.

Warning: The 1984 estimate has been scaled from the earlier count:
National scaling factors have been used: they do not necessarily reflect local circumstances.

Note: All estimated flows have been individually rounded
thus totals for all motor vehicles or other goods vehicles
may not always be the sum of the separate vehicle classes.

Figure 10.2 An example of traffic estimate output based on rotating traffic census

in adjusting for errors arising from counts, the Department of Transport's Assessment Policy and Methods division has developed general purpose micro-computer software (called ROTAN) to process count data to yield the coefficient of variation of any estimate (say, AADF) made from any number of 12 or 16 hour counts. The factors are derived from the core census data (see 10.5 above).

10.7 Sampling Procedures and Techniques

The problems of scaling up (or factoring) the number of actual observations to the total which is representative of the population being measured, is common to all sample surveys. In urban areas traffic flow through each day, week and year can be very variable. It is, therefore, important to take account of this. Most urban traffic counts can be converted to AADF in the same way as counts from the link based census and Statistics Bulletin (86) 7 (Ref. 10) describes techniques which rely only on the built-up/non built-up classification of urban roads. When AADF estimates are required from short period counts, standard expansion factors will give annual average flows and their associated coefficients of variation. The coefficient of variation, expressed as a percentage of the flow, gives a measure of the uncertainty surrounding the estimated AADF.

Every scaling factor has an associated unreliability and the result of factoring is always to worsen the overall confidence interval. Factoring should therefore be kept to a minimum and the factor with the lowest coefficient

of variation should always be chosen where a choice of factors is available.

Whilst it is, in principle, desirable to derive factors locally, a fuller understanding of the accuracy of such factors is necessary to ensure that local conditions are actually significantly different from national averages. In the absence of this knowledge national factors should be used. The Department's cost-benefit package COBA (Ref. 11) [Sco.53] gives default values for the scaling factors.

Peak and Seasonal Variations

Also of interest is the difference between the peak-hour flow and the annual average hourly flow (AAHF). Table 10.3 gives the factors to convert from AAHF into the peak-hour flow (PHF) and corresponding hourly flows ranging from 10th highest to 200th highest for three road types.

Interview Surveys

Similar problems of expanding sample data are experienced with interview surveys. Roadside interview survey data will also need expanding to represent the total traffic crossing a cordon or screenline. Usual practice is to expand the interview data to control totals established by a classified count of all vehicles crossing a cordon or screenline. The expansion procedure usually contains several steps to reflect type of vehicle, time of day, interview site and parallel non-interviewed roads and differences between the day of interview and the survey period.

Conversion of hourly flow	Types of Road					
	Main Urban		Inter Urban		Recreational Inter-Urban	
	Factor	Coeff* (%)	Factor	Coeff* (%)	Factor	Coeff* (%)
AAHF to PHF	2.630	(11)	2.825	(15)	3.890	(23)
AAHF to 10th highest hour	2.837	(14)	3.231	(20)	4.400	(23)
AAHF to 30th highest hour	2.703	(11)	3.017	(17)	3.974	(21)
AAHF to 50th highest hour	2.649	(10)	2.891	(15)	3.742	(19)
AAHF to 100th highest hour	2.549	(9)	2.711	(12)	3.381	(15)
AAHF to 200th highest hour	2.424	(9)	2.501	(9)	3.042	(13)
AAWF to AADF	0.943	(3)	0.979	(4)	1.015	(4)

Notes: AAHF is assumed to be AADF ÷ 24
      AAWF is the Average Annual Weekday Flow (Mon-Fri)
      *Coefficient of Variation

Table 10.3 Peak hour factors by road type classification

Source: TAM (Traffic Appraisal Manual) DTp (1985)

In the case of transportation surveys based upon household interviews the scaling up factor will be the inverse of the proportion of the population sampled. This proportion is usually smaller with the larger size of the population in the study area because the accuracy of the resulting information depends on the size of the sample itself, which is generally larger in large areas.

10.8 Sample Surveys—Observational Techniques

The most common requirements of observational surveys are to determine the pattern and volume of vehicle movements at a particular point on a road link, the turning movements at a junction or the pattern of traffic over a large part of the highway network. Different traffic streams can be counted manually by enumerators using hand held counters (the data being subsequently transferred to reporting forms); or by using 'data capture' portable micro-processors; or automatically using detector loops set into the carriageway. Enough enumerators should be employed to ensure adequate cover of the different movements and to permit regular breaks from what can be a monotonous job.

Where only sample periods of enumeration are undertaken, total traffic flows over the whole period are required for 'control'. This will require temporary automatic equipment which can operate continuously

Plate 10.1 Road sensors in the carriageway

and unattended. At temporary sites, pneumatic, tribo- or piezo-electric tubes may be placed across the carriageway to register the number of axles (and possibly their loads) passing in any particular time period. It is also possible to use detector loop 'mats' which are laid directly on top of the road surface, as a temporary counter. The equipment should be checked at regular intervals to confirm that the tubes are still in place and that the counter is equipped with sufficient power and recording tape to last until the next visit.

At more permanent sites the initial extra cost of installing inductive loop detectors in the road surface may well be justified on grounds of lower maintenance and supervision costs. Electronic counters may be used in association with the pneumatic tube or loop detectors which can either store the information on magnetic tape, solid state RAM, or be permanently connected by a data transmission line to a central computer. All of these detection systems need to be checked at regular intervals by manual counts to ensure that the recorded counts are compatible with visually observed information. Some sophisticated detector loop systems (see Figure 10.3 and Plate 10.1) can count the number of axles on individual vehicles and also make some attempt to record gross axle weights (piezo-electric tubes), but manually performed classified counts are still usually necessary.

Junction Counts

The counting of turning movements at junctions may require a large number of field staff but the use of video equipment with subsequent laboratory analysis should also be considered. A video camera might be positioned at a suitable vantage point (eg. in a neighbouring building or on a hoist that provides the necessary field of coverage). Several software packages (eg. VISTA—Ref. 12) have been developed for analysis of video recordings. If observers are employed substantial numbers of them may be necessary (eg. when counting a four arm junction there are twelve

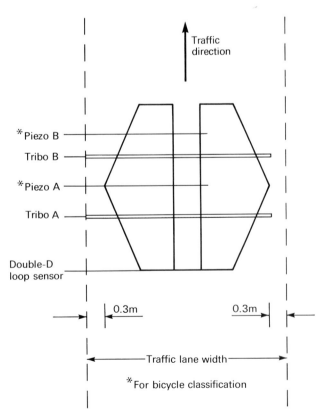

Figure 10.3 Road sensor array for vehicle classification

possible traffic movements). Savings on staff by having each enumerator observing more than one movement can lead to a reduction in the quality of the data obtained. Experience suggests that greater accuracy is achieved when vehicles are counted as they leave the junction because individual traffic streams are more easy to identify at this point.

When information on movements within a complex junction, or over a large area, is required a '**number plate survey**' may be appropriate. With this type of survey individual vehicles are identified (by the numerical part of their registration number and the year letter), together with the time when they enter the area. This information is recorded by an observer using either an enumeration form or by voice onto a tape recorder. Other observers placed in a cordon around the junction (or area) note the registration number and time as the vehicle leaves. Computer programs have been developed to match the registration numbers of vehicles entering and leaving the area in different time segments based on the estimated journey times. Usually, up to 80 per cent of the identified vehicles can be matched in this way. Developments in image processing techniques may allow the recording of number plates to be done automatically in future.

Pedestrian Counts

Pedestrian surveys are usually required to establish the flow along a footway or across a carriageway. The latter will often be required to quantify pedestrian/vehicle conflicts when assessing the need to install some form of crossing facility. For this purpose, pedestrian counts will usually be carried out over a hundred metre length of road, fifty-metres either side of the proposed crossing point. Fifty metres is taken as the maximum distance pedestrians might reasonably be expected to walk to use a formal crossing place rather than cross where they happen to be (see also Chapter 23.4). The actual distance pedestrians are willing to divert will also depend on the intervening traffic flow and on the existence of any physical barriers (eg. guard railing). Origins and destinations of pedestrian trips may only be obtained by personal interviews but surveys of pedestrians' delays at crossing points can be carried out manually or by using video equipment. Information on the use of public transport can be obtained from manual counts of people boarding or alighting at different stops or from on board interviews with passengers (see Plate 10.2). Analysis of ticket sales can produce partial and biased information due to the increasing use of travelcards and concessionary fares.

Speed Measurement

When measuring the average speed of traffic, it is important to decide how speeds at a point on the road are to be measured. Options include:

(a) use of a radar speed meter, averaging the individual speeds of vehicles directly; or

(b) timing vehicles over a short distance (L) and calculating first the average time taken (t), giving an average speed of L/t.

Of these methods, (a) would give the **time mean speed** (V_t) and (b) the **space mean speed** (V_s). Wardrop (Ref. 13) has shown that the two definitions of speed are related, thus:

$$V_t = V_s + \frac{s^2}{V_s}$$

where s is the standard deviation of the distribution of individual speeds as measured by method (b).

It is possible to calculate the time or space mean speed from either set of data by converting individual speeds into times or vice-versa.

This distinction is important because, in practice, time mean speed is used for say accident analysis at particular sites or the determination of a speed limit, whilst space mean speed is used for economic analysis and other applications of speed/flow relationships.

Plate 10.2 A bus passenger survey using electronic coding and automatic data logging

Source: Oyster Terminals

Speed Measurement Techniques

The most common method of determining the instantaneous vehicle speed measured at a point is to use the radar speed meter (Ref. 14). The speed meter should be concealed behind street furniture or inside a conveniently parked vehicle so that drivers are unaware of the observations and do not alter their normal behaviour as a consequence (see Plate 10.3).

The usual way of measuring link running or journey speeds is by the so called **moving observer method** (Ref. 15) in which a car (or light van) travels along the route at the average speed of traffic while observers record the time taken between different points and the periods during which the vehicle is stopped. A number of runs are necessary to obtain a good estimate for each period of the day being investigated. In this process the driver attempts to ensure that he passes as many vehicles as pass him in order to remove bias.

The 85th percentile spot speed (ie. the speed up to which 85 per cent of vehicles travel in free flow conditions) is generally used as a basis for highway design (see also Chapter 34.4). It can be used to help determine:

- the design speed of minor improvement schemes by measuring speeds on the approach to the improvement;

- the basis for the design of major/minor junctions;

- the basis for the settings of vehicle-actuated traffic signals at sites with speed limits of more than 30 mph; and

- speed limits.

Surveys to Assess Urban Traffic Conditions

Assessment of urban traffic conditions can be carried out by direct observations, moving car techniques, aerial photography, time-lapse cinematography and computer analysis of video-tape recordings. It will usually involve measuring one or more of the following:

- **saturation flows** at signal-controlled junctions (see also Chapter 41.9);

- **cyclic flow profiles** (ie. the average pattern of traffic flow on a road link during one signal cycle), (see also Chapters 20.9 and 20.16);

- **queue lengths,** which can be measured by observers noting at (say) one minute intervals the points at which the queue begins and ends (a distinction must be made between vehicles which are actually stopped and those which are crawling); and

- **queueing time,** as the time between the first stop to the last start but if the queue is long, an allowance should be made for the time it would have taken to cover, at normal running speed, the length of road covered by the queue. As with queue length measurements, it is important to distinguish between the time spent delayed (ie. the time taken to

Plate 10.3 Speed measurement from a vehicle

Source: Somerset County Council

decelerate to and accelerate from a stop, plus the time spent stopped) and the time spent stationary.

Car Parking Surveys

An inventory of the parking space available in an area, together with observations of the use made of it, is often required. The number of spaces, including details of where they are and whether they are privately or publicly used, can be recorded on a map of an appropriate scale. There is often difficulty in establishing the precise number of spaces available. This can be either the number of marked out parking spaces or the actual number of cars parked (which may be substantially greater than the indicated spaces). The inventory should also include kerbside capacity (estimated where individual bays are not marked), spaces in public car parks and private spaces including those within the curtilage of individual properties. Distinctions may be made between those spaces for which a charge is made, those with restricted use such as for permit holders only and those subject merely to time limits.

A quick and inexpensive assessment of the demand for parking space in a particular area can be obtained by measuring the accumulation of traffic within the study area by time of day. Using automatic traffic counters, the net accumulation of vehicles entering and leaving the study area can be measured at, say, fifteen minute time intervals. The data can then be plotted as a graph showing the accumulation of traffic for different times of the day and this provides a good proxy for parking demand. The process may be repeated on different days to determine the difference in demand for each day of the week or month. In most urban areas parking demand varies significantly during the week for a variety of reasons. Knowledge of the variation in parking demand assists interpretation of parking occupancy and parking duration surveys, which are normally limited to one day for reasons of economy.

Parking occupancy (ie. the number of spaces occupied in relation to the total available) can be obtained by observers patrolling on foot or in a vehicle. Video recording techniques are also feasible. Surveys may be used to compare different days of the week, different times of the day and the effects of different parking policies when taken over suitable periods. Aerial photographs may also be used to determine parking occupancy, but only of open, ground level parking areas.

When parking duration (ie. the length of stay of individual vehicles) is being surveyed, the parking areas should be divided into a number of patrols. The frequency of the patrol will depend on the land use characteristics of the surrounding area. A typical patrol of 60 spaces might take an observer about 30 minutes to complete. Where the land use generates short term parking, the patrol interval should be reduced to perhaps 5 minutes to achieve an acceptable level of accuracy. Portable data capture terminals can be used by observers to improve the accuracy and effectiveness of the survey. An alternative is to use video recordings taken from inside a moving vehicle, or from a high vantage point. Parking duration and accumulation can then be determined by comparing consecutive recordings. Information on parking duration in off-street car parks can be obtained from most types of automatic entry/exit ticketing systems. These do not produce the same bias against short stay parking as do periodic observation methods.

10.9 Interview Surveys

Origin and Destination Surveys of Person Movements

Surveys of personal trips are normally carried out at places of residence (eg. homes, institutions, hotels), work places or at a chosen point intercepting actual journeys being undertaken (eg. at the roadside or on a public transport vehicle). These surveys seek to discover the pattern of trip making over a given time period (usually a day) and people's need or wish to travel.

The area under study should be divided into a number of zones within an external cordon often chosen to coincide with a local government administrative boundary. Zones should preferably be of homogeneous land use and zone boundaries should, as far as possible, be drawn between different types of land use and different densities or classes of housing and workplaces, as these are likely to give rise to different patterns of trip making (see also Figure 11.3). With residence based surveys, a representative sample of the population of each zone (usually taken by household from the electoral register) is interviewed to discover individual or household travel behaviour for a specific day or over a period of one week. The results are then factored to represent the whole zone.

A major problem with this procedure is determining how many households actually live within each zone as well as determining whether the interviewed households are representative of the others within the zone. The usual source for the number of households is the most recent national census, but this can be several years out of date. Information is usually also collected on various socio-economic characteristics such as income, employment, family size and structure and car ownership, as these are the most important determinants of travel behaviour. Prediction of the changes occurring in these characteristics over time are then used to estimate future travel demand in the area (see also Chapter 11).

Origin and Destination Surveys of Freight Movement

Information on freight movements by lorries and railway vehicles can be obtained from data collected at a sample of industrial and commercial premises within the study area. However, it is very difficult to obtain a representative sample because of the wide variation in levels of freight activities taking place within the very wide range of different types of premises. It is common practice to select a sample of freight operators within the study area and then to sample a selection of vehicles used by these operators to record information on the trips made and goods carried, but this does not overcome the difficulties of obtaining a fully representative survey.

Roadside Interview Surveys

Surveys based on a sample of residences or vehicles used by freight operators will not include the trips made within the study area by non-residents or externally based transport operators. Normal practice is to collect this additional information by roadside interviews (see Plate 10.4) located on a cordon around the survey area and on screenlines that subdivide the study area. This survey technique is used to obtain information from vehicle occupants. Typically, more

Plate 10.4 A Roadside interview in progress

Source: Strathclyde Regional Council

comprehensive information on person trips is gleaned from interviews carried out for public transport journeys that cross the cordon or screenlines, than for those which take place within it.

Roadside interview surveys provide information on trips made by interviewing a sample of drivers at the roadside. This is often the only source of data on trips made by externally based residents or operators but it does require these vehicles to cross the cordons or screenlines. This may be a particular problem in urban areas where 'watertight' screenlines and cordons to intercept movements within the study area may be difficult to locate. It may not be possible or economic to establish a screenline or cordon with survey stations located on every intercepted highway. The general objective should be to achieve sample coverage of 95% of all traffic.

Information gathered at these interviews usually covers not only origin and destination but purpose of trip, vehicle occupancy and location of normal residence. The attendance of the police is necessary to extract the sampled vehicles from the traffic stream and ensure the safe operation of the survey. Survey sites should be away from busy junctions and special care is required on high speed roads. Further details of this survey procedure are given in Ref. 16.

An alternative method of acquiring roadside information is to give a questionnaire to drivers when they are stopped at the interview site, for example, at traffic signals. The questionnaire can be answered by drivers when they have completed their journey using prepaid reply forms. Although a larger number of drivers may be contacted using this method the response rate is usually very much lower than with roadside interviews and may be subject to bias if responses are more likely to be obtained from particular sections of the travelling public.

10.10 Attitude Surveys

Demands for the use of transport arise as a result of decisions made by millions of individual travellers every day. Their choices may be constrained by other members of their household, by rigid times of starting and stopping work and so on and by the availability of transport facilities. Every trip requires decisions which each individual or group of individuals have to make for themselves. One way of improving prediction of travel demands lies in obtaining a better understanding of the psychological mechanisms of choice and particularly a knowledge of which attributes of a transport system are perceived as important by individuals when making their trip choices. This applies to choices of destination, or even whether to undertake a trip at all, as well as to choice of mode or route.

Acceptance of this approach has led to the increasing use of **stated preference** methods of interview survey rather than the **revealed preference** methods which rely solely on observations of behaviour. The various methods used to measure subjective response are set out in Table 10.4. The general term **attitude survey** covers most of these stated preference techniques. Attitude surveys are used to investigate individuals' subjective response to particular proposals or policies rather than the perceptions which operators or planners may have. Attitude surveys are usually, therefore, either scheme or issue specific so as to assist in the eventual policy choice between alternatives. Attitude surveys may also be carried out at an earlier stage to identify the broad aspirations for travel and transport of those living in the area. This type of survey is generally referred to as an **opinion survey.**

Attitude surveys involve questions being put to a sample of those concerned, either by interview or in a structured questionnaire. The size of the sample will depend on the nature of the survey. It is important to ensure that the sequence and phrasing of the questions, and the manner in which they are put, allows the respondents to state their views in a way that can be measured and yet does not influence or predetermine the answers that are given.

The main techniques for measuring subjective response are as follows (examples are shown in Table 10.5):

Opinion research methods, where respondents are strictly limited in their replies and are asked to choose a particular option or merely give a 'yes/no' answer. This can be carried out by delivering questionnaires to homes or making them available at public meetings or in local community buildings. Interpretation of the responses is left to the researcher although additional information such as the respondent's address, whether they have access to a car, or which route they choose, may be helpful to any subsequent assessment.

Ranking methods, where respondents are asked to rank specified options in order of preference rather than simply choosing between items on a list. This may identify a consensus on (say) a second choice option where none existed for the first, although it may be wrong to infer that gaps between options are equal. For example, if three options are ranked in order A, B, C, option B may not necessarily be preferred to C by the same margin that A is preferred to B.

Scaling methods, where respondents are asked to rate each of the attributes on an appropriate scale. They may also be asked to relate their rating on different

STATED PREFERENCE TECHNIQUE	SCALE USED	FORM OF COMPARISON POSSIBLE	EXAMPLE OF APPLICATION
OPINION POLLS	Nominal	Frequency of nomination of a particular value, view or attribute	Choice between alternative actions
RANKING METHODS	Ordinal scale, with no implications for intervals between successive items	As above, plus an indication of the relative importance of items listed	Identification of problems/objectives as seen by public as whole or by sub-groups
SEMANTIC-DIFFERENTIAL RATING SCALES	Interval scale, usually with equal-interval properties assumed	Statistical comparison of relative valuations across several attributes	Evaluation of differences in attributes of a scheme or set of schemes
CONSTANT-SUM GAMING METHODS	Interval scale with equal intervals assumed	As semantic differential, but finer distinctions may be possible	Evaluation where constrained trade-offs need to be examined
CONJOINT ANALYSIS – TRADE-OFF METHODS	Ratio scale	Absolute magnitudes, with respect to a fixed origin	Can be used as input to forecasting models

Table 10.4 Stated preference techniques used in the measurement of subjective response

(a) EXAMPLE OF AN OPINION QUESTION

Tick the one out of the following three statements that most closely matches your view.

I think that we need to restrict lorry access at all times, even though distribution costs might increase.

I think that we need to restrict lorry access at peak times only.

I do not think that we should interfere with lorry access.

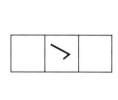

(b) EXAMPLE OF A RANKING EXERCISE

Please list the following items in their order of importance to you by writing '1' against the most important, '2' against the next in importance and so on:

Reducing traffic in the High Street   3

Increasing car parking in the High Street   4

Letting buses get right into the High Street   1

Improving pedestrian facilities in the High Street   2

(c) EXAMPLE OF A SEMANTIC DIFFERENTIAL SCALE

Consider each of the following items in turn and put a cross in the box which most closely reflects your attitude.

	Very Important	Fairly Important	Neither	Fairly Unimportant	Not at all Important
Reducing traffic in the High Street		X			
Increasing car parking in the High Street	X				
Letting buses get right into the High Street					X
Improving pedestrian facilities in the High Street		X			

(d) A FIXED-SUM FORM OF QUESTIONING

You have a budget of 100 points to allocate to the following policies. Spend your 100 points in a way which reflects the importance that you think the planner should pay to each of these –

Reducing traffic in the High Street   15   points

Increasing car parking in the High Street   10   points

Letting buses get right into the High Street   50   points

Improving pedestrian facilities in the High Street   25   points

                                           Total   100   points

(e) AN UNDEVELOPED EXAMPLE OF THE FORM OF QUESTIONING USED IN CONJOINT ANALYSIS

Consider each of the following combinations of traffic measures. Give a score of 1 to the combination that you find the most desirable, and 100 to the least desirable. Then score each of the others in terms of their position between 1 = worst and 100 = best. (If you find some equally good or bad, give them the same score).

	Attributes of Option			Score
	X	Y	Z	
Option (a)				100
(b)				70
(c)				
etc				
	level of supply/resourcing on each attribute			To be filled in by respondent

Table 10.5 Examples of techniques for measuring subjective response

scales to enable rankings to be made between attributes. The scales are usually divided in equal intervals but this is not essential. The principle of semantic differentiation must be applied to the opposite ends of the scale (ie. the ends of the scale should be the extremes of the positive and negative of a particular attribute with a neutral point in the centre). The number of points on the scale should be an odd number recognising that the more points there are the more difficulty respondents have in making a decision. In some cases, a continuous rating scale can be used between the two pole extremes.

Fixed sum gaming methods are used to measure preferences in terms of the explicit trade off between options or attributes of different schemes. For example, a respondent may be given a budget of, say, 100 points which must be allocated according to preference.

Conjoint analysis is a more complex approach to 'gaming', whereby respondents are asked to indicate a preference between different groups of attributes or options.

Choice of the method of research which is most appropriate will depend on the type of information required and the use to which the results are to be put, constrained also by resources, time available and the size of the sample to be studied. Experience is invaluable for these types of technique and it is recommended that specialist advice be sought. For example, particular care is needed in quantifying the results of an attitude survey as, depending upon the level of data obtained, only certain statistical techniques are valid. This will in turn limit the amount of information which can be derived from the survey.

10.11 Environmental Surveys

Objectives

The various impacts of traffic on the urban environment are of common concern to the general public. So far, the only explicit environmental standard set in relation to traffic is the 68 dB(A), 18 hour L_{10} noise limit (see explanation below) for compensation in connection with new roads or major improvements. Nevertheless, good design of roads in urban areas should always aim to ensure that sensitive environments are not disrupted unnecessarily and that traffic flows and compositions are managed so that environmental impacts are minimised.

A useful basic approach involves developing a hierarchy of roads (see Chapter 5), to enable large flows of through traffic to be diverted away from residential, shopping and other areas where traffic threatens safety and tranquility. This hierarchy can be

supported by traffic control measures which limit the sizes, weights and speeds of vehicles which use certain roads (eg. residential roads at night time).

In every case, it is necessary to ensure that the appropriate environmental factors are being considered (which may require an initial attitude survey in the locality concerned) and that the method being used is appropriate to the disturbance being measured. Details of survey methods relating to the more commonly perceived environmental intrusions are given in the Department of Transport's manual on environmental appraisal (Ref. 17) [Sco.44]. The most conspicuous nuisances perceived by people in residential areas, shown in the National Environment Study (Ref. 18) included:

● noise and vibration;

● pedestrian delay and the severance of communities;

● air pollution from exhaust and other emissions;

● visual intrusion of vehicles and infrastructure;

● risk of accidents and intimidation; and

● dirt and slush.

The inherently different qualities of most of these impacts, and subjective responses to them, ensure that precise measurement and evaluation is difficult. But, not withstanding this, it is important that they be fully considered in any new road design or traffic management proposal. Indeed, minimising environmental impact may be one of the main objectives of some schemes.

Noise

Noise may be defined as unwanted sound. All sound is caused by a pressure wave passing through the air which can be measured in decibels (dB). In an attempt to replicate the frequency response of the human ear, the sound pressure created by traffic noise is given an internationally agreed weighting (an A-weighting) which attenuates the very high and low frequencies. The level of exposure to traffic noise is usually measured using L_{10} which is that level which is exceeded for 10 per cent of the time, averaged over an 18 hour day from 6am to midnight. The L_{10} index is sometimes criticised for failing to measure the peaks of noise and taking no account of the base level (ie. L_{90} the level exceeded for 90 per cent of the time). Some surveys therefore use the Equivalent Sound Level (Leq), a logarithmic measure of average noise level, which is related to the sound energy.

The basic instrument used to measure traffic noise is a sound level meter with a built-in A-weighted scale. This may be hand held and readings noted instantaneously or alternatively it may be connected to an automatic data logging device for subsequent analysis.

Any measurements of existing traffic noise or predictions of future noise are unique to the location where the equipment is set up (see Plate 10.5) and the time at which the readings are taken. This is because noise is dependent upon:

- the speed, volume and composition of the traffic;

- the gradient and condition of the road surface;

- the road profile (ie. whether at grade, in cutting or elevated);

- the nature of the ground between the sound source and the receiver (and the presence of any screening such as fences, buildings or other barriers); and

- the weather (which not only affects the amount of noise generated, but can affect its attenuation over distance).

The careful selection of sites can be used to provide a guide to the amount of noise experienced, or likely to be experienced, by different groups of people under the generally prevailing traffic conditions. The details of noise estimation procedures are set out in 'Calculation of Road Traffic Noise' (Ref. 19) [Sco.54].

It is usually necessary to measure noise level in relation to buildings. Measurements should be taken on the facade of the building which is most exposed to the road. Generally, the noise source height is standardised as 0.5 m above the centre line of the traffic stream concerned, and the receiver height as 1.7 m above the ground at 1.0 m away from the facade of the building concerned.

Vibration

Certain types of vibration in buildings are recognised as being caused by low frequency ground borne waves, although the precise effects on both the structure and the occupants are not known and no widely accepted method of estimating vibration effects exists.

Many residents tend to confuse the affects of ground borne vibration with those of low frequency airborne noise. The latter, sometimes referred to as infrasound, is frequently associated with heavy vehicles passing frontage buildings. It has been found that the 'C' weighting of the decibel scale gives a better measure of the nuisance experienced from this traffic than the more commonly used dB(A) measurement.

Plate 10.5 Measuring noise near a building

Source: Travers Morgan and Partners

Pedestrian Delay and Severance

Severance has been defined as the sum of the divisive effects a major urban road or heavy traffic flow has on the inhabitants on either side of it. These effects can be either physical (ie. actual barriers to movements), or psychological (ie. perceived impediments to movement). Actual severance results in reductions in pedestrian journey frequency arising from the feeling of being cut off due to adverse changes in environmental quality (Ref. 20).

Although site specific investigations of journeys by foot have been carried out they have not been included in traffic models. This is because, firstly, the number of walking trips is large compared with trips by other modes; and secondly, the short length of most walk journeys makes it necessary to use small origin and destination zones. Finally, because pedestrians can use many routes not available to vehicles these routes would therefore have to be added to the traffic network (Ref. 21).

One feature of walking journeys that has been extensively studied is the delay road traffic causes to pedestrians crossing the road (see Figure 10.4). Two

simple measures have been adopted to express pedestrian delay, the proportion of pedestrians delayed and the mean delay to all pedestrians. It is also worth noting that the Standing Advisory Committee on Trunk Road Assessment (SACTRA) have recommended (Ref. 22) that the Department of Transport should develop values of time for pedestrians and cyclists and that these should be included in economic evaluation. The Committee also recommended further development of techniques for measuring community severance by focussing on the catchment areas of those facilities to which the vulnerable and less mobile groups need access. Pending further research in this field they recommend careful description of the likely effects.

Delay has often been considered as a proxy for other aspects of the pedestrians environment such as intimidation, worry or apprehension, danger and impatience. Some studies have attempted to establish or infer relationships between delay, annoyance and risk but with mixed success. Several studies have showed that there is a need to differentiate between groups in the pedestrian population, each with its own set of requirements in terms of facilities for crossing the road (Ref. 23).

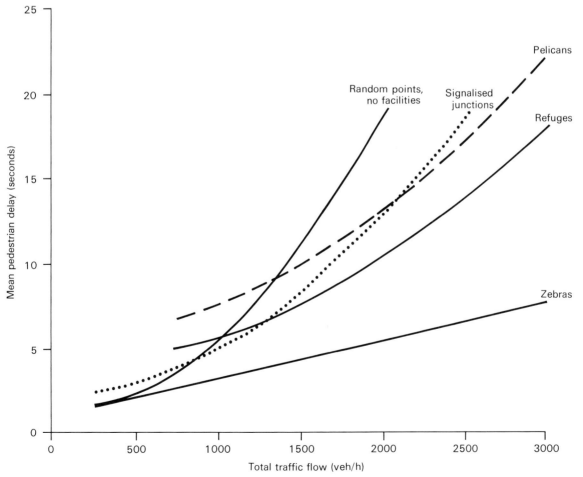

Figure 10.4 Mean pedestrian delays associated with different road crossing situations

Source: DTp/TRRL, 'Pedestrian Delay and Traffic Management', Report SR 356 (1977)

Air Pollution

As far as air pollution is concerned, there are two types of vehicle emissions:

● aerosols or particulates, such as water droplets, tetraethyl lead, dust and black smoke; and

● gases, such as carbon dioxide, carbon monoxide, various oxides of nitrogen and sulphur and numerous hydrocarbons.

Most of these emissions are generally accepted to be pollutants which are detrimental to the long term health of those exposed to them. They are all capable of measurement using specialised environmental control equipment and draft standards are being discussed at international level (eg. WHO, EEC) to limit concentrations to acceptable safety levels. Lead and carbon monoxide emissions are likely to be the subject of international agreement soon and others will no doubt follow.

Dust

Dust may act as an irritant to people with chest or eye conditions as do aldehydes and ozone, both of which combine with strong sunlight to form photo-chemical 'smog'. The proportion of the different pollutants emitted depends on prevailing traffic conditions (eg. flow, speed) and on their variability, as well as on the proportion of petrol and diesel engines. For simplicity, carbon monoxide is sometimes taken as a proxy for the general condition of the air and is measured in parts per million (ppm) by volume.

Visual Intrusion

Visual intrusion is the phrase commonly used to refer to the visual effects arising from the presence of vehicles, the road itself and any structures associated with their use. Roads and traffic do not, of themselves, constitute an intrusion. Intrusion, if it is judged to occur, can only take place in the context of views or scenes that are intruded upon. In urban areas where both viewpoint (observer) and the scene are generally fixed, the presence of roads and traffic may obscure the view or disrupt the scene. The type of intrusion which occurs will depend also on what visual task is being undertaken by the observer.

Interpretation of the visual environment has many parallels with studies of traffic noise. Two aspects common to both visual intrusion and noise are the objective content and the aesthetic content, subjectively assessed.

The most common quantitative measure of visual obstruction is the solid angle subtended at the eye where the **millisteradian** is the unit of measure. The analogous unit in noise is the sound pressure level

(SPL). The eye evaluates visual scenes so as to give more prominence to objects seen centrally than those seen peripherally. For some tasks, the visual scene may be restricted to a central field and for others a much wider view is necessary. This weighting of the visual scene is similar to the use of the A-weighting network for calculating noise levels.

It is important to distinguish between visual obstruction and visual intrusion (see Ref. 17). The **obstruction** caused by an artefact can be measured physically (eg. in terms of solid angle sub-tense) and its magnitude classified (high, medium, low). The judgement as to whether an artefact is an **intrusion** then depends on the judgement of the viewer as to the aesthetic quality of the setting.

There are three main components in assessing the visual environment:

● the object (ie. a road and its traffic);

● the viewer (at a predefined viewpoint) who may have one or more visual tasks to perform; and

● the setting (ie. the aesthetic quality of the scene, Ref. 24).

Although a quantified approach is useful in providing a consistent basis for evaluation aesthetic judgement will often be required. Aesthetic judgements can be assisted by listing those visual features which are considered to enhance or detract from the visual scene as an aid to examining the field of vision in an analytical way. For example, the presence of attractive vegetation, pleasing architectural features, surface treatments or street furniture may all add to the scene, whilst unattractive or derelict roadside buildings, evidence of poor maintenance and a general lack of vegetation may all detract from it. Whatever method is used, the intention should be to examine each situation in a thorough and systematic way.

10.12 References

Text Reference

1. DTp—'*Traffic Appraisal manual (TAM)*', DTp (1985). [Sco.44]   (10.1)

2. DTp—'*STATS 19, Accident Recording Form*', DTp (1980).   (10.1)

3. DTp—'*STATS 20, Instructions for the Completion of Road Accident Reports*', DTp (Statistics Transport C Division) (as amended) (1978).   (10.4)

4. McGuigan, D R—'*Non-junction Accident Rates and their Use in Blackspot Identification*', Traffic Engineering and Control Vol 10, No 23, (February 1983).   (10.4)

5. DTp—'*Accident Investigation and Prevention Manual (AIP)*', DTp (2nd Edition) (1986). (10.4)

6. *Local Government Act 1985,* HMSO (1985). (10.5)

7. DTp—'*ROTAN User's Guide*', DTp (STC) (1987). (10.5)

8. DTp—'*Manual of Practice on Automatic Counting*', DTp (APM Division) (1981). (10.6)

9. DTp—'*Accuracy of Manual Road Traffic Counts*', DTp (1979). (10.6)

10. DTp—'*Methods for Calculating National, Regional and County Traffic (Vehicle Bans)*', Statistical Bulletin (86)7, DTp (1979). (10.7)

11. DTp—'*COBA 9 Manual*', DTp (1981) (Amended). [Sco.53] (10.7)

12. Wootton Jeffreys and Partners—'*VISTA: Video System of Traffic Analysis*', Wootton Jeffreys and Partners (1985). (10.8)

13. Wardrop, J G—'*Some Theoretical Aspects of Road Traffic Research*', Road Paper No 36, Proceedings of the Institution of Civil Engineers, Part II (June 1952). (10.8)

14. DTp—TA 22/81 '*Vehicle Speed Measurement on All-Purpose Roads*', DTp (1981). (10.8)

15. Wardrop, J G and Charlesworth, G A— '*Method of Estimating Speed and Flow of Traffic from a Moving Vehicle*', Proceedings of the Institution of Civil Engineers, Part II (March 1954). (10.8)

16. DTp—TA 11/81 '*Traffic Surveys by Roadside Interview*', DTp (1981). [Sco.56] (10.9)

17. DTp—'*Manual of Environmental Assessment (MEA)*', DTp (1983). [Sco.44] (10.11)

18. DoE—'*National Environment Study*', HMSO (1972). (10.11)

19. DoE—'*Calculation of Road Traffic Noise*', DoE (1975). [Sco.56] (10.11)

20. DoE—Research Report No 8 '*The Environmental Evaluation of Transport Plans*', HMSO (1976). (10.11)

21. Urban Motorways Project—'*Report to DTp*', HMSO (1973). (10.11)

22. Standing Advisory Committee on Trunk Road Assessment—'*Urban Road Appraisal*', HMSO (1986). (10.11)

23. Crompton, D H—'*Pedestrian Delay, Annoyance and Risk: Preliminary Results from a Two Year Study*', PTRC Annual Summer Meeting, Seminar J, PTRC (1979). (10.11)

24. Hopkinson, R and Watson, N—'*Evaluation of the impact of roads on the visual amenity of rural roads*', DoE (1976). (10.11)

10.13 Further Information

25. Institution of Highways and Transportation—'*Guidelines for Accident Reduction and Prevention*', IHT (1986).

26. McKenzie, N B and McCallum, D G—'*A Locationally Referenced Highway Management Information System—The CHIPS Database in Scotland*', Traffic Engineering and Control, Vol 24, No 10 (1985).

27. DTp/TRRL—LR1119 '*Vibration nuisance from road traffic—results of a 50 site survey*', TRRL (1984).

28. DTp/TRRL—LR1052 '*The estimation of air pollution concentrations from road traffic*', TRRL (1982).

29. Report of the Lawther Committee—'*Lead in Air*', HMSO (1982).

30. Pennett, K and Sperring, B A—'*TRAMS*' HECB/ M/4, DTp (1980).

31. DoE/DTp/TRRL—Report SR 514 '*Accuracy of Annual Traffic Flow Estimates from Short Count Periods*', TRRL (1979).

32. DoE/DTp/TRRL—Report SR 515 '*Accuracy of Annual Traffic Flow Estimates from Automatic Counts*', TRRL (1979).

33. Advisory Committee on Trunk Road Assessment (Chairman, G Leitch)—'*Report of the Advisory Committee on Trunk Road Assessment*', HMSO (1978).

34. DoE/DTp/TRRL—Report SR 356 '*Pedestrians Delay and Traffic Management*', TRRL (1977).

35. Slatter, D A E—'*TARA: An Aid to Traffic Management and Transportation Engineers*', Traffic Engineering and Control, Vol 17, No 10 (1976).

36. Lee, T and Tagg, S—'*The Social Severance Effects of Major Urban Roads*', in Transportation Planning for a Better Environment, (Ed—Stringent & Wetzel), Plenum Press (1976).

37. Palmer, P J—'*The TARA Computer System*', BURISA Newsletter No 9 (1974).

11 Estimating Travel Demands

11.1 Policy Evaluation

Estimating the demand for travel is a highly important part of the transportation planning process as travel demands, both existing and future, will have a major influence on transport policies and the provision of transport facilities.

Background

Major advances in transportation planning philosophy and modelling capability took place in the early 1960's. At that time comprehensive transportation studies employed some form of trip end modelling which produced estimates of total travel demand. These trips were distributed and split by mode of travel to produce matrices of private and public transport movements which were then assigned to a number of highway or public transport networks. Once calibrated and validated these models were used to produce estimates of future private and public transport demand. The impacts of these forecasts were then assessed in terms of their likely effects upon the transport network.

This type of analytical assessment invariably led to the development of a strategy (or strategies) to cater for the travel demands forecast for the future and transport policies were often adopted to support these strategies.

Constraints and Influences

Although the initial reaction to the new and sophisticated demand modelling and forecasting techniques was often to plan, and sometimes to construct, major improvements to the urban highway network, restrictive financial conditions and the increasing environmental awareness of the 1970s and 1980s gradually limited the extent to which major highway improvements were carried out and more rigorous assessments and justifications are now required (see Chapters 9, 10 and 12).

Recognition of these conditions has meant that limits are often imposed on the ultimate capacity of an urban highway network by policy decisions which reflect financial circumstances and physical constraints as well as environmental and social concerns. These limits effectively determine the extent to which the demand for the use of private cars is to be catered for and hence the need to use sophisticated models to simulate the mechanisms of modal choice.

Choice of Transportation Model

In practice, transportation modelling techniques should be chosen with due regard to the circumstances in which they are to be used and this involves a choice between comprehensive modelling with few or no constraints and models which take account of practical limitations and political realities.

This chapter outlines the various stages involved in the development of conventional transportation models and considers (in 11.12 below) the alternative ways in which travel demands can be assigned to transport networks. Congested assignment models and traffic simulation models designed for more dense networks are also described and these are increasingly used to study localised traffic situations and the effects of possible new measures, without recourse to the larger and more cumbersome area-wide network models which generally use coarser representations of the network.

11.2 Transport Demand Models Generally

A model is always a simplification of reality. This simplification is obtained by describing a system in terms of the elements considered most relevant to the situation under consideration. This selective representation enables studies to be made of the likely effects of different policies and operational changes on the area and population concerned.

A perfect model would be able to reflect all possible factors which affect human choice in a way which closely matches human behaviour; but our understanding and ability to model complicated personal decisions is incomplete and even if it were possible to produce such a model it would be very complex and expensive to use. In practice, therefore, it is necessary to use a variety of models for different purposes, choosing the one most appropriate to the particular decisions to be made or problems to be examined.

The Modelling Process

Travel demand modelling generally involves two modelling processes incorporating a traffic model and a forecasting procedure.

A **traffic model** is a mechanism for estimating the way in which a transport network would be used by traffic given the distribution and characteristics of the area's population, employment and other land uses. The output would typically be the number of vehicles using each road or the number of passengers using each public transport service, but this would depend upon the objectives of the study and hence the type of model developed. Figure 11.1 provides an outline of the processes involved in a full model and these are discussed

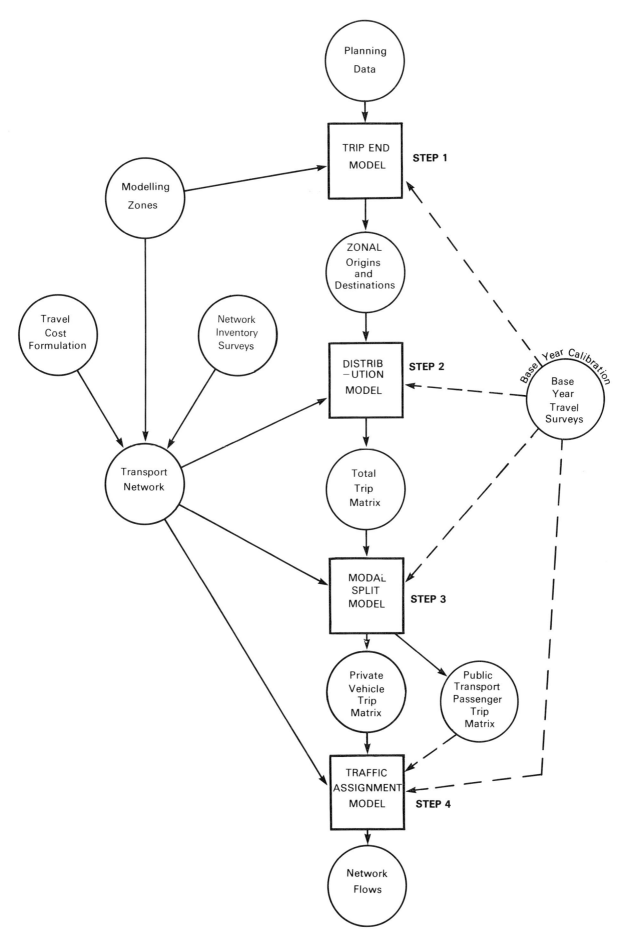

Figure 11.1 Summary of the serial traffic model (also known as the 'four-step' model)

in more detail later in this chapter. Because of its sequential operation of sub models, the full model is often known as the 'four step' or 'serial' model. Models of this type are complex, require a great deal of data and are time consuming to develop, but they can be simplified to satisfy less demanding applications. Planning data and network information are required as inputs and the model should be calibrated to recreate observed travel patterns obtained from base year travel surveys. Such a model can then be used to assess the effects of network changes, land use developments and time-based changes in population, employment and car ownership levels. This is done simply by changing the appropriate inputs and running the model again to estimate new levels of use.

In less demanding situations a localised area traffic model may be sufficient to provide the information required and there are several models of this kind available, each with its own special capabilities and limitations. In Britain models like SATURN (Ref. 22), CONTRAM (Ref. 23), and TRAFFICQ (Ref. 24) are increasingly used to test the effects of different situations on small road networks. These models and others are explained further in 11.12 below.

A **forecasting procedure** is the process by which input information required for a future year traffic model is produced. If the full serial model is to be used (see 11.4 below), future year forecasts are required at zonal (area) level for all of the demographic and land use inputs.

Alternatively, if it is less important to reflect zonal changes precisely, factors may be developed and applied to base year travel demand levels. The quality of travel forecasts is therefore dependent on the skills of town planners and economists in predicting demographic trends and national and local economic performance.

Factors in Choosing a Model

When choosing the type of model required it is important to consider the following points:

Existing information—can existing data or models be used to reduce survey requirement or simplify modelling procedures?

Policy sensitivity—can the model describe the current situation and forecast the relevant elements of travel demand in the future with the appropriate degree of accuracy, bearing in mind the robustness required for the policy decisions to be taken?

Data requirements—can the necessary data be obtained and will it be of an acceptable level of accuracy?

The forecasting period—some decisions require long forecasting periods because of their cost and economic lifespan whilst others produce quick returns in relation to their outlay and may only call for short term forecasting. The length of the forecasting period will also affect the level of uncertainty attached to the forecasts themselves and the consequence of a wrong decision will also affect the choice of model and the level of resources which can be justified.

Scale of Modelling

For the more straightforward problems a travel demand model consisting solely of observations of existing traffic movements may well suffice. If the required forecasting period is less than say five years, a simple trend extrapolation may be appropriate. Small junction or carriageway improvements which are unlikely to cause users to change their travel habits are suited to this type of approach. Local growth, however, may differ from national averages and this is likely to be most marked in the larger urban areas where congestion related factors may restrict traffic growth.

More elaborate models are required to assess the effects of a substantial change in network capacity along new or existing routes, or of major changes in land use. Models can be produced at different levels of detail to suit the particular purpose for which they are to be used.

A model suitable for assessing the broad impact of major transport policy changes (eg. doubling public transport fares or service levels, increasing highway capacity in a corridor, allocating large areas for development or radically changing parking provision or charges), will have to cover the whole area affected by the policy at a relatively coarse level; but the same model should not be expected to provide accurate estimates of traffic flows on individual roads.

A recent development of this approach has been the production of an area based model (by the Transport and Road Research Laboratory, see Ref. 1) which is intended as a quick and easy tool to help assess the effects of a wide range of possible conditions on travel patterns in the London area. This model could only examine policies which might make a sizeable impact on travel over a large spatial area. It would not, however, be suitable for forecasting traffic flows on a network but may have value as a coarse filter for testing a range of policy options prior to the more detailed assessments possible with network based land-use/transportation models.

When the local impact of a particular scheme is required a much more detailed model will be necessary but the area covered may not need to be very extensive. The model must be able to produce the required degree of detail to an appropriate level of accuracy. However, detailed models require large quantities of data, need considerable resources to develop and can be expensive to run. Moreover, the size of the study area has a disproportionately large effect on these factors. Model requirements may, therefore, conflict with practical considerations and should be planned well in advance.

In some cases, where a major scheme has both strategic and local importance, the best approach might be to develop a relatively coarse, large area model to assess strategic implications and to supplement this with a more detailed model of a smaller area to assist local evaluation.

11.3 Travel Demand and Scheme Evaluation

Travel demand models can provide information for a variety of appraisal procedures designed to assess the merits and shortcomings of alternative courses of action. Assessment techniques are discussed in more detail in Chapter 12 but they should be appropriate to the nature of the problem being addressed and the types of solution being considered. The type and scale of the scheme and its method of appraisal will influence the type and quality of information required and hence the design of the traffic model.

Effects which can be given equivalent monetary values should be included in an economic appraisal whilst other effects will generally be considered in a broader 'framework' appraisal. Whilst travel demand information is fundamental to the quantification of costs and benefits used in economic appraisals, the measures that help to quantify environmental issues are also often related to the level of use of a transport facility and may be particularly sensitive to the assignment of traffic to particular routes.

Applications of travel demand analysis in economic appraisal include:

- assessing the scale of a proposal and hence its cost relative to the estimated demand for its use;

- estimating the delays to traffic during construction or maintenance work, based on predicted travel demand;

- assessing benefits and disbenefits to travellers by incrementing time savings (positive or negative) by all users of a network, in which the traffic model can summate total person travel time by trip purpose and convert this to monetary terms by applying standard values of time;

- estimating future travel conditions, which can be used to assess the likely impact on transport operators;

- making predictions of likely road accident frequencies, which relate to the type of road or junction and anticipated traffic levels;

- assessing maintenance costs, which are heavily dependent on the number of goods vehicles using a road (measured in standard axles);

In addition, the Department of Transport's cost-benefit analysis program COBA (Ref. 2) assesses the net benefits or disbenefits to road users attributable to new road proposals. It requires networks with associated link flows, both with and without the new road or facility to be assessed.

The Department of Transport also uses a model for assessing the economic benefits of bus services in an urban area, known as the Glaister Model (Ref. 3) after its author. It is designed to examine whether there is an optimum balance between fares and service levels and to compare the amount of benefit achieved per unit (£) of subsidy. One item of data needed by the model is traffic levels (in vehicle kilometres) by type of road, which can be obtained from a suitable traffic model.

The supply and use made of parking spaces can also have an important effect on highway operating conditions particularly in and around major urban centres. Together with parking charges, they can be significant factors in choosing between modes of travel, between alternative destinations and the frequency and time of travel. Local authorities are often faced with conflicting parking requirements (eg. demand for easier parking from the business community and motorised public against the limitation of highway capacity to cope with increasing traffic volumes) and attempts have been made to develop models to help evaluate alternative parking policies. The Transport Studies Unit at Oxford University have produced a computerised simulation model, called CLAMP, and have applied it with some success. It enables the effects of various types of policy change to be assessed in terms of vehicle speeds and flows, travel times, search times and generalised cost (Ref. 4).

11.4 Defining and Building a Serial Model

Choice of Time to be Modelled

Many transport studies use 24 hour average annual daily flows (AADF) but traffic congestion in urban areas usually occurs during relatively short (typically 1 to 2 hours) peak periods and it is during these periods that most of the operational costs and benefits will be incurred. For this reason demand analysis in urban areas should concentrate on AM and PM peak periods together with a representative off peak period. In some cases it may be necessary to split a peak period into smaller 'time slices' of say 15 to 30 minutes in order to portray conditions as accurately as possible.

However, it is not possible to make reliable forecasts of future demand at such fine levels.

The Structure of the Model

A travel demand model involves estimating the number of journeys between each origin zone and each destination zone in the study area to produce a **'trip matrix'** and then allocating these journeys to alternative modes and to appropriate routes through each transport network; which is known as the **'assignment'** process.

Separate trip matrices may be developed for different trip purposes or vehicle types and then combined (or aggregated) prior to assignment. For small study areas, matrices may be estimated directly from survey data but in most cases some form of synthesis is necessary. **Synthesis** commonly involves a sequence of sub-models operated in turn, each acting on the output of the previous one and providing input for the following one, hence the term **'serial model'** (see Figure 11.1). Some or all of the sub-models may be combined or replaced by alternative methods, depending upon the purpose of the model.

An assignment model uses a logical, predetermined method of selecting the most appropriate routes through a predefined road network for each origin-destination pair in the trip matrix.

Each of the four major stages in the model involves developing mathematical relationships to replicate a known situation defined by observations. This enables the model to be **calibrated** and requires considerable amounts of survey data relating to the base year. Output from the calibrated model must then be compared with observations which have not been used in the calibration to test the accuracy of the model. This **'validation'** should be carried out at as many stages of the model building process as possible.

Obtaining an Observed Trip Matrix

An observed trip matrix is one where all the origin-destination movements have been obtained directly from surveys. It is usually only practicable for small study areas, unless large zone sizes are acceptable, but it does represent actual travel patterns reliably if the surveys have been carried out on a sufficiently large scale.

Techniques available for obtaining information on the origins and destinations of traffic include roadside interviews and number plate surveys. Careful location of observation stations on a cordon around the study area and on internal screenlines (see Figure 11.2) enable interzonal movements to be determined. Zone sizes, formed by the cordon and screenlines, should be such that journeys wholly within a zone can be neglected.

Roadside interviews are appropriate where large zones are acceptable or where non-observed movements are to be synthesised (see below). In urban areas, however, it is becoming increasingly difficult to locate roadside interview stations where traffic delays would not be excessive and without alienating the public. This can have serious effects on the size of the interview sample and the quality of data especially during peak periods. An alternative which involves shorter delays to traffic is to hand out return-paid questionnaires (see also Chapter 10).

For compact study areas and where journey purpose and the exact origin and destination are not essential, it is generally more appropriate to use a combination of number plate surveys and classifed counts. Vehicles are not delayed at all and information on routes through the study area can be obtained by judiciously siting internal screenlines.

Household interview surveys are not normally appropriate for obtaining origin-destination information for direct input to trip matrices because of the size of survey needed to obtain an adequate sample and the difficulty in determining the precise area from which to draw the sample.

A single trip matrix of all journeys may be adequate unless it is expected that some vehicle types would take different routes between the same origins and destinations (eg. because of weight restrictions on some roads), or where it is important to predict the numbers of certain types of vehicle likely to use individual links. In these cases the survey should be designed to enable individual matrices to be produced for different groups of vehicles.

Synthetic Matrices

Origin-destination movements often need to be quantified for zones where this information cannot be obtained directly from surveys (eg. because an excessively large survey would be required or because suitable survey locations are not available).

Three alternative techniques are available for deriving a synthetic matrix:

● partial matrix techniques;

● matrix estimation based on traffic counts; and

● serial models based on land use and interzonal travel costs.

The **partial matrix technique** is used to fill in missing portions of a matrix. Completed cells are used to derive a relationship between interzonal trips, zonal characteristics and interzonal travel costs from which missing cells are generated. (The theoretical basis for this approach was put forward by Kirby (see Ref. 5) and it has been practically applied by Neffendorf and Wootton (see Ref. 6) and many others).

Considerable progress has been made in recent years on the development of techniques to create a matrix where the principle data input is traffic counts (known as the 'matrix estimation' technique—see Refs. 7 and 8).

Versions of this technique are now included in some commercially available computer assignment packages. The technique is iterative and assigns an initial (or prior) matrix to a network and then factors appropriate elements of the matrix so that an improved assignment is obtained next time. The user specifies the traffic volumes appropriate to a series of links where close assigned/observed correlation is required. The procedure will, in principle, operate without a prior matrix but this is not advisable unless the study area is very small and the matrix can be well validated. There are, however, likely to be numerous origin-destination matrices which can reproduce the observed flows and it can prove difficult to achieve a unique and acceptable matrix. In general, the better the prior matrix that is used the better will be the final matrix. Possible sources for a prior matrix include earlier studies, observed movements and some form of synthesis based on zonal characteristics.

When the size of the study area and the number of zones are large the most generally used method for

producing trip matrices uses the serial model technique. Many variations have been used but the basic structure is as shown in Figure 11.1. Person trips are estimated and then, where appropriate, converted to vehicle trips at the end of the process. The technique is developed on the premise that each journey has a generation end and an attraction end. The generation end is like a reservoir of potential journeys which can be made to appropriate places of attraction. The generation end for trips made to or from home is always the home end whilst the attraction end may be the place of work, education, shopping or other activity. For journeys not made to or from home, the origin is the generation end (see also 11.7 below). Separate matrices are therefore usually developed for individual trip purposes.

Before the assignment stage can be carried out, the generation-attraction matrices have to be converted to origin-destination matrices. With a 24 hour trip matrix, the total number of trips recorded in each are identical because it is assumed that each generation-attraction trip is made once in each direction during a day. However, during any shorter period of time, some trips will be being made only in the G-A direction and some A-G. Survey data should be used to determine the proportions appropriate to that part of the day being considered (eg. in the morning peak a typical O-D matrix might consist of 70%-90% G-A movements and only 10%—30% A—G movements).

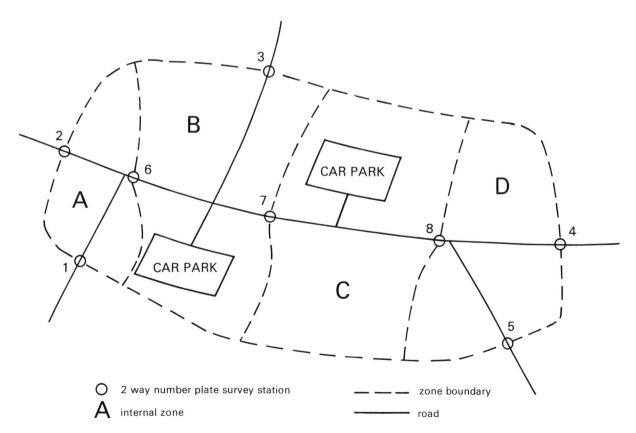

Figure 11.2 Plan showing typical design of a number plate survey from which a trip matrix may be obtained

Private (as opposed to commercial vehicle or public transport) person trips have to be converted to vehicle trips before assignment using survey data on vehicle occupancy. A typical factor to apply to a morning peak, home based, work, person trip matrix might be 0.70 although different factors may be used for different parts of the matrix.

Synthesised Commercial Vehicle Matrices

Techniques for synthesising commercial vehicle trips by serial model methods are not as well developed as for private vehicle trips. This is due to the difficulty of deriving stable relationships between types of industry and commerce and their trip making characteristics and also to the practical difficulties of designing and carrying out the surveys from which such relationships could be developed. The distribution of journeys between generators and attractors can also be very difficult to predict as different firms in the same category (eg. wholesale) can have very different patterns of distribution. Nevertheless, some studies have used this method by developing their own relationships whilst others have used the relationships developed in other studies. This 'transporting' of relationships between studies is acceptable if the study areas have similar characteristics (eg. urban, industrial, polynuclear) and the resulting model can be validated against observed information. However, the factors that affect the accuracy of transportability are not well understood and care is essential.

When a partial commercial vehicle trip matrix can be developed from survey data, it is common to complete the matrix using the partial matrix technique.

It is recommended that the number of categories of commercial vehicle for which separate matrices are developed is kept to a minimum. This is because of the difficulty in collecting data of sufficient accuracy and the uncertainties attached to the matrix development methods. It may only be necessary to differentiate between those heavy commercial vehicles which would adopt different route choice criteria to smaller vehicles (eg. to avoid roads with a weight or size prohibition and to recognise the greater attraction of roads with better alignment characteristics).

Assigning a Trip Matrix to a Network

The assignment of public transport trips and private or commercial vehicle trips to a network is carried out totally independently. A public transport assignment estimates the passenger demand for individual services and is used to help plan routes and service frequencies. A highway assignment estimates vehicular flows on roads and is used to help evaluate highway improvement proposals and related policy options. The network descriptions used by each type of assignment are very different. A journey by public transport has a number

of elements which could influence the route taken—walk to the boarding place, wait for the service to arrive, on board travelling, interchange onto another route with any inherent delay and walk to the final destination. A public transport network has to represent all this as well as each service and frequency. Various public transport assignment packages are commercially available in this country (eg. MVBus, BUSMAN, BUSMODEL—Refs. 9, 10, 11).

There are a number of different types of highway assignment packages available but all are based on the principle of selecting appropriate routes through a highway network for all the origin-destination pairs in the trip matrix. They differ in the way they select routes and in the way they represent traffic conditions on a network. It is important to select a method which best represents the way routes are chosen in reality and will provide output to a level of detail and accuracy commensurate with the decisions that have to be taken.

The general method of assignment should be decided at the outset of the study so that sufficiently accurate and detailed surveys can be organised and an appropriate trip matrix (or matrices) produced. It will also determine the level of detail required in the system of zones and in the highway network.

Assignment models require the calibration of the parameters used in the route selection procedure. This is usually done by testing alternative values and selecting those that produce the most acceptable results. The calibration stage also includes network adjustments that are deemed desirable to improve the quality of the assignment. Highway assignment models are discussed in more detail in 11.12 below.

Model Validation

Travel demand models should always be 'validated' to demonstrate how well they perform. This is done by comparing the model output with observed data not used to develop the model and is necessary to ensure that:

- the degree of accuracy of the model is adequate for the decisions which need to be taken;

- the decision makers understand the quality of the information with which they are presented;

- the inherent uncertainties can be taken into account in reaching decisions.

Where a model is based mainly on data more than about 6 years old, the validation should be carried out on a forecast (produced by the model) of present day conditions.

Validation should include:

- network validation;

- trip matrix validation; and

- assignment validation.

Network validation should confirm that the description of the modelled network is an adequate representation of the real network. Link flows, speeds and journey times should be checked and routes selected by the assignment model should be seen to be realistic.

Matrices are usually validated using screenlines of counts not previously used. Interzonal movements crossing a screenline can be identified and the appropriate cells of the matrix totalled and compared with the observed total. Screenlines should be sufficiently long to ensure alternative routes are intercepted. If O–D information is available on a screenline then some individual cells of the matrix can be validated.

The validation of assigned link flows is arguably the most important validation phase as link flows are usually central to most decisions that have to be made. The output link flows will reflect assignment model errors as well as those transmitted from the matrix and network. However, link and junction transit times are also important, especially in urban areas where delay at junctions can represent a significant proportion of the total journey time.

Validation is normally achieved by comparing output link flows with independent traffic counts. Turning volume counts would be needed to validate the most detailed assignment models. Most assignment packages are able to identify the zones or origin and destination of trips using a link (usually called 'load select link analysis'). If there are any unused roadside interviews, origin-destination data for that link can be compared—a very searching test!

The degree of accuracy to which a model should be validated depends on the applications for which it is intended and no hard and fast rule can be given. A model which is developed to compare alternative solutions to a particular problem should be most adept at reproducing those parts of the study area in the immediate region of the problem and those which may be significantly affected by any possible solution.

A great deal of reliance is placed upon the ability of the practitioner to predict the factors that are likely to prove critical when comparing the performance of competing alternatives.

The presentation of validation comparisons should always show the range of uncertainty unavoidably inherent in observed data and, wherever possible, the uncertainty associated with the model itself. This and other aspects of validation are covered in Chapter 11 of the Department of Transport's 'Traffic Appraisal Manual' (see Ref. 12) [Sco.57].

11.5 Defining the Study Area and Modelling Zones

The study area is that geographical area covered by the origins and destinations in the travel demand model and the most important criterion governing its definition is that it should include those routes which would be significantly affected by traffic rerouteing as a result of any proposal likely to be evaluated using the model.

It is advisable that, wherever appropriate, study area boundaries should coincide with major administrative boundaries to facilitate the provision of input data and the application of output summaries. Cross-checking and comparison of statistics may be possible if boundaries and screenlines can coincide with those used in other studies.

Journeys which cross the study area boundary should have their external origins (or destinations) allocated either to a system of increasingly large external zones (which should cover the whole country), or to zones which represent the points (or gateways) where they cross the study area boundary. The advantage of using external zones is that if a coarse external network is used, the possibility of long distance strategic traffic diverting to alternative routes can be assessed. It is, however, usual to include in the model only those external trips which crossed the study area boundary in the base year. The likelihood of trips being attracted into the study area should be minimised by careful choice of study area boundary but may not be eliminated altogether. An assessment of the possible scale of such rerouteing can be made using roadside interviews carried out at appropriate locations outside the study area (see also Chapter 10 for sources of national data).

The main criteria that should be considered when defining the zoning system within a study area are:

- zone sizes should be consistent with the density of the modelled network—zones normally increase in size the further they are from the area of particular interest (ie. where most change is expected);

- zones should not be smaller than is necessary to allow traffic to be loaded on to the transport network with adequate accuracy;

- boundaries should be drawn to include, wherever possible, consistent types of development within each zone (eg. residential, industrial etc.);

- zones should not contain well spaced out areas of development each with a different point of access to the network and poor intra-zonal linkages;

- zone boundaries should, where appropriate, coincide with local authority and census (enumeration district) boundaries and zone boundaries used by other studies;

• zone boundaries should coincide with screenlines and cordons used for data collection and model development.

The definition of study area and zone boundaries is often a compromise between conflicting requirements (eg. between the desire to 'improve' the model by increasing its size and complexity and the practical considerations of keeping costs down and meeting targets of timescale and adequacy). There is no substitute here for experience and professional judgement. An example of a typical zoning system is shown in Figure 11.3.

A particular problem can arise in urban areas where a large car park serves a range of destinations within a centre. Whilst an actual shop or office will be the destination for the travellers, some may park in a car park some distance away, others may park on the site itself and users of public transport may board or alight at a different point. These locations may be in different zones making assignment to a network more difficult.

11.6 Estimating Growth in Travel Demand

Changes in traffic demands may occur in a particular area over a period of time as a result of changing conditions caused by:

• residential, industrial, and commercial development;

• changes in population;

• changes in the level of economic activity;

• growth in car ownership and usage;

• the availability of alternative modes of transport and their characteristics; and

• urban transport policies, congestion and consequent effects on transport costs.

The Department of Transport monitors important factors affecting travel growth (see also Chapter 10.3) and issues forecasts from time to time for future demand expressed as expected vehicle kilometres for different types of vehicles (Ref. 13).

The Department also produces forecasts of:

• population, households, employed residents and employment;

• numbers of households owning 0, 1 and 2 or more cars;

• private vehicle trip ends by journey purposes.

These can be obtained at District Council level.

Future Trip Matrices

The provision of trip matrices for future situations involves a variety of assumptions about future growth and change. The approach adopted will depend on the resources available and the changes expected up to the end of the forecasting period. Sometimes it may be sufficient to factor an existing matrix by a single multiplier reflecting uniform growth in travel demand, but this will often be too simplistic.

Alternatively, a trip end model (see 11.7 below) may be used to estimate factors for changes in trip origins and destinations (or generations and attractions), which are then applied iteratively to the rows and columns of the matrix. This process (usually called the **Furness technique**) will converge to a point where there is little or no change in the matrix, provided the total growths in rows and columns are equal. The final matrix may be controlled to an overall level of growth obtained from national or local traffic predictions. It may be necessary to 'seed' initial values to the matrix, if for instance, development is to take place on a 'green field' site.

If the likely changes in the transport network are sufficient to make significant changes in the distribution of trips then a trip distribution model (see 11.8 below) will have to be used to derive new matrices from the forecast trip origins and destinations derived from the trip end model. If major changes in the relative attractiveness of public and private transport are also envisaged, then a modal choice model (see 11.9 below) may also be necessary.

Growth in commercial trip matrices may well have to be simply modelled by a single growth factor. The most that is likely to be contemplated is a trip end and growth factor procedure (as outlined above). This is because no well tested and practical technique for modelling freight distribution and modal choice is presently available.

Assignment of Trips to Road Networks

However they are derived, the resulting trip matrices can be assigned to networks representing the alternatives being considered (see 11.12 below).

If all of the stages of modelling described above are carried out many factors affecting trip demand will have been taken into account. This is a major undertaking, involving extensive resources in the collection and analysis of data. It can only be justified if major investment decisions are required and in many instances it will be necessary to concentrate effort on the elements of the model that are most relevant to the task in hand and to allow for effects that the model does not take into account in a less refined way.

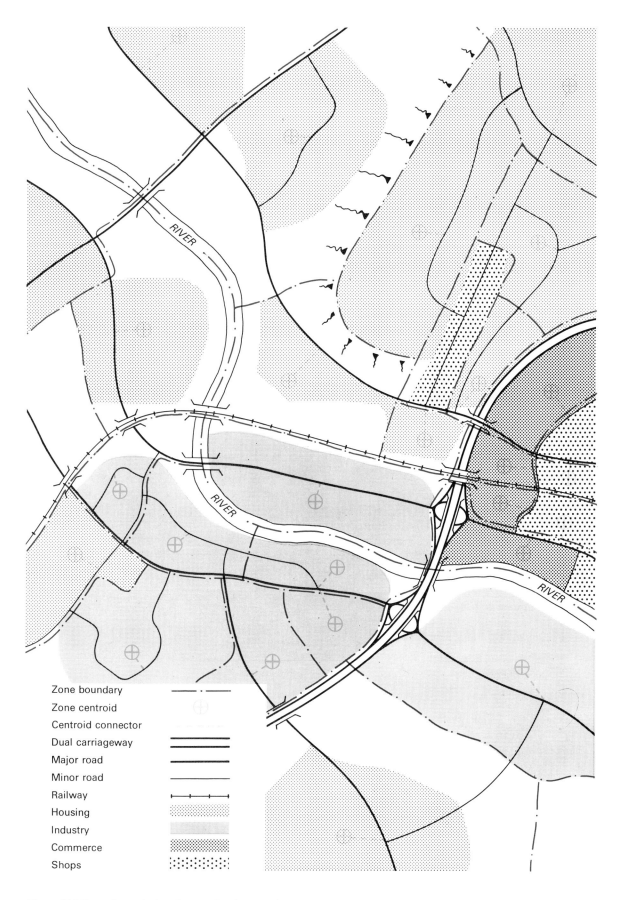

Zone boundary	—·—·—·—
Zone centroid	⊕
Centroid connector	
Dual carriageway	═══════
Major road	────────
Minor road	────────
Railway	—+—+—+—
Housing	
Industry	
Commerce	
Shops	⋯⋯⋯⋯

Figure 11.3 Part of a typical study area showing zone boundaries and connections to the road network

11.7 Modelling Trip Origins and Destinations

The origins and destinations of trips are normally referred to as trip ends. A trip end model will be required if future year forecasts are to reflect the effects of land use changes and changes in car ownership over time. Some approaches to infilling the unobserved movements in partially observed trip matrices also require trip end estimates.

Person Trips

Person trips are normally classified as being either home-based trips (with one or other end at a person's home) or non-home-based. For home-based trips, the home end is normally considered to be the 'generator' of the trip, and the other end (eg. workplaces or shops) is the 'attractor'. Trip end models for home-based trips produce zonal estimates of generations and attractions, which are converted to origins and destinations later.

Trip end estimates can be produced for a range of journey purposes including:

- home-based work;
- home-based education;
- home-based shopping;
- home-based other;
- non-home-based.

Home-based shopping trips are usually combined with home-based other for AM peak models and some studies have divided work trips into 'blue' and 'white collar'. Non-home-based trips have sometimes been classified as 'employer's business' and 'other'. Different trip purposes should have statistically significant differences in the parameters of the trip end model or of later models in the estimation process, in order to be justified.

If modal choice is being modelled (see also 11.9 below) then the trip end model will produce combined estimates of person trips for all the modes being considered, subdivided by car ownership. If modal choice is not being considered, vehicle trips are normally estimated.

Home based trip generation models may be based on zones, households or individuals. Zonal models relate the number of trips of given types generated in each zone to available data such as resident population, number of employed residents, car ownership, population density and distances from nearby urban centres. These relationships are usually estimated by linear regression using grossed up survey data.

Linear regression may also be used on survey data to estimate household or person based trip generation models, with trip making being related to such household characteristics as car ownership, household income and numbers of employed and non-employed residents, or to individual characteristics. An alternative is to cross-classify households or individuals by characteristics that have been found to influence trip making and to calculate the average trips per person or household for each of the categories so formed. This is normally called **category analysis**. A regression approach is likely to make better use of the available data.

Generally speaking, household and person-based models will reflect the factors that actually affect trip making more closely than zonal models. It is usually possible to test and (if valid) include large numbers of variables that may affect trip making. However, it must be remembered that in applying the model throughout the study area, the basic source of input data is likely to be the National Census (Ref. 14). Detailed cross-tabulations are not available from this, and weak assumptions may have to be made in order to apply the model, unless it is restricted to a few basic variables. Also, if future year forecasts are to be made, the inputs to the model may be at least as difficult to forecast as trip making itself. The more complex models may be appropriate to, for example, a detailed corridor study, where the model can be applied to the surveyed population.

Trip attractions are usually modelled using zonal regression techniques and the results are then corrected so that the total attractions match the trips generated, after allowances have been made for the net effect of trips crossing the study area boundary.

The origins and destinations of non-home-based trips are usually modelled in a similar manner to home-based trip attractions. They are often factored to an overall control derived from a household or person-based model identical in its form to a home-based trip generation model.

Models of Car Ownership

Household car ownership is generally important to a person trip end model. Car ownership models are now normally disaggregate models of a logit-type form with household income as the major explanatory variable. Experience with this type of model at a national level has shown that calibration using survey data from a single year does not provide models that are likely to adequately represent the factors which influence the growth in car ownership over time. Unless there is a series of local surveys that will enable a model encompassing dynamic effects to be developed, it is likely to be more realistic to control the overall growth in car ownership to a total derived from national forecasts, with the local model being used to estimate differences within the study area.

Commercial Vehicle Trips

Commercial vehicle trip end models are normally based on zonal regression. Numbers of employees by type of industry often provide the only suitable explanatory variables.

11.8 Quantifying Travel Costs

Trip ends represent the intention or desire to travel, but the subsequent decisions regarding choice of destination, route, mode and even time of day depend, at least in part, upon the costs which travellers will incur (or perceive they incur) on the different transport systems available to them.

In effect, each link in a highway network has an associated cost of travel along it. These link costs represent the deterrence to travel as perceived by intending travellers on that particular network and are more than just the out of pocket expenses of the traveller. In the simplest case, cost may be merely equated to travel time. More often, time and distance related costs are combined together with parking costs to define a **'generalised cost'** of travel (see also Chapter 12).

A similar approach is used to determine the generalised cost for public transport trips with appropriate time penalties built in to allow for interchange between modes. Time spent waiting and walking is usually weighted more heavily than in-vehicle time. These time related costs are added to the fare paid to form the corresponding generalised cost.

Modelling the behaviour of individuals as passengers or vehicle users, requires more than simple measurements of time and distance related costs. Crucially, an accurate representation of behaviour requires an understanding of individual's perceptions of what travel is costing them. These perceived values may differ considerably from actual resource values but it may not be easy to discover what they are. For assignment models, it may be satisfactory to experiment with alternative weightings on time and distance to discover the values which give the best fit with observed data.

The Department of Transport issues appropriate values of distance and time related costs, from time to time, in updating its Highway Economics Note 2 (see Ref. 15). These are issued primarily for use in economic evaluation of its own trunk road schemes but they can be used more generally if no other evidence is available. Users of models should also be aware that use of different values for, say, route choice and economic evaluation will produce results which are not directly comparable.

11.9 Distribution Models

The function of a distribution model is to infill any unobserved cells of a partially observed trip matrix, or to forecast the effects of changes in the transport system on the choice of trip destination.

The Gravity Model

The most common form of distribution model used in Britain is **the gravity model**. This is an aggregate model which uses zonal (and not household) trip ends and inter-zonal cost data.

The general form of a gravity model is:

$$T_{ij} = a_i b_j f(c_{ij})$$

where T_{ij} is the number of trips of a particular type between origin i and destination j.

a_i and b_j are factors relating to zones i and j (if a trip end model is used then these factors would take account of the trip end estimate so that the sum of the trips for each zone is consistent with these estimates),

c_{ij} is the generalised cost for the particular type of trip between zones i and j, and

f( )   reflects the relative propensity to make journeys in relation to their perceived cost (usually known as the deterrence of cost function).

The Deterrence Function

The deterrence function (f) may be an analytical function, the most general form of which is normally:

$$f(c) = \alpha e^{-\beta c} c^{\gamma}$$

where α, β and γ are parameters to be estimated. Or, it may be an empirical function, which simply takes on different values for different cost bands. The empirical function may give a better fit to observed data than an analytical function but requires more data.

Where the distribution model is used only for trips by a single mode, the cost will simply be the generalised costs discussed in 11.5 above. Otherwise the cost is a composite of the generalised costs by the alternative modes. It has been shown that, in order to avoid inconsistent results between distribution and modal choice models, the correct formulation for composite cost is:

$$C = \frac{1}{\lambda} \cdot \log_e \left[\sum_i e^{-\lambda c_i} \right]$$

where c_i is the cost by the ith mode, and λ is a parameter in the modal choice model (see 11.9 below).

Calibration of a Gravity Model

As with other models, the calibration of a gravity model will not ensure its validity under all circumstances since it is not possible to validate a transport demand model to cover all eventualities and study areas. It is, therefore, always advisable to perform validation checks as part of the modelling process. Examples of such checks are:

● when using a partial matrix approach, the implied trip ends for the expanded matrix should be compared with the characteristics of the zones (eg. population, employment) to check that the trip end relationships implied by this comparison are realistic; and

● when trip ends have been estimated separately, the area to area movements contained within the matrix should be reasonably similar to independently counted traffic flows across a screen line that intercepts these area to area movements.

Destination choice models based on the behaviour of households or individuals as decision making units (rather than zonal aggregates) may prove preferable in the future, because of their theoretical consistency and efficient use of data.

11.10 Modelling Choice of Mode of Travel

A modal choice model will be required if public transport proposals are being considered, or it it is thought likely that proposals for the highway/parking system (or lack of them) will lead to significant transfers of trips between modes, hence altering the modal split.

The most commonly used model is of the **logit** type, which in one form can be written as:

$$\frac{T_k}{\sum\limits_i T_i} = \frac{e^{-\lambda c_k + \delta C_k}}{\sum\limits_i e^{-\lambda c_i + \delta c_i}} \text{ where}$$

T_k is trips by mode k

C_k is cost by mode k

δC_k is a mode specific parameter (often called the 'modal handicap') to be estimated, which represents characteristics of the mode not explicitly taken account of elsewhere (it will be zero for one mode), and

λ is a general parameter to be estimated.

An alternative form is the **hierarchical (or nested) logit** model, where a primary choice is made between, say, public and private transport, and a separate equation (with a different λ value) is used for the choice between alternative public transport modes.

The parameters used in these models are now normally estimated using disaggregate data from a household survey. The generalised cost formula given above will have been determined prior to the development of the model, but the best relative weightings on the components of journey time can be determined from the data used in calibrating the model. More generally the 'C' term is replaced by a linear combination of various characteristics of the mode and the traveller. A more powerful form of choice model is called the **probit** model. These more general models are likely to be most appropriate for application in, say, a corridor study, where the relationships can be applied to the surveyed population to determine their likely reaction to changes in the transport system. If the model is to be used as part of a trip end/distribution/modal split/ assignment four step model, then simpler relationships are likely to be more appropriate.

Modal choice models are usually concerned with person trips where individuals are considered to have a choice (ie. they have a car available or can choose between alternative public transport modes). However, it is often difficult to determine whether a member of a car owning household does have a car available to him/ her.

Different relationships will almost certainly be required for different journey purposes and car ownership groups. It may also be necessary to have different relationships for different area to area movements (eg. to urban centres and peripheral areas).

The modal choice model is applied after distribution (or sometimes in its own right). From a theoretical point of view, joint models of choice of destination and mode are usually preferable and practically based disaggregate models of this type may be most appropriate in the future.

Even when disaggregate models are used in forecasting, aggregate estimates of quantities such as traffic flow and public transport patronage are usually required. Aggregation techniques such as sample enumeration must be used to obtain such estimates.

11.11 Transport and Highway Networks

A detailed specification for each **transport network** is required to carry out the traffic assignments described in 11.12 below. However, they are also required in order to estimate the zone to zone travel costs required in the distribution and modal choice models described previously.

A **highway network** (see Figure 11.3) is described in terms of nodes (usually representing junctions) and the road links connecting them (often presented as one way roads between junctions so that a two way street is represented by two separate links). In addition, nodes are required to represent zone centroids, the points where trips start and finish. They are connected to the network by notional links known as 'centroid connectors'.

Choice of Network

The level of detail to be included in the network description depends on the applications being considered. Clearly, the more roads included, the closer is the representation to the network on the ground. However, large and detailed networks require more data input, and may require unnecessary time in getting the detailed assignment correct. In general, the network should include highways not more than one hierarchical level lower than the roads for which flows are required. However, this rule of thumb may not always be possible within the resources available for study and it may be necessary to provide this amount of detail only where it is required to study a particular problem with correspondingly less detail elsewhere. Conversely, it may be necessary to provide greater detail in some areas; for example, to model realistically the way traffic from a particular zone loads onto the network. Care should be exercised to ensure that decisions on which streets to exclude do not pre-judge the outcome of the study.

Network Description

The highway network description will include link lengths and speeds or times. Other details will depend on the assignment technique to be used.

Public transport networks are built on similar principles but describe services and contain information about frequencies and fare levels.

11.12 Traffic Assignment Models

Traffic flows on the links of a network can be estimated from a combination of a trip matrix, a network description and a route choice model. Route selection procedures attempt to model drivers' behaviour in choosing the route that they (drivers) consider to be best. It has been observed that different drivers often choose different routes between any given origin and destination, especially in urban areas, for reasons such as:

● personal differences in perception of route costs, due to differences in preference or to inaccurate and incomplete knowledge about current traffic conditions; and

● increased travel costs due to congestion on heavily used links, making some routes less attractive and increasing the number of routes of similar cost between any two nodes.

Different route choice models are available and place different emphases on these aspects of urban networks. For example:

Stochastic route choice models emphasise the variations in drivers' perceptions of route cost by the use of probability distributions.

Capacity restraining models emphasise the role of congestion by systematically changing link costs as traffic flow levels change.

Assignment models can be classified according to whether or not they include these effects. Some of the more important features are summarised below.

All or Nothing Assignments

These ignore both decision mechanisms and simply assign all traffic to the least cost route on the basis of the distances and times on the input network description. They will estimate demand along broad corridor widths and are often used for this purpose. A refinement of the all-or-nothing technique includes multi-routeing in which a proportion of the trip matrix is allocated to different cost parameters.

Pure Stochastic Assignment

This method makes no attempt to model the effect of traffic flow on the costs of alternative routes, but takes account of different driver's perceptions by the use of probability distributions. This type of procedure will spread traffic over closely competing parallel routes, with more traffic going to the cheapest route.

They are mainly useful in urban modelling of all day or off peak assignments, where the average effects of traffic flow on travel costs may be less than for peak periods. The most widely used method in Britain is that devised by Burrell (Ref. 16—see also Refs. 17 and 18), but there are a number of potential pitfalls which are explained in Ref. 12.

Stochastic Assignment with Capacity Restraint

This technique uses a combination of pure stochastic and capacity restraint procedures, in which:

● all trips are assigned to the network using a 'pure' stochastic algorithm, with fixed link costs;

● the 'current' link volumes are updated by taking a weighted average of the flows between this and the previous iteration;

● the link costs are adjusted to correspond to the 'current' volumes and then the process returns to the first step and repeats; and

● iteration continues until satisfactory compatibility between flows and speeds is achieved.

It is often found that the iterative procedure described above does not converge and traffic continues to switch between competing routes for successive iterations. Methods can be adopted to damp these oscillations down but it is difficult to avoid some element of choice of end point, with the danger that this is selected when the expected result is obtained.

Wardrop Equilibrium Assignment

This is a capacity restraining procedure and in its usual form does not take account of drivers' different perceptions of costs. Its basis is that traffic arranges itself on a congested network such that all routes used between any pair of origin and destination zones have equal (minimum) costs while all rejected routes have costs equal to or greater than the minimum. In other words, under equilibrium there is no incentive for any driver to switch to another route.

This procedure has become more popular in recent years, partly because iterative procedures exist which approach the equilibrium assignment in a stable manner, thus avoiding the problems discussed above. Some versions of the model allow for different classes of vehicle (eg. goods vehicles) to be assigned using different cost formulae.

Congested Networks and Capacity Restraint

Capacity restraint procedures adjust traffic speeds according to flows. Some versions of these procedures achieve this by the use of link-based speed flow relationships (see Figure 11.4). This allows for the effect of flow on speed in a general sense, but does not allow for more detailed effects of congestion on networks, such as:

Different delays for each turn—link-based speed/flow curves do not take account of different delays experienced by, say, right turnings and straight ahead traffic at a junction.

Oversaturated conditions—it is very easy to derive a traffic matrix that will create a demand greater than can apparently be catered for by the network. This would imply a situation with infinite delay but no such conditions occur in practice. All queues eventually disappear by one means or another. Thus, it is important to model oversaturated conditions in a time dependent way with peak demands occurring for a finite time followed by a decay to off-peak conditions.

Interaction of queues—queues occupy a finite amount of road space and so may in practice interfere with other junctions.

Effects of traffic signal settings—the coordination of traffic signal controlled junctions can improve the efficiency of dealing with a demand matrix within a given network and can affect the routeings chosen by drivers.

Delays due to conflicting flows and lane sharing—these delays depend on flows on the links concerned and on other links (eg. circulating traffic on roundabouts).

Bus routes and prohibition of HGVs—the existence of traffic control measures such as these require networks to be preloaded and appropriate routeings to be specified for particular vehicle types.

Congested Assignment Models

More recently assignment models have been developed that attempt to take account of some or all of these effects. One group of such models is produced as adaptations of earlier link-based models in which the user can describe selected junctions in detail, so that delays which relate to specific turning movements can be modelled. Different types of junction (ie. traffic signals, roundabouts or priority junctions) can be specified. Delays are calculated using time dependent queueing theory, given traffic flow profiles and the traffic volumes making the various conflicting movements. Such models do not take account of effects such as linked traffic signals and the effect of variability in delay over time or route choice. They can only take account of 'queueing back' in a limited way. Examples of assignment programs of this type are HINET (Ref. 19), JAM (Ref. 20) and TRIPS (Ref. 21).

Another group of congested assignment models uses simulation techniques, rather than fixed equations to represent delays. These models represent traffic situations in a more detailed way and are capable of representing time dependent effects, such as signal coordination and allowing for different route choice with varying conditions. Examples of assignment programs of this type are SATURN (Ref. 22) and CONTRAM (Ref. 23) but these two programs take very different approaches to traffic simulation.

Traffic Simulation Models

Assignment models help to give a better understanding of the operational characteristics of a transport network and predict how it would perform if amended or subjected to different traffic loadings. Although some assignment models are now able to more accurately reflect the characteristics of individual junctions, they have to use mathematical relationships to replicate the operation of junctions. Simulation techniques have also been used to model the progression of individual vehicles through small networks so that interactions with pedestrians, other vehicles and traffic control features are represented more realistically. The essential difference between pure simulation models and assignment models is that the precise route of each vehicle passing through the network is given as part of

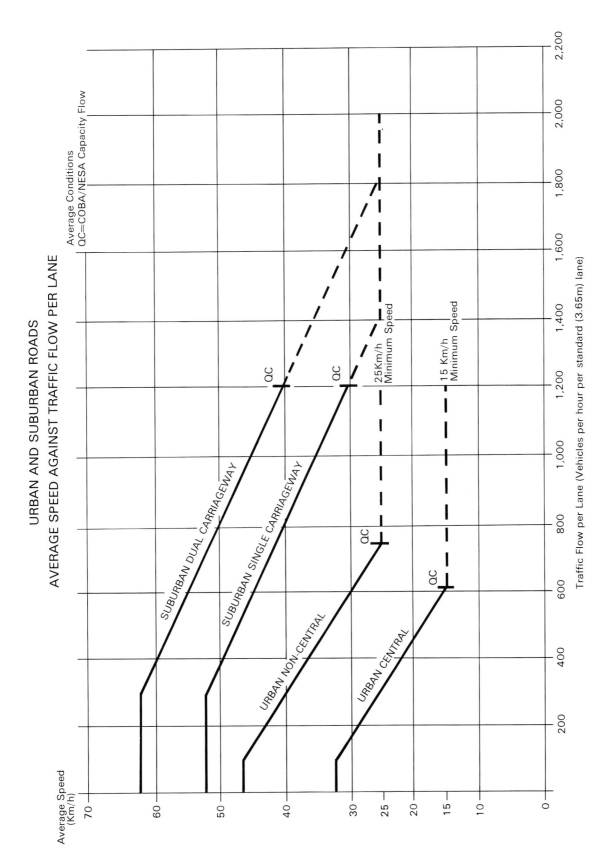

URBAN AND SUBURBAN ROADS
AVERAGE SPEED AGAINST TRAFFIC FLOW PER LANE

Average Conditions
QC=COBA/NESA Capacity Flow

Average Speed (Km/h)

SUBURBAN DUAL CARRIAGEWAY

SUBURBAN SINGLE CARRIAGEWAY

URBAN NON-CENTRAL

URBAN CENTRAL

QC

25Km/h
Minimum Speed

15 Km/h
Minimum Speed

Traffic Flow per Lane (Vehicles per hour per standard (3.65m) lane)

Source: DTp/SDD (1986)

Figure 11.4 Example of speed—flow relationships

93

the input data and changes in route choice caused by changing travel conditions are not modelled.

A traffic simulation model commonly used in Britain is the Department of Transport's TRAFFICQ (Ref. 24) in which the precise features of roads and junctions can be represented in a fully dynamic way. The model is able to represent random or predetermined incidents and can provide distributions of quantities such as queue lengths, travel times and delays.

Other models are also being developed (eg. West Yorkshire Metropolitan County Council have developed TRANSIM (Ref. 25) from a general purpose simulation program so that animated films or videos can be produced to show the progression of individual vehicles through a network. As well as assisting the design process, this can be used very effectively for presentational purposes).

11.13 Errors and Uncertainties in Demand Forecasts

Whenever traffic forecasts are used for making decisions, it is important to understand the quality of the forecasts provided. One policy option may appear better than another but the uncertainties associated with the forecasts may make the comparison unreliable.

The Department of Transport's view of the assessment of uncertainty and error in forecasting is contained in Chapters 10 and 12 of its Traffic Appraisal Manual (Ref. 12) [Sco.58, Sco.59]. Appraisals of the Department's own schemes must be carried out using the rules and guidelines set out in the manual and for other situations it provides, at the very least, a useful frame of reference.

Sources of error and uncertainty fall into three broad groups, each of which is discussed below.

Data Errors and Uncertainties

Data errors can arise in three ways:

Sampling errors—Traffic models are usually based on sampled data, which is taken to be representative of the population concerned. Provided the sampling methods are understood, confidence levels can be calculated for the values being estimated. It is possible to reduce sampling error by taking larger samples. However, beyond certain limits this is not worthwhile because the range of uncertainty will only diminish significantly with very large increases in the sample and also because possible errors due to other causes are likely to become more important.

Measurement errors—Some items, such as road lengths, can be measured very accurately, whereas other items, such as employment may only be estimates. For traffic counts, the Traffic Appraisal Manual provides ranges of likely levels of accuracy (see also Chapter 10) and methods of dealing with systematic variation by hour of day, day of week and season.

Human errors—These will inevitably arise when data is collected and processed by human beings. Good checks can minimise them. Also, when developing the model, extreme values of residual errors should be examined to ensure that they are not due to human error.

Knowledge of the likely uncertainties due to sampling and measurement error should be taken into account during the early stages of model building. There is little point in trying to produce models which validate to a greater level of precision than the accuracy of the data used. This should also be borne in mind when using the outputs from the models.

Model Specification Errors

Forecasting models are based on fairly simplified representations of human behaviour even if they appear to be complex. They are, therefore, almost bound to be incorrectly, or inadequately specified.

Errors in the form of equations used, or the omission of important explanatory variables may show up in comparisons with independent validation data but are more likely to emerge over time.

The best guide to the adequacy of a model specification is an examination of the residual errors (ie. the difference between observed and modelled values). They should be normally distributed and should not show any bias. The model should also have a reasonable theoretical basis. It should be possible to explain why the general form of the model makes sense, and why the dependent variable should vary with the explanatory variables.

In some circumstances it may be possible to develop models with alternative specifications and to combine the results. An example of this is the Department of Transport's car ownership forecasts, which are produced using both a time series model and a disaggregate household-based model (Ref. 13).

Errors of Forecasting

Obviously, the future values of the various inputs used in a forecasting model cannot be known for certain. The Department of Transport tries to take account of this by producing low and high forecasts based on different values of the important explanatory variables (eg. personal income and petrol prices). Such procedures help to ensure that decisions are robust over a range of assumptions. However, different decisions may be attractive according to which forecast is used. Whether it is better in these circumstances to give greater weight to the low or high forecast depends on the type of decision to be made and the implications of making 'wrong' decisions. Ultimately, it becomes a matter for human judgement.

11.14 References

Text Reference

1. DTp/TRRL—Special Research Branch Working Paper 33 (1986) *'The structure and calibration of the London area model'*, DTp (1986). (11.2)

2. DTp—*'COBA 9 Manual'*, DTp (1981) (Amended). [Sco.60] (11.3)

3. Glaister, S—*'Urban Public Transport Subsidies: An Economic Assessment of Value for Money'*, DTp (1983). (11.3)

4. Bates, J and Bradley, M—*'The CLAMP parking policy analysis model'*. TEC Vol 27 No 7/8, (July/Aug 1986). (11.3)

5. Kirby, H R—*'Theoretical requirements for the calibration of gravity models'*. Paper to PTRC Urban Traffic Model Research Seminar, PTRC (Dec 1971). (11.4)

6. Neffendorf, H and Wootton, H J,—*'A Travel Estimation model, Based on Screen-time Interviews'*, PTRC Summer Annual Meeting (July 1974). (11.4)

7. Van Zuylen, J H and Willumsen, L G—*'The most likely trip matrix estimated from traffic counts*, Transportation Research Vol 14B No 3 (Sept 1980). (11.4)

8. Willumsen, L G—*'Estimation of Trip Matrices from Volume Counts'*, PTRC Annual Summer Meeting, PTRC (July 1982). (11.4)

9. MVA Systematica—*MVBus Network Monitoring Program*. MVA (1986). (11.4)

10. Wootton Jeffreys and Partners—*'BUS-MAN users guide'* Wootton Jeffreys and Partners (1981). (11.4)

11. C Buchanan & Ptnrs—*'BUSMODEL User Guide'*, Collin Buchanan and Ptnrs. (11.4)

12. DTp—*'Traffic Appraisal Manual (TAM)'*, DTp (1985). [Sco.61] (11.4)

13. DTp—*'National Road Traffic Forecasts (Great Britain)'*, DTp (1984). [Sco.62] (11.6)

14. Office of Population Censuses and Surveys—*'Census 1981: National Report'*, HMSO (1983). (11.7)

15. DTp—*'Highways Economic Note 2'*, DTp (1985). (11.8)

16. Burrell, J E—*'Multiple route assignment and its application to capacity restraint'*, 4th International Symposium on the Theory of Traffic Flow (1968). (11.12)

17. Dial, R B—*'A probabilistic multipath traffic assignment which obviates path enumeration'* Transportation Research, Vol 5 (1971). (11.12)

18. Van Vliet, D and Dow, P D C—*'Capacity-restrained road assignment'* Traffic Engineering and Control, Vol 20 No 6, (1979). (11.12)

19. Transport Planning Associates—*'HINET Manual'*, Transport Planning Associates (1981). (11.12)

20. Wootton Jeffreys and Partners—*'JAM users guide'*, Wootton Jeffreys and Partners (1980). (11.12)

21. MVA Systematica—*'TRIPS Manual'*, MVA Systematica (1982). (11.12)

22. Van Vliet, D—*'SATURN: a users guide'*, Institute for Transport Studies, University of Leeds (1981). (11.2, 11.12)

23. DTp/TRRL—Supplementary Report SR 735 *'Users guide to CONTRAM Version 4'*, DTp (1982). (11.2, 11.12)

24. Transpotech Ltd.—*'TRAFFICQ Manual'*, MVA Systematica (1983). (11.2, 11.12)

25. Foster, D and Smare, A D—*'Development of TRANSIM—a display orientated traffic simulation model'*, Municipal Engineer, Vol 110 No 6 (1983). (11.12)

11.15 Further Information

26. DTp—*'Highways Economic Note (HEN)1'*, DTp (1985).

27. Robertson, D I—*'Estimating origin—destination flows by simulating trip choice'*, Traffic Engineering and Control, Vol 25 Nos 7 and 8 (1984).

28. Bell, M G H—*'The estimation of junction running flows and their confidence intervals from measurements of link volumes: a computer program'*, Traffic Engineering and Control, Vol 24 No 4 (1983).

29. DTp—*'QUADRO Manual'*, DTp (1982).

30. DTp/TRRL—Report SR 735 '*A user guide to CONTRAM version 4*', DTp (1982).

31. DTp/TRRL—Report LR 939 '*MIDAS: a computer program to estimate delays at junctions*', DTp (1980).

32. DTp/TRRL—Report LR 941 '*PICADY: A computer program to model capacities, queue and delays at major/minor junctions*', DTp (1980).

33. Logie, D M W—'*TRAFFICQ: a comprehensive model for traffic management schemes*', Traffic Engineering and Control, Vol 20 No 11 (1979).

34. Hall, M D Van Vliet, D and Willumsen, L G—'*SATURN—a simulation assignment model for the evaluation of traffic management schemes*', Traffic Engineering and Control, Vol 21 (1978).

12 Economic and Environmental Appraisal

12.1 Introduction

Identifying Schemes

Local authorities [NI.1] should develop their highway and traffic schemes side by side with policies for the development and other use of land so that schemes are brought forward as part of the planning of the area as a whole and their objectives are compatible with it. The planning process may identify parts of the existing highway network where a new road, a major alteration to an existing road or a traffic management scheme would be beneficial on economic, traffic, environmental or safety grounds, or to allow development to proceed. However, as there are usually practical limitations on the number of schemes on which investment might be made during any given planning period (because of limits on available investment capital and the time needed to obtain the necessary consents), it is usually necessary to select those schemes which will achieve the greatest net benefit to the community as a whole as part of a coordinated transport policy. For this reason many highway authorities develop ranked lists of schemes to be pursued as a planned programme.

Developing Schemes

Once a decision in principle has been made that some form of scheme is required to meet identified problems, it will be necessary to:

- consider a range of feasible alternative options, (including that of taking no action, ie. do-nothing);

- assess the extent to which each scheme meets the required economic, environmental, social and traffic objectives;

- proceed with public consultation and participation to inform and take account of the responses of those people affected by the different alternatives;

- select a prepared scheme and where appropriate secure its inclusion in an approved or adopted structure plan, local plan or unitary development plan and obtain planning permission;

- include the scheme in the 'firm' programme and arrange capital funding; and

- initiate procedures for acquiring any land necessary to construct the scheme.

(NB: A fuller explanation of procedures for scheme development is provided in Chapter 35).

Scheme Development Time and Flexibility

The lead time for most large highway construction schemes is usually at least five years and the time required for each of the above operations will vary from scheme to scheme. Events occurring during this time may influence the detailed design which evolves. For instance, the design may need to be amended to take account of a particular development proposal which arises during scheme preparation, or to ameliorate the scheme's effect on a group of nearby residents identified during public consultation. A scheme may also be brought forward in the programme if it meets the criteria for funding by one of the ad hoc (or temporary) sources of finance which occur for local government capital construction from time to time (eg. the urban development programme initiated by the Industrial Development Act 1982) [NI.2].

Traffic management schemes usually take less time to implement because there is often less land take involved (sometimes none) and new construction is minimized. The time frame appropriate to different options can be a major factor in the choice of scheme.

It has in the past been the practice of some local authorities to protect routes for which long term improvements are envisaged by 'as-and-when' safe-guarding on the development or redevelopment of adjacent land. Because of the indeterminate timescale or nature of such improvements they have often not been included in any formal plan. Department of the Environment Circular 22/84 (Ref. 1) [Sco.63] recommends that only firm proposals should be safeguarded for development control purposes and that they should be included in development plans.

12.2 Comparison Between Alternatives

The comparison between mutually exclusive alternatives for a scheme and consideration of a set of independent schemes should be based on the relative costs and benefits resulting from operational, financial, environmental and safety effects on different sections of the community, both direct and indirect and in the short and long term. Most of these effects can be directly quantified but some can only be measured in a way which allows a monetary equivalent value to be applied. The essential point in any comparison is that the basis should be fair and consistent. Likewise, alternative proposals should always be based upon the same set of values and standards of geometry, safety and operation, so that their costs and benefits can be compared in an equitable way. Where a series of small schemes can have a larger impact than the sum of their individual effects, they should be assessed as a group.

12.3 The Framework Approach

Given that various effects of schemes will be measured and presented differently it is important that they be brought together in a way which allows the total effects of any one particular option, and the differences between options, to be readily seen. The Department of Transport uses a framework approach [Sco. 64]. The framework consists of a matrix setting out data which summarises the expected direct and indirect impacts on different groups in the community for each of the alternative options for a proposed scheme. Some local authorities have used more complex frameworks where scores and weights are attached to both the impacts themselves and the groups they affect.

The use of a framework permits a comparison of both quantifiable and non-quantifiable costs and benefits in a comprehensive and consistent way. It allows environmental and social consequences to be considered in a standardised format alongside the economic effects.

This method follows the recommendations of the Leitch Report (Ref. 2). The methods used by the Department of Transport are set out in the Manual of Environmental Appraisal (MEA) (Ref. 3) [Sco.65]. This manual aims to ensure consistency in the appraisal of trunk road schemes but the principles are also applicable to non-trunk road schemes, both for new construction and in the management or enhancement of existing transport infrastructure.

Under the Department's method, an analysis is made of the different ways in which different groups of people will be affected. The MEA divides the impacts into the following categories:

Group 1   the effects on travellers;

Group 2   the effects on occupiers of property;

Group 3   the effects on users of facilities;

Group 4   the effects on policies for conserving and enhancing the area;

Group 5   the effects on policies for development and transport; and

Group 6   financial aspects.

The level of detail demanded in the MEA for Groups 1–3 is reproduced in Table 12.1. The particular policies affected in Groups 4 and 5 are determined by reference to statutory documents (eg. Structure and Local Area Plans in each case). The effects in Group 6 are generally obtained from cost benefit analysis using COBA (Ref. 4) [Sco.66], but see also section 12.4 below.

An example of an environmental consideration under Group 2 is given by the impact of traffic noise on residents. Figure 12.1 illustrates how the noise impact of three different levels of traffic can be presented for public consultation, with the corresponding data on houses affected by the change being entered into the framework for evaluation.

SACTRA Report (1986)

The Standing Advisory Committee on Trunk Road Assessment (SACTRA) recommended in its 1986 report on Urban Road Appraisal (Ref. 5) that the framework approach should be extended to include a clear descriptive statement of the objectives and problems which a scheme is designed to meet and the extent to which each option achieves them. The Committee also recommended that the assessment should indicate the main points that have arisen in any public consultation, since these would be important factors which should influence the option chosen. The Committee's recommended framework approach is illustrated by a case study in Chapter 14 of their report.

12.4 Using the Concept of Environment Capacity

An alternative approach that might be used to develop road schemes of acceptable environmental quality involves making use of the concept of environmental capacity (as described in Chapter 6). The technique involves modelling the relationship between traffic flow and environmental factors such as noise and pedestrian delay and, starting with existing or assigned flows, iteratively adjusting the scheme design (and hence the value of these parameters) until an acceptable balance between traffic access and the environment is achieved. For further information see Refs. 6, 7 and 8.

12.5 Traffic and Economic Effects

The extent to which the traffic, economic and related environmental effects of proposals can be estimated, depends on the traffic forecasting and modelling techniques used. These were discussed in Chapter 11. The choice of technique is a matter for professional judgement and will depend upon individual circumstances. SACTRA (Ref. 5) recommended that the methods chosen should be as simple as possible given the constraints of the situation. This approach should avoid unnecessary complexity and cost. The choice of traffic models should take account of the probable use of the results in other parts of the appraisal. For example, changes in traffic flows and journey times will form part of the assessment of economic effects.

GROUP 1 TRAVELLERS – SUMMARY OF IMPACTS TO BE CONSIDERED

Component Sub Groups	Impacts to be considered					
	Time Savings or Delays (2)	Changes in Vehicle Operating Costs (2)	Accident Reductions (2), (3)	Driver Stress	View from the Road	Amenity and Severance
Vehicle Drivers and Passengers	X	X	X	X	X	
Cyclists (1)			X			X
Pedestrians			X			X

The more important impacts are denoted by X.

NOTES
1. This sub group to be included only where an appreciable flow of cyclists is expected.
2. Normally expressed in monetary terms and discounted to a stated base year.
3. Supplemented by assessments of the numbers of casualties prevented.

GROUP 2 – OCCUPIERS OF PROPERTY – SUMMARY OF IMPACTS TO BE CONSIDERED

Component sub groups Occupiers of:	Impacts to be considered					
	Demolition No.	Noise Change dB(A) L_{10} 18hr (1)	Visual Effects	Severance	Disruption during Construction	Landtake hectares
Residential Property including Farmhouses	X	X	X	X	X	
Industrial and Commercial Property	X	X	X	X	X	
Schools and Hospitals	X	X	X	X	X	
Public or Social Buildings	X					
Recreational Space						X
Agricultural Land				X	X	X

The more important impacts are denoted by X.

NOTES
1. Public Inquiry frameworks will express this impact in terms of the numbers of properties experiencing noise changes within stated ranges of decibels. Public Consultation frameworks will not use decibels. Instead the properties affected will be classified by their distance from the centre-line of the proposed new road in bands up to a normal maximum of 300 m. For existing roads, the numbers of properties likely to experience at least a doubling or halving of the present traffic flow during the fifteen years after opening will be deemed to indicate the comparative effect of noise change.

GROUP 3 – USERS OF FACILITIES – SUMMARY OF IMPACTS TO BE CONSIDERED

Component Sub groups – Users of:	Impacts to be considered			
	Vehicle/ Pedestrian Conflict	Noise	Visual Intrusion	Severance
Shopping Centres	X	X		X
Public Buildings such as Churches Libraries or Community Centres		X		
Recreational Areas and Facilities	X	X	X	X

The more important impacts are denoted by X.

NOTES
1. The component sub groups are general examples only. For each scheme, the facilities likely to be affected and the relevant effects must be identified from local data.
2. The boundary between groups 2 and 3 is not well defined and in cases of doubt, the effect on the people concerned should be entered in the group containing the most relevant impacts. Care must be taken that double counting does not occur inadvertently.

Table 12.1 Frameworks indicating impacts on different groups

Source: DTp Manual of Environmental Appraisal (1983)

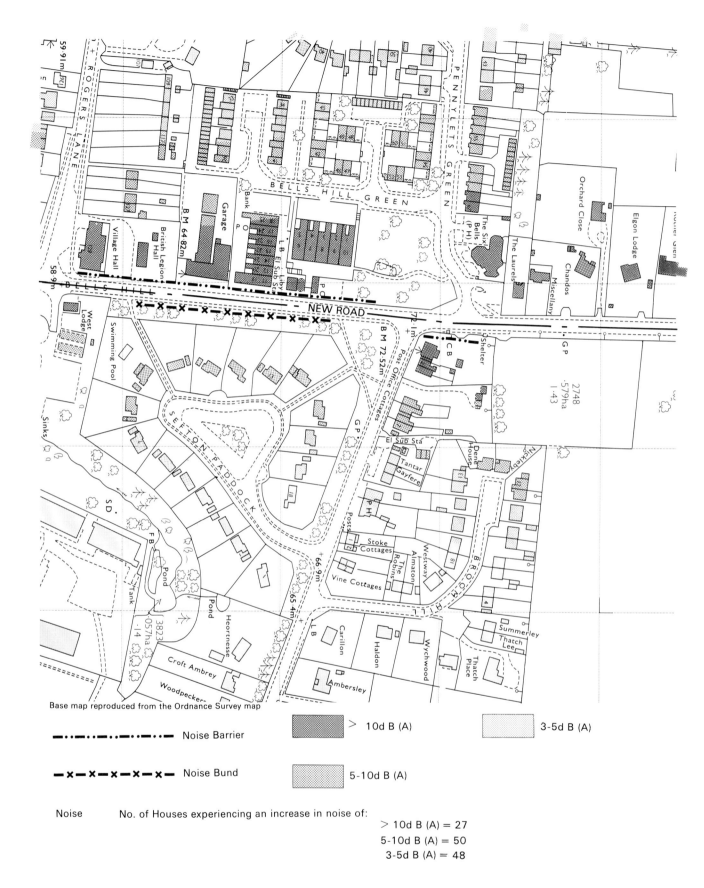

Base map reproduced from the Ordnance Survey map

▬·▬·▬··▬·▬·▬··▬ Noise Barrier

▬×▬×▬×▬×▬×▬ Noise Bund

> 10d B (A)

5-10d B (A)

3-5d B (A)

Noise　　No. of Houses experiencing an increase in noise of:

> 10d B (A) = 27
5-10d B (A) = 50
3-5d B (A) = 48

Figure 12.1 Illustration of the effect of road noise on housing

Source: DTp Manual of Environmental Appraisal (1983)

The main costs and benefits which should be included in an economic assessment are those associated with (Ref. 5):

- the cost of providing the new facility;

- delays to traffic during construction;

- travellers, including car and public transport users, goods vehicles, cyclists and pedestrians;

- transport operators;

- accidents;

- maintenance; and

- enforcement of traffic regulations.

This should include those effects which it is possible to measure in monetary terms but not all of these will be relevant to every scheme. However, there may be other economic effects which cannot be measured in these terms. Such effects should be included separately where relevant. As a general rule, a flexible approach will be necessary to include those factors which are relevant and to leave out those which are not.

Capital Costs

The main items of capital costs arise from:

- surveys, design and administration, including site supervision and materials testing;

- the costs of acquiring the land to construct the scheme and of any necessary accommodation works;

- the costs of construction, including the main engineering and ancillary contracts such as the cost of altering or accommodating public utilities;

- compensation costs, for example, for severance and noise nuisance; and

- capital renewal (as opposed to routine maintenance) costs during the life of the scheme.

These costs account, typically, for only about 10% to 15% of the total cost of providing, maintaining and operating a new road when amortised over a 30 year (assumed) useful life.

Delays to Traffic During Construction

The delays to traffic during construction of a scheme and subsequent maintenance can be an important factor to take into account, particularly in urban areas. The Department of Transport has developed a computer program called QUADRO (QUeues and Delays at ROadworks—Ref. 9) which calculates delays and their consequences for vehicle operating costs and accidents. However, this program was developed for use in rural areas and, although it can be used with urban schemes, detailed representation of complex diversionary routeing is not practicable. Where

QUADRO is not suitable, delays can often be estimated by using the traffic model constructed for the main traffic analysis.

Effects on Travellers

The main categories of travellers to be included are car drivers and passengers, public transport crew and passengers, goods vehicle drivers and passengers, motor cyclists, pedal cyclists and pedestrians. The main effects to be taken into account are changes in journey time and consequential monetary costs (accidents are dealt with separately below).

The **value of time** associated with each road user is intended to represent the value to individuals of the leisure time they give up in order to travel (which could have been spent on other useful activities) and the cost to the employer of travel during working hours. The Department of Transport publishes values for use in its own assessments and these are commonly used by other authorities carrying out economic evaluation. Full details are given in the Department of Transport's Highway Economics Note 2 (Ref. 10). However, the results of research into these values produce changes from time to time and the results of new research in 1987 are now available (Ref. 11).

Most new highway schemes will reduce specific operating costs per vehicle-km but some traffic management schemes could increase them. Any savings in fuel, wear and tear and depreciation should be seen as a tangible benefit of the new road. Vehicle operating costs can be divided into fixed costs, (those incurred simply to place the vehicle on the road such as the time dependent depreciation cost, garaging, vehicle insurance and vehicle excise duty) and variable costs which relate to how the vehicle is used (notably the fuel cost, tyres and general wear and tear) which is a function of the speed and distance the vehicle travels. Only the latter are likely to vary as a result of a scheme, the fixed costs can, therefore, often be ignored. Estimates of the cost of operating different types of vehicle are regularly updated by the Department of Transport. Forecasts of the numbers of vehicles of different class assigned to the different options for the new road can then be used to compare the operating costs per vehicle-km of using the existing, unimproved road network with that of the new.

Transport Operators

Urban road schemes may have significant impacts on public transport. As well as possible changes in operating costs, patronage and, in turn, revenues may change. These effects should also be taken into account but it is important to ensure that they are not included twice. The effects of changes in the supply of and demand for car parking spaces on car park operators, should also be included, if significant.

Accidents

Scheme assessment should include consideration of its likely effect on road safety and the expected level of accidents. This can be a vital consideration, particularly if a new scheme looks likely to increase accident risk. Accidents can be costed and the Department of Transport (Ref. 12) gives values for the cost of accidents based on 3 components:

(i)   the direct financial costs to individuals and organisations involved (eg. damage to vehicles and police and medical costs);

(ii) the opportunity cost of lost output to the economy for those killed or injured; and

(iii) an allowance for the 'pain, grief and suffering' resulting from personal injury or death.

Although the Department presents figures of accident rates for each road type in its COBA Manual (Ref. 4) [Sco.67], these may be too general for use in specific urban schemes and local data should be used whenever possible (see Tables 12.2 and 12.3) [Sco.68 and Sco.69].

Classification of Link-type	COBA 9 Link Accident-type	Average Accident Rate	
		Link-only	Combined links and junctions
New links			
Single Carriageway	2	0.16	0.25
Dual (AP) Carriageway	3	0.11	0.19
Motorway	4	0.11	0.11
Existing links			
Urban A	9	0.34	1.22
B	10	0.49	1.55
Other	11	0.67	1.77

Table 12.2 Average accident rates used in COBA 9 (PIAs per million veh-kms) [Sco.68]

Source: DTp COBA 9 Manual (1981)

Type of Accident / Class of Road	Urban[1] Roads	Rural[2] Roads	Motorways	All Roads
Fatal Accidents	191,800	210,300	237,700	201,420
Serious Accidents	10,280	13,600	13,700	11,260
Slight Accidents	1,290	2,260	2,500	1,500
All Injury Accidents	5,940	13,670	14,550	7,780
Damage Only Accidents	600	720	860	620
Average Accident Cost per Injury Accident (including an allowance for damage only accidents)	9,750	17,010	18,400	11,480

1 Urban roads are defined for this purpose as those roads (other than motorways) with speed limits of 40mph or less.
2 Rural roads are defined for this purpose as those roads (other than motorways) with speed limits over 40mph.

Table 12.3 Average cost of an accident (£s) by severity and type of road (1985) [Sco.69]

Source: DTp Highway Economics Note No 1 (1986)

Maintenance Costs

The routine costs incurred in maintaining the highway to a satisfactory operating standard will include minor repairs, resurfacing, cleaning, lighting and snow clearance, but exclude structural repair and renewal which should be regarded as capital items.

Enforcement of Traffic Regulations

The costs of enforcing traffic regulations should be estimated in consultation with the police and compared with enforcement costs for the existing situation. They should only be included when a significant change seems likely.

12.6 Cost Benefit Analysis Methods

Having determined the appropriate monetary value for the different quantifiable elements of cost and benefit, these may then be compared to establish whether a particular proposal will result in a net economic gain or loss. This form of evaluation is akin to economic Cost Benefit Analysis (CBA). The principal inputs to this economic evaluation process are the travel costs and times taken per trip in the two situations (ie. with and without the proposed scheme). These inputs are crucially dependent on the output of the traffic forecasting and modelling exercise. Two basic modelling procedures are in general use (see also Chapter 11):

- assuming a **fixed demand matrix** of trips (ie. where the scheme does not affect travel demands in terms of origin and destination of movements, mode of travel and time of travel); and

- allowing variations in the demand matrices for the two situations with and without the proposed scheme (ie. the **variable matrix** approach, where any reduction in the perceived (unit) cost of travel will result in an increase in the amount of travel undertaken).

The fixed trip matrix assumption has the advantage of being relatively simple to apply. It is used as far as possible by the Department of Transport in connection with its trunk road schemes and is embodied in the Department's cost benefit analysis program COBA (Ref. 4) [Sco.66]. However, some urban schemes may cause changes to travel behaviour which extend beyond simple reassignment of trips and SACTRA (Ref. 5) have recommended that where this situation is likely to occur it should be modelled and included in the evaluation. Many local authorities use four stage transportation planning models which take account of possible re-distribution of trips and model the wider transport effects. Even so, other relevant effects such as the re-timing of journeys and the generation of completely new trips as a result of a scheme are generally not modelled. This is an area in which considerably more research is needed before particular modelling techniques can be recommended, but the various possibilities should not be ignored.

Consumers' Surplus

Assuming that the different responses to a proposed scheme can be measured and predicted, the economic evaluation of these changes is relatively straightforward. It is usually based on the concept of 'consumers' surplus' which means the difference between the generalised cost a traveller would be willing to incur for a trip and the cost he actually incurs (or believes he incurs, where perceived costs and resource costs differ). The difference between the consumer surpluses calculated for the two situations with and without the proposal for each zone to zone movement by each mode, is then calculated to provide a measure of the overall benefit of the scheme. The method can be applied to both fixed and variable trip matrices and a detailed explanation of this method and the factors to be determined in the calculation of costs is contained in the current COBA Manual.

Discounting Costs and Benefits (Net Present Value)

The benefits and costs measured by the above formulae should be applied to every year over the life of a scheme. Typically there will be costs of design and implementation at the start of a scheme, whereas maintainance costs and losses to those adversely affected will be spread over the life of the scheme. Benefits will also be spread over the life of the scheme, but may increase (eg. as traffic increases) over time. On the basis that having something worth £P (at today's prices) in t years' time is only worth as much as having $£P/(1+r)^t$ now, where r (% per annum) is called the discount rate, the difference in incidence of costs and benefits over time is taken into account in calculating the net present value (NPV). This is defined, as follows:

$$NPV = \sum_{t=0}^{t=n} \frac{(b_t - c_t)}{(1+r)^t}$$

where b_t and c_t are respectively the benefits and costs in year t, and n years is the estimated life of the scheme. It should be noted that b_t and c_t should be expressed in constant prices (usually present day prices) as the discount rate has nothing to do with allowance for inflation. The choice of discount rate is a matter for economic judgement. The Treasury provides guidance on this for public sector projects and currently (in 1987) the Department of Transport uses 7 per cent per annum.

In terms of the effects expressed in money equivalents, the bigger the NPV the better the scheme. In the case of alternative schemes, the more costly one will usually only be preferable if the NPV of the extra benefits exceeds that of the extra costs. It is worth noting that this comparison of alternatives is possible even if some of the common effects of the alternatives are not fully known. It is sufficient to know that they will be the same for both schemes. If there were no constraints on resources, it would be economically worthwhile carrying out any scheme having a positive NPV (or for mutually exclusive alternatives, that with the higher NPV). However, in the real world this is seldom the case and there are usually additional qualitative factors to consider as well. Generally speaking, the aim should be to choose schemes with the highest NPV that have acceptable environmental consequences.

Net Present Value/Cost

If the aim is to maximise the total NPV of all schemes implemented within a single budget constraint, the criterion NPV/C (where C is the cost of the individual scheme) may be used to rank schemes, the best value schemes being those with the highest value of this ratio. Any scheme with a value of NPV/C of less than 1.0 should of course be rejected.

Internal Rate of Return

Another economic ratio called the internal rate of return (IRR) has also been suggested as an alternative criterion to that of the NPV especially in cases where the value of discount rate is uncertain. However, some care is necessary as it can result in inconsistencies in project choice where the criterion for ranking has not been specified in advance. For a full discussion of this ratio see Ref. 13.

First Year Rate of Return

A simpler method, which avoids the necessities of both forecasting future costs and benefits and of discounting their values over time, is the so called first year rate of return (FYRR).

$$\text{FYRR} = \frac{\text{net benefit in first year after completion of scheme}}{\text{cost of design and implementation}}$$

This should be used only where the schemes being assessed are closely comparable, with the same expected lives and very similar profiles of cost and benefit, preferably with a fairly uniform predicted annual net benefit. In these circumstances, the first year rate of return can be used in place of NPV to summarise the effects expressed in terms of their money equivalents. Where the above conditions are not satisfied, use of this or other ratios of benefit to cost, unless properly defined, can give seriously misleading results. However, following SACTRA's recommendations in 1986, it may be useful to present a FYRR alongside the NPV as an aid to scheme selection and programming.

SACTRA also suggested that economic benefits and costs should be presented in a suitably disaggregated form to illustrate their effects on different groups of people at different times of the day as cost-benefit analysis does not in itself take any specific account of time or spatial distribution effects. These effects may be very important when decisions on alternative schemes have to be made at the political level.

To summarise, economic indicators such as the Net Present Value and other single measures of economic worth are important, but should not be presented in isolation. They represent only part of the accumulated information which should be assembled in making a choice based upon sound judgement.

12.7 Environmental Appraisal

Introduction

The environmental impact of alternative road scheme proposals should influence the choice between options rather than being treated as a secondary matter. The procedure adopted for assessing the environmental impact of proposals should aim to:

● identify the relevant environmental factors;

● measure, as far as possible, and predict as appropriate the environmental effects on the different groups of people affected;

● determine how these effects should be valued and (if possible) compared;

● specify a format for presentation of the data; and

● integrate the results with those from the economic and operational evaluation to assist decision makers to determine which option should be chosen.

The first two points are dealt with in Chapter 10 but the remaining points are discussed here.

Valuation and Comparison

There are, broadly, four ways in which environmental impacts might be evaluated. These are:

Environmental standards: Most methods of evaluation use environmental standards or thresholds to identify acceptable levels of environmental effects. In practice, the choice of a particular standard depends upon agreement between affected parties as to what is acceptable or reasonable in relation to the resource cost of achieving it. It is difficult to base such standards on an objective assessment where the impact is annoying rather than physically harmful. A technique for measuring subjective response (see Chapter 10) is essential in these cases to assess the economic costs of environmental nuisance.

Monetary equivalent values: Various compensation tests have been tried (notably for noise nuisance in the vicinity of airports) to measure directly an individual's personal evaluation between income and environmental disturbance. Generally, these studies have been poorly controlled and their results reflect the complex multivariate nature of the evaluation process. They have failed so far to produce a satisfactory set of monetary equivalent values for general application.

Points scoring systems: Different levels of environmental impact can be assigned relative scores just as different impacts themselves can be given relative weights. This method is dependent on judgement and the consequent arbitrary determination of the maximum score. Alternatively, it can be done using an agreed voting system, either by a select panel or a wider constituency.

Impact statements: There are difficulties in identifying, measuring and summarising environmental impacts but check lists and frameworks can be devised for describing the impact of each option under agreed headings.

The conclusion must be that environmental factors are undoubtedly difficult to evaluate. The assessment of scheme options is essentially comparative and their various environmental impacts will vary from person to person affected. The overall environmental benefit or disbenefit will rely on a balance of benefit to some community groups at the expense of others; or improvement in one aspect of the environment at the expense of another. For example, a noise barrier can itself be a visual intrusion. Evaluation methods should be capable of accepting subjective valuations as well as objective measures such as material costs and should deal with both short term and long term effects such as longer-term ecological and health effects. In addition to assessing alternative schemes, the assessment techniques should enable unacceptable options to be eliminated at an early stage and should allow for changes in environmental conditions.

As a starting point, a strategic evaluation of the network should establish, in broad terms, the scale of environmental impact over a wide area and the consequences of particular investment or policies. Later, complementary scheme evaluation should be able to assess the specific effects of particular proposals at given locations. The use of an assessment framework allows the environmental effects, however measured, to be set against the economic consequences of each scheme.

12.8 Appraisal of Road Safety

There are two alternative approaches which may be used to predict future accident rates at a site after treatment. The first approach is simply to group all the 'before' accidents into two classes:

- those which one would expect the treatment to reduce (treatable accidents); and

- those which the proposals would not reduce (non-treatable accidents).

It is then assumed that the 'after' accident frequency will be equal to the 'before' frequency of untreatable accidents plus the percentage remaining of the treatable ones. This approach is commonly used in practice and is simple to apply.

The second approach is to attempt to establish a numerical relationship between accident frequencies and the physical characteristics of sites, based on observations over a large sample. A study by the TRRL (Ref. 14) has led to the production of a simple model for predicting accident frequencies on rural two way roads in terms of highway alignment and other basic characteristics (such as the presence or absence of an access point at the site in question). However, potential applications for models of this kind appear to be limited by the fact that they can deal with only a narrow range of physical characteristics. They may not account for the oddities of circumstance which sometimes lie at the root of the problem at a blackspot where, for example, the road geometry may be unexceptional. It remains to be seen whether such models can in future be applied successfully to the appraisal of remedial schemes in urban areas.

12.9 References

Text References

1. DoE—Circular 22/84 *'Memorandum on Structure and Local Plans: The Town and Country Planning Act 1971: Part II (as amended by the Town and Country Planning (Amendment) Act 1972, the Local Government Act 1972 and the Local Government, Planning and Land Act 1980),'* HMSO (1984). [Sco.63]   (12.1)

2. Advisory Committee on Trunk Road Assessment (Chairman G Leitch)—*'Report of the Advisory Committee on Trunk Road Assessment'*, HMSO (1978).   (12.3)

3. DTp—*'Manual of Environmental Appraisal (MEA)'*, DTp (1983). [Sco.65]   (12.3)

4. DTp—*'COBA 9 Manual'*, DTp (1981) (Amended). [Sco.66]   (12.3, 12.6)

5. Standing Advisory Committee on Trunk Road Assessment—*'Urban Road Appraisal'*, HMSO (1986).   (12.3, 12.5, 12.6)

6. Crompton, D H and Gilbert, D—*'Bath Environmental Capacity Study'*, Imperial College of Science and Technology (1976).   (12.4)

7. Crompton, D H et al—*'Environmental Capacity and Traffic Management: Report to DTp,'* Imperial College of Science and Technology (1978).   (12.4)

8. Organisation for Economic Cooperation and Development—*'Effects of Traffic and Roads on the Environment in Urban Areas'*, OECD (1973).   (12.4)

9. DTp—*'QUADRO Manual'*, DTp (1982).   (12.5)

10. DTp—*'Highways Economic Note (HEN) 2'*, DTp (1985).   (12.5)

11. DTp—*'Values for Journey Savings and Accident Prevention—A Consultation Document'*, DTp (1987).   (12.5)

12. DTp—*'Highways Economic Note (HEN) 1'*, DTp (1985).   (12.5)

13. Wohl, M and Hendrickson, C—*'Transportation, Investment and Pricing Principles: an Introduction for Engineers, Planners and Economists'*, Wiley (1984).   (12.6)

14. DTp/TRRL—Report LR 1120, *'Accidents at 4 arm Roundabouts'*, TRRL (1984).   (12.8)

12.10 Further Information

15. DTp—*'The Government Response to the SACTRA Report on Urban Road Appraisal'*, HMSO (1986).

16. DTp—*'Value of Travel Time Study'*, (Consultants: ITS Leeds, TSU Oxford, MVA). DTp (1986).

17. DoE—Research Report No 8, *'The Environmental Evaluation of Transport Plans'*, HMSO (1976).

18. DTp—*'Mathematics Advisory Unit (MAU) Note 255'*, DTp (1975).

13 Public Consultation and Participation

13.1 Introduction

Attitudes and expectations towards public consultation have developed since the 'Skeffington Report' (People and Planning—Ref. 1) in 1969 which concluded that public consultation is a 'necessary and desirable procedure'.

The many benefits afforded by greater public participation in the decision making process include:

● a better understanding of public views and preferences;

● the opportunity to take account of minority interests and detailed local knowledge;

● better organised planning and appraisal of schemes and policies with less disruptive and time consuming arguments during later stages; and

● improved access to information and openness in government.

Public participation and consultation should provide a valuable channel of communication between decision makers and those most affected by the consequences of particular policies and/or schemes.

Statutory Requirements for the Planning Process

Highway and traffic schemes included in structure plans, local plans and unitary development plans will be subject to the statutory requirements for publicity, public participation and consultation required for all matters proposed to be included in a development plan. The steps authorities should take to meet those requirements are described in the Memorandum accompanying DoE Circular 22/84 (Ref. 2, see also Chapter 3) [Sco.70]. Briefly, they involve giving all interested parties adequate opportunities to make objections and representations on matters to be included in the relevant plan and making them aware of their opportunity to do so [NI.13, NI.50].

13.2 Deciding Upon the Level of Public Involvement

Before embarking on any public involvement or publicity, four important questions need to be considered:

Who should participate?

In theory, all those who have legitimate interests should take part. Care must be taken to try to ensure that they do so otherwise public consultation and examination, by attracting the attention of vociferous interest groups but under-representing the views of other substantial groups who fail to respond, could result in an unrepresentative sample of public views being obtained. Where transportation planning is concerned it is quite usual to categorise the public according to the nature of their interest. A key task for the planner will be motivating and involving those people who do not usually exert political influence and deciding what weight to attach to responses from different sources.

At what stage in decision making is participation desirable?

It is now widely accepted that the public should be involved in all stages of the planning of schemes. In practice this has proved difficult either because of impatience or incomprehension of planning procedures or because of an inability on the part of the public to sustain a lengthy and intense involvement. Thus, the public voice often becomes more noticeable at a late stage (eg. at a public inquiry) when the local impact issues are more prominent, rather than at an earlier stage when broad principles are being decided. If public involvement occurs only at this late stage, issues can become personalised and create a mood of confrontation. Carefully designed opinion surveys carried out earlier can help reduce this conflict (see also Chapter 10) but, the stage at which the public can most usefully be involved will vary according to the proposal under consideration and decisions on this must be carefully weighed, not least because the resource costs involved can be substantial (see below).

It is also worth noting two points in particular from the SACTRA report (Ref. 3). Firstly, that there will be benefits in terms of quality of design and decisions, if a deliberate effort is made to involve the public in identifying transport problems as soon as possible (see also Chapter 8.5), and secondly, the need for flexibility in the choice of procedural steps, including consultation, according to the size, nature and complexity of scheme proposals.

Which methods of consultation and participation are most appropriate?

The methods chosen should reflect the purpose for which public participation is being undertaken. Thus, participation may consist of informing, information gathering or more interactive involvement between the planner and the public. Whilst, ideally, these activities should proceed together, it may be desirable to give or to gather information as a self-contained activity. Whatever path is followed, the intention should be to develop public confidence and a continuing dialogue over time.

What level of resources should be allocated to participation and consultation?

This will be a matter for judgement bearing in mind the issues under consideration and the use to which the information is to be put. Clearly, the resources allocated to public participation in the preparation of, say, a Structure or Unitary Plan will be greater than for a minor traffic management scheme, even though the response and interest generated may be proportionally much less. It is important that sufficient resources are allocated to carry out the level of consultation judged to be appropriate and not simply to create an illusion of it, or to carry out what amounts to a public relations exercise. There may, however, be occasions when publicity and public relations are justified in their own right.

13.3 Methods of Public Consultation

Public consultation may have one or more of the following objectives:

- to inform those affected by a particular proposal or policy;

- to explain the proposals and/or the policies behind them; and/or

- to gather opinions or responses.

There are many techniques which may be used including the distribution of leaflets and handouts, public exhibitions and meetings or the use of press, radio and television. Choice and suitability of technique should be matched with objectives (see Figure 13.1).

Gathering opinions or responses is recognised as a difficult task and in addition to considering how to measure response, judgements are necessary on whose response should be gathered, how structured should be the form in which it is gathered and whether experts should be employed. Representative or random samples of individuals, households, or groups may be used as the source of response. At the group level, consultative groups or panels may be formed on the basis of some chosen system of selection. Responses may be in verbal or in written form or alternatively, a number of kit and game based activities may be used. With individuals, it is possible to pursue a greater depth of questioning but there is usually a trade off between more detail and volume of response, for a given level of expenditure.

An alternative to deliberate sampling is to use the returns from self completion forms which may be distributed to households or to passers-by at key locations, or to people attending a meeting or exhibition (see Plate 13.1). The major problem with this approach is that the level of response is often poor and it is difficult to determine how representative it is of the public at large. Responses are likely to be heavily biased towards those personally motivated by, and aware of, the issues under consideration. It is, therefore, important to decide who to approach and

	Dispersal of Information	Gathering of Information	Production of Interaction
Behaviour and Attitude Survey		●	
Existing Political Structure	□	□	●
Press/Mass Media	●		□
Leaflets/General Publicity	●		□
Detailed Reports	●		□
Consultative Groups	□	●	□
Community Workers	□	□	●
Exhibitions	●	□	□
Study Groups/Kits	□	●	□
Public Meetings	●	□	□
Co-option to Committees		□	●
Comment Forms		●	

● Principal Use

□ Relevant

Figure 13.1 Techniques for public involvement and their major functions

Source: Based on work by Hampton (1977)

Plate 13.1 Typical local exhibition of alternative scheme proposals

Source: Leicestershire County Council

how, and the use to which the information being gathered is to be put.

If attitudes or opinions are being investigated at a very early stage in the planning process, public consultation may have the simple purpose of testing general or average perceptions and discovering the extent to which a consensus view exists. In this case, a random selection of respondents may be appropriate. If, however, the consultation is taking place at a much later stage, the investigations are more likely to be used in the evaluation of projects or to contribute to an impact statement. In this case, structured sampling (that is the positive selection of individuals, to reduce the bias of the sample) should be undertaken to ensure that different interests are represented.

When carrying out consultation it is important that:

● information is reduced to the simplest form consistent with the case to be presented or opinion being sought;

● care is taken to ensure that the recipients of information are clearly identified and that proper coverage is obtained (eg. if an exhibition is to be held it may be necessary to provide a range of sites);

● information contained in handouts or household leafleting should not be based totally on the maps and diagrams which are familiar tools of planning. Large numbers of the general public do not find it easy to understand information presented in this way;

● consideration be given to the use of tape/slide presentations or other repeatable forms of audio visual presentation since these may be the most effective means of providing information. This is particularly important where some form of persuasion/presentation of the case for a particular project is being attempted;

● recognition be given to the fact that whilst the mass media have particular presentation skills and can provide a ready made channel for communications, their involvement may lead to loss of or change in the reporting emphasis desired by the planner. Good relationships and briefing are required for this to work well.

As an example of large scale consultation, a major exercise in public consultation was carried out by the Department of Transport in four areas of London in 1986. The purpose of consultation was to identify particular problems prior to consideration of optional or complementary solutions. A variety of techniques were used in order to obtain a response from the public. These included leaflets to all householders in the study areas (evoking only a small response), contact with known local groups, public advertisements inviting comments and the setting up of semi-structured group discussions using sampling to provide a respresentative response. Not surprisingly, the latter technique produced the greatest amount of information but a wide opportunity was extended for the general public to make its views known. Specialist market researchers were employed for this project using standard qualitative research techniques and examples of the publicity material used are shown in Figures 13.2, 13.3 and 13.4.

109

Figure 13.2 Typical advertisement announcing the start of a study and inviting representations

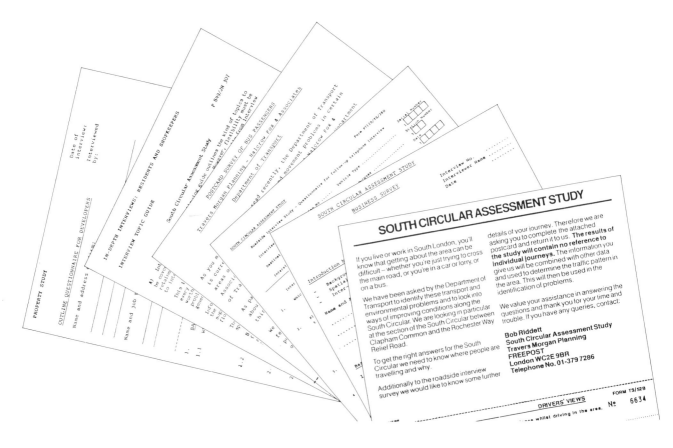

Figure 13.3 A selection of data collection forms used to obtain the public's views

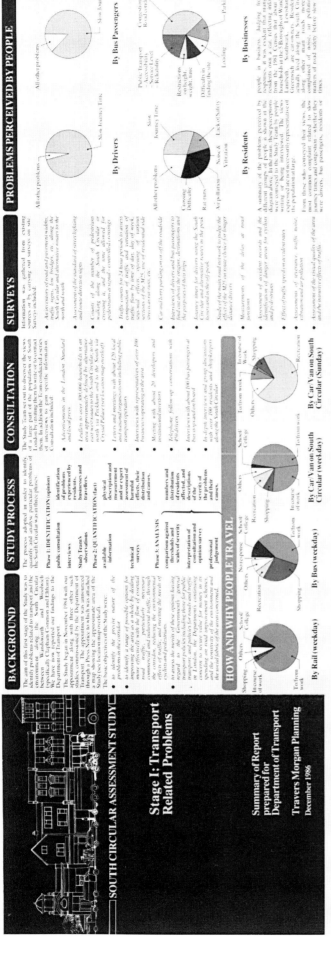

Figure 13.4 Informatory leaflet explaining background, techniques used and findings from consultation and surveys

111

13.4 Public Inquiries and Examinations in Public

When are Inquiries Necessary?

A public inquiry or examination in public may be held for a number of reasons and the procedure to be followed will depend upon the proposal being considered. Typically, highway and traffic matters will be publicly examined for the following reasons:

● when a public inquiry is called following the referral to the Secretary of State of a planning application which has implications for an approved development plan or which otherwise raises issues of more than local importance and which he decides should be called in for his own determination;

● when an examination in public is required before the approval of a structure plan or a unitary development plan, or where a public local inquiry is required to consider objections to a local plan or a unitary development plan [Sco.71];

● when a public inquiry is called by the Secretary of State into a proposed trunk road;

● when a public inquiry is held as the result of the Secretary of State proposing a Compulsory Purchase Order (CPO) or a similar proposal by a highway authority (under Highways Act 1980 [Sco.72] and Acquisition of Land Act 1981 powers [Sco.73]), (Refs. 4 and 5); or

● when a public inquiry is held as a result of objections to certain types of traffic regulation order (under the Road Traffic Regulation Act 1984) (Ref. 6).

Joint Planning and CPO Inquiries

Where a scheme involves additional land for highway purposes and requires formal planning approval, even when the planning authority is the same body as the highway authority, the usual planning procedures relating to planning applications under the Town and Country Planning Act 1971 [Sco.74] (Ref. 7) will have to be complied with. In these circumstances it may be advantageous to arrange a joint planning and CPO inquiry so that the process of investigation into the purpose and design of a scheme does not have to be examined twice, with consequent saving on the time and resources of all involved.

The Conduct of an Inquiry

The general procedure for the conduct of a public inquiry involves:

● the appointment of an Inspector [Sco.75] by the appropriate Secretary of State;

● the proponents of the proposal under examination present their case;

● the objectors to the proposal put their case;

● if appropriate, neutral parties may be called upon to present factual information which may be relevant;

● the Inspector produces a report of the proceedings including his conclusions and recommendations;

● the Secretary of State or the local planning authority (depending on the purpose of the hearing of inquiry) notifies the parties concerned of his decision (and may make a public announcement if appropriate).

At public inquiries, witnesses may be cross-examined by those with opposing views and re-examined by their own representatives. The conduct of the Inquiry, including the order in which the parties are heard, is largely at the discretion of the Inspector. It is also common for the Inspector to visit the sites concerned.

Strict rules govern the conduct of these events (Refs. 8, 9, 10 and 11) [Sco.76] and the fact that different parties may employ an advocate, often a barrister, and call expert witnesses, means that the proceedings can sometimes take on the tone of a court room. This can tend to favour the professionals and those more familiar with the surroundings. However, Inspectors are conscious of the need for unrepresented participants to be given an effective hearing and they will try to ensure that members of the public who have something relevant to say are not inhibited from making their views known.

13.5 References

Text Reference

1. Ministry of Housing and Local Government—'*People and Planning; Report of the Committee on Public Participation in Planning (Skeffington Report)*,' HMSO (1969).   (13.1)

2. DoE—Circular 22/84 '*Memorandum on Structure and Local Plans: The Town and Country Planning Act 1971: Part II (as amended by the Town and Country Planning (Amendment) Act 1972 and the Local Government, Planning and Land Act 1980)*', HMSO (1984). [Sco.70, Sco.72, Sco.73, Sco.74]   (13.1)

3. Standing Advisory Committee on Trunk Road Assessment—'*Urban Road Appraisal*', HMSO (1986). [Sco.76]   (13.2)

4. *Highways Act 1980,* HMSO (1980).   (13.4)

5. *Acquisition of Land Act 1981*, HMSO (1981).   (13.4)

6. *Road Traffic Regulation Act 1984*, HMSO (1984).   (13.4)

7. *Town & Country Planning Act 1971*, HMSO (1971). (13.4)

8. *Town & Country Planning (Inquiries Procedure) 1974* SI No 419, HMSO (1974). [Sco.77] (13.4)

9. *Highways (Inquiries Procedures) Rules 1976* SI No 721, HMSO (1976). (13.4)

10. *Compulsory Purchase by Ministers (Inquiries Procedure) Rules 1967*, SI No 720, HMSO (1967). (13.4)

11. *Compulsory Purchase by Public Authorities (Inquiries Procedure) 1976*, SI No 746, HMSO (1976). (13.4)

13.6 Further Information

12. Alterman, R et al—*'The Impact of Public Participation on Planning'*, Town Planning Review, Vol 55, No 2 (1984).

13. Galin, D—*'Applications of the Citizens Participation Approach to the Quality of Service'*, Traffic Engineering and Control, Vol 24, No 2 (1983).

14. Butler, M and O'Brien, J—*'The Role of Public Participation: St Albans Town Centre Redevelopment'*, PTRC Summer Annual Meeting, Seminar C, PTRC (1980).

15. Mynors, P L B and Moore, M D—*'Public Involvement in Road Planning: the Leicester Experiment'*, Highway Engineering, Vol 25, No 11 (1978).

16. Hampton, W and Walker, R—*'Public Participation and Structure Planning: the Case in Teeside'*, University of Sheffield (1977).

17. Boaden, N and Walker, R—*'Samples Surveys and Public Participation'*, University of Sheffield (1976).

18. Stringer, P and Plumridge, G—*'Consultation with Organisations on the N E Lancashire Plan'*, University of Sheffield (1974).

PART 3 TRAFFIC MANAGEMENT OBJECTIVES, TECHNIQUES AND PROCEDURES

14 The Objectives and Techniques of Traffic Management

14.1 Introduction

The term 'traffic management' is used to describe the process of adjusting or adapting the use of an existing road system to meet specified objectives without resorting to substantial new road construction. Traffic management may be undertaken on a small or large scale, either by itself to improve conditions in an area where new transport infrastructure is not envisaged, as an interim measure pending new construction, or as a temporary arrangement to accommodate short term demands. Traffic management may also be carried out in association with the construction of a new road or car park or other infrastructure changes, to help accommodate the consequential changes in traffic patterns.

Traffic patterns on an urban road network are complex and change continuously with time and with operating conditions. The context in which traffic movements develop is illustrated in Figure 14.1 which also shows the role that traffic management can play in influencing and controlling them.

14.2 Objectives of Traffic Management

Traffic management is usually undertaken to achieve some, or all, of the following objectives:

- a reduction in road accidents;
- environmental improvement;
- improved access for people and goods;
- improved traffic flows on primary and distributor roads.

These objectives can conflict with one another and balances may have to be struck which are appropriate for the particular road or area. There are often trade-offs between different objectives but almost any traffic management scheme is likely to affect road safety, the environment and traffic movement. Such effects should, therefore, always be taken into account in the design of a scheme, even if some of them are consequential to the main objective of the scheme.

Traffic management can be used to achieve particular benefits in inner city areas when it may form part of wider proposals associated with housing or industrial improvement areas (see also Chapters 4.2 and 31.1 and Plates 19.6 and 19.7). In these circumstances traffic management is usually aimed at improving the environment and creating new facilities like play streets or improved access to commercial areas.

The use of traffic management techniques in respect of access and mobility, road safety and the environment are discussed in more detail in Chapters 16, 18 and 19 respectively.

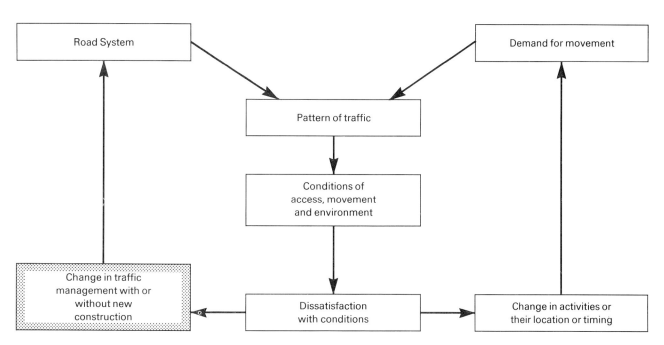

Figure 14.1 The context of traffic management

14.3 Techniques and Powers

There are four principal types of traffic management technique:

- those which involve a physical alteration to the road system;

- those which involve some form of regulatory measure;

- the provision of information for road users; and

- the introduction of charges for the use of facilities (eg. parking).

Most schemes will include a combination of such measures.

Powers

The main legislative provisions and procedures for making physical changes to the road system and for regulating its use are contained in the Road Traffic Regulation Act 1984 (Ref. 1) [NI.7], the Highways Act 1980 (Ref. 2) [Sco.78, NI.5] and the Town and Country Planning Act 1971 (Ref. 3) [Sco.79, NI.3], together with the associated regulations and orders.

The relevant procedures are summarised in Chapter 15 and specific traffic management measures of various kinds are discussed in Chapters 18-27.

Physical Measures

Physical alterations to the road system may be undertaken for a variety of purposes. Examples are:

- re-allocation of existing highway space (to assist pedestrians, cyclists, parked or other stationary vehicles—including delivery vehicles, public service vehicles and general vehicular traffic) by introducing changes of level, bollards and other physical barriers, kerbs or differences in surface colouring or texture;

- alterations to road layout at junctions, often allied to changes in the type of control or range of permitted movements (eg. right or left turn bans);

- closing (or opening) roads to particular classes of vehicular traffic in one or both directions (for some or all of the time) by installing (or removing) physical barriers;

- changes to surface level, texture or alignment to control the speed of traffic;

- coordinating the phasing of traffic signals;

- the provision of (or alteration to) traffic signs and road markings, either to reinforce other physical measures or for regulatory or informatory purposes;

- the provision of crossing facilities for pedestrians and/or cyclists;

- the provision of stopping places (of various kinds) for public service vehicles and shelters for passengers;

- the provision of taxi ranks; and

- alterations to landscaping and street furniture (including surface treatment) for environmental improvement.

Because many physical measures do not rely on any order or traffic sign they are essentially self-enforcing. Thus driver compliance is assured without the presence of a law enforcement officer or resourse to legal penalty.

Traffic Regulation

Methods of regulating the use of the road include:

- control by traffic signals;

- imposition of speed limits;

- introduction of one-way operation;

- restrictions on the directions of movement at junctions;

- restrictions on parts of the carriageway for use by specified classes of vehicle;

- exclusion of vehicles by size or weight (with or without exemption for access);

- limitations on parking and loading (including special provision for parking by those with a mobility handicap) and control of footway parking; and

- temporary regulations for special events (eg. road works, developments and emergencies and other temporary occurrences).

Regulations can be applied for some or all of the time and are usually of a prohibitive rather than permissive nature.

Compliance and Enforcement

In most cases the prohibited activity still remains physically possible for a driver (or rider). The effectiveness of traffic regulations is therefore helped by their acceptance by the general public, as sensible, necessary and lawful; and by an appropriate level of enforcement by police officers or traffic wardens. Since enforcement is costly and can have adverse effects upon relations between the police and the public, excessive reliance upon enforcement alone should be avoided whenever possible. Compliance can be helped by physical measures such as changes to kerb lines to discourage prohibited movements and by clear traffic signing and road marking, including the provision of information about alternatives to the prohibited action. Regulations whose purpose is not readily apparent to road users are less likely to be complied with.

Road User Information

Information provided for road users is not confined to the traffic signs and road markings required in connection with physical and regulatory measures or to give advance warning of hazards.

Clear and comprehensive direction signing (see Chapter 43) and lane marking reduces uncertainty and encourages traffic to follow routes which are consistent with traffic management objectives. Comprehensive and clearly legible naming of streets can also assist drivers and reduce the uncertainty which can lead to accidents.

Direction signing for cyclists and pedestrians can encourage them to use safer routes and crossing places especially where there are many visitors. Systematic signposting of car parks, perhaps including information on the availability of spaces and of service areas (see Plate 20.1), encourages their use and reduces parking and loading in places where it is either prohibited or inconsistent with traffic management objectives.

Maps designed especially for car drivers, lorry drivers and coach drivers can also be helpful, particularly for visitors. In some places multi-language information signs may also be beneficial.

Further advances in information technology may see the widespread use of in-car information systems to assist direction finding and route selection.

The quality of information about public transport, including opportunities to park and ride, can influence modal choice and hence the overall level of traffic and the demand for parking places.

Charging Systems

Charging for the use of the specific parts of the road system is usually confined to charging for on-street and off-street parking, imposing tolls for the use of bridges and tunnels and, less directly, influencing the level of public transport fares by means of subsidy (though the opportunities for this were considerably curtailed by the Transport Act 1985—see Ref. 4 and Chapter 26.1) [NI.2].

Charging moving vehicles for the use of road space, though a potentially powerful management technique in the context of traffic restraint, would require new legislation as it is beyond the scope of present local authority powers in this country (see also Chapter 23).

14.4 An Introduction to Scheme Appraisal

Once a general requirement for changes in the traffic management of some part of the road system has been

identified, it will be necessary to assemble the relevant data using the techniques described in Chapter 10. The evaluation of small schemes could be based simply on local counts and trend forecasts, whereas larger schemes, likely to cause more widespread changes and rerouteing of traffic, will involve the study of wider ranging movements using methods such as origin and destination surveys. These data can be used as inputs to computerised models capable of simulating the operation of the affected roads and junctions so that 'before' and 'after' effects of the proposed scheme can be compared. Such models can provide estimates of future traffic patterns as a basis for assessing the likely effects of the scheme on access and mobility and (to the extent that the techniques allow) safety and the environment. The various modelling techniques which can be used are described in Chapter 11.

Traffic assessments of this kind should be used as part of the input to a scheme appraisal of the kind discussed in Chapter 12, which will assist decision making on whether to proceed with any proposed scheme. Where the outcome of the appraisal is inconclusive it is sometimes appropriate to implement a scheme experimentally, using experimental traffic regulation orders [NI.14]. Not all schemes are suited to this kind of approach but if it is done and the scheme is subsequently made permanent, it may then be necessary to improve the quality of any features of the scheme which may have been installed in a temporary form during the experimental period.

Techniques of traffic management are described in following chapters of this manual, in which Chapters 18–23 deal with measures affecting road users generally whilst Chapters 24–27 deal with measures for specific classes of traffic like heavy goods vehicles, cyclists and pedestrians.

14.5 References

Text Reference

1. Road Traffic Regulation Act 1984, HMSO (1984). (14.3)

2. Highways Act 1980, HMSO (1980). (14.3)

3. Town and Country Planning Act 1971, HMSO (1971). (14.3)

4. Transport Act 1985, HMSO (1985). (14.3)

14.6 Further Information

5. ALBES/DTp—'*Highways and Traffic Management in London—A Code of Practice*', HMSO (1986).

6. Association of Municipal Engineers—'*Traffic Management State of the Art Report No 1.*', Municipal Engineer Vol 1. No 3: pp 253–274 and Report No 2 Municipal Engineer Vol 1 No 4 pp 311–325, ICE (1984).

7. DTp/TRRL—Report SR 568, '*The design of traffic management schemes*': Proceedings of a seminar held at TRRL, DTp (1978).

15 Statutory Procedures for implementing Traffic Management Measures

15.1 General Principles

Although some management of traffic can be achieved without involving statutory procedures, most schemes require the making of the requisite orders.

Highway authorities in Britain (and some other authorities) are empowered under the Road Traffic Regulation Act 1984 (RTRA 1984—Ref. 1) (see also Chapters 3 and 4) [NI.7] to make Orders to regulate the speed, movement and parking of vehicles and to regulate pedestrian movement. As indicated in Chapter 14.3, enforcement will be easier to achieve if Orders are only introduced for good reasons and are supported by clear, unambiguous traffic signs. There will, however, inevitably be occasions when signs and road markings will need to be reinforced by physical barriers or restrictions.

When drivers do not comply with Orders and are convicted of an offence, the courts may impose penalties such as fines or the endorsement of a licence, or even disqualification from driving (Ref. 2) [NI.7]. The procedures for making orders are laid down by the Secretary of State and must be strictly observed by the order-making authority. The procedures generally involve consultation on, and publishing of, proposals and the consideration of objections. In some circumstances Public Inquiries must (or may) be held.

15.2 Procedures for making Traffic and Parking Orders

There are a number of different regulations which specify the procedures for making traffic and parking orders under the RTRA 1984 [NI.15]. These regulations are amended from time to time and in 1986 the following were in use (in England and Wales):

- The Local Authorities' Traffic Orders (Procedure) (England and Wales) Regulations 1986, Statutory Instrument 1986 No 179 (Ref. 3) [Sco.80]. These regulations are most widely used as they cover the main types of traffic and parking orders.

- The London Authorities' Traffic Orders (Procedure) Regulations 1986, Statutory Instrument 1986 No 259 (Ref. 4). Equivalent provisions for London.

- The Secretary of State's Traffic Orders (Procedure) (England and Wales) Regulations 1986, Statutory Instrument 1986 No 180 (Ref. 5) [Sco.81]. Prescribing the procedures the Secretary of State must use.

- The Control of Parking in Goods Vehicle Loading Areas Orders (Procedure) (England and Wales)

Regulations 1986, Statutory Instrument 1986 No 181 (Ref. 6).

All of these regulations specify in fairly precise terms the procedures which are to be used. There are variations between them for different order making authorities and between the procedures required for orders of different types or purposes (eg. permanent, temporary or experimental orders). There are, however, certain general similarities and the most common permanent orders involve the stages shown in Figure 15.1 [Sco.82].

Consultation

From Figure 15.1 it can be seen that before an Order is made the Chief Officer of Police must be consulted together with the highway authority (if the authority making the order is not that body) and organisations representing people who use the road affected (unless there are no such organisations). In practice it is common to consult with local residents, the emergency services, and representatives of commerce and industry as well as organisations representing pedestrians, cyclists, motorists and bus and freight operators; but the extent of consultation is for the order making authority to decide upon.

Notices

Notices which set out the proposals and invite objections must then be placed in the local press and the London Gazette [Sco.83]. At the same time notices must be placed in prominent positions at the site and these must be maintained for a minimum of 21 days. During this period a copy of the draft Order, a statement of the authority's reasons for making the Order and a map of the roads affected must be placed on deposit for inspection by the public at all reasonable times. Any objections must be considered by the order-making authority.

Public Inquiries

Under certain circumstances (outside London) a public inquiry must be held when objections have been made but in other circumstances it is a discretionary power exercisable by the authority if they so wish. The procedures for holding a Public Inquiry are also set down.

Objections

If, after considering objections, the Order-making authority decides to proceed with the making of the Order then the objectors must be informed of the reasons in writing and the appropriate notices placed

NOTES

Generally: powers to make an order are provided in the Road Traffic Regulation Act 1984, as amended by the Local Government Act 1985. Procedures for doing so are specified there and in the Local Authorities' Traffic Orders (Procedure) (England and Wales) Regulations 1986. The signs relating to an order must conform to the Traffic Signs Regulations & General Directions 1981.

1. Consult police, highway authority (if not order-makers) & any interested organisations. Also traffic commissioner if S19 or 38 (i)(a) order.

2. Advertise proposals & effects in local newspaper & London Gazette.
Display street notices in area affected.
Make relevant documents available for inspection.
Allow 3 weeks for objections to be made (4 weeks for SS 83(2) & 84 orders)
Further consultation required for MDC orders affecting other MDCs, trunk roads or S of S reserve powers on UTCs. No publicity needed for certain S9 orders.

3. Order can be modified at any stage so as to be less restrictive. But modifications cannot be made to an order to which the S. of S. has given consent. If an order is to be made more restrictive, all the preceding stages must be repeated.

4. A public inquiry must be held if the order is under:
a) S1, 37 or 45 and prohibits loading or unloading, due to 09.30.-16.30 & 18.30.-08.00. ⎫
b) S9 and prohibits loading or unloading, due to come into effect within 6 months of the expiry of a similar S9 order. ⎬ & there are unwithdrawn objections.
c) S1, 37 or 45 and requires traffic to proceed in a specified direction or prohibits traffic from doing so. ⎭
d) S9 and requires traffic to proceed in a specified direction or prohibiting traffic from doing so, due to come into effect within 6 months of the expiry of a similar S9 order. ⎫ & there are unwithdrawn objections from local service operators or other PSV operators charging separate fares.
e) S19 and prohibits PSVs from using a road. ⎭

A public inquiry may in any case be desirable.
The inquiry must then be arranged and notice advertised & displayed on site.
At least 21 days to elapse before inquiry held.
Report and any recommendations of inquiry must be considered.
If order will vary from recommendations arising from compulsory inquiry, papers must be sent to S. of S. and making delayed for up to 1 month.

5. S. of S. consent is required if the order:
a) prevents access for more than 8hrs in 24 & there are unwithdrawn objections from owners etc. of affected premises.
b) prevents access for more than 8hrs in 24 & prevents boarding/alighting from buses & there are unwithdrawn objections from operators or prevents loading/unloading & there are any unwithdrawn objections.
c) applies to a trunk road.
d) directs that a principal road becomes or ceases to be a restricted road.
e) applies a speed limit to a principal road or applies a speed limit of less than 30 mph on any road.
f) varies or revokes an order made under the direction of the S. of S. within 12 months.
g) makes provision for a road within 12 months of the S. of S. varying or revoking a similar order on that road.
The full case with any objections must then be submitted to S. of S.
The S. of S. may require an inquiry to be held or a modification to the order, or both, before giving consent. He may withold consent.
S. of S. determination may be required for MDC cases. He may require inquiry or modification to order or may determine order be abandoned.

6. Send police notice of making or order, including operative date.
Notify objectors of reasons for making order in spite of outstanding objections. Make documents available for inspection.

7. Advertise notice of making of order, including operative date (no earlier than publication date) in local paper & London Gazette and full effects, within 14 days.
The London Gazette notice may be abbreviated.
Operative date for consolidation order must be 14 days or more after publication.

8. Signing for a scheme must be fully considered before decision taken to introduce order, and erected after order made.

Not required for consolidations, disabled exemptions or substituting metric or gross weights

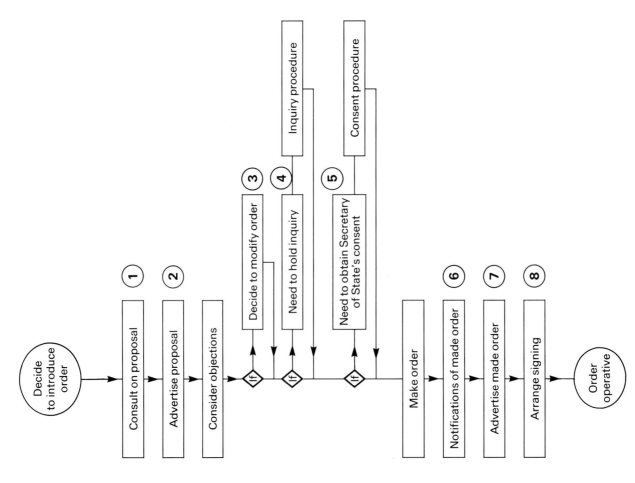

Figure 15.1 The main stages in the making of a traffic regulation order [in England and Wales—Sco.82]

in the press. The chief officer of police must also be informed.

Making the Order

If the Order is modified to take account of objections it may not be necessary to re-advertise providing the revisions do not substantially change the proposals. When the Order is made, steps must be taken forthwith to provide the appropriate traffic signs to bring it into effect and these must be in accordance with the current Traffic Signs Regulations and General Directions (Ref. 7) (although other signs may be specially authorised by the Secretary of State).

Validity of Orders

The validity of an order may be questioned during the six weeks after it is made on the grounds that it is outside the authority's powers, or that the interests of the applicant were prejudiced by the authority's failure to follow the specified procedures. It may not be questioned after this period.

Duration of Traffic Orders

Traffic Orders may be permanent, experimental (up to 18 months) or temporary (up to 3 months in areas outside London but extendable with the consent of the Secretary of State). Any order can be revoked at any time.

Experimental orders are subject to different (and shorter) procedural requirements in respect of the publication of proposals and objections.

The procedures for temporary orders are described in schedule 3 of the RTRA 1984.

There is no right of objection to a temporary Order. In circumstances where there is a likelihood of a danger to the public or of serious damage to the highway, a highway authority may take immediate action to prohibit or restrict the use of a road by the placing of an appropriate notice (see S14(3) RTRA 1984). Such a notice can continue in force for up to 14 days.

Police Powers

The police also have powers to control traffic and to regulate the use of the highway in emergencies and on other special occasions.

Exemptions

It is common practice to include exemptions for certain classes of vehicle, or for particular purposes, within a traffic regulation or parking order. As examples, these exemptions often include;

- emergency services (ie. the police, fire and ambulance services);

- statutory undertakers and other public bodies involved in the construction and maintenance of the highway and the services located within it;

- vehicles needing access for weddings, funerals or removals;

- post office and security vehicles making collections and deliveries of mail, cash or valuables.

It is also common to exclude from the effect of waiting restrictions vehicles which are stopping for the purpose of picking up or setting down passengers and their luggage and also vehicles being loaded or unloaded, but each order will require careful consideration on its own merits to take account of local circumstances. Other exemptions may also be necessary to meet local requirements.

These exemptions do not need to be shown on the signs introduced to effect the regulations.

15.3 The Purposes of Traffic Regulation Orders

Traffic Regulation Orders (TROs) constitute a major category of traffic order.

The powers provided by the RTRA 1984 [NI.7] (Sections 1 and 2 for local authorities outside London) allow a highway authority to make a TRO to control the movement and waiting of vehicles for the following reasons:

'(a) for avoiding danger to persons or other traffic using the road or any other road, or for preventing the likelihood of any such danger arising; or

(b) for preventing damage to the road or to any building on or near the road; or

(c) for facilitating the passage on the road or any other road of any class of traffic (including pedestrians); or

(d) for preventing the use of the road by vehicular traffic of a kind which (or its use by vehicular traffic in a manner which) is unsuitable having regard to the existing character of the road or adjoining property; or

(e) for preserving the character of the road in a case where it is specially suitable for use by persons on horseback or on foot; or

(f) for preserving or improving the amenities of the area through which the road runs.'

The criteria appropriate for making Orders similar to TROs in London under section 6, are more specific and are set out in Schedule 1 of the 1984 Act and by cross referencing to Section 1 (see also Chapter 6.1).

Secretary of State's Approval

If a TRO prevents vehicular access to premises for more than 8 hours in any 24 hours it must fulfil certain strict conditions. If there are unwithdrawn objections to such an Order by the owners or occupiers of those premises then the Secretary of State's approval is required before the Order is made.

15.4 Common Types of Traffic Regulation Order

The restrictions on the use of the highway which are most commonly imposed by a TRO are set out below:

One Way Streets

These are usually introduced to improve traffic flow and sometimes form part of a package of measures including prohibitions on turning movements at junctions.

Prohibition of Classes of Vehicle

Orders may be made to prohibit all vehicles or certain classes of vehicle from using a road for all or part of the time. Typical examples are:

all vehicles prohibited—this can be used to prevent vehicles from using shopping or other streets for certain periods of the day, where pedestrian activity is high. Alternative, and sometimes more appropriate, powers are contained in Section 212 of the Town and Country Planning Act 1971 (Ref. 8) [Sco.84, NI.3] (see 15.8 below, Chapter 23 and Ref. 9);

all motor vehicles prohibited—which allows pedal cycles and horse drawn vehicles to continue to be used on the road. Again the use of Section 212 of TCPA 1971 [Sco.84, NI.3] can be more appropriate (see 15.8 below and Ref. 9);

prohibitions of specified classes of vehicle—which may be by weight, width, length or by description, like 'buses' (which are defined in Regulation 3 of the Road Vehicles (Construction and Use) Regulations 1986— Ref. 10) [NI.16], cycles or horsedrawn vehicles;

prohibitions with exemptions for specified classes of vehicles—commonly used for providing priority for buses or cyclists (eg. no right turn except for buses).

Specified Exemptions (by Vehicle Type or Activity)

In addition to the standard exemptions for emergencies other exemptions may be applied to suit local conditions although the extent to which this is possible may be constrained by the regulations relating to the use of the prescribed signs. It can also lead to complex signing which is difficult for drivers to read and understand quickly.

The most common exemptions are for buses (to give them priority in some locations), for cyclists (for reasons of safety and convenience) and for access or loading (in order to maintain reasonable access to adjacent premises).

Another alternative is to specify exemptions by reference to permits issued to particular persons (eg. for security constrained deliveries to banks or jewellers' shops) [NI.17]. However, the use of permits should be avoided whenever possible as they are administratively cumbersome and can result in a selection of different coloured permits being displayed.

It should also be noted that excessive use of exemptions can result in a general perception that the Order is not being adhered to. This may bring the Order into disrepute and create enforcement difficulties.

Orders for Environmental Purposes

Traffic Regulation Orders which specifically prohibit or restrict heavy commercial vehicles are sometimes introduced to protect particularly sensitive roads or structures, or larger environmental areas, or to specify through routes. Orders relating to general traffic, such as are described elsewhere in this paragraph, may also be introduced for environmental reasons [NI.18].

Control of Particular Turning Movements

Vehicle turning movements can be controlled in two ways using traffic regulation orders supported by:

restrictive signs—which prevent certain manoeuvres being carried out and are indicated by a sign within a red roundel; or alternatively,

permissive signs—which make certain manoeuvres mandatory and are indicated by a sign with a blue background.

Orders of this kind may be introduced at junctions to control turning movements or to create one-way streets. Where a number of turns are to be banned at a particular junction then, for clarity, consideration should be given to making the permitted manoeuvres mandatory rather than describing the restricted turns. Exemptions to these Orders may be provided as with other Orders (eg. 'except for buses').

N.B. Certain types of regulatory signs do not require the support of a traffic regulation order. These include Stop, Give-Way, Keep Left or Right and some others (see also 17.2 and the current Traffic Signs Regulations and General Directions).

15.5 Control of Waiting and Loading

In theory, any vehicle parked on the highway (other than in a designated parking place) could be considered to be causing an obstruction, although in practice evidence of the obstruction being caused would normally be necessary if prosecution was envisaged. Custom and practice in Britain has been that vehicles are permitted to park at the kerbside where it is safe to do so except at those places where parking is specifically prohibited. There are several prohibitions on waiting including those:

● in the vicinity of pedestrian crossings, (ie. within the controlled areas of a zebra or pelican crossing as indicated by the extent of the zig-zag markings or on the approach to a pelican crossing as indicated by studs across the approach lanes);

● where double white lines are provided in the centre of the carriageway (to reduce the risks associated with overtaking where visibility is poor—although loading is still permitted);

● in parking places reserved for a specific type of vehicle (eg. motorcycles) or class of vehicle user (eg. disabled drivers or residents); and

● where a traffic regulation order preventing waiting has been made and is indicated by the appropriate yellow lines and supplementary signs (or for other measures such as box junctions).

Other Advice on Waiting

In addition, drivers are advised not to wait at places indicated by advisory markings which may be used at entrances to schools, hospitals and ambulance or fire stations, or in the vicinity of junctions and other hazards identified by the Highway Code (Ref. 11). Although failure to observe the Highway Code is not an offence in itself it may have a bearing on any subsequent criminal or civil proceedings.

Duration of Restrictions Introduced by TRO

Traffic Regulation Orders may be introduced to prohibit waiting at any time, or to restrict waiting at certain times of the day or on certain days of the week, or to limit the length of stay.

Application to Public Service Vehicles

Prior to the enactment of the Transport Act 1985 (Ref. 12) [NI.2] 'stage carriages' were exempt (under S3(4) of RTRA 1984) from waiting restrictions. This was because the road service licence could itself impose restrictions. As service licences have been abolished (in areas outside Greater London) this universal exemption has now been revoked so that there are now no statutory exemptions for public service vehicles except those provided specifically by order making authorities.

N.B. there is a saving which preserves the exemption for stage carriages on orders made before the 26th of October 1986, which will continue in force until the 1st of January 1989.

Exemptions for Picking Up and Setting Down or for Loading

It is common practice for a TRO to include an exemption from waiting restrictions for picking up and setting down passengers and their luggage, and for the purposes of loading and unloading. However, there will be circumstances in which these exemptions will not be appropriate and they should not be automatically included. Each site must be considered on its merits.

If a proposed no-waiting order prevents loading/unloading and there are unwithdrawn objections, a public inquiry must be held (outside London) unless the prohibited period is between 08.00 and 09.30 or 16.30 and 18.30.

Bus Stop Clearways

Bus stop clearway orders are a special type of waiting restriction under which no vehicles other than buses can stop. They are employed to keep bus stopping places free from other traffic and have standardised times of operation between 7am and 7pm [Sco.85]. They are indicated by special bus stop clearway prohibition signs and bus stop cage markings incorporating a thick, single yellow line.

Urban Clearways

These may be appropriate when no waiting is to be permitted during morning and/or evening peak periods. They usually include the exemption for picking up and setting down and are indicated by the appropriate signs and broken line carriageway markings and kerb 'blips'. They can be used to cover more extensive periods of the day if necessary.

Rural Clearways

Rural clearway restrictions can be used in urban areas and apply at all times of the day and on all days of the week. They are appropriate to main roads and fast arterial roads where stopping of any kind should be prevented. Rural clearways are not indicated by road markings and rely solely on the provision of traffic signs which should be erected at regular intervals (Ref. 7).

Special Signing in Environmental Areas

The extensive use of standard yellow road markings may be visually intrusive in environmentally sensitive areas. This effect can be reduced by the use of the narrower yellow lines (50 mm wide) permitted by the

Traffic Signs Regulations and/or a paler shade of yellow (see Chapter 5 of the Traffic Signs Manual (Ref. 13) for advice on suitable shades of yellow). However, care needs to be taken to lay the lines neatly and different shades of yellow should not be used on adjacent lengths of line. The Department of Transport [Sco.86] is willing to dispense with yellow lines and rely on zone entry signs and repeater plates in certain types of pedestrian zone where the street has been fully paved (see Ref. 14). In other environmentally sensitive areas the Department [Sco.86] is prepared to consider dispensing with yellow lines on an experimental basis provided the waiting restrictions are uniform throughout the area, the entry of other than purely local traffic can be discouraged (by physical measures or traffic regulation orders) and adequate alternative parking is available just outside the zone. In all cases where yellow lines are to be dispensed with the signing arrangements require prior authorisation by the Secretary of State.

15.6 The 'Orange Badge' Scheme for Disabled Persons

Section 21 of the Chronically Sick and Disabled Persons Act 1970 (Ref. 15) [NI.19] provides for a prescribed form of badge, the 'Orange Badge', to be issued by local authorities for motor vehicles used by disabled persons.

Local authorities are required, under the Local Authorities' Traffic Orders (Exemptions for Disabled Persons) (England and Wales) Regulations 1986, Statutory Instrument No 178 (Ref. 16) [Sco.87, NI.2], to include exemptions in traffic orders for Orange Badge holders which enable them to park for as long as they wish where others may wait only for a limited time and to park for up to two hours [Sco.88] on single or double yellow lines when 'no-waiting' restrictions are in force. The latter does *not* apply where loading and unloading is also prohibited.

The scheme is described in a Department of Transport leaflet and Circular 4/82 (Ref. 17) [Sco.89, Wa.9] covers the criteria for issuing badges. The scheme does not apply in certain areas of Central London where local authorities have applied their own schemes to suit local circumstances.

15.7 Other Types of Orders

Local authorities [NI.1] are empowered to make a range of orders under Road Traffic Regulation Act 1984 provisions [NI.7] but they also have powers to make Orders similar to traffic regulation orders which require the same or a similar procedure to be followed. Some of the more commonly used orders are described in 15.8–15.12 below.

15.8 Stopping Up and Diversion of Highways

There are several ways in which a highway may be stopped up. Two of the more common are:

Using Highways Act Powers;

Section 14 of the Highways Act 1980 (Ref. 18) (Section 18 for special roads) [NI.20] provides for the making of orders authorising a highway authority, inter alia, to stop up or divert a highway. Alternatively, in England and Wales, a highway authority can apply to a magistrates court under section 116 of the Act on the grounds that the highway is either unnecessary or can be diverted so as to make it nearer or more commodious to the public [Sco.90]. Footpaths and bridleways may be stopped up or diverted under powers provided in Sections 118 and 119.

Using Planning Act Powers;

Section 209 of the Town and Country Planning Act 1971 (Ref. 8) [Sco.91, NI.21] gives the Secretary of State for Transport [and, in Wales, the Secretary of State for Wales], power to stop up any kind of highway if he is satisfied that this is necessary to enable development to be carried out in accordance with planning permission [Sco.92]. By virtue of Section 216 [Sco.93] the Secretary of State may in certain circumstances anticipate the granting of such a planning permission. Conditions may be attached such as the provision or improvement of another highway. An Order under this Section removes all public rights of way.

Section 210 [Sco.94] allows local authorities to stop up footpaths and bridleways if they are satisfied that this is required to enable development to be carried out. Again, a valid planning permission is required, and conditions can be attached regarding the provision or improvement of another footpath or bridleway.

15.9 Extinguishment of Vehicular Rights

Where a local planning authority adopt, by resolution, a proposal for improving the amenity of part of their area which involves a highway, an Order can be made extinguishing the existing vehicular rights (under Section 212 of the Town and Country Planning Act 1971) [NI.22]. Such an Order can apply to any non-trunk road and can provide for specific vehicles or classes of vehicles to be exempted. This method is commonly used when streets are pedestrianised. The Order would be made by the appropriate Secretary of State [Sco.95]. Where vehicles are still physically able to gain access to such an area, it may be necessary to institute a Traffic Regulation Order creating relevant offences to back the intention of the Section 212 Order (see also Ref. 9) [Sco.84].

15.10 Parking Orders

There are many different types of on-street parking schemes which can be created under the powers provided in Part IV of the RTRA 1984 as amended by the Road Traffic Regulation (Parking) Act 1986 (Ref. 19) [NI.7].

The procedures followed when making orders are prescribed in the procedure regulations listed in 15.2 above. A brief guide to various types of parking schemes which have been used is given below.

On-Street Parking

A highway authority (outside London) may by Order (Section 32 of RTRA 1984) [NI.23, Wa.10] authorise the use of part of the road as a parking place for the purpose of relieving or preventing congestion provided that (Section 36):

- it does not unreasonably prevent access to premises adjoining the road; and

- it does not unreasonably prevent the use of the road or cause a nuisance.

Equivalent powers for use within London are provided in Section 6 of RTRA (see Schedule 1 paragraph 15).

On-Street Parking for Payment

Local authorities [Sco.96, NI.23] may designate paying parking places on the highway (Section 45 of RTRA 1984) but must use devices or apparatus for charging that have been approved by the Secretary of State. Such places are often associated with adjacent waiting restrictions.

Traffic wardens are usually employed by the Police to enforce the restrictions and issue excess charge and fixed penalty notices. In addition local authorities may employ their own enforcement officers who may issue excess charge notices or prosecute offending motorists. They may not, however, issue fixed penalty notices.

An Order may specify that parking places are restricted to certain classes of vehicle (eg. coaches), may exempt certain vehicles from charges, or specify that the holders of specified permits are exempt from charges or time restrictions (eg. for residents or commercial users).

Local authorities [Sco.96] are required to exempt from parking charges and time limits vehicles lawfully displaying an Orange Badge, (see 15.6 above) except in certain areas of Central London where the national scheme does not apply.

Residents and Permit Parking Schemes

Parking places may be specially designated [NI.2] for use by certain groups of people and may be controlled by issuing and displaying permits. Permits may also be made available to indicate exemptions from time restrictions or charges. In such cases the Order must state which groups are eligible to apply for a permit (eg. residents of a particular street). Permits can be issued for specific vehicles or for a particular individual or organisation.

Parking Places Provided for Use by Particular Individuals or Groups of Users

The use of parking places may be restricted by order to particular users where local circumstances require it. For example, this facility has been used for:

- vehicles displaying an 'orange badge';
- motorcycles, mopeds and pedal cycles;
- buses, coaches or taxis;
- police vehicles, and those in use by other emergency vehicles;
- doctor's vehicles;
- vehicles loading or unloading;
- diplomats' vehicles (Ref. 20).

Controlled Parking Zones (CPZs)

Composite Orders may be made which in addition to designating on-street parking places include the ancillary traffic regulations in an area, such as waiting and loading restrictions. This approach creates controlled parking zones, avoids the necessity for separate Orders for each street and simplifies the signing so that signs are only required at the entry and exit points to the zone and at locations where restrictions apply which are different from those in the main zone Order.

Provision for Buses and Coaches

Local authorities (outside London) [Sco.96, NI.24] may (Section 19 RTRA 1984) provide stands on highways for use by public service vehicles and regulate their use and may appoint by order, (Section 38) on or off-street parking places as bus or coach stations. In the latter case the authority may also provide waiting rooms, ticket offices etc.

Provision for Taxis

Parking places can be designated specifically for use by 'hackney carriages' [NI.25]. These include public service vehicles as well as taxis.

Private hire vehicles can wait at such places but cannot ply for hire from them; only licenced taxis (under Section 37 of the Town Police Clauses Act 1847 (Ref. 21)—outside London, or Section 6 of the Metropolitan Public Carriage Act 1869 (Ref. 22)—within London) can do this.

In addition, taxi ranks (also known as stands) can be appointed on the highway by the appropriate Commissioner of Police in London or the appropriate

Chief Constable outside London. Where all stopping by vehicles other than taxis is to be prevented, these ranks will need to be protected by a traffic regulation order [Sco.97]. Taxi ranks should be signed using the appropriate signs and road markings shown in the current edition of the Traffic Signs Regulations and General Directions.

Off-Street Parking

Local authorities [Sco.96, NI.26] may, subject to certain conditions, provide and maintain off-street car parks (Section 32 RTRA 1984). They may enter into arrangements for these to be operated by others on their behalf or grant licences to others to provide off-street car parks. A local authority [Sco.96] may by Order (Section 35 of RTRA 1984):

● restrict the vehicles or class of vehicle permitted to use the car park and the conditions under which they do so;

● set charges and utilise approved equipment or devices for their collection; and

● remove vehicles left in contravention of the order.

15.11 Cycling and Cycle Tracks

Cyclists are entitled to cycle on 'highways'. This includes carriageways (except motorways and other roads from which cyclists have been excluded) and bridleways (so long as they give way to pedestrians and horse riders using the 'way') and cycle tracks. [Sco.98, NI.27].

It is illegal for cyclists to ride on any footway or footpath. Furthermore it is an offence under S.72 of the Highways Act 1835 (Ref. 23) to cycle on any footway, and an offence may be created in respect of specific footpaths under traffic regulation orders or local byelaws.

There are a variety of ways in which facilities can be provided to assist cyclists (see Chapter 24). Statutory procedures to convert part or all of a footpath to a cycle track are contained in the Cycle Tracks Act 1984 (Ref. 24) and the Cycle Tracks Regulations 1984 (SI No 1431) (Ref. 25). Statutory powers to convert footways are contained in the Highways Act 1980 (detailed guidelines on conversions are given in Refs. 26 and 27).

15.12 Speed Limits (See also Chapter 22)

Orders may be made to establish either a maximum or a minimum speed limit. The procedures followed are prescribed in the regulations listed in 15.2 above. All roads in Britain are subject to a maximum limit whereas

very few have a minimum limit. In addition, various classes of vehicle are subject to a vehicle maximum speed limit (see Schedule 6 of RTRA 1984) [NI.28]. Signs may also be erected to indicate a local advisory maximum limit (eg. those used on motorways during adverse weather conditions). Failure to comply with an advisory sign is not itself an offence but it may provide strong evidence of criminal liability (such as under Section 2 or 3 of RTA 1972) or civil liability.

Responsible Authorities

The Secretary of State is responsible for speed limits on trunk roads but retains reserve powers for all roads. Local authorities are responsible for speed limits for all roads in their area (except trunk roads) but must obtain the consent of the Secretary of State to introduce or alter a limit on a principal road (see also Tables 5.3 and 5.4) [NI.29].

National Limits

There is a national maximum speed limit which applies to all roads unless a lower local limit is in force. The national limits are currently:

Motorways and dual carriageways—70 mph
Single carriageways —60 mph

Restricted Roads

A road will be a restricted road if there is on it a system of street lighting by lamps not more than 200 yards apart or if, by an order under Sections 82 and 83 of the RTRA 1984, the status of a restricted road is imposed [Sco.99, NI.30]. The speed limit on a restricted road is 30 mph. An order under Section 84 of the 1984 Act may impose a speed limit of more than 30 mph on a road which would otherwise be a restricted road. Whilst that order is in force the road will not have the status of a restricted road (see Section 84(3)) but that status will automatically revive if the Section 84 order is revoked and there is a system of street lighting as mentioned above. All roads without such a system of lighting and not covered by an appropriate order are not restricted. A maximum limit of less than 30 mph requires the consent of the Secretary of State but in practice is rarely granted.

Signing

Speed limit signs must be provided at the terminal points of the Order. On trunk and principal roads they are required to be lit whereas on other roads they should be lit or made of reflective material. In addition reflectorised repeater signs are required:

● on roads other than restricted roads; and

● on restricted roads where lights are more than 200 yards apart [Sco.100], or where there is no street lighting.

Special care should be taken to ensure that the appropriate speed limit signs are erected at the junctions between roads where different limits apply and if necessary, when new roads are adopted. At roundabouts between roads where different limits apply, the junction should be restricted to the limit applying on the majority of approaches; if there is an equal number, then the lower limit should apply.

15.13 Pedestrian Crossings

The provision of a formal pedestrian crossing imposes restrictions and duties on road users such as giving precedence to pedestrians under certain circumstances and prohibiting waiting on the approaches to the crossings. Before a formal crossing is introduced the highway authority must carry out certain procedures. They must:

● consult the chief officer of police;

● give public notice of the proposal; and

● inform the Secretary of State in writing.

The layout of formal pedestrian crossings must conform to the current regulations. Local authorities may also make arrangements for the provision of school crossing patrols to assist children in crossing the road between the hours of 8am and 5.30pm. More detailed information on the introduction of formal crossing facilities is provided in Chapter 24.

15.14 References

Text Reference

1. Road Traffic Regulation Act 1984, HMSO (1984). (15.1)

2. Road Traffic Act 1972, HMSO (1972). (15.1)

3. Local Authorities' Traffic Orders (Procedure) (England and Wales) Regulations 1986, Statutory Instrument 1986 No 179, HMSO (1986). [Sco.80] (15.2)

4. London Authorities' Traffic Orders (Procedure) Regulations 1986, Statutory Instrument 1986 No 259, HMSO (1986). (15.2)

5. Secretary of State's Traffic Orders (Procedure) Regulations 1986, Statutory Instrument 1986 No 180, HMSO (1986). [Sco.81] (15.2)

6. Control of Parking in Goods Vehicle Loading Areas Orders (Procedure) (England and Wales) Regulations 1986, Statutory Instrument 1986 No 181, HMSO (1986). (15.2)

7. Traffic Signs Regulations and General Directions 1981, Statutory Instrument 1981 No 259, HMSO (1981). (15.2)

8. Town and Country Planning Act 1971, HMSO (1971). [Sco.101] (15.4)

9. DTp/Welsh Office—Local Transport Note 1/87, 'Pedestrian Zones—Getting the Right Balance', DTp/Welsh Office (1987). (15.4)

10. Road Vehicles (Construction and Use) Regulations 1986, Statutory Instrument 1986 No 1078, HMSO (1986). (15.4)

11. The Highway Code, HMSO (1987). (15.5)

12. Transport Act 1985, HMSO (1985). (15.5)

13. DTp—'Traffic Signs Manual', published by HMSO in 14 chapters (1977 onwards). (15.5)

14. DTp—TA/41/83, 'Pedestrian Zones— Signs', DTp (1983). (15.5)

15. Chronically Sick and Disabled Persons Act 1970, HMSO (1970). (15.6)

16. Local Authorities' Traffic Orders (Exemptions for Disabled Persons) (England and Wales) Regulations 1986, Statutory Instrument 1986 No 178, HMSO (1986). [Sco.87] (15.6)

17. DTp—Circular Roads 4/82, 'Orange Badge Scheme of Parking Concessions for Disabled and Blind People', DTp (1982). [Sco.102, Wa.11] (15.6)

18. Highways Act 1980, HMSO (1980). (15.8)

19. Road Traffic Regulation (Parking) Act 1986, HMSO (1986). (15.10)

20. The Vienna Convention on Diplomatic Relations (Cmnd.1368), HMSO (1961). (15.10)

21. Town Police Clauses Act 1847, HMSO. (15.10)

22. Metropolitan Public Carriage Act 1869, HMSO. (15.10)

23. Highways Act 1835, HMSO. (15.11)

24. Cycle Tracks Act 1984, HMSO (1984). [Wa.13] (15.11)

25. Cycle Tracks Regulations 1984, Statutory Instrument 1984 No 1431, HMSO (1984). (15.11)

26. DTp—Circular Roads 1/86, 'Cycle Tracks Act 1984', The Cycle Tracks Regulations 1984, DTp (1986). (15.11)

27. DTp—Local Transport Note 2/86, 'Shared Use by Cyclists and Pedestrians', DTp (1986). [Sco.103] (15.11)

15.15 Further Information

28. The 'Pelican' Pedestrian Crossing Regulations and General Directions 1987, Statutory Instrument 1987 No 16, HMSO (1987).

29. ALBES/DTp—'*Highway and Traffic Management in London, A Code of Practice*', HMSO (1986).

30. DTp—Circular Roads 6/84, '*i, Road Traffic Regulation Act 1984; and ii, Parking for Disabled People*', DTp (1984). [Wa.12]

31. DTp—Circular Roads 2/84, '*Orange Badge of Parking Concessions for Disabled and Blind People*', DTp (1984). [Wa.9]

32. DTp—Circular Roads 4/83, '*Speed Limits*', DTp (1983). [Sco.105, Wa.14]

33. Disabled Persons (Badges for Motor Vehicles) Regulations 1982, Statutory Instrument 1982 No 1740, HMSO (1982).

34. DTp—'*Door to Door; Guide to Transport for Disabled People*', DTp (1982).

35. DTp—TA 19/81, '*Reflectorisation of Traffic Signs*', DTp (1981). [Sco.106, Wa.15]

36. DTp—Circular Roads 1/80, '*Local Speed Limits*', DTp (1980). [Sco.104]

37. DTp—Circular Roads 23/75, '*Car Parking for the Medical Profession*', DTp (1975). [Sco.108, Wa.16]

38. DTp—Circular Roads 31/74, '*Resident Parking Schemes*', DTp (1974). [Sco.107, Wa.17]

39. The Zebra Pedestrian Crossings Regulations 1971, Statutory Instrument 1971 No 1524, HMSO (1971).

40. Vehicles Excise Act 1971, HMSO (1971).

16 Access and Traffic Movement

16.1 Introduction

The concept of designating a hierarchy of roads for different functional purposes has been described in Chapter 5 and the objectives of achieving improved road safety and environmental conditions are dealt with in Chapters 18 and 19 which follow. Alongside these objectives adequate provision must be made for traffic requiring access to every part of an urban area whilst recognising the different nature of access required for the many activities which take place within the urban scene.

Urban areas typically consist of a complex interaction of land use types which usually include fairly well defined residential, shopping or industrial areas whilst elsewhere very mixed land uses may exist side by side with one another, sometimes in conditions of extreme conflict.

Although development planning objectives usually aim to separate activities which do not by their nature, operate in harmony with one another (eg. heavy industry and domestic residence) most of our towns and cities have historic roots which existed well before current planning procedures and ideas were established. Substantial changes to existing patterns of land use can take a long time to bring about and it will often be necessary to devise schemes which will achieve the best compromise between access requirements and an acceptable environment.

16.2 Types of Access Requirement

Vehicular Access

Each type of land use has its own characteristics of vehicular access requirement. For example, **industrial, manufacturing** and **commercial** premises will all have a requirement for access by heavy goods vehicles, the size and frequency of collections and deliveries being dependent upon the nature of the business carried out. Large scale heavy industrial activities, such as mining and steelworks often have rail connections for carrying bulk materials but these will not dispense with the need for adequate vehicular access.

Shops and offices generate demands for vehicular access, but in terms of volume most of the demand is for access by private cars for those who use or work in these areas. In addition there will be a need for access for delivery and service vehicles.

Residential properties require vehicular access for residents and visitors as well as more occasional access for large vehicles for purposes such as removals, deliveries, refuse collection and emergencies.

Sports and recreational facilities generate demands for access of all kinds and are particularly characterised by the fluctuation and peakiness of their demands, which can be extreme on major occasions.

Public buildings such as schools, libraries and hospitals, are often located in residential areas yet give rise to significant levels of vehicular movement.

Other Access Requirements

All premises and areas of land require appropriate standards of access by foot and there is often also a need to ensure that access on a bicycle, or for vehicles carrying disabled people is available (see also Chapters 24 and 25 which give details of facilities for pedestrians and cyclists).

The needs of disabled people will require special attention, particularly at public buildings and further information is given in Chapter 24.13.

16.3 Influencing Access Requirements

Careful planning of new developments should ensure that varying needs for access do not conflict unnecessarily and are catered for by suitably designed roads (see also Part 4 which deals with highways and traffic arrangements for new development).

In existing built-up areas demands for the use of private cars to gain access to shops and offices can be limited and reduced by measures such as the provision of efficient and comfortable public transport and by limiting the provision of parking; ensuring also that the parking which is available is well located in relation to the main distribution and access roads as well as the destinations creating the major demands (see also Chapter 23 which discusses various techniques for limiting road traffic).

The location and design of transport interchanges needs careful consideration so that transfers between cars, buses and trains can be made easily, thus encouraging use of the most direct and efficient forms of transport and reducing demand for the use of private cars.

16.4 Through and Local Traffic Movement

Many urban areas have to cope with through traffic as well as local traffic which has either, or both, origin and destination within the area. Local traffic needs must be catered for but traffic management schemes should aim to remove through traffic from environmental areas and direct it onto the primary road network (see also Chapters 5 and 19).

The general aim should be to provide, as far as is practicably possible, reasonably uncongested progress along fairly direct routes for through traffic. In some areas the capacity of the existing road network may be insufficient to meet this aim and more extensive measures, like route improvements or even new roads, may need to be considered.

This type of traffic management can involve directing through traffic onto less direct routes, but the extra distances involved may be proportionally quite small for long distance traffic. Diversion of local traffic can, however, cause considerable inconvenience and increased costs. This is particularly so for cyclists and pedestrians, especially those with a mobility handicap. Therefore, routes for cyclists and pedestrians should always be kept as direct as possible.

Measuring Accessibility

In assessing the extent to which a scheme or schemes meet the needs of access traffic the concept of 'crowfly' journey speeds has sometimes been used. It is included as an option within the CONTRAM (see Chapter 11) method of studying the design of traffic management schemes (Ref. 1) and involves estimating the time to travel between origin and destination pairs through the street network. This is converted to a journey speed on the basis of the straightline distance between the origin and the destination. The result is a 'crowfly' speed. Schemes which force trip makers to use circuitious routes produce low crowfly speeds. In practice peak-hour crowfly speeds of below 6 miles/hour would be a cause for concern, as would an inequitable distribution of speeds across the O–D matrix.

16.5 Road Links

The treatment appropriate to road links between junctions should reflect the extent to which they serve the functions of through movement, local distribution and access to frontage premises.

Primary and District Distributors

Where no frontage access is required, all of the available carriageway space can be used to bring the layout of the road as close as practicable to the standards for new road links (as discussed in Chapter 37). In these cases, road alignment, width and carriageway markings should assist the free flow of traffic reflecting the importance of the traffic movement function and the role of the street in the hierarchy, whilst taking into account the requirements of cyclists and pedestrians and without encouraging speeds that are excessive in relation to the surroundings and subsidiary functions of the link.

Local Distributors and Access Roads

Where local distribution and access functions need to be served, there are two possibilities. If sufficient road width is available it may be possible to separate the local and through traffic. Alternatively, and more frequently, it may be necessary to reduce the capacity and use of the road for through movement in order to provide for local access needs.

The types of measure which might be considered include road markings and footway extensions to create permanent laybys for parking, loading and unloading. These can also serve to separate the footway from moving traffic and provide scope for planting and landscaping.

Carriageway Narrowing

In some areas it may be beneficial to consider narrowing the carriageway of local distributor and access roads to preserve just sufficient width to provide for their desired functions. This can be achieved in a variety of ways but should take account of the existing road construction, particularly crossfalls and drainage.

It is sometimes useful to create a chicane type of alignment to reduce vehicle speeds and improve the appearance of the road, particularly when complemented with hard or soft landscaping treatment.

The additional space made available can be used for residential parking, which is of particular value to older or terraced property which may not provide off-street parking space. Alternatively, footways can be widened or cycling facilities introduced.

16.6 Choice of Junction Type

Road junctions are particularly important because of their effect on traffic capacity (because the capacity of a road system is usually constrained by its junctions) and also their effect on route choice (because route choices are made at junctions and the layout and system of control of junctions can influence route selection). Detailed information on the design of junctions is provided in Chapters 38–42 but an introduction to the various types of junction available is given below.

Priority Junctions

Priority junctions establish the precedence of one road over another and can help to reinforce the designated road hierarchy. Layout and lane marking at such junctions can be used to encourage or discourage particular turning movements and can make turning prohibitions largely self-enforcing. Staggering of cross-roads or closure of a particular arm of a junction can reduce the attractiveness of a route for through movement as well as reducing accident risk by removing the number of conflict points which can occur.

Signalised Junctions

Signal-controlled junctions, with the flexibility offered by variations in layout and signal timings (including co-ordination of timings) can also be used to reinforce the hierarchy by favouring one route over another in terms of capacity and vehicular delay. They also provide the opportunity to encourage or prohibit turning movements and to help pedestrians to cross at junctions. For these reasons they are a very powerful control measure and are widely used in urban areas (see also Chapter 20 on urban traffic control).

Roundabouts and Gyratory Systems

There are several different types of roundabouts and gyratory systems and their use and suitability depends upon the physical layout of the site, the nature of the approach roads and the objectives for traffic control. The types available are 'normal' roundabouts with a kerbed centre island more than four metres in diameter; 'mini' roundabouts with a flush or slightly raised central marking; gyratory systems composed of a series of one-way streets linked to form a circulatory system; and 'ring' junctions where the arms of large existing roundabouts are treated individually to create a series of small junctions.

The use of roundabouts has to be carefully judged in relation to the expected flows of traffic making different movements through the junction. Where the balance of flows is suitable, roundabouts provide good opportunities for vehicles to turn right and to provide free flow conditions when capacity is not exceeded by demand.

Choice of Junction Type

The through traffic function of major roads can be strengthened by appropriate use of junctions of different types encouraging or preventing different movements. Traffic wishing to join or leave major routes can be given opportunities and enouragement to do so at places where the manoeuvres involved are safest and consistent with the overall traffic management objectives for the area.

At all types of junctions the requirements of pedestrians and cyclists are especially important, particularly where the roads concerned are passing through busy urban conditions (see also Chapters 24, 25 and 38).

16.7 Frontage Access to Premises

The treatment of frontage access should be closely associated with a road's major functions within the road hierarchy. Uncontrolled access to premises fronting a major road can substantially reduce traffic flows and create severe road safety hazards as vehicles attempt to leave, merge with or cross traffic streams. For these reasons attempts should be made to limit or control frontage access on primary and district distributors, but inevitably there will be situations where this is not fully practicable.

In many urban streets, frontages, particularly pavement areas, are used as an extension of the property itself, to provide parking or trading areas. It may be necessary to limit this kind of activity, particularly when the land in question is a part of the highway and especially where it interferes with the safety or convenience of passers-by.

On roads serving as local distributors and access roads different standards may be appropriate to provide an acceptable level of access to premises and sites. Whenever possible, access should be provided within the curtilages of the premises served, using, for example, forecourts, paths, driveways, yards, unloading bays and car parks on private property. However, the ways in which pedestrians and vehicles are able to approach premises and the opportunities provided for vehicles to stand there, should be appropriate to the activities taking place and consistent with safety, peace and quiet, privacy and an attractive outlook for occupiers, especially residents. An example of the kind of improvement which can be brought about is shown in Plates 16.1 and 16.2.

16.8 Access Requirements for Particular Kinds of Traffic

As well as providing for access and movement by traffic in general, traffic management should cater for the needs of particular kinds of traffic as discussed in Chapters 24–27, only key points relating to access and movement are mentioned here.

Pedestrians and Cyclists

Pedestrians and cyclists need special consideration where their desired routes pass along or across roads having an appreciable through movement function, at junctions and where they have to share access with vehicles in close proximity.

Plate 16.1 An example of poor conditions of access to rear garaging

Plate 16.2 A similar situation showing the benefits of improvement

Parking Information

Drivers need clear information in advance about access and parking, especially where traffic management measures are complicated and there are likely to be many visitors unfamiliar with the area.

Public Transport

Buses and other public service vehicles need to be able to stop close to their passengers' origins and destinations to minimise inconvenience to passengers whilst considering the effects on other traffic. They can sometimes be given priority in congested areas with little or no detriment to other traffic. Wherever possible, bus routes should avoid detours to maximise accessibility and minimize operating costs.

Goods Vehicles

Goods vehicles need clear information about preferred routes and about permitted times and places for loading and unloading. They also need adequate clearances for width and height and advance notice of constricted parts of the road system.

Emergency Vehicles

Emergency vehicles need reasonably direct and unobstructed routes to all premises and help in avoiding or negotiating congestion (see also Chapter 17 and Chapter 20.3).

Disabled Persons

People with a mobility handicap need good access for wheelchairs and for the vehicles which carry them.

Pedestrian routes need to be easily negotiated by people in wheelchairs or with little or no vision.

Many of these requirements need careful and detailed design which can benefit from timely consultation with relevant groups and organisations (see also Chapter 24.13).

16.9 References

1. DTp/TRRL—LR 841. '*CONTRAM: a traffic assignment model for predicting flows and queues during peak periods*', DTp (1978). (16.5)

16.10 Further Information

2. ALBES/DTp—'*Highways and Traffic Management in London—A Code of Practice*', HMSO (1986).

3. GLC/ALBES—'*Code of Practice for Local Authorities/Emergency Services in the preparation of traffic management schemes*', Joint Traffic Executive and Association of London Borough Engineers and Surveyors (ALBES), GLC (1983).

4. DTp—Advice Note 4/80 '*Access to Highways: Safety Implications*', DTp (1980).

17 Provision of Access for Emergency Vehicles

17.1 Introduction

Traffic management measures are sometimes designed to discourage the use of certain routes by introducing road closures, prohibited turns and physical restrictions of various types. Care must be taken to avoid measures which unduly restrict access by emergency vehicles which are usually taken to include fire tenders and ambulances but could in some circumstances also include a variety of other specialist services such as Civil Defence and Military Vehicles.

The fire service is generally opposed to the use of the most stringent physical measures such as barriers and road closures because of the detrimental effect they have on the emergency response times laid down by the Home Department. Ambulance service requirements are usually satisfied by the fire service standards.

The police tend to prefer physical measures, including road closures, which are self-enforcing and therefore reduce the demands on police manpower; but thoughtless and obstructive parking near to barriers or other constraining devices can create additional problems for the emergency services.

17.2 Measures to be Employed

Consultation

To avoid creating access difficulties the emergency services (and a variety of other bodies—see Chapter 15) should be consulted during the development of proposed traffic management and environmental schemes, especially if they involve some form of restriction on the movement of vehicles. (See also Chapter 1 of the ALBES Code of Practice for local authorities and emergency services—Ref. 1).

Maintenance

All traffic management measures, particularly those that include barriers and automatic gates, should be regularly maintained to ensure that they are operating as intended.

Design Features

Different types of schemes will benefit from particular attention to avoid creating difficulties for emergency vehicles and the following points should be considered:

Road closures. Whenever roads are closed or culs-de-sac created it may be necessary to provide space for vehicles to turn around. Adequate signing should be provided in advance to warn of the obstruction and allow alternative routes to be used. Where a road is severed it may be necessary to re-name one end of it to avoid confusion and access difficulties.

Barriers. Where barriers are erected and there is sufficient space, a lockable gate should be provided using a standard key to open all padlocks. Openings

Plate 17.1 An example of provision of access for emergency vehicles at a width restriction

Source: Royal Borough of Kingston Upon Thames

should have a minimum width of 3.0 m (4.3 m if there is an angled approach) and obstructive parking must be prevented. Automatic barriers should have a manual over-ride in case of electrical failure (see Plate 17.1).

Traffic Regulation Orders. These should incorporate exemptions for emergency vehicles to allow an unimpeded access (see Chapter 15.4).

Posts and bollards. Posts and bollards should be of a standard design and arranged so that the fire service are able to open a fire path of 3.0 m width by unlocking only one bollard or post. Alternatively, a captive padlock with a length of chain might be provided. Frangible bollards or pivoted posts can also be used but pivoted posts must be less than 150 mm high when laid down flat.

Width restrictions. Width restrictions should provide a path for emergency vehicles. If this means using footpaths these should be ramped, strengthened and free from obstructions.

Paved carriageway crossovers. At these points the fire path should be ramped and clearly marked (see Plate 17.2).

Road humps. Road humps can cause damage to emergency vehicles travelling at higher speeds than other traffic and they can also reduce response times.

They are not suited for use near to hospitals or medical centres because of their effect on patients travelling in ambulances [Sco.109].

Pedestrianised areas and shared surfaces. In all such areas there should be a clearly defined fire path providing an operating width of at least 3.6 m with a preferred width of 4 m and capable of supporting point loads of 18 tonnes. Where buildings require the use of special ladders to gain emergency access to upper floors, the width of the path should be 5.0 m. The fire path should be clear of obstructions such as trees or canopies and should have a ramped access (see Plate 17.3). It should also be kept free from parked vehicles.

Street markets. The siting of stalls should be arranged so that they do not obstruct individual premises, fire hydrants or indicator plates. Any temporary wiring to stalls should be at a height of at least 5.0 m. Vehicular traffic will usually be excluded but a fire path of 3.0 m must be attainable by unlocking only one post or bollard, where these exist.

General measures. One-way streets should allow normal access and not increase response times. Traffic Regulation Orders may be used to inhibit obstructive parking.

Traffic Signals. In circumstances where traffic conditions consistently make egress from Fire and

Plate 17.2 A firepath to assist turning at a traffic island

Source: Royal Borough of Kingston Upon Thames

137

Plate 17.3 Ramped firepath access to a pedestrian area using removeable posts

Ambulance Stations difficult for emergency vehicles, traffic signals activated from within the station can be provided. The use of 'green waves' in UTC systems, to assist emergency services, is discussed in Chapter 20.

17.3 Exemption from Traffic Regulations

It is an offence under Section 22 of the Road Traffic Act 1972 (Ref. 2) [NI.31] to fail to comply with the indication given by certain traffic signs. This provision does not apply to all signs, only those given in the current Traffic Signs Regulations and General Directions, including for example, Stop, Give-Way, Turn left or right, No-Entry, and some others. All vehicles must comply with the signs and local authorities cannot generally give exemptions.

Other types of regulatory traffic signs need to be supported by a Traffic Regulation Order, made by the highway authority and these can include specific exemptions for emergency vehicles. Examples include

All-vehicles prohibited, Bus lanes, No left or right turn, and many others.

These distinctions should be borne in mind when devising and implementing schemes and providing for the needs of emergency services.

17.4 References

Text Reference

1. GLC/ALBES—*'Code of practice for local authorities/emergency services in the preparation of traffic management schemes'*, Joint Traffic Executive and Association of London Borough Engineers and Surveyors, GLC (1983).   (17.2)

2. Road Traffic Act 1972, HMSO (1972).   (17.3)

17.5 Further Information

3. Miller, R J H—*'The difficulties faced by the fire service'*, PTRC Seminar J, pp 243–251. PTRC (1981).

18   Road Safety

18.1 Road Accidents in Urban Areas

The Urban Environment

About three quarters of road accidents occur on built-up roads (Ref. 1). The urban road environment is often complex and makes heavy demands on road users. Junctions occur at frequent intervals, shops and advertisements compete with traffic signs for road users' attention and parked vehicles can restrict manoeuvring space and hamper visibility. Above all, vehicles and pedestrians are brought into potentially dangerous proximity to one another.

Those Most at Risk

Road users in general are exposed to greater risks in urban areas than elsewhere but these risks vary greatly with the mode of travel. Statistically, pedestrians, cyclists and motorcyclists are more likely to become involved in accidents than vehicle occupants per unit distance travelled and their injuries are more likely to be serious or fatal. Young and elderly pedestrians and teenage cyclists and motorcyclists are particularly vulnerable.

Other factors such as the consumption of alcohol or the use of drugs by road users and adverse environmental conditions, such as inclement weather or darkness, also affect accident risk.

Effects on the Public

Road accidents cause great distress and are costly to the community. In purely economic terms they represent a substantial loss of national resources (Ref. 2) and in social terms they cause personal pain, grief and suffering. An efficient and systematic approach to accident prevention and mitigation is, therefore, clearly desirable.

Public attitudes often seem contradictory. Attempts to influence road user behaviour can meet with resistance and are sometimes seen as infringements on personal liberty (eg. wearing of crash helmets or seat belts). However, when a particularly severe accident occurs those involved or living in the locality are often vociferous in their demands that local measures be taken at the site in question, whether or not these are likely to be effective in preventing future accidents. As a result, local authorities are often put under presssure to treat particular sites when a more comprehensive, prioritised and systematic approach could be more effective.

Distribution of Accidents

Accidents are not spread uniformly over the road network. They tend to form clusters at particular places like town centres or junctions on major roads. On other parts of the road network including residential streets, accidents are usually more scattered. It is notable that two thirds of all accidents occur at junctions.

Accidents which are grouped together in clusters can often be reduced by focussing attention on a small part of the network which may benefit from physical measures such as improvements to lighting, signing or road layout. But accidents which are more scattered, such as pedestrian accidents in residential areas, will require a more widespread and generalised approach often involving education and publicity rather than just physical measures.

18.2 Accident Remedial Work

Accident savings can often be obtained as a valuable and intentional by-product of a traffic management scheme and some schemes are implemented purely, or largely, for safety reasons. However, a systematic approach to the problem of accident reduction has been shown to lead to greater benefits in relation to costs than by pursuing one-off schemes.

A systematic appraisal of all the sites of particular types which could be treated in a local authority's area, together with the different forms of treatment which could be applied, will help to achieve good use of resources devoted to such schemes.

Alternative Approaches

Programmes for remedial treatment may be of several different kinds, for example:

Blackspot programmes, are the most generally used type of programme. Treatment is individually tailored to suit those sites which are likely to yield the highest economic rate of return from accident reduction.

Mass action programmes, in which a particular type of remedy is selected (for example, anti-skid surfacing) and a systematic search made for sites which are likely to benefit from that form of treatment, resulting in economies of scale in the use of such treatments.

Route programmes, in which the principal accident sites along a continuous stretch of major road are treated together. Measures considered might include improved street lighting, improved road markings, parking controls, the redeployment of turning movements between junctions and alteration of speed limits.

Area programmes, in which treatment is applied systematically within an area (usually a residential area). Measures might include access controls to reduce through traffic, use of road humps and diagonal barriers at cross-roads to reduce speed; and selected road closures.

During the early stages of remedial work within an urban area, a blackspot programme is likely to give the most cost-effective results. But later, when the majority of high yield sites have been dealt with, a more widespread approach using a route programme or an area programme may be more beneficial. However, new blackspots can develop over time and a continuous programme of monitoring and review is needed, including sites which have already been treated.

These types of approaches are particularly suited to suburban areas where large numbers of distributed accidents happen, but where dense clusters of accidents occur, blackspot treatments will remain most effective.

Specialist Teams

Experience has shown that systematic remedial work is most effectively undertaken by a team of specialists capable of undertaking the processes of:

- budgetting and target setting;
- screening of sites;
- detailed analysis of candidate sites;
- selection of sites for treatment;
- design and implementation of treatment; and
- monitoring and evaluation.

Further guidance on the setting up and execution of remedial programmes is provided by the Institution of Highways and Transportation (Ref. 3) and the Department of Transport (Ref. 4).

18.3 Selection of Sites for Treatment

Sites should be selected for treatment on the basis of a screening process carried out against selected criteria. It is common practice to use the total number of accidents which have occurred at the site within the last three years (a period long enough to give an indication of the average annual frequency with reasonable confidence) as an initial test.

What is regarded as a blackspot may vary considerably from one part of the country to another. In a dense metropolitan area a site may be recognised as a blackspot if it has, for example, twelve accidents in three years. In a less urbanised area a site with four accidents in three years might be regarded as exceptional.

Sites with very high accident frequencies are not necessarily good candidates for simple remedial measures as they may have more deep-seated problems which might require more drastic solutions.

It will, therefore, be clear that great care is required in selecting sites for treatment since the likelihood of a particular site benefiting from remedial work is more important than a high accident rate alone, even though the latter may give rise to public pressure for a quick solution.

An example of an accident remedial site before and after treatment is shown in Plates 18.1 and 18.2. A systematic investigation of accident locations identified this junction as the location of 26 personal injury accidents in the eight year period 1979–87.

Traditional 'stick' diagrams were produced (Figure 18.1) to identify the dominant accident type and a site inspection was carried out prior to the preparation of remedial measures. In the three year period following the construction of a mini-roundabout (Figure 18.2) just one accident occurred.

Use of Accident Data

Accident rates are often expressed in terms of accident frequency per vehicle movement through the site (or per vehicle-kilometre if the site is a section of road) and can help to show whether the accident frequency is unusually high in relation to the amount of traffic at the site. Hence they may give an indication of the presence of some deficiency which ought to be investigated. As an example, whilst it is not unusual to find several accidents per year in a busy shopping street, these might arise from a variety of causes and accordingly, be difficult to treat. A similar accident frequency on a residential street in the suburbs could point towards a localised deficiency which might well be remedied.

Accident maps, which show individual accidents plotted on a network overlay are another valuable aid to investigation work. When used with a table of accident rates (as indicated in the previous paragraph) these can help to reveal sites where the accident occurrence is unduly large in relation to the amount of traffic at the site. Once sites have been identified, those sites most likely to be amenable to treatment should be analysed first. Those sites with a high incidence of recurring accident patterns are likely to offer the best opportunity for successful treatment.

Detailed Site Analysis

The detailed analysis of individual sites requires a description of each accident, including details of the movements of each road user involved, together with

Plate 18.1 Example of an accident remedial site before treatment

Source: London Accident Analysis Unit

Plate 18.2 . . . and after treatment

Source: London Accident Analysis Unit

LOCATION: THE RIDGEWAY/SLADES HILL/WINDMILL HILL/OAK PARK ROAD

REFERENCE:

	1	2	3	4	5	6	7	8	9	10
POLICE REF	YF00164	YF00046	YF00105	YF00103	YF00167	YF00133	YF00259	YF00214	YF00200	YF00241
DAY	TUE	SUN	SUN	SAT	FRI	THU	FRI	FRI	THU	WED
DATE	01/07/80	01/03/81	26/04/81	25/04/81	03/07/81	28/05/81	14/09/79	14/08/81	06/08/81	29/08/79
TIME	21.05	22.55	02.05	08.05	13.35	07.20	18.05	19.10	16.05	22.15
DARK/LIGHT	LIGHT	DARK	DARK	LIGHT	LIGHT	LIGHT	LIGHT	LIGHT	LIGHT	DARK
WET/DRY	WET	WET	WET	WET	DRY	WET	DRY	DRY	WET	DRY
SEVERITY	SLIGHT	SLIGHT	SERIOUS	SLIGHT	SLIGHT	SLIGHT	SERIOUS	SLIGHT	SLIGHT	SLIGHT
CONFLICT	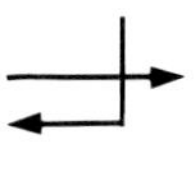	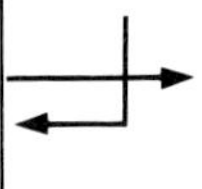	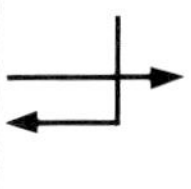	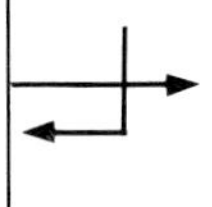	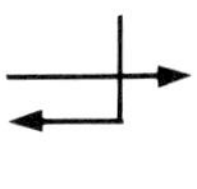	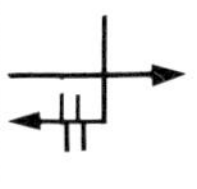	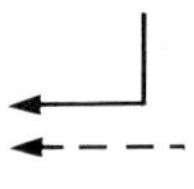	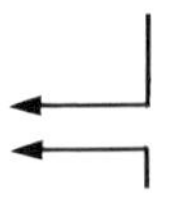	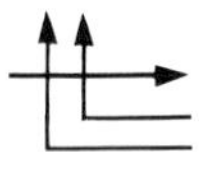	
PEDS ON X										
CONTRIB F										
EASTING	53170	53170	53170	53169	53171	53170	53170	53170	53170	53170
NORTHING	19672	19672	19670	19673	19672	19672	19673	19673	19673	19673

REFERENCE:

	11	12	13	14	15	16	17	18	19	20
POLICE REF	YF00251	YF00183	YF00209	YF00231	YP00219	YF00319	YF00233	YF00171	YF00186	YF00211
DAY	THU	MON	WED	SUN	WED	TUE	WED	FRI	THU	SUN
DATE	06/09/79	28/07/80	27/08/80	21/09/80	10/09/80	09/12/80	09/09/81	10/07/81	23/07/81	29/07/79
TIME	11.05	20.10	09.30	09.30	20.40	18.55	14.35	11.05	15.05	13.25
DARK/LIGHT	LIGHT	LIGHT	LIGHT	LIGHT	DARK	DARK	LIGHT	LIGHT	LIGHT	LIGHT
WET/DRY	DRY	DRY	DRY	DRY	DRY	DRY	DRY	DRY	WET	WET
SEVERITY	SLIGHT	SERIOUS	SLIGHT	SLIGHT	SLIGHT	SERIOUS	SLIGHT	SLIGHT	SLIGHT	SLIGHT
CONFLICT		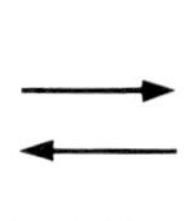								
PEDS ON X										
CONTRIB F										
EASTING	53170	53170	53170	53170	53170	53169	53170	53170	53170	53170
NORTHING	19673	19673	19673	19673	19673	19673	19672	19673	19674	19672

REFERENCE:

	21	22	23	24	25	26				
POLICE REF	YF00095	YF00125	YF00050	YF00007	YF00048	YF00194				
DAY	SAT	TUE	SAT	THU	WED	WED				
DATE	18/04/81	01/05/79	24/02/79	15/01/81	27/02/80	06/08/80				
TIME	22.05	14.25	06.55	08.15	16.05	09.50				
DARK/LIGHT	DARK	LIGHT	LIGHT	LIGHT	LIGHT	LIGHT				
WET/DRY	DRY	WET	DRY	SNOW	DRY	DRY				
SEVERITY	SLIGHT	SLIGHT	SLIGHT	SLIGHT	SLIGHT	SLIGHT				
CONFLICT	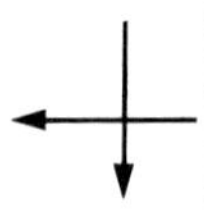	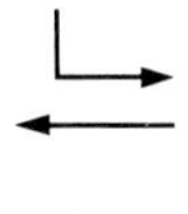	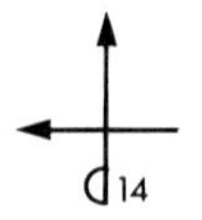	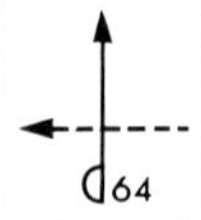		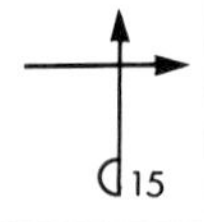				
PEDS ON X			0	0	0	0				
CONTRIB F										
EASTING	53169	53170	53170	53169	53170	53170				
NORTHING	19672	19672	19672	19674	19672	19672				

PERCENTAGES

PEDS	15
WET	38
DARK	23
R/TURNS	35
HEAD ONS	31

YEARLY FIGURES

SEVERITY	1979	1980	1981	1982	TOT
SLIGHT	5	6	11		22
SERIOUS	1	2	1		4
FATAL					0
TOTAL	6	8	12	0	26

Figure 18.1 A typical 'stick' diagram used to study accident causation

Source: London Accident Analysis Unit

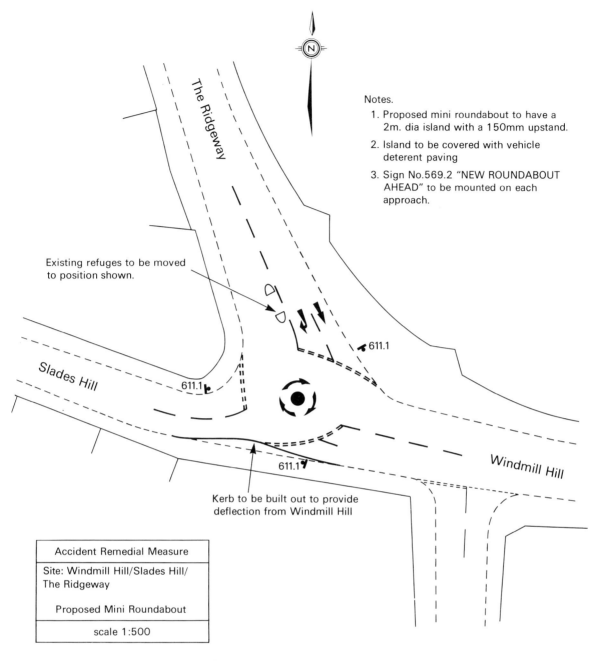

Existing refuges to be moved to position shown.

611.1

611.1

611.1

Kerb to be built out to provide deflection from Windmill Hill

The Ridgeway

Slades Hill

Windmill Hill

| Accident Remedial Measure |
| Site: Windmill Hill/Slades Hill/ The Ridgeway |
| Proposed Mini Roundabout |
| scale 1:500 |

Figure 18.2 An accident remedial scheme plan

Source: London Accident Analysis Unit

road lighting and weather conditions at the time (see also 10.4). The likely saving in accidents associated with the proposed remedial treatment can usually be estimated from experience at other sites. The rate of return on the cost of treatment can then be estimated using the Department of Transport's published figures for the monetary costs of accidents, together with an estimated costing for the remedial work involved. The reliability of such estimates will be related to the volume of data available and the experience of those involved.

Selection of Priority Sites

In principle, the sites with the highest rates of return should be treated first because this criterion leads to the maximum saving in accidents for every pound invested. However, in practice only single sites and routes can be assessed strictly according to this criterion and even with these there is no guarantee that some of the more worthwhile sites will not be eliminated during the initial screening where the criteria for selection are relatively crude. The only reliable method of avoiding this is to use sophisticated criteria for selection including the identification of sites with above average occurrence of particular categories of accident. Computer based analysis techniques can now make this a feasible proposition because of their rapid data handling capabilities.

Monitoring and Evaluation

The last stage in the process involves evaluation of the success of the measures introduced. This can best be accomplished if the accident data base is equipped to record data on the type of measures introduced and the timing and cost of implementation (see also 18.4 below).

Types of Hazards and Remedial Measures

A summary of the road characteristics which can affect road safety is provided in Table 18.1 together with remedial measures which could be considered. Traffic engineering measures that might also help to alleviate these problems are discussed in subsequent chapters.

18.4 Monitoring and Evaluation of Accidents and Site Characteristics

Research has shown that whilst it is possible to determine accident rates for individual categories of site for the country as a whole with reasonable accuracy, it is difficult to predict changes in accident frequency at particular sites.

Changes in accident frequency or type arise because either the flow of vehicles or pedestrians changes or there is a change in the physical characteristics of the site. In the former case it is possible to use known relationships for predicting accident frequencies as a function of exposure; and these provide a reliable guide for quite large numbers of similar sites considered together. In the latter case, if the changes in the site layout are small, it may be possible to estimate the changes in accidents using information based upon comparable measures. If, however, the site layout has changed appreciably, it is normally not possible to make reliable predictions of future numbers of accidents, but improved techniques are being developed (see also Ref. 5).

Monitoring the Effects of Remedial Measures

When monitoring the effectiveness of remedial treatment at a site, accident data before treatment and data for at least three years afterwards should be compared. Although in practice shorter time periods often have to be used, they will be statistically less soundly based.

Practitioners should be aware of three factors which can affect the validity of any comparison:

● changes in other factors, not associated with the treatment given to the site, may cause changes in accident rates (eg. national advertising campaigns or changes in legislation). Such changes can be compensated for by comparing the before and after frequencies with those of nearby 'control' sites over identical periods;

● random fluctuations in accident frequencies can occur and these can be relatively large even when there has been no change in the underlying mean accident rate. A statistical test of significance should be carried out to determine how easily the observed change in the number of accidents could have occurred by chance;

● a site selected for treatment is often one where a high accident rate has been observed in the past in the short term and this can produce an unusually high accident rate within the statistical fluctuation expected in average values. In this case a reduction in the number of accidents would be likely to occur even if there had been no change in the underlying mean accident rate for the longer term. This effect can be monitored by matching pairs of sites provided suitable pairs can be found; the site receiving treatment being matched with a similar site not receiving treatment. An alternative method of statistical analysis uses a large group of sites to estimate the average regression effect.

Evaluating the Benefits

An evaluation of the benefits derived from remedial work requires the calculation of the estimated money savings achieved by a reduction in accidents as described in Chapter 12. Normally (for schemes where the main purpose is the reduction of accidents) the assessment can be based on the estimated first year rate of return. High rates of return can be achieved by accident remedial schemes. The achievement of such rates is a very cost-effective way of using these resources and also provides a strong argument for diverting more resources to such schemes from other areas of expenditure where lower rates of return are achieved.

Road Safety Audit

It is now becoming increasingly common for local authorities to carry out a road safety audit of all highway and traffic schemes. By allowing an experienced safety engineer to check schemes before implementation amendments can be made which will improve the safety of the final scheme without a lot of abortive work. Safety audit should be seen as an on-going process which should start at the concept stage and continue throughout the detailed design of the scheme.

18.5 Information and Publicity

Road accidents involve, and are inevitably caused by, the people who use the road system, which includes every member of society. Whilst the physical environment and vehicle design can contribute to accidents and their effects, it has been shown (Ref. 6) that road user error is a factor in about 95% of road accidents.

Education and training programmes mounted at both local and national level should aim to raise the level of understanding and skills of road users and assist in

Characteristics which affect road safety	Remedial measures
Road Layout	
Horizontal alignment: substandard provision associated with accidents involving loss of control and overtaking. Overdesign associated with excessive speed. Horizontal curves can reduce visibility.	Appropriate geometric standards, layout and surface materials can help reduce speed and skidding. Speed control devices. Superelevation can reduce likelihood of loss of control, improves drainage and grip in wet weather. Signs and markings can give advance warning of hazards. Anti-skid surfacing.
Vertical alignment: poor visibility at crests associated with overtaking accidents on two-way roads. Down grades can increase stopping distance.	Appropriate geometric standards as above. Crests and sags should not contain sources of unexpected conflict such as turning or parked vehicles, or pedestrians crossing. If this is unavoidable then displaced centre lines at crests and mini roundabouts at sags can help.
Carriageway width: wide roads associated with greater risks for pedestrians crossing. Excessive speeds relating to the character of the road rather than to that of the road environment.	Refuges and pedestrian crossings. Footbridges and subways Speed control devices and road narrowing. Sheltered parking with footway extensions where pedestrians waiting to cross are visible to drivers.
Junctions: accidents associated with conflicting movements.	Reduce and simplify conflicts by closures, banned movements, one-way street, improved junction control and reducing the number of junctions. Clearer provision for pedestrians at junctions or at convenient points nearby.
Road Surface	
Surface texture: accidents due to skidding and badly maintained surfaces.	Rough or permeable textures give better skid resistance and additional tyre noise may have safety advantages for pedestrians and others. Special anti-skid treatment at critical braking points such as approaches to pedestrian crossings and signals. Proper maintenance programme and reinstatements.
Markings: smooth markings can lead to skidding. Poor visibility and lack of markings can lead to confusion.	Use marking material which is visible at night and effective in the wet. Markings should promote discipline and alert drivers to hazards.
Road Margins	
Kerb:	Vertical kerbs give protection to pedestrians and positive drainage yet cause problems to those with a mobility handicap. Provide lowered kerbs at specific points.
Hard shoulder and central reserve:	Valuable safety margin for out-of-control vehicles – the wider the margin the lower the probability of severe impact. Use crash barriers where space is at a premium.
Lighting: A poor standard or design can cause undue reflection off wet roads. Bad spacing can create unnecessary shadows.	Correct spacing and height for lighting columns. Special illumination of pedestrian crossings.
Vehicle Access to and from the Carriageway	
Frontage development: conflicting access movements to and from frontage development associated with accidents on major arterials.	Reduce conflicts by providing access elsewhere – access road, rear access.
Parked and loading vehicles: reduce visibility for pedestrians and constrict carriageway. Deflect cyclists. Contribute to accidents at junctions.	Waiting and loading restrictions. Provision for on and off-street parking. Provision for deliveries.

Table 18.1 Summary of road characteristics which can affect road safety

improving attitudes and behaviour. Although a relationship between such programmes and accident reduction is not easily demonstrated it does not detract from their value but underlies the need to ensure that the programmes are well defined and effectively presented.

Publicity programmes should complement traffic engineering measures aimed at accident reduction and should be designed to achieve specific objectives in terms of improved behaviour, knowledge or attitudes for specific target groups (eg. child pedestrians, drivers, etc.). Priority objectives and target groups should be determined by rigorous accident analysis. Ideally, this should be supplemented by collecting and analysing road user behaviour, knowledge and attitude data, reviewing past experience about the effectiveness of different campaigns (ie. the extent to which they achieved their objectives, if at all) and carrying out small scale survey/discussion group research to assess likely impact and effectiveness of different potential campaign themes and approaches. A useful guide to campaign design is contained in a booklet entitled 'Manual on road safety campaigns' (Ref. 7).

Methods of Communicating Road Safety Information

The process of informing and influencing the public on matters relating to road safety can be undertaken at different levels. National campaigns are organised by the Department of Transport (see below) [Wa.18]. Local authorities, on the other hand, may need to undertake campaigns dealing with problems of general concern (eg. cycle awareness) or to promote and reinforce the introduction of specific local safety measures (eg. at a dangerous junction).

There is a variety of methods available for disseminating information, including television, radio, cinema, roadside posters, the press, leaflets and exhibitions; so a decision on the appropriate medium will depend upon the resources available and the target group and objectives selected. Guidance on media selection is included in the OECD manual referred to above but as a general guide the more local the issue the more precise and 'immediate' should be the targeting.

Thus television can achieve the widest coverage and can demonstrate manoeuvres and movement. However, it is relatively costly and removed in time and space from the road situations it is intended to influence. Use of the local press allows for maps and diagrams to be reproduced as do displays, exhibitions and publicity leaflets.

Roadside posters have a number of advantages at the most local level. They are quick and relatively cheap to erect, can be location specific and of immediate relevance. On the other hand they need to be carefully sited so that they can be easily seen and read without distracting drivers' attention or becoming confused with other road signs and, for ease of comprehension, the message conveyed needs to be clear and concise.

General campaigns are often best targetted at particular groups of road user (eg. the elderly or cyclists) and should impart a simple and specific message.

The effectiveness of a campaign will depend not only upon the way in which the message is presented but upon its timing. Campaigns should be timed to coincide as closely as possible with the highest risk levels associated with the accident problem being targetted. The intensity and duration of campaigns will depend partly upon the resources available. Sustained long term campaigns probably have the greatest effect upon behaviour but a series of short, intensive campaigns can also be effective.

Where local authorities intend to promote campaigns associated with accident problems of a general nature they should have regard to national initiatives and consult the Department of Transport on priorities and coordination in order to ensure maximum impact. Campaign effort associated with purely local issues can be most effectively deployed if it is coordinated locally with the efforts of other agencies such as the police.

The progress of each campaign should be carefully monitored and its impact evaluated to judge its own effectiveness and to guide future policy or publicity. Reference should be made to the OECD manual or the RoSPA Road Safety Programme Manual (1984) (Ref. 8) for further information on evaluation methodology.

School Age Children

The aim of road safety education in schools should be to produce safe road user behaviour for life through a comprehensive continuous and developmental programme of education from the time children start school until the time they leave. Despite the efforts of road safety officers and some teachers, current school programmes often fail to meet these requirements.

Nevertheless, comprehensive programmes relating to all aspects of the safe use of the highway should be developed jointly by road safety officers, teachers and the police to provide a graduated process of instruction and learning, geared to the requirements, capabilities and ages of the children concerned. To be successful such a programme must have the active support, assistance and involvement of head teachers and the teaching staff generally, encouraged by the local authority. The police consider involvement in the field of safety education for school children to be especially beneficial because it helps to develop closer liaison, cooperation and the exchange of information between children and the police.

146

Plate 18.3 Examples of the Department of Transport's road safety campaign material

Source: Department of Transport

To effectively cover an age range from 5 to 18 years necessarily requires a wide curriculum and advice on its content is contained in RoSPA's 'A Curriculum for Road Safety Education' (Ref. 9).

For younger children the aim should be to increase their awareness of danger on the roads, especially from the actions of others, and to help them understand the many different facilities provided to make roads safer (eg. school crossing patrols, zebra and pelican crossings, guardrails, traffic islands etc.), how to use them and to teach them basic safe personal behaviour (including use of the Green Cross Code—Ref. 10). For older children the programme will need to cover a wider range of topics in greater depth including cycle training and perhaps even vehicle driver training.

At all ages the effectiveness of training will be increased if, in addition to classroom presentations, safety projects are developed, practical training is provided and competitions concerned with road safety are organised.

National Road Safety Campaigns

The Department of Transport organises publicity campaigns on many kinds of topics of national significance. When preparing their own campaigns, local authorities should take account of the Department's plans which are discussed during the planning stages with representatives of all local authorities through their associations. Complementary local publicity, to back up national campaigns, can be very effective and the Department is always ready to give assistance to any local authority to enable this to be done. Even where additional local publicity is not proposed, local authorities can make use of the Department's publicity material, which is provided free of charge, to ensure that it is given the widest possible coverage (see Plate 18.3).

Road safety material is also available from other organisations such as the Royal Society for the Prevention of Accidents (RoSPA) who make a considerable contribution towards road safety matters.

18.6 References

Text Reference

1. DTp—'*Road Accidents Statistics, Great Britain*', DTp (1985). (18.1)

2. DTp—'*Road Accident Costs. Highway Economics Note No 1*', DTp (updated annually). (18.1)

3. IHT—'*Guidelines for Accident Reduction and Prevention in Highway Engineering*', Institution of Highways & Transportation (1986). (18.2)

4. DTp—'*Accident Investigation Manual*', Distributed by the Royal Society for the Prevention of Accidents (RoSPA) (1986). (18.2)

5. DTp/TRRL—Report LR 1120, '*Accidents at 4-arm roundabouts*', DTp (1984). (18.4)

6. The Royal Society for the Prevention of Accidents (RoSPA)—'*Road Safety Handbook*', RoSPA (1984). (18.5)

7. OECD—'*Manual on road safety compaigns*', OECD (1975). (18.5)

8. RoSPA—'*Road Safety Programme Manual*', Guidelines for Research, Design, Monitoring and Evaluation of Education, Training and Publicity Activities, RoSPA (1984). (18.5)

9. RoSPA—'*A curriculum for Road Safety Education*', RoSPA (1984). (18.5)

10. DTp—'*The Green Cross Code*, HMSO (1986). (18.5)

18.7 Further Information

11. DTp/TRRL—Report RR 101, '*The current state of road safety education in primary and middle schools*', DTp (1987).

12. DTp '*The Highway Code*', HMSO (1987).

13. Association of London Borough Road Safety Officers—'*Handbook for Road Safety Officers*', ALBRSO (1984).

14. Sabey, B E—'*Road Safety in the 80's*', Report to Symposium 'Recent Developments and Research in Road Safety, Remedial Measures', University of Salford (Sep 1983).

15. RoSPA—'*Educating the Road User*', RoSPA.

16. DTp—TA 24/81 '*Road safety during installation and maintenance of permanent traffic signals and related equipment on all purpose roads*', (Amendment No 1. 7/2/83), DTp (1981). [Sco.110]

17. DTp/TRRL—LR 929, '*The relationship between road lighting quality and accident frequency*', DTp (1980).

18. DTp—Circular Roads 12/75. '*Duty of Local Authorities to promote road safety*', DTp (1975). [Wa.19]

19. DoE—'*Pedestrian Safety Manual of Advice*', HMSO (1973).

N.B. In addition, there are a number of TRRL reports issued in the LR and SR series. Details of these can be obtained from TRRL (see Preface).

19 Environmental Protection and Enhancement

19.1 General Objectives

All highway improvement and traffic management schemes should seek to make a positive contribution to the environment whenever possible. However, improvements for the travelling public are often incompatible with the needs of pedestrians, cyclists or local residents and an appropriate balance will need to be achieved between improving the environment of an area and improving accessibility for vehicles (see also Chapter 16 which considers access requirements).

In some cases the major aim of a traffic management scheme will be to achieve significant environmental benefits for a specific street or area. In others, traffic throughput, road safety or improved access may be the major objective; but in all schemes the concept of limiting traffic flows on local distributors and access roads to a level compatible with their environmental capacities should be considered (see also Chapters 5 and 6 on roads hierarchy and concepts of capacity).

19.2 Environmental Factors

The environmental consequences of traffic in urban areas affect the physical fabric of towns and cities and the health and well-being of people living in, working in and visiting these areas as tourists or for shopping or business.

The consequences of traffic movement which adversely affect the environment are:

- noise,
- vibration,
- pollution from exhaust fumes,
- dust and dirt,
- visual intrusion,
- accident risk,
- severance, and
- nuisance from parked vehicles.

All of these are seen as inconveniences or nuisance and sometimes as a danger to health, although evidence for this may be difficult to find. Although each factor is measurable in some way, individual perception of their severity and impact will always be subjective and will be related to personal values, levels of tolerance and expectations, often built up over many years. Despite these difficulties it will be necessary to establish the size and nature of each problem, using techniques which will enable comparisons to be made between one area and another. Ultimately, a judgement will need to be made. (See also Chapters 10 and 12 which deal with data collection and assessment and the Department of Transport's Manual of Environmental Appraisal (Ref. 1) [Sco.111] which contains detailed descriptions of these factors and their method of measurement.)

An introduction to the main characteristics of the principal environmental factors is given below:

Noise

Traffic noise can have detrimental effects on the tranquility of an area and is particularly annoying at night when it can affect sleep. Traffic noise comes from the interaction of tyres and the road surface, from engines, exhausts and brakes, and in the case of many heavy goods vehicles, from the body of the vehicle itself and supplementary machinery such as refrigeration units. Noise is accentuated by braking and acceleration at junctions and by high speeds. It can also be increased by poor maintenance of vehicles and road surfaces and by poor driving. Heavy and light railways in urban areas can also generate high noise levels near to the tracks and at stations.

Peaks of noise are particularly vexing and heavy lorries and motorcycles are often seen as the worst offenders. Noise can have different characteristics and a noise can be regarded as a nuisance even though it may not register a high decibel level.

Vibration

There are two forms of vibration from vehicles; that which is caused by the contact of the vehicle with the road surface and transmitted through the ground; and that which is caused by low frequency sound waves. Research has shown that rattling or buzzing windows and shaking floors are common manifestations of traffic vibration and that worry about damage to property is an important source of nuisance (Refs. 2 and 3).

Pollution

Exhaust emissions are generally regarded as objectionable and a hazard to health although there is no evidence that demonstrates direct effects at normal atmospheric concentrations. People normally think of such pollution as 'fumes', a combination of dirty smoke and bad smells. Exhaust emissions consist of gases, lead and other suspended particles and black smoke. In general, diesel engines produce less gaseous emissions than petrol engines (and no lead). However, diesels are the main source of black smoke, particularly if they are poorly maintained and are therefore perceived to be the worst offenders.

Dust and Dirt

Dust and dirt have been shown to be important sources of environmental nuisance which bother many people both in and out of doors (Refs. 4 and 5).

Visual Intrusion

Visual intrusion is one of the more subjective environmental factors and is difficult to measure. Visual quality relates to the presence of stationary or moving traffic in the context of individual perceptions of the visual quality of the street as a whole. The quality of the built environment is also affected by the presence and design of street furniture, traffic signs and signals and parking meters, as well as landscaping and townscaping features like pavings, walls and kerbing and street lighting.

Accident Risk

Perception of accident risk, as well as actual risk, is important to the quality of the environment (see also Chapters 10 and 18 which deal with accident data and road safety). The fear and intimidation which people experience when in close proximity to large, noisy and fast moving vehicles has an adverse effect on their feelings of safety and is thus highly detrimental. These fears are accentuated in residential streets where children play and in places where footpaths are narrow and heavily used.

Severance

The term severance is used to describe the divisive effects an urban road (or railway) has on the inhabitants on either side of it. It may result from the construction of a new route or from increased traffic volumes on an existing route.

The effects usually take the form of a change in the distribution and number of trips that people make due to the perceived deterrence of a major barrier in their midst. The number of trips between the two sides of the route are likely to decrease and journey times may be increased. Young children, the elderly and people with restricted mobility are affected more than others.

Parked Vehicles

Inconsiderate parking of vehicles causes danger and nuisance. Vehicles which are parked on footways cause inconvenience to pedestrians and may put them at risk, as well as damaging the construction of the footway. Parking of heavy goods vehicles in residential areas is visually intrusive and causes noise and pollution, often at unsocial hours of the day or night.

19.3 Conflicting Demands

All drivers or passengers in vehicles are also at some time pedestrians and each person also has his or her place of residence. Despite this, individuals tend to adopt different sets of values when they occupy their different roles at work or at home. For every road or area there will be those who demand freedom of vehicular access as well as those who wish to restrict vehicle movements.

Decision makers have to recognise these facts of life just as they must recognise the necessity to permit commercial vehicles to have an adequate level of access to their destinations since the economic welfare of the nation is reliant on efficient and effective delivery of all kinds of goods and services.

The balance between the need for access and environmental protection is sometimes difficult to establish and may on occasion, not afford the level of protection which the resident population demands, perhaps because existing street patterns and land uses prevent major changes in the short term.

There will always be limits on the extent to which it is possible to protect people from the effects of traffic in an urban environment but this should not prevent efforts being made to achieve the best possible level of protection in proportion to the costs, of all kinds, involved in achieving it.

19.4 Typical Areas for Treatment

Certain types of area or situation are particularly likely to suffer from detrimental effects of traffic. These include:

Historic Towns

Old buildings and street patterns can possess a unique character and charm which may suffer great detriment from traffic and every effort should be made to protect them (see Plate 19.1). Although on rare occasions it may be necessary to demolish historic buildings to make provision for traffic, this should only be contemplated when all other feasible alternatives have been examined.

Inner Cities and Traditional Town Centres

The decline of old and traditional shopping areas can be accelerated by crowded, noisy and polluted streets as people with access to cars transfer their shopping or business to more pleasant environments elsewhere.

Residential Areas

Residential areas can suffer from unwanted through traffic making detours to avoid congested main routes.

Plate 19.1 Environmental treatment in a historic town retaining access for vehicles

Source: Civic Trust

The adverse effect of heavy lorries and non-residential car parking are, a typical concern.

Severed Areas

Some areas of land can become isolated by the effects of a major transport route (road or rail), effectively cutting them off from the surrounding area. This can bring marked commercial and social consequences.

Areas Near Major Junctions

Starting, stopping and queueing traffic causes more noise and pollution than a continuous traffic stream.

Effects of Traffic Management

Schemes designed for some other purpose may have unwanted consequences for the environment, such as changed traffic routeing in residential streets or simply a proliferation of signs and road markings.

Temporary Disturbance

Areas near to major new works (road or development) can suffer for fairly long periods from the noise of construction machinery and the dirt and noise of vehicles passing to and from the site.

19.5 Measures to Improve the Environment

Measures which improve or protect the environment can be considered in three groups:

general traffic management schemes, which may have some other major objective but can also improve the environment;

environmental traffic management schemes, designed specifically to improve some aspect of the environment; and

measures to minimise environmental impact.

A general description of each of these groups is given below but information on the detailed design of different types of scheme is contained in subsequent chapters (eg. Chapter 24 for pedestrian schemes, Chapter 27 for the mangement of heavy vehicle movements).

Use of General Traffic Management Techniques

The concept of an environmental area was introduced (in Chapter 1) as an area where environmental intrusion from moving or stationary vehicles should be minimised.

An environmental area might include various kinds of land use which could produce a considerable amount of traffic within the area but there should be no traffic which has no need to be there.

All new traffic management schemes should try and avoid creating unnecessary environmental problems in the first place and aim to improve the environment in general, whilst keeping an overall balance between accessibility and environmental protection.

Traffic management techniques applied in environmental areas, should endeavour to:

● maintain a human scale to the area;

● not exceed the environmental capacity of the streets in the area (see Plate 19.2);

● be compatible with other urban planning policies (maintaining close links with planners and architects);

● consider and provide for the needs of public transport as appropriate;

● segregate car, public transport, lorry, cycle and pedestrian routes where this is beneficial;

● consider giving priority to access on foot and by bicycle;

● limit access by car to the periphery of main shopping areas;

● reduce through traffic (see Figures 19.1 and 19.2);

Plate 19.2 Road narrowing at the exit from a residential street   Source: TRRL

BY JUNCTION PRIORITY   BY A SERIES OF STREET END CLOSURES

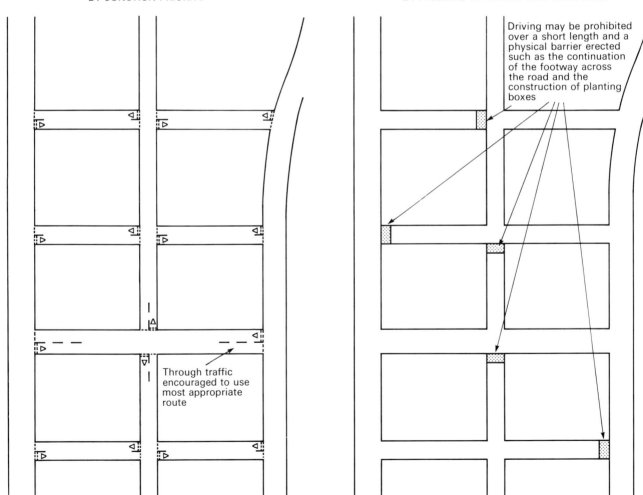

Through traffic encouraged to use most appropriate route

Driving may be prohibited over a short length and a physical barrier erected such as the continuation of the footway across the road and the construction of planting boxes

Plate 19.1 Environmental treatment in a historic town retaining access for vehicles

PIMLICO PRECINCT

Shops

Entry streets (one way)

Additional paving

Parking areas

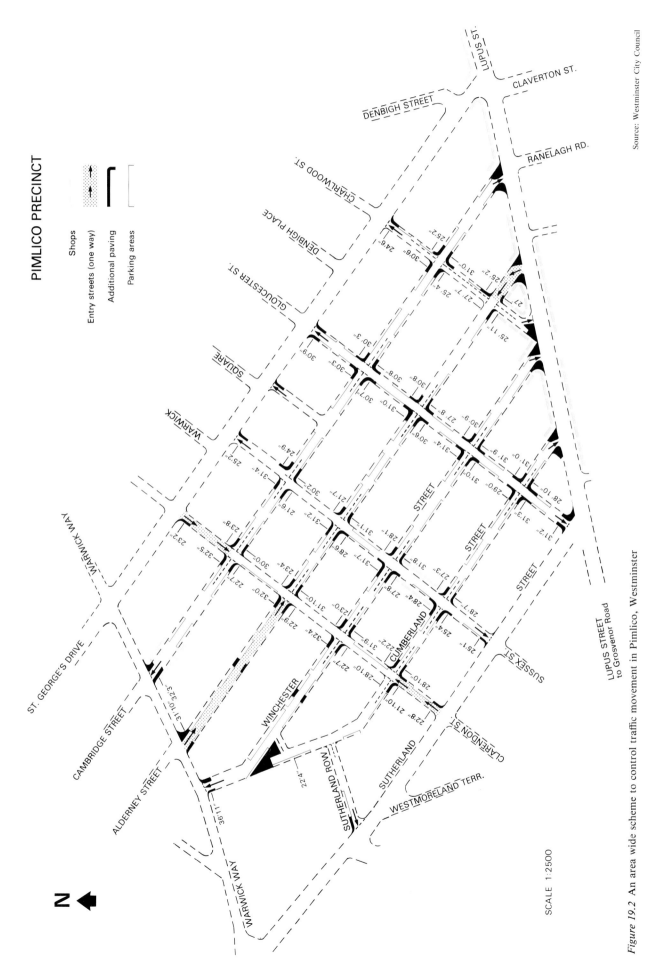

SCALE 1:2500

Figure 19.2 An area wide scheme to control traffic movement in Pimlico, Westminster

Source: Westminster City Council

153

Plate 19.3 Use of varied and textured carriageway surfacing to control vehicle speeds near a pedestrian area

● remove non-essential car parking (eg. commuters);

● avoid major new construction and street widening;

● control speed and use landscaping features to enhance the character of the road and discourage through-traffic (see Plate 19.3);

● coordinate signal controlled junctions to allow continuous traffic flow and reduce noise caused by the stopping and starting of vehicles;

● use coloured and textured surfaces, street furniture, vegetation, water features, seating and shelter to enhance the visual appearance of the street scene (see Colour Plate 19.4); and

● maintain high standards of maintenance and reinstatement to help reduce noise and vibration.

Specific Environmental Improvement Schemes

Traffic management schemes may also be designed to reinforce planning measures and improve the environment. Examples are:

● lorry management schemes and the licensing of lorry depots subject to consideration of amenity and environmental factors (see Chapter 27);

● pedestrianisation of shopping areas and other facilities to assist pedestrians (see Chapters 24 and 31);

● creation of play streets and emphasis on the residential area of certain places on the lines of the 'woonerven' system used in Holland (Refs. 6 and 7—see also Plate 19.5);

● creation of suitable parking schemes (see Chapters 20 and 31); and

● dealing with traffic matters in inner city regeneration programmes (see Plates 19.6 and 19.7).

For further details see also DoE, Area Improvement Notes No's 5, 6, 7 and 9 (Refs. 8, 9, 10 and 11).

Other Measures to Minimise Environmental Impact

Where specific environmental protection measures are not appropriate for some reason, other general

Plate 19.5 An example of the Dutch 'Woonerven' system

Note: A number of European countries have introduced measures intended to reduce the amount of through traffic in established residential areas and thereby create an enhanced environment where pedestrian activity predominates. Many Dutch towns and cities have established 'Woonerven' (residential precincts) the main features of which are:

● a repaving of the existing street with a variety of materials together with planting and street furniture designed to create an attractive street scene. Features which suggest the division of the street into areas for different types of traffic are excluded in order avoid any presumed priority for vehicles;

● the introduction of features such as sharp bends, road humps and local narrowing to reduce vehicle speeds and discourage through traffic. Parking is only permitted in specific areas; and

● the reinforcement of physical measures with regulations which lay down a code of behaviour for road users.

Similar features have been used to create 'dorpserfs' (village yards) and 'winkelerfs' (shopping yards) in other areas. Although a Woonerf is expensive to provide and maintain and the controls are quite restrictive, the resulting environment is inherently safer and is generally accepted to be more pleasant for residents.

measures to reduce intrusion can be considered, such as:

● providing noise insulation for buildings (possibly under The Noise Insulation Regulations 1975 (Ref. 12) [Sco.112, NI.2] where this is appropriate—see also Chapters 10 and 34);

● landscaping, screening and planting to minimise the effects of noise and visual intrusion; and

● careful siting of traffic control equipment and signs using the smallest size of sign possible while maintaining legal and safety requirements (eg. fixing signs to walls and street lighting columns where appropriate).

19.6 Evaluation of Environmental Measures

General Considerations

● As with any other traffic management scheme, environmental schemes should be evaluated to determine whether they are good value for money and in order to prioritise or rank schemes in different areas.

Plate 19.6 Environment treatment in a sensitive inner city area before . . . .

 Source: Civic Trust

Plate 19.7 . . . . and after.

Source: Civic Trust

Remedial measures intended to produce environmental benefits may also produce road safety benefits as vehicles are diverted onto new or improved roads and might also improve traffic performance. However, scheme evaluation must take account of any peripheral effects at or close to the boundaries of a scheme, which could be adverse if much traffic is excluded from an environmental area and seeks other routes. Transferring a problem from one area to another will seldom provide a satisfactory solution.

Any environmental gain resulting from remedial action will have cost implications resulting from construction, maintenance and administration. There may also be costs resulting from increased journey times and distances and the loss of facilities previously enjoyed by the occupants of vehicles.

It is difficult to place any universally accepted values on environmental benefits because of their subjective nature but it may be argued that the burden of travel costs would be more fairly distributed by implementing a scheme because the costs caused by the journey would be no longer 'subsidised' by the reduced environmental quality previously experienced by residents and pedestrians.

The evaluation of environmental measures is dealt with in the DTp Manual of Environmental Appraisal (Ref. 1) [Sco.111] and a useful and simple alternative technique for evaluating environmental schemes is given in the ALBES' (Association of London Borough Engineers and Surveyors) Code of Practice (Ref. 13). This method aims to provide a quantified assessment of all environmental factors, using proxy parameters in some cases. This type of technique provides a useful comparative guide which should help decisions to be made in an objective and consistent way. (Further details on scheme assessments are also given in Chapter 12.)

Evaluation of Lorry Control Measures

Many environmental schemes are aimed at the removal of heavy commercial vehicles from unsuitable areas (see also Chapter 27). As with other environmental schemes attempts should be made to quantify the effects. It is useful to evaluate a scheme in terms of the effects it will have on numbers of people and property and a method for this also is given in the ALBES Code of Practice (see reference above). The method itemises factors like numbers and time distribution of heavy commercial vehicles of different classes, persons, dwellings and sensitive land uses affected and road safety hazards.

Costs and benefits must also be considered. Costs usually arise from:

● implementation;

● operating costs of the scheme (eg. enforcement and maintenance);

● additional costs for HGV operators (arising from diversions);

● additional costs for other road users (including public transport operators).

Benefits might arise from:

● reduced road maintenance costs (less damage from large and heavy vehicles);

● fewer accidents;

● savings from reduced congestion.

Operator's Costs

There are three basic ways of calculating changes in vehicle operators's costs:

● the simplest method uses an all-in per kilometre cost figure for each of the different types of vehicle affected;

● a more detailed method takes account of changes in journey speed on different routes as well as distance and is based on an assessment of the runnings costs for the vehicles involved; and

● the most sophisticated method adopts the techniques recommended in the DoE Lorry Plans Advice Note (Ref. 14).

19.7 Decision Making

With quantitative measurements available for several different study areas, it will be possible to identify those with the most severe problems. However, the severity of the problem is not the only factor to be considered in determining priorities for action. It is important to consider whether effective solutions are possible. For example, it may be better to improve areas with less severe problems where worthwhile results can be obtained rather than to attempt to solve the worst problems if there is little prospect of success.

When the problem has been evaluated and benefits and costs have been assessed for alternative schemes it will be possible to make a value judgement on the desirability and probable effects of implementing a particular scheme. A decision to implement will depend upon a local authority's policies towards improving the environment and upon the competing demands for funding other projects. These decisions will ultimately be made at the political level.

Use of standardised and systematic techniques will be of great value in presenting schemes for decision. Schemes involving traffic regulation orders may involve public inquiries and the data collected will enable the facts to be presented in a clear and objective way.

19.8 References

Text Reference

1. DTp—Manual of Environmental Appraisal, DTp (1983). [Sco.111] (19.2)

2. DTp/TRRL—Report LR 1020, *'Vibration from Road Traffic at 14 residential sites'*, DTp (1981). (19.2)

3. DTp/TRRL—Report LR 1119, *'Vibration nuisance arising from road traffic—results of a 50-site survey'*, DTp (1984). (19.2)

4. Morten Williams, J, Hedges, B and Fernando, E—*'Road Traffic and the Environment'*, Social and Community Planning Research, London (1978). (19.2)

5. DTp/TRRL—Working Paper 85, *'Traffic nuisance in Great Britain'* (Unpublished—available on personal request only) (1985). (19.2)

6. SWOV—*'Towards safer residential areas'*, Institute for Road Safety Research SWOV/Ministry of Transport, Netherlands (1984). (19.5)

7. Royal Dutch Touring Club—*'Woonerven. A new approach to Environmental Management in residential areas and the related traffic legislation'*, RDTC (1980). (19.5)

8. DoE—Area Improvement Note 5 *'Environmental design in four general improvement areas'*, HMSO (1972). (19.5)

9. DoE—Area Improvement Note 6 *'The design of streets and other spaces'*, HMSO (1973). (19.5)

10. DoE—Area Improvement Note 7 *'Parking and garaging in general improvement areas'*, HMSO (1973). (19.5)

11. DoE—Area Improvement Note 9 *'Traffic in general improvement areas'*, HMSO (1974). (19.5)

12. Noise Insulation Regulations 1975, Statutory Instrument 1975 No 1263, HMSO (1975). [Sco.112] (19.5)

13. ALBES/DTp—*'Highways and Traffic Management in London'*, HMSO, London (1986). (19.6)

14. DoE—*'Vehicle operating costs for the evaluation of lorry plans'*, Lorry Advice Note, HMSO (1976). (19.6)

19.9 Further Information

15. DTp/TRRL—Report SR 806, *'A user's guide to the computer programs for predicting air pollution from road traffic'*, DTp (1984).

16. DTp/TRRL—Report SR 774, *'A National Survey of Lorry Nuisance'*, DTp (1983).

17. Wood, A A—*'Traffic management and the environment'*, PTRC Seminar L, pp 201–213, (1982).

18. DTp—*'Traffic Signs Manual'*, (Chapter 1), HMSO (1982).

19. DoE/DTp/TRRL—Report SR 778, *'Review of some effects of major roads on urban communities'*, DoE/DTp (1982).

20. Jones, I D—*'Environment versus accessibility: the traffic management policy options for town and city centres'*, PTRC Seminar J, pp 229–241 (1981).

21. DoE/DTp/TRRL—Report LR 1015, *'Environmental effects of traffic changes'*, DoE/DTp (1981).

22. Watkins, L H—*'Environmental Impact of Loads and Traffic'*, Applied Science (1981).

23. DoE/DTp/TRRL—Report SR 536, *'Roads and the environment: a collection of papers'*, DoE/DTp (1980).

24. Report of the Inquiry into, *'Lorries, People and the Environment'*, conducted by A Armitage, HMSO (1980).

25. Buchanan, C et al—*'Traffic in Towns'*, HMSO (1963).

20 Urban Traffic Control

20.1 Background

Using traffic signals at road intersections allows vehicle movements to be controlled by allocating time intervals during which separate traffic demands make use of the available road space. Signal equipment and control techniques have evolved to cope with a wide range of intersection layouts and complex traffic demands—including pedestrians crossing at the intersection. Moreover, traffic signals provide relatively efficient intersection control within limited road space. Consequently they are frequently adopted as the means of traffic control at busy urban junctions.

Traffic signals are also widely used to provide pedestrian crossing facilities at sites remote from intersections. Techniques have also been developed in which traffic signals are used to assist pedal cyclists, public service vehicles or emergency service vehicles at particular sites.

Allocating the amount of time available, as well as the space, for particular vehicle movements adds a further dimension to the overall control of traffic. The allocation of both road space and road time in a coordinated manner can be extended to include the coordination of road time at adjacent signal sites to secure the control of vehicle movements over a section of road network. This is the basis of the majority of present day urban traffic control (UTC) schemes. By taking account of the available road space at intersections and balancing the road time between individual traffic signals it is possible to derive widespread advantage in terms of freer flowing traffic and reduced journey times. The benefits of coordination and the frequency of traffic signal installations in urban areas means that use of these techniques is becoming commonplace.

Coordination between adjacent traffic signals involves deriving some form of plan or strategy on the occurrence and extent of individual signal timings and introducing a system to electronically link the signals together in order to impose the plan or strategy. Much of the development work behind today's UTC schemes was carried out by the Transport and Road Research Laboratory. Control strategies have been devised and tested which are now applied in urban areas throughout the world.

Nowadays, traffic signals are often selected as the preferred means of intersection control in urban areas as they can be easily incorporated into existing UTC systems. It is expected that around 40 per cent of traffic signal installations in Britain, including pedestrian crossing facilities, will eventually be part of UTC systems.

Detailed advice on the design of traffic signals for individual intersection control is given in Chapter 41. Pedestrian, pedal cyclist and public service vehicle facilities involving the use of traffic signals are described in Chapters 24, 25 and 26 respectively.

20.2 Operational Objectives for UTC Systems

UTC systems have become popular for two reasons; they can make the best use of existing network capacity and reduce journey times without creating adverse environmental effects (indeed by reducing congestion and delay they can help in reducing vehicle noise and pollution); and they can provide the basis for an expanded control system incorporating such features as variable message signs, congestion monitoring, emergency service vehicle priority and other intervention strategies.

UTC can be used to influence the pattern of traffic in an area to pursue predetermined objectives, or alternatively to optimise the performance of existing traffic signal systems.

Objectives usually include getting the best traffic performance from a network by reducing overall delay to vehicles and the number of times that they have to stop. Other performance criteria can also be used such as minimising fuel consumption or pollution, but there is usually little practical difference between the effects of adopting one or the other of these criteria.

Further objectives might be to attract or deter traffic from particular routes or areas, to give priority to specific categories of road user or to arrange for queueing to take place in suitable parts of the network, for example, where the noise and fumes of waiting vehicles would cause less irritation to passers-by or residents, or where convenient road space exists for queuing.

The needs of pedestrians, cyclists and those with a mobility handicap should not be overlooked. When congestion is reduced and vehicle speeds increase, pedestrians can experience more difficulty in crossing the road and Pelican crossings must be linked with signal-controlled junctions within a UTC system.

Plate 20.1 A car park information system with variable messages

Source: Devon County Council

20.3 The Potential Benefits of UTC

The potential benefits which can be obtained from the installation of a UTC system include:

- a reduction in vehicle journey times, number of stops, fuel consumption and environmental pollution;

- creating priorities for buses and bus routes (see also Chapter 26);

- giving priority to emergency vehicles responding to incidents and reducing vehicle attendance times by using special signal timing plans to favour key routes from fire stations;

- implementation of diversion schemes to deal with emergencies or special events and other control strategies such as tidal flow schemes;

- improved fault monitoring and maintenance of equipment leading to a reduction in the delays and potential road safety hazards caused by faulty equipment;

- improved utilisation of car parks and a reduction in the amount of circulating traffic by providing car park information systems as part of UTC (see Plate 20.1); and

- the creation of a constantly updated centralised data bank of traffic information.

As an example of what can be achieved, in November 1983 a SCOOT system (see 20.10 below) was installed by Hampshire County Council in Southampton where the traffic signals were previously uncoordinated. A detailed study was carried out covering 37 of the SCOOT links which represented approximately one quarter of the network. This found that:

- peak hour journey times were reduced by 18 per cent in the morning and 26 per cent in the evening;

- peak hour delays were reduced by 39 per cent in the morning and 48 per cent in the evening;

- bus journey times in the evening peak were reduced by 39 per cent.

The economic benefits for the whole SCOOT area (at 1979 prices), excluding accidents and reduced fire response times were estimated at £600,000 per annum

Plate 20.2 A typical UTC operations centre

Source: Hampshire County Council

compared with an installation cost of £700,000. The system will eventually be expanded to consist of 256 outstation addresses including 90 SCOOT nodes.

A typical UTC operations centre is shown in Plate 20.2.

20.4 Identification of Areas Suitable for Signal Coordination

Adjacent signal controlled junctions should be considered for coordination when the vehicle arrivals are platooned as a result of the control at upstream junctions and when link travel times are less than 20–30 seconds or 50 seconds in particularly free-flowing conditions. Coordination can be achieved between as few as two junctions (even between two signal controlled crossings) or on a network area-wide basis. Simple schemes can utilise the coordination capabilities of modern traffic signal controllers. Larger area-wide schemes, making use of a central control computer, become worthwhile when there are about a dozen junctions and pedestrian crossings under signal control within a single locality and the traffic pattern exhibits cyclic downstream platooning at least during peak periods.

It is common to divide a UTC network into sub-areas and this should be considered when:

● groups of adjacent signals require different plans or strategies;

● relatively long distances occur between groups of signals;

● well defined major routes exist with few significant cross movements;

● queuing space becomes a critical feature at particular junctions;

● complex movements have to be accommodated within a relatively small area.

Coordination between sub-areas can be adjusted to meet demands. It is common for individual sub-areas to share the central computer for economy but operate independently.

The TRRL have developed a simple method for deciding which groups of adjacent signals are likely to be worth coordinating and the scale of benefits which should result (Ref. 1). A program called COORDBEN is available and has been used successfully in the UK and overseas (see also 20.15 below).

161

20.5 The Concept of Coordination

Signal coordination means controlling the starts and durations of the green periods at adjacent sets of signals along a route or within a network.

Common Cycle Times

To maintain signal coordination from cycle to cycle each junction must operate with a common cycle time or a simple multiple of it (eg. pelican crossings can often complete two cycles in the time needed for adjacent street junctions to complete one cycle).

Offsets

The green periods occuring at each junction are staggered in relation to each other by specifying an offset time for each junction with respect to adjacent junctions. The offset is the starting time of a specified stage at the junction relative to a common time base of one cycle (this is illustrated in Figure 20.1).

Time-Distance Diagrams

Using a time and distance diagram (see Figure 20.2) offsets can be calculated to produce a 'green wave' to the predominant traffic flow and to optimise coordination to the opposing flow (on the same route). In practice, diagramatic techniques do not always produce the best possible settings and when more than one or two conflicting traffic streams have to be considered, the problem becomes more complicated and computerised techniques should be employed as discussed in 20.9 below.

A method for calculating signal timings at a single junction is provided in Chapter 41.

20.6 Signal Control Equipment

Specifications

All signal equipment used on public highways in Britain must conform to standards laid down by the Department of Transport (Ref. 2).

Coordination

Traffic signals in a UTC area are usually controlled by a central computer which sends electronic instructions by telephone type cables to each junction. Coordination may also be achieved using 'cableless link' units which use timing devices to implement preset signal timings. These units are microprocessor based and operate by having a synchronised time reference at each junction, usually maintained by coordination with regular pulses from the mains supply, so that the need for cable connections between junctions is eliminated (Ref. 3).

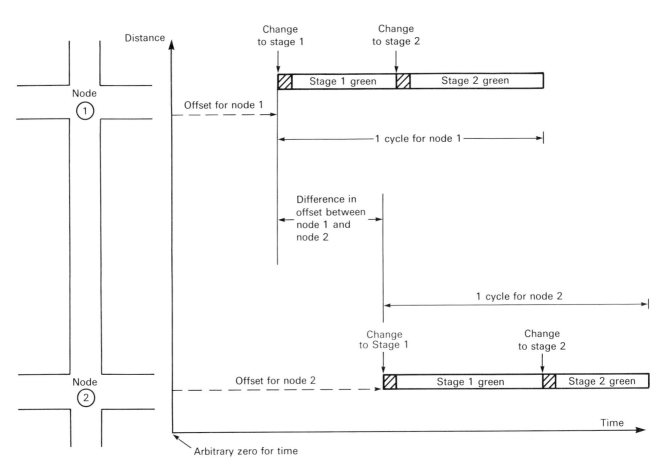

Figure 20.1 Illustration of the term 'offset'

Source: DoE/DTp/TRRL (1975) Report LR 888
'User guide to TRANSYT version 8'

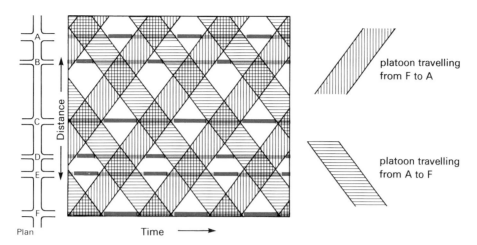

Figure 20.2 A time and distance diagram for linked traffic signals

platoon travelling
from F to A

platoon travelling
from A to F

Source: 'Traffic Signals; Road Technical Paper 56.' (1966) HMSO

Although cableless systems do not have the same scope or flexibility as a centrally controlled system and equipment operation cannot be modified or monitored centrally, they can be useful as a backup facility in the event of computer failure, or for small groups of signals in places where the expense of a central computer is not justified.

20.7 Alternative Methods of Signal Coordination

Two basic types of UTC system are currently in use and are based on different control strategies. These are:

● **fixed-time control systems;** and

● **traffic-responsive control systems** which can be divided into traffic responsive plan selection, and fully traffic responsive control systems.

20.8 Data Requirements for UTC

Calculation of signal settings for either of the above control strategies requires a considerable amount of data including:

● a representation of the network, typically as nodes (junctions) and links (one-way approaches to nodes);

● link lengths;

● traffic flows, including turning flows within junctions;

● saturation flows for each link;

● free flow journey speeds or times for each link; and

● details of the cycle of signal operations for each junction, including intergreens, minimum greens, stage sequence, and appropriate geometric and traffic parameters.

The suitability of the resulting signal settings for the network depends on the accuracy both of the input data and of the traffic model within the computer program. Fixed time signal plans are calculated from average flow values, and cannot respond to the variability of traffic flows which often occurs except by switching to alternative plans. This has led to the development of traffic responsive systems. Considerable time and effort is needed to update fixed time plans, whereas traffic-responsive systems keep themselves up to date and obviate the need for periodic recalculation of plans.

20.9 Fixed-Time Systems (including TRANSYT)

Signal Plans

Fixed-time systems operate with a set of predesigned signal plans, each of which can be implemented at any time on receipt of a command from the central control point.

A signal plan is a collection of coordinated settings for all the signals in a network and, although it can be calculated by manual methods in simple cases, computer techniques are usually used.

The preparation of signal plans involves representing the traffic conditions in the network numerically and calculating an index of performance with respect to which the signal timings are optimised (this procedure is described in the later section on TRANSYT).

The signal settings in each plan are fixed in that the green periods and offsets do not vary from cycle to cycle. Thus, fixed-time systems can control known patterns of traffic, rather than respond to demand. This can be both a strength and a weakness of such systems.

Types of Signal Plan

A typical fixed-time system will have different plans for morning, evening and off-peak weekday conditions and for weekends. It is likely that there will also be plans for evening and night-time conditions, and for specific occasions such as processions or sports events. If the network also has traditional vehicle detection equipment (see Chapter 41), the fixed-time system may also switch to isolated vehicle actuated (VA) operation during the night, during periods of low flow or if some fault occurs at the central controller. However, the cost of maintaining vehicle detectors is difficult to justify for these purposes alone and reversion to full isolated VA operation is becoming less widely used.

Ageing of Signal Plans

The benefits offered by the initial signal plan implemented on-street will depreciate over time as traffic conditions change and the plan becomes less appropriate. It has been estimated that signal plans degrade by about 3% per year and so the initial benefit can be lost within five years. The ageing process arises from:

● any general increase or decrease in traffic over the whole or parts of the network;

● changes in flows of traffic on different links resulting from re-routeing or altered traffic demands; or

● alterations to the street network.

It is also worth remembering that when a new plan is first implemented congestion is reduced in a consistent way because of the fixed nature of the plan. Vehicles often re-route to take advantage of the less congested routes and in so doing alter the distribution of flows within a network. This can create a need to update the plan but, in practice, such action is taken rather infrequently because of the time and costs involved.

Plan Selection

A fixed-time system may, typically, involve between 4 and 8 changes of plan during a normal weekday. It is often difficult to decide exactly when to change plan in order to respond to day-to-day variations in flow level but changes should be timed to relate to daily flow profiles. Sometimes plan changes are carried out in response to a manual command resulting from visual monitoring of conditions using closed circuit television cameras (CCTV). However, the most common method is to change plans at a particular time each day determined historically by expected traffic conditions.

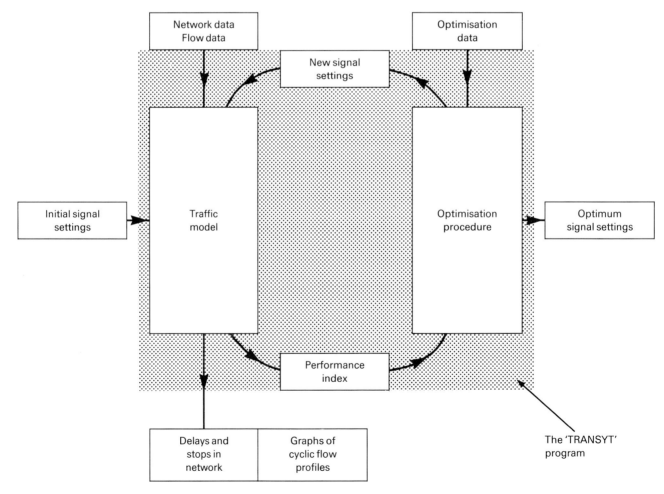

Figure 20.3 The structure of the 'TRANSYT' program

Source: DoE/DTp/TRRL (1975) Report LR 888
'User guide to TRANSYT version 8'

As this will take place irrespective of prevailing traffic conditions, it may cause some disruption to traffic and reduce the overall performance of the network whilst adjustments take place. For these reasons changing plan too frequently also has a detrimental effect and it is generally better to change plans during off-peak periods, whenever this is possible (Refs. 4, 5 and 6).

TRANSYT

In Britain, the most widely used technique for calculating fixed-time signal settings is the TRANSYT 8 computer program developed by the TRRL (Ref. 7).

The program models traffic behaviour, carries out optimising procedures and then predicts the best signal settings (see Figure 20.3 for the program structure). The program also provides extensive information about the performance of the network including estimated delays, numbers of stops, journey speeds and fuel consumption (Ref. 8).

TRANSYT models traffic behaviour using histograms to represent the arrival patterns of traffic. These are called cyclic flow profiles because they represent the average pattern of traffic flow during one signal cycle (see Figure 20.4). It is important to check that the predicted cyclic flow profiles give a reasonably accurate representation of actual traffic behaviour and parameters within the program can be altered to achieve this. (See also Ref. 9 and Chapter 10).

The signal-optimising part of the program looks for a good fixed-time plan which will keep down the level of congestion by minimising a performance index for the network. The performance index is a weighted combination of the costs of delay and stops on all links and specific links can be weighted so that the optimising process derives more benefit from reducing delay and stops on these links at the expense of others. These weightings can be used to give priority to buses, allowing for differences between their movement and that of other traffic along each link to be taken into account (Ref. 10).

20.10 Traffic-responsive Systems (including SCOOT)

Basic Principles

Traffic-responsive control systems monitor traffic conditions in a network by some form of detection and react to the information received by implementing appropriate signal settings. Thus, systems of this kind adapt themselves to traffic patterns and respond to traffic demands as they occur.

Traffic Responsive Plan Selection

In this method of responsive control the information obtained from on-street detection is used to select the most suitable plan from a library of pre-calculated plans. Although this method provides a degree of self-adaption to traffic conditions, it still requires the preparation of fixed-time plans, rather than providing a gradual evolution of signal timings in response to changing traffic conditions. Furthermore, there is no convincing evidence that systems which change fixed plans on the basis of flows and congestion measurements perform any better than the simpler procedure of changing plans by time of day.

The SCATS system developed and implemented in Sydney, Australia (Ref. 11) is a type of UTC system which uses background traffic control plans selected in response to traffic demand. The optimum signal timings and phasings within these plans are determined according to traffic conditions. In addition to selecting appropriate signal plans the system also contains a simple method of assessing the desirability of linking major junctions, a facility which may be useful on some signal-controlled arterial roads where particularly

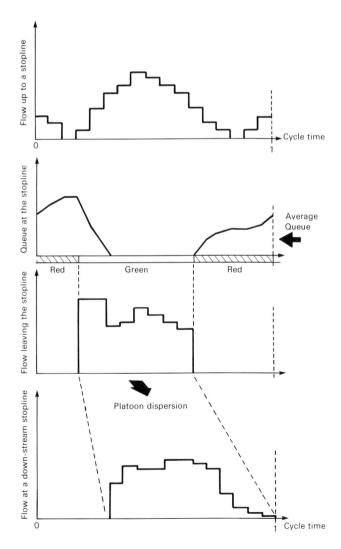

Figure 20.4 Cyclic flow profile in the 'TRANSYT' model

Source: DoE/DTp/TRRL (1975) Report LR 888
'User guide to TRANSYT version 8'

large and unpredictable variations in traffic levels and patterns may occur.

Fully-Responsive Control Systems

To overcome the problems of plan preparation and plan changing, a fully responsive strategy called SCOOT was conceived by the TRRL and developed by the Department of Transport and British signal manufacturers (Ref. 12).

SCOOT has now been introduced in several cities in Britain and subsequent performance assessments have shown significant benefits over both fixed-time systems (including TRANSYT) and isolated control (Ref. 13).

SCOOT is primarily a signal control technique and as such is a type of UTC system. The structure of SCOOT is similar to that of TRANSYT in that both methods use a traffic model of a network which predicts the delay and stops caused by particular signal settings. However, unlike TRANSYT, the SCOOT model is 'on-line' and monitors traffic flows continuously from on-street detectors. SCOOT uses this information to recalculate its traffic model predictions every few seconds and then makes systematic trial alterations to current signal settings, implementing only those

alterations which the traffic model predicts will be beneficial. The structure and principles of SCOOT are illustrated in Figures 20.5 and 20.6.

Advantages of Fully-Responsive Systems

The advantages of a fully-responsive strategy such as SCOOT over fixed time systems are:

● there is no need to prepare or update fixed-time plans;

● there are no sudden changes in signal settings— instead, new plans are continuously evolved;

● trends in traffic behaviour can be followed without requiring longer term predictions of average flows; and

● the system will adjust itself to respond to incidents which occur (eg. accidents) and data on the traffic situation are available to operators.

Table 20.1 gives a summary of the advantages and disadvantages of each type of UTC system. It should be noted that SCOOT and TRANSYT UTC systems can operate in adjacent parts of urban areas. In general, SCOOT is most valuable in central areas where congestion is high and flow patterns are complex and

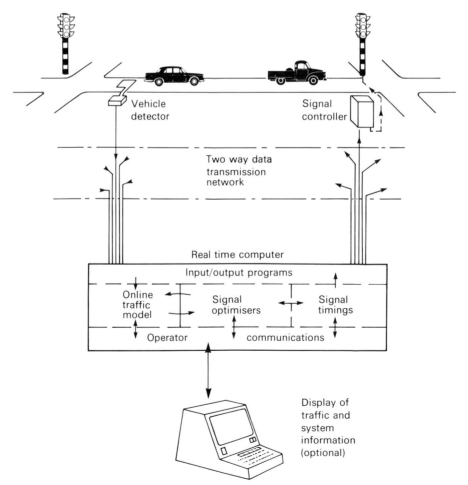

Figure 20.5 The flow of information in a 'SCOOT' UTC system

Source: DoE/DTp/TRRL (1981) Report LR 1014

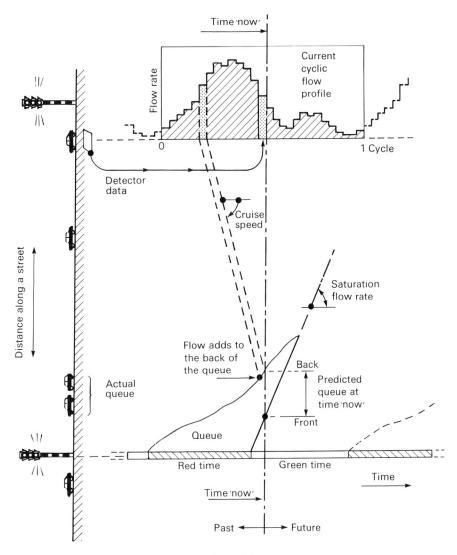

Figure 20.6 Principles of the 'SCOOT' traffic model

Source: DTp/TRRL (1981) Report LR 1014 'SCOOT: A Traffic responsive method of co-ordinating signals'

variable. Fixed time TRANSYT UTC systems can best be employed where congestion levels are generally lower and flow patterns consistent, such as on radial arterials. In practice SCOOT has shown up to 12% reductions in delay in comparison with fixed time control. (Ref. 13).

20.11 Fault Monitoring

Improved maintenance of traffic signal equipment can be achieved at junctions operating under UTC as they can be monitored continuously and remotely to identify faults, thus enabling maintenance work to be initiated more swiftly than by the conventional method of periodic checking and reporting. Both on and off-line computer fault monitoring and analysis systems have been developed and similar benefits are achieved through periodic, 'dial-up' monitoring of signal installations which are not on UTC.

20.12 Car Park Information Systems

Car park information systems can be incorporated into UTC systems. The aim is to monitor vehicles entering and leaving car parks and display information on the availability of spaces to drivers by means of variable message signs. The signs are controlled by the UTC central computer and should be located at key locations in the areas of car parks (see Plate 20.1 for illustration).

20.13 Priority Routeing for Emergency Vehicles

'Green waves' can be implemented through UTC systems to give priority for emergency vehicles travelling through the network and this is especially effective when used in conjunction with automatic detection equipment for these vehicles (Ref. 14). Fire appliances generally follow predetermined routes to incidents and it is relatively easy to devise special plans to cater for them.

Type of UTC system	Advantages	Disadvantages
Fixed time	• Cheaper to install and maintain. • Can be implemented using non-centrally controlled equipment. • Familiarity with settings for regular users. • 'Green waves' more easily implemented. • Can favour specific vehicle types more easily.	• Needs large amounts of data to be collected and updated. • Signal plans may require updating. • Disruption of plan changing. • Requires operator reaction to incidents. • Cannot deal with short term fluctuations in flow levels.
Responsive plan selection	• Can deal with some day-to-day fluctuations. • Plan change times could be more appropriate. • Might be valuable on arterial routes. • Cheaper than fully responsive control as fewer detectors required.	• Requires as much or more data to be collected as for fixed time systems. • Detector failure possible. • Needs decisions on thresholds for plan change. • May plan change for wrong reason. • Difficult to foresee all plan needs.
Fully responsive	• Less data needed to be collected in advance. • Plan evolves so avoids problems with plan changing and updating. • Can deal with short and long term fluctuations in flow levels. • Automatic reaction to incidents. • Monitors traffic situation throughout the area.	• Detector failure possible. • More expensive to install and maintain. • Requires central control. • Maintenance critical.

Table 20.1 Summary of the advantages and disadvantages of different types of UTC system

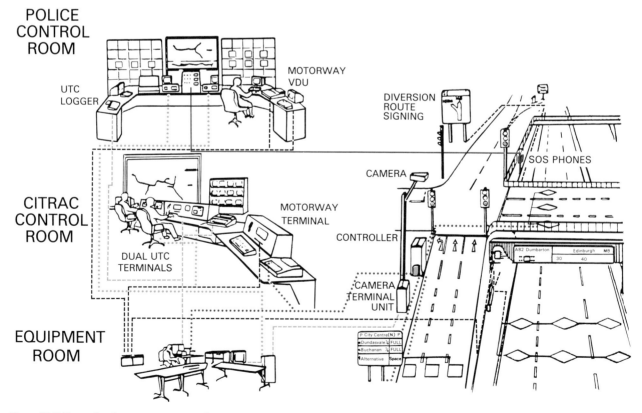

Figure 20.7 Example of a motorway control system (CITRAC)   Source: Mowatt, AMM and Young, AD (1986) 'CITRAC—The first five years' Traffic Engineering and Control volume 25 No 5.

20.14 Control of Urban Motorways and Major Roads

Systems have been developed which integrate traffic control for a city street network with the management of traffic flows on urban motorways. A notable example is the CITRAC system in Glasgow (Ref. 15 and Figure 20.7). Such systems enable the UTC control centre to respond to traffic conditions on the motorway, such as accidents or lane closures and to implement diversions from motorway exit points using the local street network.

20.15 Measuring the Effectiveness of UTC

Methods

The effectiveness of a UTC system is usually assessed using moving car techniques to measure traffic flow speeds (see Chapter 10). This method can be rather expensive but a reasonable indication of the benefits of signal coordination can be obtained using limited measurements of the journey times along various key routes in the UTC area. It is important that traffic flow levels are also measured and corrections made for their effects upon journey time.

Other methods of assessment which have been used involve aerial photography, time-lapse photography or computer analysis of video-tape recordings. All of these methods are, however, labour intensive and generally cost more than the use of moving car techniques.

Predicting the Benefits of Signal Coordination

A simple method of predicting the benefits of coordinating signals has been developed by the TRRL (Ref. 1).

This information is necessary to decide whether it is worthwhile extending an existing UTC system or implementing a new one. The method predicts the annual benefits of coordination in monetary terms from traffic data which is normally readily available. The simple computer program COORDBEN, mentioned in 20.4 above, is available from the TRRL to help to perform the calculations.

20.16 References

Text Reference

1. Robertson, D I and Hunt, P B—'*A method of estimating the benefits of coordinating signals by TRANSYT and SCOOT*', Traffic Engineering and Control, Vol 23, No 11 (1982). (20.4)

2. DTp—'*Specification MCH 0010B, UTC: Notes for Guidance for Local Authorities*', DTp (1984). (20.6)

3. Rudland, P—'*Cableless Linking of Traffic Signals*', Traffic Engineering and Control, Vol 15 No 1 (1973). (20.6)

4. Bell, M C—'*A survey of the methods used to define and change signal plans in the UK*', Transport Operations Research Group (TORG) Research Report 50, University of Newcastle upon Tyne (1983). (20.9)

5. Bell, M C et al—'*Plan-Change Algorithms for Area Traffic Control Systems*', TORG Research Report 51, University of Newcastle upon Tyne (1983). (20.9)

6. DTp—*Specification MCE 0360, 'Urban Traffic Control: Functional Specification*', DTp (1984). (20.9)

7. DoE/DTp/TRRL—Report LR 888, '*User Guide to TRANSYT version 8*', DoE/DTp (1975). (20.9)

8. DoE/DTp/TRRL—Report SR 934, '*Coordinating traffic signals to reduce fuel consumption*', DoE/DTp (1980). (20.9)

9. Robertson, D I—'*Cyclic Flow Profiles*', Traffic Engineering and Control, Vol 15 No 14 (1974). (20.9)

10. DoE/DTp/TRRL—Report SR 266, '*Bus TRANSYT—a user's guide*', DoE/DTp (1977). (20.9)

11. Lowrie, P R—'*The Sydney Coordinated Adaptive Traffic System, principles and methodology algorithms*', Proceedings of IEE International Conference (1982). (20.10)

12. DoE/DTp/TRRL—Report LR 1014 '*SCOOT: a traffic-responsive method of coordinating signals*', DoE/DTp (1981). (20.10)

13. DTp/TRRL—Leaflet LF 1025, '*SCOOT—the UK traffic-responsive signal coordination system—a summary of the latest assessment surveys*', DTp (1986). (20.10)

14. Griffin, R M and Johnson, D—'*Northampton fire priority demonstration scheme—the "before" study and EVADE*', Traffic Engineering and Control, Vol 21 No 4 (1980). (20.13)

15. Mowatt, A M M and Young, A D—'*CITRAC—the first five years*', Traffic Engineering and Control, Vol 25 No 5 (1984). (20.14)

20.17 Further Information

16. Robertson, G D—'*Handling Congestion with SCOOT*', Traffic Engineering and Control, Vol 28 No 4 (Apr 1987).

17. Bell, M C and Bretherton, R D—'*Ageing of Fixed-Time traffic signal plans*', IEE 2nd International Conference on Road Traffic Control, London (1986).

18. Transportation Planning Associates—'*Report: The Evaluation of Urban Traffic Control in Worcester*', TPA (1986).

19. Chandler, M J H and Cook, D J—'*Traffic Control Studies in London: SCOOT and Bus Detection*', PTRC Proc. Annual Summer Meeting Vol p 269 pp 111–128 (1985).

20. Selby, D L and Powell, R J—'*SCOOT in Southampton*', PTRC, Proc. Annual Summer Meeting Vol p 269 pp 97–109 (1985).

21. DTp—TA 14/81, '*Procedures for the Installation of Traffic Signals and associated equipment*', DTp (1981).

22. DTp—TA 16/81, '*General Principles of Control by Traffic Signals*', DTp (1981). [Sco.114 and 115]

23. DTp—TD 7/80, '*Type Approval of Traffic Control Equipment*', DTp (1980). [Sco.113]

24. DTp—Memorandum H2/77, '*Bus Priority at traffic signals using selective detection*' (corrigendum 25/10/77), DTp (1977).

25. MoT/RRL—Report LR 253, '*TRANSYT: a traffic network study tool*', MoT, (1969).

26. Webster and Cobbe—'*Traffic Signals; Road Technical Paper 56*', HMSO (1966).

21   On-street Parking

21.1 Introduction

Drivers usually assume that they will be able to park their vehicles within a reasonable distance of their final destination, sometimes accepting that in congested areas this might involve some time searching for a space.

Drivers' personal judgements of what constitutes an acceptable place to park vary considerably in terms of location and size of space and any parking fees charged. Judgements are influenced by the purpose and urgency of the trip, the ownership of the car (eg. company owned) and personal affluence, as well as by individual attitudes and behaviour patterns.

For many journeys finding a space involves little difficulty as kerbside parking is tolerated, if not encouraged, on most urban roads. However, in the areas of highest demand such as town centres, shopping and business districts, particularly at peak times, the demand for parking space often exceeds the amount of space provided. This may be the result of deliberate restrictions on the amount of space made available, or purely as a result of circumstances in which demand for parking space exceeds supply.

21.2 The Importance of Parking Policies

A local authority's [Sco.116, NI.1] parking policy should be determined as an integral part of local transport policy and within the planning framework provided by structure plans, local plans and unitary development plans. The role of streets as channels for through traffic, local traffic and access and their non-transport functions, will all need to be considered when deciding their possible use for parking. Traffic management schemes can affect the on-street space available for parking by restricting parking facilities in order to improve road capacity or safety. Alternatively, schemes can control the use of on-street parking spaces to pursue a range of objectives such as providing space for residents or disabled persons or ensuring that a continuous turnover of parking space is made available for visitors. A variety of measures capable of producing these effects are described below.

Waiting Restrictions

Waiting restrictions and parking controls should complement each other. Restrictions can govern where and when drivers are prohibited from waiting whereas parking controls can establish places where drivers may park subject to stipulated conditions. These measures

can directly influence the volume and nature of traffic in an area. Congestion can be reduced by giving more road space to moving vehicles or by providing sufficient parking provision to avoid cruising and reversing manoeuvres by drivers searching for a parking space. The function and character of a road can be greatly affected by determining where and when different categories of vehicle are permitted to park.

21.3 Statutory Powers

The powers to control waiting and loading and to provide and charge for on-street parking are provided by the Road Traffic Regulation Act 1984 (Ref. 1), amended by the Road Traffic Regulation (Parking) Act 1986 (Ref. 2), together with their associated regulations and orders [NI.32].

Highway authorities may prohibit waiting on-street for all or part of the day and may limit the duration of any waiting permitted. Restrictions may also be applied to prevent loading/unloading. Usually, loading restrictions are only applied during peak traffic hours but they can be used more extensively if necessary. A traffic order must be made in accordance with the procedure set out in the current procedure regulations (see also Chapter 15).

Waiting and loading restrictions are very widely used in urban areas but care should be taken to ensure that they are only used where they are really needed and at times when traffic conditions justify them.

Measures of this kind are often beneficial in shopping streets and near junctions. They can also protect bus stops, allow for vehicle access to the kerb to pick up and set down passengers and allow loading and unloading to take place at the kerb during defined periods. Care should be taken to ensure that restrictions introduced incrementally over many years in response to isolated circumstances are not inconsistent with each other, as this would be confusing to motorists. For the same reason it will be beneficial to standardise on hours of operation.

21.4 Making Use of On-street Parking Space

The availability of on-street parking space can make a significant (sometimes the major) contribution to the total parking stock of an area and hence increase its attractiveness to drivers.

The amount of road space made available for parking in an area will depend on the highway authority's parking policy, which should take account of the road space required for moving vehicles, environmental considerations, the local parking demand and the extent to which parking facilities are available off-street.

Determining Demand

Parking needs for an area will need to be determined for the area in question taking account of shopping, business, delivery and servicing requirements. They will also vary with the time of day, day of week and season and the duration of stay required. Parking surveys should be carried out to determine the total parking stock and the characteristics of demand as discussed in Chapter 10.

On-street spaces are usually regarded as the most convenient places to park, particularly for those with a mobility handicap who wish to avoid walking long distances. Where there is no provision for off-street servicing, on-street loading and unloading spaces will also be required for delivery vehicles.

Determining Priorities

In busy urban areas the demand for on-street space frequently exceeds the amount which is physically available so policy decisions have to be made on how to share out the available space amongst the various groups which wish to use it. Priorities need to be established and the demands of local residents and traders are usually satisfied first, with demands for long term parking for such groups as commuters or workers being regarded as less essential. It is usually desirable to preserve a certain amount of short stay parking (less than 4 hours) for visitors to the area and a number of control measures are available to limit parking duration.

Time Limits and Charges

Time limits may be imposed and charges levied to maximise the use of space available (see also 21.10 below). This will also ensure that those who use the facilities bear the cost of their provision and maintenance. Where demand for parking exceeds supply, demand can be regulated and reduced by raising the level of the parking charges. Drivers themselves can then decide whether a particular jouney by car justifies the parking cost.

Designated Spaces

Particular kerbside areas may also be designated for use by specified individuals (eg. doctors or diplomats) or groups of people (eg. residents or disabled persons).

Charges can generally be made within schemes of this kind [NI.33].

Shared Spaces

It is also possible to designate spaces for more than one use, with or without charges. This provides a very flexible form of control in which, for example, residents exhibiting a permit might park free of charge (or with a charge) and visitors might have a time limit and/or have to pay (Refs. 2 and 3) [Sco.117, NI.33].

21.5 Resident's Parking Schemes

Residential streets on the fringes of town centres and near suburban railway stations often attract commuters, shoppers and other visitors to park for long periods. This results in local residents having difficulty in parking near their homes if they do not have private driveways or garages.

Resident's parking schemes are often introduced to assist those living in the area and make town centres and fringe areas more attractive places to live. They are particularly applicable to areas with older terraced housing where there is seldom any off-street parking available within the curtilage of the dwelling. In view of the constraints which these schemes impose on both residents and non-residents, considerable care must be taken to ensure that they are justified (see Ref. 4.) [Sco.118, NI.33].

Investigations for such schemes should consider:

- the size of the area which would need to be treated, bearing in mind the alternative locations which might be used by displaced parkers and the effects on streets just outside the area;

- the type of measure to apply (whether the scheme needs to be applied to whole streets or only short lengths of street and whether restrictions by time of day are appropriate);

- the enforcement implications resulting from the type of measure to be introduced;

- the advantages and disadvantages to residents and any inconvenience to non-residents;

- criteria for allocating permits for residents (if used); and

- how to cater for guests, servicing and emergency vehicles.

Four alternative methods of control are described in Table 21.1, together with their advantages and disadvantages.

Method	Description	Advantages	Disadvantages
Resident or permit holder only parking	Permits to park are issued with or without charge to residents	• Usually ensures that residents can park in the streets at any time, subject to total residential demand	• Inflexible • Can be over-restrictive and affect normal activities such as servicing and visitor parking • Does not necessarily guarantee residents a space
Limited waiting with exemptions (Not recommended – see DTp Circular Roads 31/74) [Sco. 118]	A traffic regulation order is made imposing waiting restrictions in the area with specific exemptions for residents	• Permits reasonable level of access for other vehicles • Sometimes preferred by the police as it reduces the number of complaints about offenders from residents	• Does not necessarily guarantee residents a space • Residents still subject to the laws of obstruction and under certain circumstances may be prosecuted • Parked vehicles on a restricted street may encourage other drivers to disregard restrictions • May be difficult to enforce
Parking places with exemption from charges (or separate charges) for residents	Parking places are designated by traffic regulation order with exemption from charges or separate permit charge for residents	• Does not remove all the kerbside parking from the on-street parking stock • Offers considerable flexibility	• Does not necessarily guarantee residents a space • Equipment costs incurred
Restriction by time of day	Waiting is limited for specific periods (for example, during a morning peak period to discourage commuter parking).	• Relatively easy to enforce • Does not impinge too heavily on normal activities	• Only effective where problems are caused by all day parking • Residents are also unable to park during the restricted periods

Table 21.1 Measures to implement resident's parking schemes [NI.2]

21.6 Controlled Parking Zones

Where it is necessary to introduce waiting and loading restrictions in all, or most, of the roads in a particular area and to combine these with designated parking spaces, it will usually be more convenient to create a Controlled Parking Zone (CPZ) which can provide a variety of different types of waiting or loading facility at designated places, whilst preventing waiting elsewhere.

CPZs require an order to designate the various parking places and the rules governing their use and a further waiting and loading restriction order covering all the parts of streets within the CPZ area which are not designated as parking spaces.

In environmentally sensitive areas it may be desirable to dispense with the use of the usual yellow line road markings and to use instead traffic signs like 'paved zone' or 'controlled parking area'. A narrow pale yellow line can also be used (see paragraph 15.5 for more details). However, any such proposals involving signs which are not prescribed in the current Traffic Signs Regulations and General Directions (Ref. 5) require the authorisation of the Secretary of State.

21.7 Parking for Disabled People

Consideration should be given to allocating the most convenient spaces for the exclusive use of people with a mobility handicap and to introducing lowered kerbs at adjacent footways in order to assist wheelchair users.

Provision for the mobility handicapped is also made under the Orange Badge Scheme whereby vehicles being used by a badge holder may park for up to two hours on yellow lines, without time limit where others may park only for limited periods and without charge or time limit at parking meters (see also Chapters 15.6, 24.13, and Refs. 6, 7 and 8) [Sco.119].

In cases of special hardship holders of Orange Badges may apply to the local highway authority for a designated disabled person's space outside their home or business premises. If such a space is provided it does not give an exclusive right to park and will be available for the use of other badge holders.

21.8 Parking for Other Categories of Road User

Loading/Unloading

Consideration should be given to providing other designated spaces to meet particular needs. For example, loading bays may be necessary along streets with commercial premises and special provision may also be required at places where cash, mail or other valuables are delivered or collected (see also 15.3).

Medical Practitioners/Diplomats

Medical practitioners with residences or surgeries in busy areas may also need an exclusive space and some parking spaces in central London are reserved for the use of diplomats (Ref. 9 and Chapter 15.10) [Sco.120, NI.33].

Buses and Coaches

Vehicles used to provide public transport services often have a need to wait for extended periods, apart from the usual requirement for stopping places for picking up and setting down passengers. In some cases it may be appropriate to designate particular places for use as bus stands to serve as crew change, terminus or schedule adjustment points.

Special facilities (preferably off-street) should be provided near places attracting many tourists or visitors and on-street coach meters may be appropriate in some circumstances (see Plate 21.1).

Each case should be treated on its merits and useful guidance is provided in the ALBES Code of Practice (Ref. 10).

21.9 Layout of Parking Spaces

Careful consideration must be given to the siting of any on-street parking places to take account of the following points:

● to avoid creating a road safety hazard by obstructing visibility near bends, junctions or places where significant numbers of pedestrians cross the road;

● to create suitable crossing points for pedestrians to avoid the inconvenience and danger caused by long unbroken rows of parked vehicles;

● to avoid impeding the free flow of traffic at places where this is important to the role of the street in question;

● to maintain reasonable and adequate access to premises including access for loading and unloading, particularly where there are security considerations (eg. for mail or bank deliveries); and

● to avoid obstructing access to fire hydrants, interfering with traffic detection loops etc.

Individual bays should be large enough to permit most drivers to park reasonably quickly, avoiding any danger or significant interruption to traffic flow. If individual bays are not marked, the number of cars that can park in a length of road may be greater than if it were

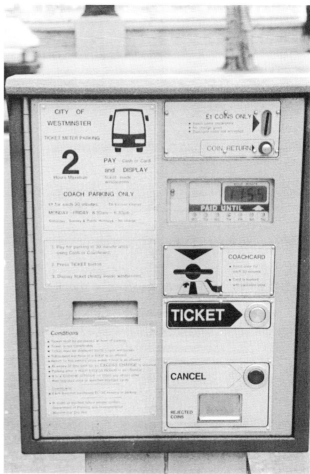

Plate 21.1 Meters for coach parking

marked out. If there is a charge for use of a particular bay then the bay must be marked.

Size and Position of Bays

Parking bays can be parallel to the kerb or angled to it. Typical layouts for waiting and parking controls applied to different categories of road are indicated in Figure 21.1. The minimum size for a bay parallel to the kerb should be 1.7 m in width and 4.5 m in length but variations up to 2.5 m and 6.0 m respectively are common to allow for different site conditions and sizes of vehicles. Wider bays should be provided where the space is for the use of those with a mobility handicap. In addition there may be some local need for motor-cycle parking (see also Refs. 5 and 11) [NI.34].

Wide streets give scope for both moving and stationary vehicles to be accommodated. Making streets one-way to improve capacity can often allow additional parking spaces to be provided. Layouts should minimise environmental intrusion; for example by arranging parking on one side of a street only or using landscaping to hide parked vehicles.

Clear Road Widths for Traffic

The extent to which it is necessary to preserve a clear width of carriageway for traffic flow depends upon the type of road in question and some suggested widths are given below for locations remote from road junctions where some disruption to traffic movement may be tolerated:—

On **main traffic routes** (with 24 hour flows in excess of 5000 vehicles) and roads carrying HGV's with 3 or more axles or a frequent two way bus flow, the minimum clear running width should preferably be 7 metres with 6 metres as the absolute minimum.

On **lesser traffic routes** (with 24 hour flows between 2000 and 5000 vehicles) the preferred minimum clear running width is 6 metres, with 5 metres as the absolute minimum.

On **minor roads** (with 24 hour flows between 500 and 2000 vehicles) the preferred minimum clear running width is 6 metres with 4.5 metres as the absolute minimum.

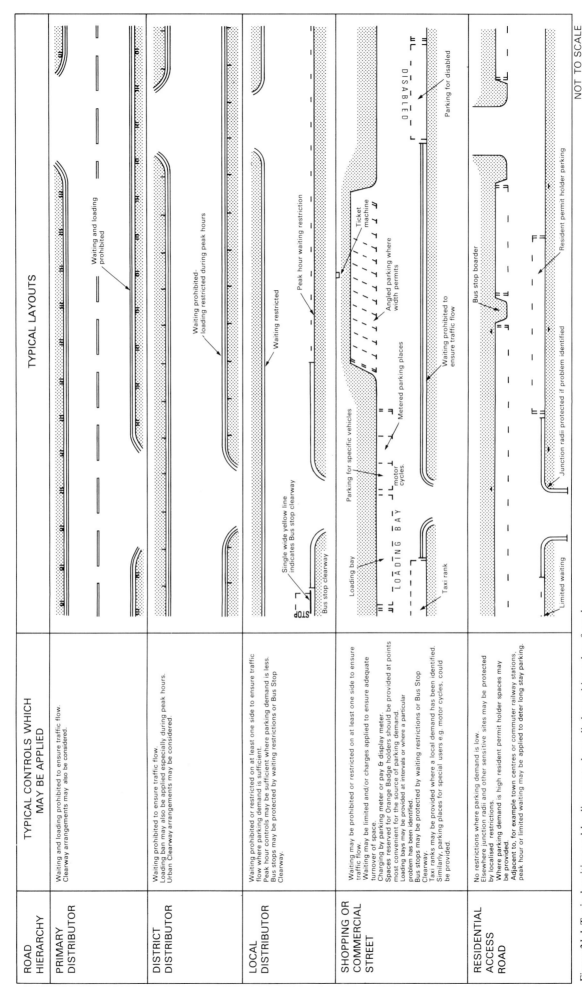

ROAD HIERARCHY	TYPICAL LAYOUTS	TYPICAL CONTROLS WHICH MAY BE APPLIED
PRIMARY DISTRIBUTOR		Waiting and loading prohibited to ensure traffic flow. Clearway arrangements may also be considered.
DISTRICT DISTRIBUTOR		Waiting prohibited to ensure traffic flow. Loading ban may also be applied especially during peak hours. Urban Clearway arrangements may be considered.
LOCAL DISTRIBUTOR		Waiting prohibited or restricted on at least one side to ensure traffic flow where parking demand is sufficient. Peak hour controls may be sufficient where parking demand is less. Bus stops may be protected by waiting restrictions or Bus Stop Clearway.
SHOPPING OR COMMERCIAL STREET		Waiting may be prohibited or restricted on at least one side to ensure traffic flow. Waiting may be limited and/or charges applied to ensure adequate turnover of space. Charging by parking meter or pay & display meter. Spaces reserved for Orange Badge holders should be provided at points most convenient for the source of parking demand. Loading bays may be provided at intervals or where a particular problem has been identified. Bus stops may be protected by waiting restrictions or Bus Stop Clearway. Taxi ranks may be provided where a local demand has been identified. Similarly, parking places for special users e.g. motor cycles, could be provided.
RESIDENTIAL ACCESS ROAD		No restrictions where parking demand is low. Elsewhere junction radii and other sensitive sites may be protected by localised restrictions. Where parking demand is high resident permit holder spaces may be provided. Adjacent to, for example town centres or commuter railway stations, peak hour or limited waiting may be applied to deter long stay parking.

NOT TO SCALE

Figure 21.1 Typical waiting and loading controls applied to a hierarchy of roads

176

Method	Advantages	Disadvantages
Parking meters	<ul><li>Enforcement straightforward.</li><li>Help impose physical parking discipline.</li><li>Generate revenue.</li><li>Useful for short stay.</li><li>Help match demand to supply.</li><li>Potential of electronic versions.</li></ul>	<ul><li>Relatively expensive to install, operate or adjust to new charges.</li><li>Environmentally intrusive.</li><li>Cannot be used to favour specific drivers.</li></ul>
Ticket-dispensing machines (Pay and Display meters)	<ul><li>Enforcement relatively easy.</li><li>Cheaper and less intrusive than meters.</li><li>Suitable for short and long stay.</li><li>Potential for separate residents' tariffs.</li></ul>	<ul><li>Drivers have to walk to meter.</li><li>Extra signing required.</li></ul>
Parking discs	<ul><li>Relatively cheap to operate.</li><li>Environmentally unobtrusive.</li></ul>	<ul><li>Enforcement difficult.</li><li>Generate no revenue.</li><li>Can discriminate against visitors.</li></ul>
Parking permits/Season tickets	<ul><li>Enforcement easy.</li><li>Availability can be restricted to specific types of user.</li><li>Generate revenue.</li><li>Can be issued for varying time periods.</li></ul>	<ul><li>No control over duration.</li><li>Fraud possible as holders can allow others to use them.</li><li>Fraudulent requests.</li><li>Administration effort required.</li></ul>
Pre-purchased cards cancelled and displayed by user	<ul><li>Enforcement relatively easy.</li><li>Cheap to implement and operate.</li><li>Environmentally unobtrusive.</li><li>Generate revenue.</li><li>Price can be changed easily.</li></ul>	<ul><li>Risk of fraud.</li><li>Need for outlets to sell – reduces income.</li></ul>
Limited waiting	<ul><li>Cheap to install and modify.</li></ul>	<ul><li>Enforcement very difficult.</li><li>Markings and signs can be environmentally intrusive.</li><li>Generates no revenue.</li><li>Need substantial patrolling.</li></ul>
Specific vehicle priorities (e.g. mobility handicapped, motorcyclists, car pools)	<ul><li>Spaces can be marked.</li></ul>	<ul><li>Enforcement can be difficult.</li><li>Permits need to be displayed when vehicles used in a specific way.</li></ul>

Table 21.2 Control devices and systems for on-street parking

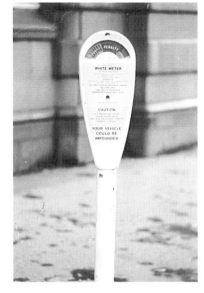

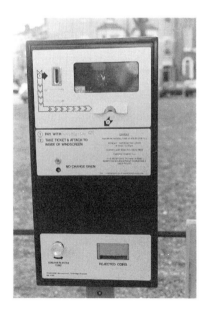

Plate 21.2 Typical meter head and 'pay and display' systems

Source: P Ostler (TRRL), S Sexton Esq, Newcastle City Council

178

In very **minor residential roads**, short culs-de-sac, etc., (with 24 hour flows less than 500 vehicles) the clear running width should be at least 3.5 metres. This does not permit the free flow of two-directional traffic but it is sufficent to allow access for emergency and service vehicles.

21.10 Devices for Control and Collection of Charges

Any device used for collecting charges for on-street parking must be approved by the relevant Secretary of State and should:

- be reasonably economical to install and maintain in relation to estimated revenue;
- be simple to use and easily understood by drivers;
- be secure and reliable;
- deter fraud and assist enforcement;
- comply with current regulations; and
- be flexible enough to allow the charges and time periods to be readily adjusted.

General approvals are issued by the relevant Secretary of State to cover individual categories of device conforming with appropriate British Standards. Special approval may be given for equipment which does not comply with the General Approval; for example, to allow experiments with novel or non-standard devices.

A number of control devices and systems for on-street spaces are listed in Table 21.2 together with some of their advantages and disadvantages. Plate 21.2 illustrates a number of the meter head systems that are currently available.

21.11 Enforcement

The present system of excess charging at on-street spaces and the issuing of fixed penalty tickets is only effective when adequate manpower resources are available for enforcement. Where resources are limited, they may best be concentrated on locations which suffer most from indiscriminate parking, like major traffic routes.

The process of enforcement was made more effective in 1986 when unpaid fixed penalty notices became automatically registered as fines with a 50% surcharge enforceable through the courts (Ref. 12) [NI.7].

Although this system is labour intensive it is assisted by the use of computerised driver and vehicle licence records held by the DVLC at Swansea. The use of traffic wardens can release the more highly trained police manpower for other duties.

The various types of enforcement action and their relative advantages and disadvantages are given in Table 21.3.

Vehicle Removals

Both the police and local authorities have powers to remove broken down, abandoned or illegally parked vehicles from the street [NI.35]. Local authorities are, however, restricted in removing illegally parked vehicles to those at parking places designated by an order (they can also remove vehicles parked contrary to the conditions of an order from off-street parking places). The police have powers to remove from the street vehicles which are either parked in contravention of a parking or waiting order or are parked in a dangerous or obstructive manner.

Penalty	Advantages	Disadvantages
Fixed penalty	• Relatively inexpensive • Some deterrent value	• Only effective if followed up
Removal of vehicles (Towing away)	• Moderate deterrent value • Payment of fee unavoidable • Useful when vehicle causing obstruction	• Relatively expensive • Time consuming • Alienates public opinion • Police must keep vehicle safe and secure
Wheel clamping	• High deterrent value • Cheaper than towing away • Less time consuming and disruptive than towing away • Visible (publicity effect) • Payment of fee unavoidable • More productive than vehicle removal for high intensity enforcement	• Not effective in dealing with vehicle causing obstruction • Difficulties in areas where vandalism and theft prevalent

Table 21.3 Types of penalty imposed for illegal parking

Wheel Clamping

Wheel clamping (see Plate 21.3) is currently available only in areas designated by the Secretary of State for Transport [NI.2] but any highway authority may apply for particular areas to be designated. If approved in principle this requires a Parliamentary Order (Statutory Instrument). Advice on the suitability of particular areas for wheel clamping can be obtained from the Department of Transport but this usually requires that the area be within a controlled parking zone, that adequate enforcement resources can be made available and that the scheme is supported by the police.

Plate 21.3 A Wheel clamp in use in central London   Source: TRRL

Local Authority Parking Attendants

Local authorities [NI.1] can employ their own staff to enforce the conditions of designated off-street and on-street parking places. Their powers are more limited than those of traffic wardens. They can issue excess charge notices at designated parking places but cannot issue fixed penalty notices.

21.12 Pavement Parking

Pavement parking causes problems. Parked vehicles obstruct pedestrians and are a hazard to disabled, blind and elderly people. Heavy vehicles can damage pavements and underground services.

It is already illegal to park on the pavement where yellow line waiting restrictions operate, or if the vehicle is a heavy commercial one, or if the vehicle is left in a dangerous or obstructive position. It is also an offence under Section 72 of the Highways Act 1835 to drive upon the footway.

If and when the provisions of the Road Traffic Act 1972, as amended by Section 7 of the Road Traffic Act 1974 (Refs. 13 and 14), are brought into force, all parking on verges, central reservations and footways in urban areas will be prohibited, save where exemptions are applied. These exemptions would relate either to certain classes of vehicle (under regulations made by the Secretary of State for Transport [Sco.121]) or to specific roads (as determined by the local authority).

Because the introduction of these national measures has been delayed by shortage of police and local authority resources, London, Worcester and Hereford have taken private act powers to ban pavement parking. Only the London ban has so far been introduced (in 1985) although some other authorities have used traffic regulation orders under the RTRA 1984 to achieve the same end.

When contemplating the introduction of such bans it is important for local authorities to consider their wider effects and the availability of alternative legal parking facilities, especially in older areas where off-street parking space may be limited.

The use of suitably designed bollards can also provide an effective physical means of preventing vehicles mounting footpath areas (see Colour Plate 19.4).

21.13 References

Text References

1. Road Traffic Regulation Act 1984, HMSO (1984).   (21.3)

2. Road Traffic Regulation (Parking) Act 1986, HMSO (1986).   (21.3, 21.4)

3. DTp—Circular Roads 6/86, *'Road Traffic Regulation (Parking) Act'*, DTp (1986). [Wa.20]   (21.4)

4. DTp—Circular Roads 21/74, *'Resident Parking Schemes'*, DTp (1974). [Sco.118, Wa.21]   (21.5)

5. DTp—*Traffic Signs Regulations and General Directions'*, Statutory Instrument 1981 No 859, HMSO (1981).   (21.6, 21.9)

6. DTp Circular 4/82. *'Orange Badge Scheme of Parking Concessions for Disabled and Blind People'*, (1982). [Sco.122]   (21.7)

7. DTp—Circular Roads 2/84, *'Orange Badge Scheme of Parking Concessions for Disabled and Blind People*, DTp (1984). [Sco.119, Wa.22]   (21.7)

8 DTp—Circular Roads 6/84, *'Parking for Disabled People'*, DTp (1984). [Sco.119, Wa.23]   (21.7)

9. DTp—Circular Roads 22/75 *'Car Parking for the Medical Profession'*, DTp (1975). [Sco.120, Wa.24]   (21.8)

10. ALBES/DTp—*'Highways and Traffic Management in London: A Code of Practice'*, HMSO (1986).   (21.8)

11. DTp—*'Traffic Signs Manual'*, Chapter 5, HMSO (1980).   (21.9)

12. Transport Act 1982, HMSO (1982).   (21.11)

13. Road Traffic Act 1972, HMSO (1972).   (21.12)

14. Road Traffic Act 1974, HMSO (1974).   (21.12)

21.14 Further Information

15. DTp—*'Tourist Coaches in London—Parking and Access'*, DTp (1986).

16. DTp—*'Pavement Parking'*, Consultation Paper, DTp (1986).

17. Removal and Disposal of Vehicles Regulations, Statutory Instrument 1986 No 183, HMSO (1986).

18. Wheelclamping Orders, Statutory Instruments 1986 Nos 1224 and 1225, HMSO (1986). [Wa.25]

19. DTp—Circular Roads 2/85, *'Parking Meters: General Approval'*, DTp (1985).

20. DTp/TRRL—PA13 91/86 *'Parking in Central London—Survey Autumn 1985'*, DTp (1986).

21. DoE/DTp/TRRL—Report LR 1136, *'The effects of wheel clamping in central London'*, DoE/DTp (1984).

22. DTp—*'Door to Door: Guide to Transport for Disabled People'*, DTp (1982).

23. Cima, B and Hildebrand, L—*'Evaluation of the Washington D C Parking Enforcement Programme—Final Report'*, UMTA-Ma-06-0049-USDoT (1982).

24. OECD Road Research Group—*'Evaluation of urban parking systems'*, OECD Paris (1980).

25. DTp—Circular Roads 19/78 and Local Government (Miscellaneous Provisions) Act 1976, Section 37 (1978). [Wa.26]

26. The Control of Parking in Goods Vehicle Loading Areas Orders (Procedure) (England and Wales) Regulations 1986, SI 1986 No 181 (1986).

27. Fixed Penalty (Procedure) Regulations 1977, Statutory Instrument 1977 No 1711, HMSO (1977).

28. The Road Traffic (Owner Liability) Regulations 1975, Statutory Instrument 1975 No 324, HMSO (1975). [Sco.126]

29. DTp—Circular Roads 21/74, *'Definition of Goods Vehicles in Parking Place Orders'*, DTp (1974). [Sco.124, Wa.27]

30. DTp—Circular Roads 22/74, *'Parking Meters and Parking Control Equipment: General Approval'*, DTp (1974). [Sco.123, Wa.28]

31. DTp—Circular Roads 53/72, 'Disc Parking', DTp (1972). [Wa.29]

32. British Standards:
    BS 4684/1971 Clockwork Parking Meters
    BS 4469/1973 Car Parking Control Equipment
    BS 6571/1985 (Part I). Specification for Coin Operated Clockwork Parking Meters.

33. DoE—*'Lorry Parking, The Report of the Working Party'*, DoE (1971).

34. Functions of Traffic Wardens Order 1970, Statutory Instrument 1970 No 1958, HMSO (1970). [Sco.125]

35. University of Edinburgh Research Unit/Central Council for the Disabled, *'Planning for Disabled People in the Urban Environment'*, University of Edinburgh (1969).

36. Vienna Convention on Diplomatic Relations (Cmnd 1368) HMSO (1961).

22 Measures for Influencing Vehicle Speed

22.1 Introduction

Measures for influencing the speed of vehicles fall into two categories;

- speed limits imposed by statute, regulation or order, including those which limit the permissible speed of travel by certain types of vehicle (eg. commercial vehicles, caravans) and

- physical measures to control vehicle speeds, with or without regulations.

22.2 Speed Limits

Powers to restrict vehicle speeds are provided in Part VI of the Road Traffic Regulation Act 1984 (Ref. 1) and Schedule 6 of that Act defines maximum speeds for vehicles of certain classes (see also 15.10) [NI.36]. Most roads in urban areas are subject to a 30 mph (50 kph) limit, but some roads may have higher limits depending upon local conditions. Advice on speed limits is contained in Department of Transport Circulars (Refs. 2 and 3) [Sco.127].

Speed limits are often the subject of intense local debate and pressure, with opposing groups taking different views on a particular issue. For example, local residents often wish to lower speed limits near their homes or schools whereas people passing through an area may press for higher limits, particularly where the road appears to be of a high standard.

Typically, consideration is given to:

- lowering a higher limit;

- raising a lower limit (often more difficult in terms of public reaction); or

- applying limits of less than 30 mph in particular areas (subject to the consent of the Secretary of State—in practice rarely given).

Requests are also occasionally made for the application of specific limits at particular times, rather than a general limit valid at all times, but this type of measure is not permitted under existing legislation in Britain. However, legislation has recently been enacted in the Netherlands and Denmark to permit speed limits of only 30 kph (18 mph) in some existing residential areas.

22.3 Selecting Appropriate Speed Limits

Before deciding to change an existing speed limit, the appropriate authority (see Ref. 1) must consider all relevant factors. The police view is important and the Chief Officer of Police must be consulted before any order is made. The characteristics of the road, such as its alignment, the level and type of frontage activity and the accident rate, must be taken into account along with the prevailing speed of vehicles. The measured 85th percentile speed (see Chapter 10) is used for this purpose and this provides one of the principal indicators of what is likely to be a realistic speed limit and one which is observed in practice. However, in urban areas other characteristics of the road will also need to be taken into account after selecting the most appropriate limit.

Speed limits for new roads should be determined at the design stage taking account of hierarchical role, frontage characteristics and intended function. The design standards used should be appropriate for the expected speed of travel (see also Chapter 34).

Speed limits are frequently not observed by motorists when they appear unsuited to the character of the road and its environment. In these circumstances they may require extensive enforcement and it may be necessary to introduce physical measures to encourage lower speeds. An unrealistically low speed limit may create enforcement difficulties for the police and should be avoided. In practice raising an unrealistically low limit can result in a slight lowering of speeds, better compliance and a reduction in accidents.

Frequent changes of speed limit should also be avoided except when transitional lengths of 40 or 50 mph may be appropriate between lengths where national limits and lower urban limits apply. Maximum limits should not be applied to lengths of road of less than half a mile and a series of short lengths with successively lower speed limits approaching the boundary of an urban area is to be avoided.

22.4 Use of Minimum Speed Limits

Minimum speed limits can be introduced to maintain traffic flow in special circumstances such as on sensitive structures (eg. bridges or tunnels) where standing loads might cause difficulties. In practice they are rarely used.

22.5 Physical Measures to Reduce Speed

22.3 above referred to the use of design standards commensurate with intended vehicle speeds in the design of new roads. On existing roads, a variety of

Physical measure	Description	Use
Road humps	Single hump or a series extending across the carriageway at right angles to the direction of flow.	Best used as part of an area-wide scheme and especially appropriate on access roads where layout encourages speed. Should not be used on major routes. Subject to extensive criteria.
Bar markings	Standard marking is 90 yellow transverse lines applied over about 400 metres, the spacing between which progressively reduces towards the hazard.	On approaches to roundabouts on major routes. Subject to extensive criteria.
Rumble areas	Continuous length of carriageway with coarsely textured surface designed to produce a rumble which increases with speed within vehicles driving over it.	In urban areas but consider noise nuisance if adjacent to residential development.
Rumble strips Jiggle bars	A series of lateral bands of surface treatment designed to cause intermittent noise within vehicles driving over them. Variable spacing and dimensions.	For use on roads with high flow levels. More applicable to local distributors than access roads. More effective than a rumble area but consider noise nuisance if adjacent to residential development.
Road narrowing	The aim is to break up long straight sections of road by alternate extension to each side of the road and by the addition of refuges and turning bays.	Can be continuous over a long length or at a point. Check visibility, pattern of pedestrian movement, parking provision and passing bays.
Junction modifications	Reduction of kerb radii, change of junction type and change of markings.	At isolated junctions or as part of an area-wide scheme.
Shared surfaces	Elimination of a separate footway and creation of a kerbless profile. Use of different surface textures and colours, landscaping and planting.	Access roads within residential areas. City shopping centres. Use in conjunction with other measures.

Table 22.1 Physical measures for controlling vehicle speed

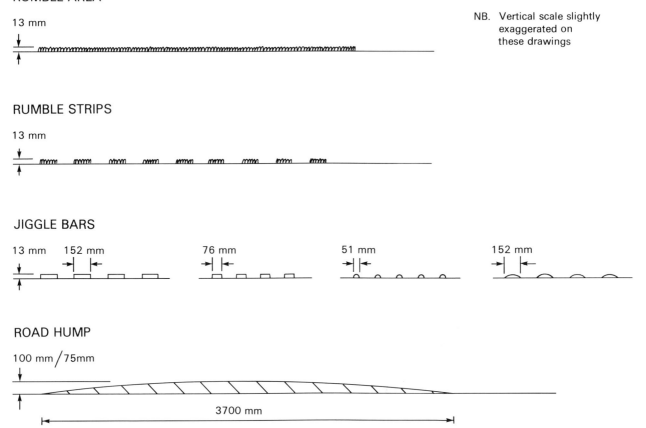

RUMBLE AREA

13 mm

NB. Vertical scale slightly
exaggerated on
these drawings

RUMBLE STRIPS

13 mm

JIGGLE BARS

13 mm   152 mm   76 mm   51 mm   152 mm

ROAD HUMP

100 mm / 75mm

3700 mm

Figure 22.1 Examples of physical devices to control speed

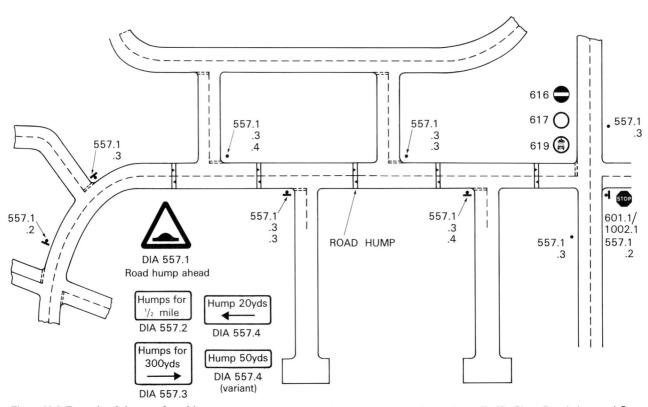

DIA 557.1
Road hump ahead

557.1
.3
.4

557.1
.3
.3

557.1
.3

557.1
.3

557.1
.2

557.1
.3
.3

557.1
.3
.4

557.1
.3
.3

ROAD HUMP

557.1
.3

616
617
619

601.1/
1002.1
557.1
.2

Humps for
½ mile
DIA 557.2

Humps for
300yds
DIA 557.3

Hump 20yds
DIA 557.4

Hump 50yds
DIA 557.4
(variant)

Figure 22.2 Example of the use of road humps

NB. Diagram numbers refer to Traffic Signs Regulations and General Directions 1981.

Plate 22.1 Use of road humps
Source: 'The Surveyor'

Plate 22.2 Use of rumble strips
(textured surfacing)
Source: Hampshire County Council

Plate 22.3 Use of jiggle bars
Source: S Sexton Esq

Plate 22.4 Use of road narrowing and central
islands to reduce speed in Germany
Source: C Hass-Klan Esq

physical measures may be necessary to reduce vehicle speeds to a level more suited to the roads' physical characteristics. They are broadly of two types; those that involve changes to the highway geometry, such as road narrowing or junction modification; and those that vary the carriageway surface to improve driver awareness of vehicle speed and thus inhibit speeding (eg. rumble strips, road humps). A description of the most commonly used measures is given in Table 22.1 and in Figures 22.1 and 22.2 and examples of their use are illustated in Plates 22.1 to 22.4.

N.B. Some of these measures have legal implications and reference should be made to the appropriate Department of Transport Advice Notes and Circulars listed in 22.7.

22.6 References

Text Reference

1. Road Traffic Regulation Act 1984, HMSO (1984). (22.2)

2. DTp—Circular Roads 1/80, *'Local Speed Limits'*, DTp (1980). [Sco.127, Wa.30] (22.2)

3. DTp—Circular Roads 4/83, *'Speed Limits'*, DTp (1983). [Sco.127, Wa.31] (22.2)

22.7 Further Information

4. DTp—TA -/87, *'Signing and Siting of Road Humps'*, DTp (1987). [Sco.129]

5. DTp—Circular Roads 8/86, *'Road Humps'*, DTp (1986). [Sco.129, Wa.32]

6. DTp—TD 6/79, *'Transverse Yellow Bar Markings at Roundabouts'*, DTp (1979). [Sco.128]

7. DTp—Circular Roads 17/78. *'Transverse Yellow Bar Markings at Roundabouts'*, DTp (1978). [Sco.128, Wa.33]

23 Measures for Limiting the Amount of Road Traffic

23.1 Introduction

A number of transport policy options were explained in Chapters 7 and 9 demonstrating that it is sometimes desirable to control the level of traffic in an area, or using a particular route, in order to achieve the desired balance between accessibility, traffic movement and satisfactory environmental conditions.

Some traffic management measures (eg. junction control or bus priority) can affect patterns of trip making but they are usually aimed at specific locations and their effectiveness in restraining overall traffic levels is usually very limited.

Other measures, usually known as traffic restraint (or demand management) techniques, can be designed to encourage trip makers to respond to imposed conditions in specific ways, for example by:

● changing their mode of travel;
● changing their time of travel;
● using a different route;
● making the trip to an alternative destination; or
● not making the trip at all.

A reduction in the level of traffic is not usually seen as an end in itself and should be allied with other clearly defined objectives such as the pedestrianisation of a major shopping street, or improvements for essential traffic requiring access to an area.

Very few restraint schemes, other than those involving some form of parking control, have been implemented in Britain but a number of more radical measures have been attempted in other countries such as Singapore, Hong Kong and Bangkok (see Ref. 1).

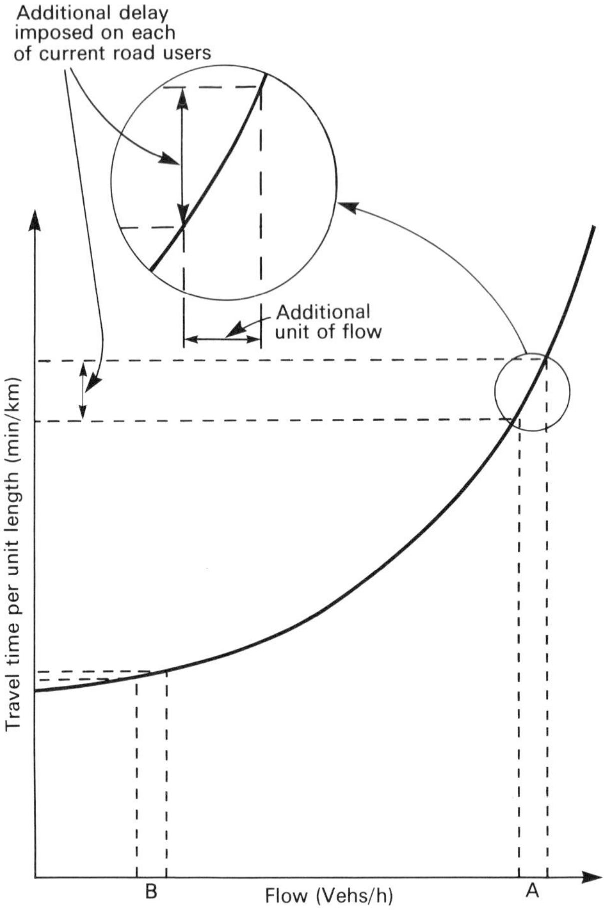

23.2 The Objectives and Effects of Traffic Restraint

Traffic Flow Efficiency

In congested conditions, each additional vehicle in a traffic stream adds to the total time spent and costs incurred by those already there. This is illustrated in Figure 23.1 which represents a typical travel time versus flow relationship. When choosing to make a trip each road user usually perceives only his or her own travel time and not the additional delay that the presence of their vehicle imposes on others. Thus, as traffic flows increase the overall costs of resources like time and fuel increase disproportionately more.

There are also other factors to be considered and the following objectives are those usually associated with

Note: An additional user at high flow levels (A) generates much more delay to current road users than the additional traveller at low flow levels (B).

Figure 23.1 Travel time versus flow relationship (on a congested link)

traffic management and do not include other more wide ranging objectives such as, for example, the stimulation of public transport as an end in itself.

Effects of different types of vehicle: some vehicles impose greater costs than others because of their size or performance characteristics, whilst others are more efficient as carriers of people because their occupancy is higher per unit area of road space occupied. For these reasons some restraint schemes aim to distinguish between low and high efficiency vehicles measured by the number of people carried (eg. an occupancy of four people or more gives exemption from a charge).

Effects in different areas: analysis of potential restraint schemes should cover complete areas to identify which would benefit most.

Variations in travel time: some people place a greater value on achieving consistency in travel times than achieving an average time saving. This is particularly noticeable with public transport passengers who are adversely affectecd by irregularity in bus arrival time.

Theoretically, traffic restraint measures should aim to ensure that road users perceive the costs they inflict on all other road travellers by making a payment of an appropriate magnitude to cover total delays and environmental costs. In this way the user will only undertake a journey if what is gained from it at least equals the disbenefits to the community imposed by it (but see also 'Equity' below). However, this approach also means that those who cannot afford the 'full' cost of the journey are prevented from undertaking it, regardless of the value of the trip to the community or the individual.

Environmental Protection

Traffic imposes many environmental disbenefits (see Chapters 12 and 19) and restraint measures can reduce them. It is important to identify particular environmental problems because each will require a different approach. For example, noise and pedestrian/vehicle conflicts are best tackled by reducing all traffic in the risk areas, whereas concern over vibration and visual intrusion might require an emphasis on restraint of commercial vehicle movements.

Land Use Planning

Traffic restraint may assist in revitalising inner city areas, particularly when it allows pedestrianisation schemes to be implemented.

The question of traffic restraint in inner city areas does, however, produce a variety of opposing arguments. On the one hand a poor environment with dense traffic noise and fumes is blamed for loss of trade and patronage of local shops and business, whilst on the other hand, lack of accessibility for vehicles is also cited as a reason for commercial decay of retail outlets.

Clearly then, restraint schemes must be carefully designed to retain essential traffic whilst deflecting that which makes no local contribution or has no intrinsic reason to be in the area. This is not easy to achieve as the mechanisms of restraint are often fairly crude and may, for example, rely simply on an ability to pay.

Equity

It has been explained that traffic restraint is intended to achieve a re-distribution of costs and benefits between road users and the population in congested areas. A more equitable distribution can be obtained by:

- restraining those who impose a net burden on vehicle users as a group;

- protecting space-efficient and essential vehicles from congestion (eg. buses, emergency and service vehicles);
- reducing the environmental impact of traffic on residents and pedestrians; and
- reducing the amount of through traffic.

Although these 'equity' arguments are used as the major justification for traffic restraint, equity issues can also be used against restraint proposals.

The most frequent criticism is of the adverse effects of fiscal controls on lower income car users, but it is important to note that inequities can also arise through transfering traffic problems to other areas, imposing regulatory controls affecting people who have no travel alternatives and inflicting time penalties on those who place a high value on time savings.

It is therefore necessary to identify the full range of equity issues arising from a restraint scheme and to consider its effects separately by user type, location, income level and journey purpose (or need), on both road users and other groups in the community.

23.3 Scheme Design and Assessment

Before implementing any scheme involving traffic restraint it is important to assess whether its objectives are sufficiently important to justify its various effects and whether restraint is the most efficient and widely acceptable means of achieving them.

It is also important to ensure that the costs of implementing and operating the scheme do not exceed the projected cost savings and that benefits in one area are not achieved by transfering the problem elsewhere.

Forecasting the Effects of Restraint Schemes

It is often difficult to estimate what level of traffic restraint is required to achieve particular objectives. For example, the 'Zone and Collar' scheme implemented in Nottingham (see Ref. 2) aimed at a 10% reduction in traffic based on the difference between congested October peak flows and less congested August flows; although in practice it failed to achieve it.

In Inner London, target traffic reductions of up to 50 per cent were based on the objective of achieving environmental improvements without new road building (Ref. 3).

In some cases, assessments have been based on transport demand models, as was the case in Central London where a target reduction of 1/3 in peak traffic was based on an estimate of the proportion of car users likely to switch routes or modes as a result of introducing charges for a supplementary licence.

Alternatively, the most appropriate level of restraint could be decided as a result of site trials in which the restraint penalty is gradually increased until the required traffic conditions are obtained. This approach was used in the traffic restraint scheme imposed in Singapore where the final level for the supplementary licence fee was fixed after an initial period with an experimental fee.

Summary of Design Principles

Effectiveness: Restraint should be effective in its aim which may be reducing congestion and environmental intrusion. It must bear directly on those journeys which contribute to perceived problems, or at least on a sufficiently large proportion of them for its effects not to be undermined. It also requires a restraint penalty large enough to produce the desired effects.

Flexibility: As the precise effects of restraint techniques are likely to be somewhat uncertain, it is important that a restraint scheme is flexible so that any over or under restraint can be corrected as and when necessary.

Selectivity: Selectivity is crucial as restraint should always bear most heavily on those journeys which cause the greatest problems whilst affecting essential or efficient trip making least. Nor should it impose hardship on those who have little alternative in terms of choice of route, mode, time or destination.

Simplicity: Controls need to be simple for users and for operators. Users need to be able to understand the controls and the response expected of them. The operator needs a method which is within his legal powers and is inexpensive to introduce and administer whilst making fraud or violation difficult.

Containment: The scheme should be largely self-contained in its effects. It should avoid transferring congestion or environmental intrusion to other areas or times and avoid imposing greater problems for other modes or for those not travelling. Some of these effects (particularly the changes in parking location, time of travel and car occupancy) will be difficult to predict. Equally, it should avoid creating future problems by, for example, causing unwanted land use changes.

It can be seen that there is likely to be considerable difficulty in devising a scheme which can satisfactorily meet all of the above conditions and compromises have been necessary on those schemes which have been implemented. A decision to implement such a scheme will ultimately be made at the political level where the potential advantages will need to be weighed against any unwanted effects.

23.4 The Measures Available

Methods of restraint can be categorised in the following ways;

- schemes which affect the ownership or keeping of a vehicle (either generally or in specific areas),

- schemes which affect the destination of a journey (generally involving some form of parking control), and

- schemes which affect the usage of a vehicle.

Controls on Ownership and Keeping of Vehicles

It is useful to draw a distinction between controls on ownership and keeping of vehicles (although the legal definitions of these terms differ from country to country). In this chapter, ownership refers to vehicles owned by residents or businesses in a particular area, whether or not the vehicles are actually garaged in that area. 'Keeping' refers to the garaging of vehicles in the area concerned irrespective of their ownership.

The difficulty with measures which control vehicle ownership and/or keeping is that they do not necessarily affect those journeys that contribute to congestion or which are regarded as unnecessary; neither do they provide alternatives for those who are affected.

Controls on Journey Destination

Most studies in Britain in the 1960s proposed parking control as the most readily available means of traffic restraint because of its effects on the attractiveness of the destination for car drivers.

Parking control measures can:

- be physical controls imposed by removal of existing spaces or restriction on provision of new spaces;

- be regulatory controls imposed by confining parking to selected locations and by allocating spaces for designated users (eg. residents and the disabled);

- control the times space is available and the duration of each stay;

- control the use of parking meters and other systems for imposing restraint by price.

Privately Controlled Off-Street Parking: Control of on-street parking alone leaves a major loophole as a means of restraint, as drivers can avoid the controls by parking in privately owned and controlled off-street spaces. Typically in urban areas, on-street space provides between a tenth and a third of all non-residential parking stock; the remainder includes publicly and privately operated public car parks and private parking associated with commercial development.

It is estimated that between 30 and 60 per cent of parking space in urban areas is outside local authority control and this substantially reduces the effectiveness of any form of parking restraint. Naturally, these percentages will vary from area to area.

Effects on Through Traffic: Parking controls cannot affect through traffic, which often accounts for a third of the traffic entering city centres and it has been argued that general growth in traffic can nullify the benefits achieved by restraint on public parking.

The effects of parking restrictions may therefore be limited unless private parking and through traffic can be controlled; or in areas where they do not create significant problems.

Peripheral Effects of Parking Control: The main adverse effect of parking controls can be the transfer of parking demand to fringe areas, resulting in the displacement of both congestion and environmental intrusion. Little is known of the distances which drivers are prepared to walk to avoid parking controls or their effects on safety, but in practice it may be necessary to extend on-street controls for up to 1 km beyond the main target area.

Parking controls can also lead to transfer of trips to other destinations and in turn to the decline of retail and business activities (see also Chapter 21 and 30).

Controls on Moving Vehicles

Controls on moving vehicles can be introduced in various ways including physical measures, controls on the level and location of congestion, use of regulations and fiscal means.

Physical controls: Physical controls on moving vehicles include those traffic regulations which deny access to specific streets or routes. A wide range of environmental management measures fall into this category (see also Chapter 19) but most have too little effect on routeing to be considered as restraint measures in themselves. However, traffic cell systems and mazes, which result in re-routeing over wide areas, can be considered as a form of restraint, and there is some evidence that the area-wide application of road humps (see also Chapter 22) can also be effective in this way.

In cell or area based systems, local distributors and access roads are connected together to create identifiable areas for control purposes. Vehicle access to a specific cell is normally reasonably direct but the road system within the cell is designed so that there are no direct routes between cells. Thus, through routes are made extremely difficult or impossible. Street mazes operate in a similar way, the difference being that no clear cells are created.

Such measures are aimed primarily at reducing through traffic and are effective in confining it to major routes.

However, they have little effect on traffic terminating within the area and this makes them attractive when accessibility to those areas needs to be preserved.

Generally, controls of this kind are permanent but they are often introduced initially using experimental regulations which can be modified in the light of experience. A scheme should be made permanent as soon as it is found to cater adequately for traffic, so that the full environmental benefits can be obtained and any complementary work, like landscaping or paving, can be carried out.

Direction signing: These types of systems require clear and effective traffic signing to assist drivers. Cell systems need to identify the route to individual cells. Mazes present greater problems since the barriers to movement are less obvious and they make even greater demands on detailed local knowledge. It is therefore necessary to ensure that through route signing is provided at entry points to the system and it may be necessary to provide map type signs within it.

Since cells and mazes involve re-routeing, adequate alternative routes are essential otherwise the environmental problems will just be transferred to other residential streets or to shopping areas on the major roads. The more successful schemes usually involve a limited amount of road improvement to create the bypass to cater for the diverted traffic, although the traffic restraining effect is correspondingly reduced.

Congestion related measures: Controls on the congestion experienced by moving vehicles impose restraint through the application of penalties in the form of extra travel time and uncertainty.

It has been suggested that organised delay or planned congestion would provide a positive and equitable form of restraint since all users would be equally penalised. In practice, measures have usually concentrated on controlling the location of congestion on pre-determined routes at places where congestion would cause the least adverse effect. This technique is sometimes complemented by priority measures to relieve public transport vehicles from the delays affecting other vehicles. Storage space needs to be provided for queueing vehicles and controls must not be evaded.

It should, however, be noted that the use of controlled vehicular delays may be counter productive if the time penalties involve a resource cost greater than the benefits achieved. Furthermore, its equity is questionable as although the time penalty is imposed equally on all road users it inevitably bears more heavily on those for whom time is more valuable and on those with no option but to use their vehicles during the period of control. Moreover, what might be regarded as essential traffic is subjected to the same delays as non-essential traffic.

Delay based controls are simple to understand and are achievable within existing legislative powers, but problems of enforcement can occur and the implications of, for example, widespread violation of traffic signals caused as a result of frustration, would be a matter for concern and might lead to an increase in accidents.

Regulatory controls: Measures involving some form of preferred vehicle status can be imposed by regulation and many systems have been conceived though few have been implemented. Two types of regulatory control worthy of mention are permit based systems and time allocation systems.

Permit Based Systems allow permits to be allocated on the basis of need with consequent exclusion of vehicles without permits. Qualification for permits can take several forms:

● permits limited to identifiable and essential users such as the disabled, doctors or residents;

● permits allocated to more efficient vehicles (eg. vehicles with four or more occupants are exempted from area licensing charges in Singapore);

● schemes based on a simple percentage allocation of permits chosen at random;

● schemes based on a demonstrated need to make the particular journey.

Time Allocation Systems allocate travel time slots to vehicles to some pre-determined formula. For example, the 'odds and evens' systems operated in Athens and Lagos, in which odd numbered vehicles are permitted to enter the controlled area on certain days of the week and even numbered vehicles on the others.

Permit based systems can be effective in reducing congestion and environmental intrusion but can cause intense arguments on the way permits are allocated and can lead to fraud and corruption.

With the 'odds and evens' system, traffic is not necessarily reduced by a half, as those whose vehicles are permitted on a given day may elect to make additional journeys which in effect, replace journeys by those who are restricted. This type of system imposes restraint without any rational form of discrimination.

Fiscal controls: A commonly cited principle behind fiscal methods is aimed at charging drivers the difference between the average cost which they perceive and the costs they force other drivers to incur (ie. the marginal social cost).

There are a variety of ways in which these charges can be made. One method involves the use of a meter on the vehicle triggered by a device at the roadside, or a central charging computer triggered by the detection of an electronic 'number plate' on the vehicle, as in the Hong Kong experimental trials (see Ref. 4).

The system of charging and location of pricing points can vary. True marginal cost road pricing is difficult to achieve but close approximations can be obtained by increasing the number of pricing points, pricing periods and rates for different vehicle types. For practical reasons, simpler charging methods may be preferable involving, for example, the purchase of a special licence to enter an area, or to use a vehicle within it, or cash tolls for the use of tunnels and bridges surrounding the urban area (e.g. Manhattan Island, USA).

Fiscal restraint can be designed to affect those vehicles which contribute most to congestion costs by charging a price for road use at congested times and in congested locations. Fiscal methods are generally flexible but their effectiveness depends on the response of drivers to price, which should be determined by field trials as little is known at present.

Equity of Control by Price: It is often argued that because pricing indicates willingness to pay rather than need, it will bear most heavily on the less well-off and is, therefore, a regressive form of restraint. The balance of this argument will depend upon the prices charged, the distribution of income amongst the vehicle users affected and the alternative options available to them. Perhaps the strongest argument in favour of restraint by pricing is that it does allow freedom of choice and requires the driver to decide much more critically whether the full cost of his or her journey is really justified.

It is also argued that fiscal measures are less wasteful of resources. A fiscal measure achieves its effects by increasing the money component of generalised cost whereas a delay based measure achieves its effects by increasing the time component of generalised cost. However, whilst the money collected through fiscal measures may be used to compensate some users (directly or indirectly through road improvements, bus subsidies and so on), wasted time is lost forever.

Implementation of Fiscal Controls

Fiscal controls can be implemented by:

toll systems at the entries and exits of the controlled area—simple to operate but care should be taken to prevent large queues forming at peak periods;

pre-purchased licences, which should allow for regular and occasional users; and

electronic road-use pricing systems, where each vehicle is fitted with equipment to interact with roadside units when entering or leaving the controlled area (see Figure 23.2).

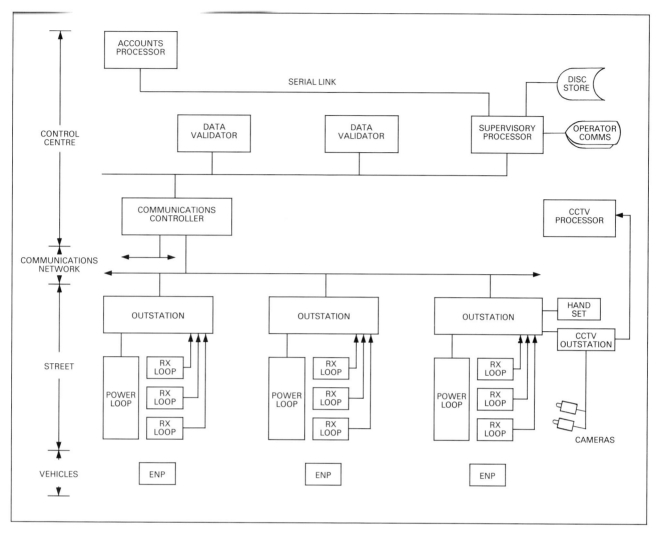

ENP :   Electronic Number Plate fitted underneath the vehicle
POWER LOOP : Loop energising all ENPs crossing the site
RX LOOP :   Receiver loops overlapping the power loop to ensure no vehicles are missed due to lack of lane discipline

DATA CAPTURE SYSTEM

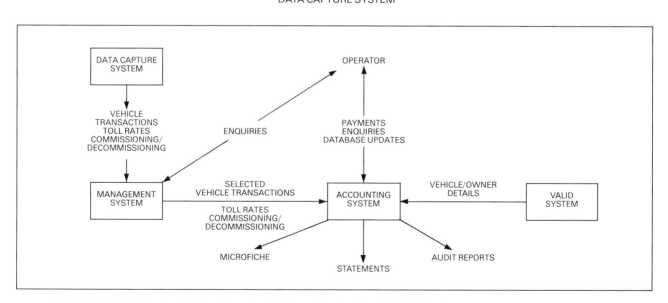

VALID SYSTEM : Government's vehicle licensing system (Vehicle and Licensing Integrated Data System).

ACCOUNTS PROCESSOR

Figure 23.2 The electronic road pricing experiment in Hong Kong

Source: 'Electronic Road Pricing in Hong Kong', Traffic Engineering
and Control volumes 26 and 27 (1985, 1986)

23.5 References

1. May, A D—*'Traffic Restraint—a review of the alternatives'*, Transportion Research, (Special Issue *'Road Pricing'* Vol 20A No 2) (1986).   (23.1)

2. DoE/DTp/TRRL Report LR 805,—*'Nottingham Zones and Collar study—overall assessment'*, DoE/DTp (1977).   (23.3)

3. Cracknell, J A et al—*'Physical restraint: Greater London's cordon restraint study'*, Traffic Engineering and Control, Vol 16 No 9 (1975).   (23.3)

4. Dawson et al—*'Electronic Road Pricing in Hong Kong'*, Traffic Engineering and Control, Vol 26, Nos 11 and 12 and Vol 27, Nos 1 and 2 (1985, 1986).   (23.4)

23.6 Further Information

5. OECD Report to Environment Committee Group (as yet unpublished)—*'Case Study on Gothenberg'*, OECD Paris (1984).

6. DTp/TRRL SR 734—*'Travel behaviour and traffic restraint: a study of households in Oxford'*, DTp (1982).

Text References

7. OECD—*'Integrated Urban Traffic Management'*, OECD Paris (1978).

8. Watson, P L and Holland, E P—*'Relieving traffic congestion: The Singapore area license scheme, SWP 281'*, The World Bank, Washington (1978).

9. Holland, E P and Watson, P L—*'Traffic restraint in Singapore'*, Traffic Engineering and Control Vol 19 No 1 (1978).

10. Herald, W S—*'Auto restricted zones: plans for five cities'*, Urban Mass Transportation Administration Report, Department of Transportation, Washington, United States (1977).

11. Lane, R and Hodgkinson, D M—*A permit system for traffic restraint'*, Traffic Engineering and Control Vol 17 No 3 (1976).

12. DoE—Research Report No 14. *'A study of some methods of Traffic Restraint'*, DoE (1976).

13. DoE—*'The Control of private non-residential parking: a consultation paper'*, DoE (1976).

14. GLC—*'A study of supplementary licensing, London'*, GLC (1974).

15. OECD—*'Techniques for improving urban conditions by restraint of road traffic'* OECD Paris (1973).

16. MoT—The Smeed Committee Report, *'Road Pricing—The Economics and technical possibilities'*, HMSO (1964).

Plate 19.4 Sensitive use of surface treatment and street furniture to indicate pedestrian priority   *Source: Greater London Consultants*

Plate 24.4 Typical pedestrianised area with cycle parking   *Source: Peterborough City Council*

Plate 24.5 Pedestrianised area with provision for public transport   *Source: Devon County Council*

Plate 26.2 A with-flow bus lane   *Source: G. Crow Esq.*
(NB this type of traffic sign has now
been superseded by white on blue signs)

Plate 33.1 An example of a covered shopping mall　　　　　　　　*Source: Photo Mayo*

Plate 33.7 An example of an aesthetically pleasing multi storey car park　　　　*Source: British Parking Association*

Plate 34.1 An example of the softening effect of vegetation on new road construction   *Source: British Road Federation*

Plate 41.1 Linked signals on a gyratory system   *Source: Devon County Council*

24   Facilities for Pedestrians

24.1 The Importance of Pedestrians as Traffic

All road users are pedestrians for one or more stages of every journey. Shorter distance journeys are likely to be made on foot and over 60% of journeys under 1.5 kms long are made solely on foot but pedestrian journeys rarely exceed 3 km for most trip purposes. In urban areas about one third of all journeys are made entirely on foot.

Pedestrians, particularly the young and elderly, are the most vulnerable group of road users. It is essential to consider their needs within the transport system to give them equal and sometimes greater consideration with other road users and to plan accordingly.

The great majority of pedestrian movement is local in nature and takes place on footways adjacent to carriageways. It therefore follows that the problem of pedestrian/vehicle conflict must be an important consideration in highway design and traffic management. Attention needs to be paid to minimising risk and providing facilities for pedestrians which are primarily safe, convenient and pleasant to use.

Pedestrian activities can differ in nature between trips concerned only with direct travel between two points and those which have a more diverse or recreational character. In some areas footways are also used as play space or places where people might be expected to congregate and talk. All of these aspects should be considered in the design of pedestrian facilities.

24.2 Making the Best Use of Existing Footways and Footpaths

Widening Footways

In areas of high pedestrian activity it will be important to consider how best to use existing highway space and in particular, the proportions devoted to vehicular and pedestrian traffic. In some areas it may be possible to widen the existing footway to avoid the necessity for pedestrians to step into the carriageway where the footway is too narrow for the demands placed upon it.

Measures which increase the capacity of the footway and reduce the time taken for pedestians to cross the road can be especially useful where pedestrian movements cannot be concentrated at a formal crossing place. The loss of carriageway capacity for moving vehicles can sometimes be reduced if bays are provided for bus stops and arrangements are made to control

loading and any on-street parking, thus preserving an adequate running width.

Corner Radii

The use of small radii kerbing at corners can help pedestrians cross the mouths of side roads by causing a reduction in the speed of turning vehicles and reducing the carriageway width at the bell mouth; but there may be an increased risk of large vehicles mounting the kerb and it is sometimes advantageous to provide extra protective features such as bollards. The balance between pedestrian amenity and junction capacity can be critically dependent on the choice of corner radii and obstructive parking is also more likely with tighter radii—a further factor which may need to be considered.

Surface Treatment at Junctions

In some areas it may also be beneficial to continue the main road 'footway' across a junction. This may not necessarily involve a closure of the side road but would require a change of level for vehicles rather than pedestrians. This type of measure can assist pedestrian movements by giving them precedence and prominence by encouraging drivers to manoeuvre more slowly (see Plate 24.1). The use of coloured and textured surfaces can be effective in reinforcing the change in priority.

Plate 24.1 Footway paving continuing across side road junctions

Source: S Sexton Esq

Maintenance

The standard of maintenance and repair of facilities plays an important part in reducing both real and perceived danger and inconvenience for pedestrians. Footways with uneven surfaces or otherwise in a poor state of repair are particularly hazardous to people who have poor sight or are unsteady on their feet.

Maintenance activity is especially important following temporary reinstatements by public utilities and their contractors. Adequate signing and lighting of works is essential and a level walking surface should be maintained at all times.

Other General Points

Vegetation should not be allowed to obstruct the footpath and should be regularly trimmed. Where temporary building works are to take place, it should not be assumed that the footway can be obstructed in preference to the carriageway and appropriate arrangements should be made to ensure that a safe and level footpath of adequate width is maintained. Isolated and less well used footpaths should not be allowed to fall into disrepair. Some more remote areas can be particularly prone to vandalism and assaults on pedestrians and the design of facilities should aim to minimise this by not creating hidden refuges and by producing an open aspect. The provision of a good standard of street lighting with vandal proof fittings is also invaluable in these areas.

Footway Obstructions

Poorly sited street furniture can prevent full use of the footway and impede visibility for road users. It creates particular difficulties for physically disabled people especially those who are blind or partially sighted. It is sometimes possible to site equipment like traffic signal controllers, lighting columns and poles for signs at the back edge of the footway rather than at the kerbside. Informatory signs for pedestrians should be provided where they can be useful but should also be sited with care. The display of goods or commercial signs on the footway can also be obstructive to pedestrians and draw motorists attention away from the road. Equally, parking on the footway is highly obstructive and can damage the surface. Powers are available to penalize offenders (see Chapter 21.12) but in some locations physical measures like posts or raised kerbs will be necessary to prevent it.

Routes for Footpaths

New footpaths should be arranged to suit known pedestrian routes wherever possible and should be considered at the earliest stages of any new development (see also Chapter 31 on the development of residential areas). Some authorities have chosen to leave the exact location of surfaced footpaths in open areas until after a development is complete, so that the surface can then be laid along the worn paths which indicate precisely where people wish to walk.

24.3 Pedestrian Refuges

Pedestrian refuges (or traffic islands) are the most common and generally the least costly type of crossing aid for pedestrians and their installation is not so tightly prescribed as the siting of pelican or zebra crossings. They permit pedestrians to concentrate on crossing one stream of traffic at a time by creating a relatively safe waiting point, usually in the centre of the carriageway.

Refuges are often appropriate at sites where pedestrian crossing movements are concentrated but are insufficient in number to justify a more formal crossing (see Plate 24.2 and 24.4 below). Where movements are less concentrated, pedestrians sometimes cross near to a refuge using the space between traffic streams as a 'shadow' refuge. In these situations it may be beneficial to erect guardrails along the edge of the footway to focus crossing movements at the refuge.

Plate 24.2 A pedestrian refuge   Source: S Sexton Esq

The reduced width of carriageway resulting from installing a refuge can reduce vehicle speeds, but sufficient width is still needed to permit safe passage of the largest vehicles likely to use the road.

Where a crossing problem has been identified, it may be necessary to consider the imposition of a ban on vehicles waiting in the vicinity of the refuge, to avoid pedestrians being masked by parked vehicles.

Design and Location of Refuges

Refuges should normally be 1.8 m wide and never less than 1.2 m wide. Openings or dropped kerbs should be provided in the centre island to assist pedestrians, especially those with prams and users of wheelchairs. Dropped kerbs should be provided on both footways opposite the refuge. Internally illuminated bollards should be placed at each end of the refuge with an illuminated beacon post in the centre if appropriate, so long as it does not obstruct pedestrians; this will enable the refuge to be quickly identified by pedestrians and motorists. Crossing points should be well illuminated by street lighting or, where necessary, by supplementary floodlighting.

At major/minor junctions, the provision of traffic islands which serve as refuges will help pedestrians to cross the minor road or indeed the major road if there is an established need for a crossing point. It is preferable to provide separate crossing points away from the junction where road widths are narrower and traffic movements are more straight forward, but if they are sited too far away they will not be effective because pedestrians will continue to cross at the junction rather than walk the extra distance involved.

A refuge on the minor road of a T-junction should preferably be set back so that the end nearer the junction is at least 3.0 m behind the continuation of the kerb line of the major road. The layout and positioning of all traffic islands and refuges should be checked to ensure that there is adequate clearance for the largest type of vehicles expected to use the junction bearing in mind the type of property to be served in the locality. Provision of a refuge could mean that a junction needs to be widened or kerb radii increased to enable long vehicles to turn but this should not involve excessively large radii which cause pedestrians greater difficulty in crossing the road. For further details, see Ref. 1 [Sco. 130].

Refuges are often beneficial on local distributors acting as bus routes, especially where crossing movements are drawn to a particular location near local shops or a bus stop. Refuges are particularly valuable where a zebra or pelican crossing cannot be justified by numerical criteria (see 24.4 below).

Refuges should not be sited directly opposite bus stops because they can prevent other vehicles in the traffic stream from overtaking a stationary bus or may create a condition where vehicles attempting to overtake a bus collide with the refuge itself.

24.4 Formal Pedestrian Crossings

Formal pedestrian crossings provide pedestrians with priority over vehicular traffic for part of the time. They may be:

- school crossing patrols;
- zebra crossings;
- pelican crossings; or
- pedestrian facilities at signal controlled junctions.

Although demands are frequently made for formal pedestrian crossings, these types of crossings should only be considered at sites where positive benefits for the convenience and safety of pedestrians are likely to be obtained. For example, if a zebra crossing is installed at a site where it is not used for long periods of the day drivers may tend to ignore it, with the risk of bringing it and other crossings of this type into disrepute. Furthermore, some formal crossings tend to

have a low but steady accident rate for accidents of certain types and their installation at sites with little or no previous accident record can have an adverse affect on road safety.

The following factors should be considered when assessing whether a formal crossing should be provided:

- the level of pedestrian/vehicle conflict (quantified);
- the current accident record and that which is likely to prevail following installation of a new facility; and
- the benefits to pedestrians in terms of convenience, safety and reduced delay against any additional delay incurred by vehicle occupants.

The Department of Transport recommends empirically based criteria in order to assess whether the volume of potential conflicts between pedestrians and vehicles is sufficiently high to justify a formal crossing.

The criteria are based on PV^2 where;

P = the pedestrian flow (pedestrians/hour) across a 100 m length of road centred on the proposed crossing site, and

V = the number of vehicles in both directions (vehicles/ hour).

The PV^2 value should be the average over the four busiest hours of the day and a formal crossing is normally justified where the calculated value of PV^2 is greater than 1×10^8. Where there is room for a central refuge this figure is increased to 2×10^8. Figure 24.1 shows the type of crossing recommended for the different combinations of pedestrian and vehicle flows.

At locations where appropriate values of PV^2 are not achieved, a formal crossing may still be justified:

- where there is substantial community severance;
- at sites adjacent to community centres, homes for the elderly, infirm or blind, hospitals or clinics, outside school entrances and in busy shopping areas;
- where there are significant numbers of heavy vehicles (300 vehicles/hour during the four busiest hours); and
- where there are pronounced seasonal variations in the number of pedestrians.

For further details, see Refs. 2, 3, 4 and 5 [Sco. 131, NI. 37].

24.5 School Crossing Patrols

The County Road Safety Officers' Association has provided (see Ref. 6) advice and guidance on the

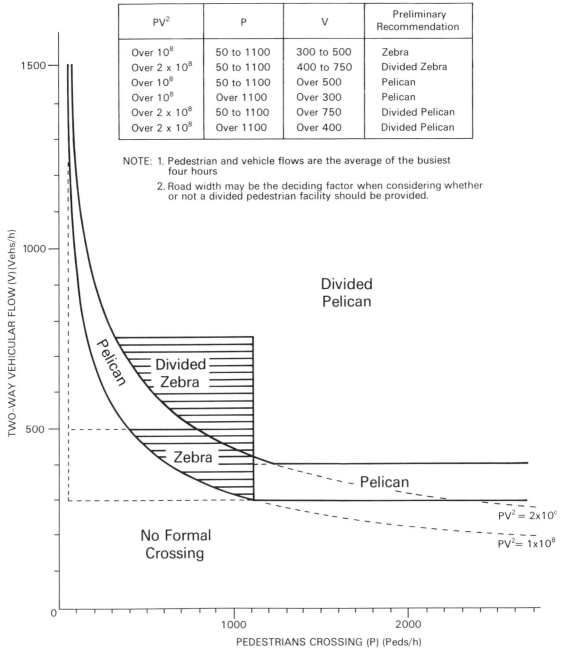

PV^2	P	V	Preliminary Recommendation
Over 10^8	50 to 1100	300 to 500	Zebra
Over 2 x 10^8	50 to 1100	400 to 750	Divided Zebra
Over 10^8	50 to 1100	Over 500	Pelican
Over 10^8	Over 1100	Over 300	Pelican
Over 2 x 10^8	50 to 1100	Over 750	Divided Pelican
Over 2 x 10^8	Over 1100	Over 400	Divided Pelican

NOTE: 1. Pedestrian and vehicle flows are the average of the busiest four hours

2. Road width may be the deciding factor when considering whether or not a divided pedestrian facility should be provided.

Figure 24.1 Suggested warrants for formal pedestrian crossing facilities

Source: TD4/79 DTp (1979)

provision of school crossing patrols. The decision to introduce a patrol will depend largely on site character-istics and the police, the highway authority and the education department will usually be involved (see also Refs. 7 and 8) [Sco. 132 and Sco. 133].

With school crossing patrols, drivers are required to stop when signalled to do so by an authorised person exhibiting a 'Stop—Children' sign. Advance warning signs giving notice of the crossing point should be erected and flashing amber lights may be added at difficult sites when:

● the 85th percentile speed of cars is greater than 35 miles/hour (see also Chapter 10);

● the forward visibility to the patrol is less than 100 m, or exceptionally;

● on any road where difficulties arise due to lack of suitable gaps in the traffic flow.

24.6 Zebra Crossings

Zebra crossings can be provided at relatively low cost but are unsuitable:

● where traffic is heavy and fast moving, as pedestrians wishing to establish precedence find it difficult to judge the speeds and stopping distances of approaching vehicles;

- in busy shopping streets and opposite railway stations, as high and continuous pedestrian flows may dominate the crossing and delay traffic excessively; and

- at special sites such as contra-flow bus lanes because of the uncertainty which they can cause to pedestrians.

In these circumstances, a pelican crossing will usually be preferred.

The effect of pedestrians using a zebra (or pelican) crossing on pedestrian and vehicular delays may be determined by using a formula which takes into account pedestrian flow, the time taken for pedestrians to cross and vehicle flows (see Ref. 9).

Zebra Crossing Undivided

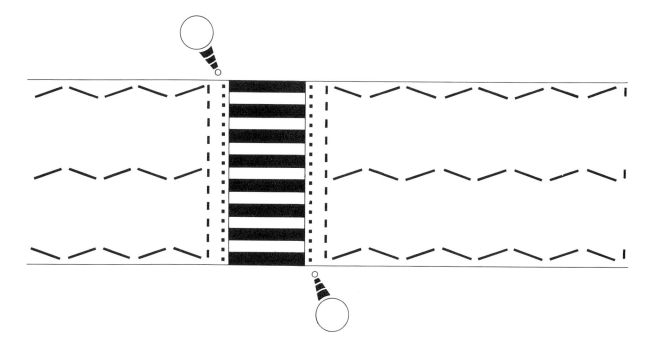

Zebra Crossing Divided

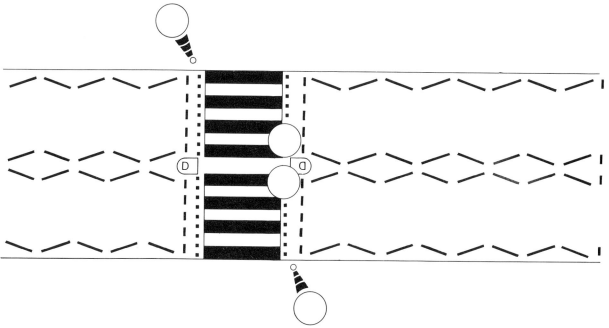

Figure 24.2 Suggested Layouts for zebra crossings

Pedestrians using a zebra crossing have right of precedence over vehicles only when they step on to the carriageway. The purposes of the zig-zag markings which indicate the zebra controlled area are to:

● extend waiting and parking bans to both sides of the crossing, thereby improving the conspicuity of the crossing for drivers;

● provide a ban on overtaking on the approach to the crossing; and

● discourage pedestrians from crossing within the zig-zag area except on the crossing itself.

Zebra crossings and road humps (see Chapter 22) [Sco. 134] may be made coincident.

Where the carriageway is more than 10.0 m wide, provision of a central refuge should be considered either integral with, or as an alternative to, a zebra crossing. Where both a central refuge and a crossing are provided pedestrians should be encouraged to treat each side of the street as the separate crossings which they are.

Recommended layouts for zebra crossings are shown in Figure 24.2.

In countries outside the United Kingdom zebra stripes are used differently, often at signal-controlled crossings. Their main purpose is usually to attract the attention of drivers but the stripes themselves do not indicate precedence for pedestrians. The legal requirements for pedestrians vary from country to country and in many places it is an offence to cross the road away from the recognised crossing points provided. In Britain, there is little regulatory control of pedestrians and there is no law requiring pedestrians to use crossings or to observe signals. Control must therefore be effected by good design.

24.7 Pelican Crossings

Pelican crossings help in areas of high pedestrian flow by providing specific safe pedestrian crossing periods and give a direct indication to motorists of pedestrians' legal right of way (see Plate 24.3). By placing an upper limit on the time the crossing may be occupied by pedestrians, they reduce the delays to vehicles which can occur with zebra crossings when pedestrian flows are very high.

Pelican crossings are more appropriate than zebra crossings in the following situations;

● where there are significant numbers of elderly and infirm pedestrians,

Plate 24.3 Typical staggered pelican crossing   Source S Sexton Esq

● at sites with high approach speeds, where a pelican with vehicle detection should be used,

● where pedestrian flow is heavy and a pelican will prevent pedestrians establishing a continuous flow on the crossing,

● at special sites such as contraflow bus lanes, and

● in areas operating under urban traffic control, as pelican crossings can be linked with traffic signals.

The 'Pelican' Pedestrian Crossing Regulations and General Directions 1987 (Ref. 2) now prohibit vehicles from stopping on both sides of the crossing and provide for pelicans to be given zig-zag markings on each side of the crossing to make this prohibition clear [NI. 2]. Recommended layouts for pelican crossings are shown in Figure 24.3.

On dual carriageways and on single carriageways more than 15.0 m wide, pelican crossings should be of the staggered type of layout which operates as two separate crossings. The staggering should preferably be left-handed so that pedestrians stepping onto the central reserve or refuge turn towards the approaching traffic to give them a better view of it. The central storage area should be large enough to accommodate the expected numbers of pedestrians gathered during each signal cycle.

Details of the standard settings and timings for pelicans are given in Ref. 4 [Sco. 131]. A feature which helps minimise delay to vehicles is the flashing amber/flashing green man period in the signal sequence. During this period pedestrians have right-of-way if they are already on the crossing but they should not start to cross; drivers may proceed during this phase if there are no pedestrians on the crossing. The phasing of the signals can also be amended to allow for the change in the driver's signal from red to flashing amber to be delayed at wider crossings. This gives pedestrians more security

Pelican Crossing on Two Way Road
without Central Refuge.

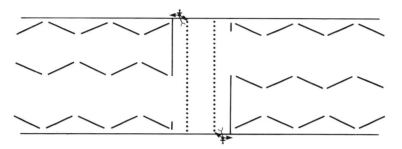

Pelican Crossing on Two Way Road
with Central Refuge.

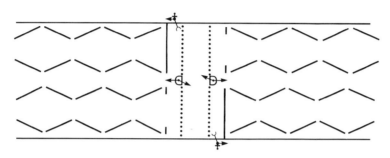

Pelican Crossing of Two Way Road
Left Hand Stagger (Preferred).

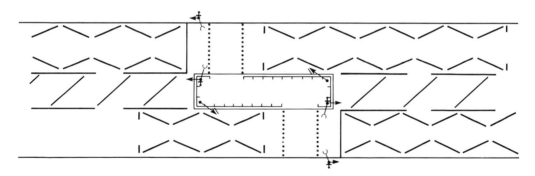

Pelican Crossing on Two Way Road
Right Hand Stagger.

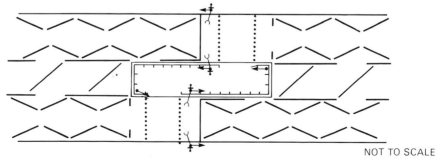

NOT TO SCALE

Figure 24.3 Layouts for pelican crossings

199

on wider crossings—particularly the elderly and people with disabilities. In some instances a two second extension of the steady green man may represent a sensible alternative to the delayed flashing amber.

An audible signal in the form of a pulsed tone emitted during the steady green man display may be provided at straight-cross pelicans to assist the visually handicapped. They are not recommended for use at staggered pelicans because of the possible confusion between audible signals on the two halves of the crossing. The 1987 Regulations also provide for tactile indicators to assist the visually handicapped. These indicators will be particularly suitable at crossings where it is not possible to provide an audible signal (see also 24.13 for textured surfacing).

24.8 Siting of Crossings

Crossings should not normally be placed immediately beside a priority junction because of the danger to pedestrians from turning traffic. Pelican crossings should not be sited close to a give-way or stop line to avoid the danger of drivers mistaking pelican signals for signals controlling the junction itself.

Great care is required when siting crossings near roundabouts. In particular a pelican crossing should not give the impression that it is controlling the roundabout, but if it is too far away pedestrians may choose not to use it. Alternatively, if it is too near, the entry and exit flows to the roundabout may be reduced with a consequent reduction in capacity and risk of blocking. The effect of blocking back can be evaluated using the ARCADY 2 program developed by the Department of Transport (Refs. 10 and 11—see also Chapter 40).

24.9 Provision for Pedestrians at Signal-controlled Junctions

At signalled junctions specific facilities for pedestrians can be incorporated using separate "green man" pedestrian aspects. It is possible to provide a full signal stage (all red to traffic) during which pedestrians have right-of-passage. However, this can result in a considerable loss in vehicular throughput and it is often possible to arrange the signal staging so that pedestrians may cross individual arms of the junction whilst traffic is moving elsewhere, thus reducing the effect on vehicular delay. This type of provision is commonly known as 'walking with traffic' and further details are given in Chapter 41 and Ref. 13 [Sco. 135].

In urban traffic control schemes, it is important to consider whether measures can be taken which benefit the movement of pedestrians as well as vehicles. For example, one-way systems can assist the provision of combined pedestrian/vehicle stages because there are fewer vehicle movements to cater for. Banned movements can also help pedestrians without unduly reducing capacity. It should also be noted that the TRANSYT system for UTC (see Chapter 20) can allow pedestrian flows and delays to be taken into account in coordinating traffic signals and pedestrian 'progression' can be achieved through suitable timing of signal stages and 'offsets' between nearby junctions.

The United Kingdom differs from many countries in that it does not provide a positive signal for pedestrians to be shown concurrently with a signal for conflicting turning traffic (ie. left turning traffic), which is required to give way to pedestrians.

24.10 Shared Facilities

Facilities for pedestrians can sometimes be combined with those for other road users. This may have particular advantages where there is insufficient space to allow exclusive facilities for each class of road user. However, care should be taken not to put, for example, pedestrians and cyclists together to the possible detriment of both. Scope for space sharing should be recognised but facilities for pedestrians and cyclists should be separate wherever possible.

For further details see Chapters 25 and 31.

24.11 Pedestrianisation

Certain areas, or particular lengths of road, experience high levels of pedestrian activity. Such places may be potential candidates for some form of pedestrianisation scheme. These schemes are most commonly introduced in shopping and market areas but they can also be beneficial in high intensity office areas and in conservation areas or other places where environmental conditions are highly valued (see also Chapter 31 which deals with the development of residential areas). Examples of pedestrianised areas which illustrate a number of thoughtful design features are shown in Colour Plates 24.4 and 24.5.

Pedestrianisation allows the creation of an environment which respects a human rather than a vehicular scale. However, to be successful, such schemes require satisfactory provision to be made for local and through traffic and for public transport and parking, including in particular the access needs of mobility handicapped people. Access for servicing of premises in the restricted area and for emergency vehicles must also be provided. Decisions on the most appropriate type of measure are therefore usually controlled by the existing characteristics of the street or area in question but there are a variety of options from which to choose depending upon the extent to which vehicles can or should be excluded. The options range from full pedestrianisation, with total vehicle exclusion, to partial or part-time pedestrianisation, with some or all vehicles excluded to differing degrees, at different times of day or on different days of the week.

Highways can be pedestrianised under section 212 of the Town and Country Planning Act 1971 (TCPA Ref. 13) [Sco. 136, NI. 3] or by traffic regulation order (TRO) under the Road Traffic Regulation Act 1984 (RTRA Ref. 14) [NI. 7]. In both cases exemptions can be made for any class or classes of vehicle, for all or part of a day, for certain days of the week or for any other limited period of time. The provisions of the two Acts in this respect are not, however, interchangeable and for this reason it may sometimes be advisable to supplement orders under the TCPA with a TRO. Generally speaking there is greater scope for making environmental improvements (eg. by introducing benches or flower beds) following a TCPA order but such an order has enforcement limitations. On the other hand, although the power to make physical alterations is limited under RTRA, sanctions are provided for breach of an order under this Act so that it may be necessary to back up a TCPA order with a TRO and its associated signing, to facilitate enforcement.

Full Pedestrianisation

By excluding all vehicles (or all motor vehicles) for all of the time, with exemptions only for emergency and maintenance vehicles, full pedestrianisation usually allows the carriageway to be eliminated and enables the street to become a continuously paved area with consistent surface textures. It does, however, depend upon viable arrangements for delivery and service vehicles, such as rear access, loading bays and/or provision for delivery by trolley. It will also require the use of adjacent roads for local access and as bus routes. Compliance with any vehicle exclusion orders should be encouraged by good design; for example, the approaches to the pedestrianised area should give the clear impression that vehicles would be intruding into the pedestrians' environment. As indicated above, TCPA powers would normally be used to create this kind of scheme but where compliance difficulties are encountered or envisaged, complementary orders under both Acts should be made.

Partial Pedestrianisation

Local circumstances can make it impracticable to totally exclude all vehicles from an area all of the time. Suitable exemptions (in addition to those for emergency services, statutory undertakers etc.) may then need to be made for particular purposes, the most common of these being for orange badge holders' vehicles (for disabled persons), delivery vehicles, public transport

and pedal cycles; or at certain times of day (see Chapter 15.2).

One of the more difficult issues is whether to allow entry by public transport service vehicles and a decision is likely to be dependent upon the opportunities available to provide an adequate and satisfactory service elsewhere without penetrating the pedestrianised area itself. Many schemes, both including and excluding buses have been implemented and there is little evidence to suggest that road safety is impaired if the presence of buses is properly catered for. They do, however, detract from the environmental quality of the townscape and perpetuate the need for pedestrians to remain aware of their existence when walking in the area.

In some cases the lack of suitable alternative routes for local or through traffic (eg. at peak hours), may require that restrictions upon the vehicular use of the street or area be limited to certain times of the day and similar restrictions can also be introduced to deal with the problem of deliveries to shops or other commercial properties where alternative arrangements cannot be made.

Clearly, any departure from full vehicle exclusion restricts the scope for environmental treatment of the area. Where significant volumes of traffic are to be permitted for part of the day few permanent features can be introduced, although moveable barriers can be provided to assist enforcement. Where vehicle encroachment is permanently limited (eg. to public transport service vehicles), footways can often be widened and in these circumstances, provision for vehicles should be made to minimum standards consistent with safety. Features such as guardrails, ramped footways or large radius kerbs at corners facilitate easier and speedier access by vehicles and should be avoided. The overall aim should be to design for people and not for vehicles and attention to detail is important if the maximum environmental benefit is to be achieved.

Signing

Signing is an important consideration in pedestrianisation schemes. For aesthetic reasons it should be kept to the minimum consistent with legal requirements and driver comprehension. Sign clutter should be avoided.

It should be noted that exemptions for vehicles being used by emergency services, statutory undertakers, local authorities in pursuance of statutory powers or duties and security carriers do not need to be signed, although exemptions for other categories of vehicle do.

For further information on the design of pedestrian schemes see Refs. 15, 16 and 17 [Sco. 137].

24.12 Grade Separation

Grade separation between pedestrian routes and roads carrying vehicular traffic is potentially the safest type of crossing facility for pedestrians, provided such routes are easy and convenient to use. However, pedestrians prefer crossings to be at a single level. Use of grade separated facilities can be encouraged if there is no change in level for pedestrians and the grade separation is effected mainly by changes to the vertical profile of the carriageway whilst the footway level remains unaltered, but this can be relatively expensive unless the natural ground contours favour it (see Plate 24.6). The potential safety benefit of grade separation may not be realised if many pedestrians continue to make hazardous crossings at road level rather than make strenuous and time consuming detours.

The choice between a footbridge and a subway or pedestrian underpass may be made on economic grounds (footbridges are usually cheaper) although the visually intrusive aspects of a footbridge and the anti-social behaviour associated with both bridges and subways will also be factors. For pedestrians, the change of level associated with a footbridge is often greater than that for a subway, owing to the headroom required for vehicles passing underneath.

Factors which might justify the provision of either footbridges or subways include high pedestrian and vehicle flows, lack of alternative facilities, favourable site topography, poor accident records, road type in the hierarchy and the prospect of a good economic return. In the main, they should be considered for major roads with high approach speeds and high volumes of traffic with high pedestrian flows, or where pedestrian severance is acute.

The environment should be favourable to the design and the horizontal and vertical alignments should be compatible with the main pedestrian desire lines. Footbridges should have the easiest type of access ramp, preferably not stepped; and subways should have a clear view through from entrance to exit. Escalators can also be considered (see also Chapter 33).

Subways in particular can attract anti-social behaviour. This can be minimised by good design which avoids places of concealment and by the provision of

Plate 24.6 At—grade pedestrian footbridge (carriageway dips beneath)

Source: Leicestershire County Council

Plate 24.7 Pedestrian subway with good lighting and surface treatment

Source: S Sexton Esq

Plate 24.8 Subway approaches covered by video recording (inset)

Source: Telford Development Corporation

adequate, vandal proof lighting (see also Plate 24.7 and Plate 24.8 which illustrates a novel approach to personal security). Commercial sponsorship can also encourage use of subways and reduce nuisance.

The walking surfaces of bridges, ramps and steps should be slip resistant and guardrails should be used to discourage crossing at road level and encourage use of the new facility.

For further details, see Refs. 18, 19 and 20.

24.13 Consideration of Those with a Mobility Handicap

Disabled people, the elderly, those with reduced mobility and even the able bodied when temporarily encumbered with shopping bags or escorting small children, have special needs which must be recognised by highway engineers and planners. Difficulty in walking or boarding buses is common and special

facilities or features in public areas can mean the difference between making a journey or staying at home for those with a mobility handicap and can also help the able-bodied to move more easily and freely. Such facilities can achieve the greatest benefit when they are provided in areas with high concentrations of older people and adjacent to buildings often visited by, or catering specifically for the needs of, the disabled.

There are a number of measures with wide application including dropped kerbs and non-slip, ramped footways at all pedestrian crossing points, whether formal or not, particularly when adjacent to parking places reserved for Orange Badge holders. However, it should be noted that whilst wheelchair users need lowered kerbs, guide dogs for the blind are taught to respond to normal upstanding kerbs. To resolve this conflict, a textured surface has been developed by the Department of Transport (see Plate 24.9). Advice has been issued to all local authorities recommending the use of the surface at all pedestrian crossings where the surface has been ramped (see Ref. 21),

Plate 24.9 Textured surfacing to assist blind persons at a zebra crossing

Source: Department of Transport

Other more innovative techniques include audible devices such as the 'talking' pelican installed in Lothian Region, Scotland (Ref. 22) to assist the blind at signal controlled crossings where standard devices are not considered sufficient; the 'talking bus stop' on trial at Weston Super Mare, which provides information on bus timetables and arrivals; and key controlled pelican crossings installed in Edinburgh in 1984.

Further information is also available in the Institution of Highways and Transportation publication 'Providing for People with a Mobility Handicap' (Ref. 23).

24.14 Guardrails

Guardrails should be considered where it is appropriate to channel pedestrians onto crossing facilities and away from dangerous sites. At zebra crossings, the guardrails should ideally cover the length of the zig-zag area on both sides of the crossing.

Guardrails can be used to alter patterns of pedestrian movement as part of any road safety measure. They should be used in short lengths in front of school entrances, recreation grounds and footpaths to prevent children running straight onto the carriageway. Asymmetric (or off-centre) positioning can deflect emerging pedestrians and encourage them to face on-coming traffic before crossing the road. At busy locations, such as congested junctions and railway or bus stations, guardrails can be used to keep pedestrians off the carriageway but they should be used sparingly on local distributors as they cause inconvenience to pedestrian movement.

Where guard railing is used at bus stops access to the carriageway will be necessary, but the guard railing should be continued along the queueing area. It is sometimes necessary to leave gaps in the railings to accommodate trees or street furniture. These gaps should be small enough to prevent children squeezing through. Alternatively, it may be preferable to resite the obstruction if this is practicable.

Where loading and unloading is unavoidable it is necessary to provide gates or removable panels. In practice, openings of this kind are often left open for long periods, thus removing the continuous protection that the barrier should provide. It is therefore necessary to make arrangements to ensure that they are used properly.

Plate 24.10 Special guard railing at a pedestrian crossing to assist visibility before . . . .

Plate 24.11 . . . . and after installation.

Source: Hugh Logan Engineering Ltd—Manufacturers of VISIRAIL

Guard rails should be set back (normally 500 mm) from the kerb to give adequate clearance for passing vehicles and should also leave sufficient room on the footway for two prams to pass (usually taken as 1.2 m). Widening of the pavement may sometimes be necessary before guard rails can be erected.

Specially designed guardrails which do not impair vision are available and should be used wherever visibility is important (eg. adjacent to junctions or pedestrian crossings—see Plates 24.10 and 24.11).

The disadvantages of guardrails, apart from their obtrusive appearance and their cost, is that they prevent pedestrians from crossing a road wherever they wish and their extensive use can encourage diagonal crossing. Accordingly, their use should normally be confined to district and primary distributor roads and only at junctions and other particularly hazardous locations on local distributor and access roads. The deterrent value of guardrailing against illegal or obstructive parking could be an additional consideration at critical locations.

24.15 Street Lighting

The provision of street lighting can make a considerable contribution to the urban scene in terms of improved road safety, increased personal security and environmental improvement when sympathetically designed; it is therefore especially beneficial to pedestrians.

High intensity floodlights can illuminate locations with poor night-time accident records. Their main area of use will be on local distributors where there are pedestrian crossing facilities or where the carriageway alignment changes (eg. on sharp curves).

24.16 Anti-skid Treatment

It is important to provide anti-skid treatment on the carriageway approaches to pedestrian crossings, as well as at junctions which exhibit high proportions of accidents involving braking in wet conditions.

24.17 References

Text Reference

1. DTp—TA 20/84, '*Junctions and accesses: the layout of major/minor junctions*', Advice Note, DTp (1984). [Sco.130] (24.3)

2. The 'Pelican' Pedestrian Crossing Regulations and General Directions 1987, Statutory Instrument 1987 No 16, HMSO (1987). (24.4, 24.7)

3. The 'Zebra' Pedestrian Crossings Regulations, Statutory Instrument 1971 No 1524, HMSO (1971). (24.4)

4. DTp—TD 28/87, '*Pelican and zebra crossings*', DTp (1987). [Sco.131] (24.4)

5. DTp—TA 51/87, '*Design considerations for pelican and zebra crossings*', DTp (1987) and corrigendum. [Sco.131] (24.4)

6. County Road Safety Officers Association, '*School crossing patrol service, Advice and Guidance*' (1986). (24.9)

7. DTp—Circular Roads 41/75, '*School crossing patrol signs*', DTp (1975). [Sco.132, Wa.34] (24.5)

8. DTp—Circular Roads 14/78, '*Traffic signs*', DTp (1978). [Sco.133, Wa.35] (24.5)

9. Griffiths, J D, Hunt, J G and Marlow, M—'*Delays at pedestrian crossings*', Traffic Engineering and Control, Vol 25 Nos 7/8, Vol 25 No 10, Vol 26 No 5 (1984–1985). (24.6)

10. DTp—TA 44/77, '*Capacities, queues and delays at road junctions: computer programs ARCADY 2 and PICADY 2*', DTp (1975). (24.8)

11. DTp/TRRL—Report RR 35, '*ARCADY 2: an enhanced program to model capacities, delays and queues at roundabouts*', DTp (1986). (24.8)

12. DTp—TA 15/81, '*Pedestrian facilities at traffic signal installations*', DTp (1981). (24.9)

13. The Town and Country Planning Act 1971 (as amended), HMSO (1971). [Sco.136] (24.11)

14. Road Traffic Regulation Act 1984, HMSO (1984). (24.11)

15. May, A D et al—'*Attitudes to town-centre pedestrian streets and buses: a case study in Barnsley*', Traffic Engineering and Control, Vol 23 No 11 (1982). (24.11)

16. Parker, J—'*Urban design and pedestrianisation schemes*', PTRC Seminar, British Institute of Management (1985). (24.11)

17. DTp—LTN 1/87, '*Pedestrian Zones—Getting the Right Balance*', DTp (1987). (24.11)

18. DTp—BE 1/78, '*Design criteria for footbridges and sign/signal gantries*', DTp (1978). (24.12)

19. DTp—TD 2/78, '*Pedestrian subways: layout and dimensions*', DTp (1978). [Sco.137] (24.12)

20. DTp—TD 3/79 *'Combined pedestrian and cycle subways: layout and dimensions'*, DTp (1979). [Sco.137]   (24.12)

21. DTp—Circular DU 1/86, *'Textured Footway Surfaces at Pedestrian Crossings'*, DTp (1986). [Wa.36]   (24.13)

22. McCann, V and Cross, B—*'The "talking" Pelican crossing—the introduction of a novel aid for the blind'*, Traffic Engineering and Control, Vol 23 No 5 (1982).   (24.13)

23. IHT—*'Providing for people with a mobility handicap, Guidelines'*, Institution of Highways & Transportation, London (1986).   (24.13)

24.18 Other Information

24. DTp—LTN 2/86 *'Shared Use by Cyclists and Pedestrians'*, DTp (1987).

25. DTp/TRRL—Report LR 1064, *'Walking as a mode of transport'*, DTp (1983).

26. DTp—TA 41/81 *'Pedestrian Zones—Signs'*, DTp (1983).

27. Landles, J R—*'The overall effect of accidents at sites where zebra crossings were installed'*, Traffic Engineering and Control Vol 24 No 1 (1983).

28. DTp—*'Electronic mobility and communication aids for disabled people'*, Report of Working Group, DTp (1982).

29. DTp/TRRL—Report SR 724, *'The effect of zebra crossings on junction entry capacities'*, DTp (1982).

30. DTp—*'Pedestrian Safety; Manual of Advice'*, HMSO (1973).

31. Todd and Walker—*'People as pedestrians'*, The Office of Population Censuses and Surveys, HMSO (1980).

32. DTp/TRRL—Report SR 567, *'The known risks we run: The Highway'*, DTp (1980).

33. DTp/TRRL—Report LR 933, *'Age-related differences in the road crossing behaviour of adult pedestrians'*, DTp (1980).

34. Crompton, D H—*'Pedestrian delay, annoyance and risks—preliminary results of a two year study'*, PTRC Summer Meeting—proceedings (1979).

35. University of Edinburgh Research Unit/Central Council for the Disabled, *'Planning for disabled people in the Urban Environment'*, University of Edinburgh (1969).

25 Measures to Assist Cyclists

25.1 Introduction

Despite some recent evidence of declining use on a national scale, the 1970s and 80s have seen an upsurge of interest in the use of pedal cycles in certain areas and cycling is now seen by many to be a convenient, cheap and healthy mode of transport and exercise, particularly for local journeys.

However, the level of accidents to cyclists causes great concern as cyclists are amongst the most vulnerable groups of road users and are very exposed to injury as a result of collisions with motor vehicles, or from other hazards they may encounter.

Their special vulnerability means that the needs of cyclists must always be considered by highway and planning authorities. Provision for cyclists can often be included in traffic management schemes at little extra cost. Furthermore, special measures specifically for cyclists can be cost-effective for the community in terms of their safety, environmental and social effects.

The introduction of measures for cyclists can sometimes release a suppressed demand for cycling which in turn can lead to:

● some increases in cycle journeys by existing users;

● some new users being attracted to the mode; and

● diversion to new routes which now become attractive.

It must also be borne in mind that cycling activities are very widespread and local authorities allocate their resources amongst a very wide range of services and facilities. For these reasons it is likely that the majority of cycling will continue to take place on existing roads where special facilities do not exist.

25.2 The Legal Position on the Use of Cycles

The pedal cyclist (and users of electrically assisted cycles) hold a unique position among vehicle users. Their vehicles do not have to be registered or taxed and as a consequence, neither are they required to be insured. The users of such vehicles do not have to pass a test or hold a licence and there is no lower or upper limit on the age at which cyclists can start or stop riding cycles, with the exception that users of electrically assisted cycles must be at least 14 years of age. A cyclist cannot be disqualified from cycling or have his (or her) driving licence (if he or she has one) endorsed for cycling offences. There is no annual check on the mechanical condition of cycles.

Cyclists are only entitled to cycle on 'ways' where they have legal authority to ride. They are entitled to ride on carriageways, except motorways or roads from which they have been excluded by a traffic regulation order. Contravention of most of these prohibitions constitutes an offence. Cyclists are also entitled to ride on cycle ways or cycle tracks, which they may or may not share with pedestrians; and on bridleways, where they will be sharing with both horse riders and pedestrians.

A cyclist has no general right to ride on a footway or on a footpath and it is an offence under Section 72 of the Highway Act 1835 (Ref. 1) (ie. it contravenes a specific regulation) to do so on a footway [Sco.138, NI.27]. Cyclists have no right to cycle across a zebra or pelican crossing (see Chapter 15.9).

It is illegal for a cyclist to contravene an order extinguishing vehicular rights (if this includes pedal cycles) made under the Town and Country Planning Act 1971 (Ref. 2) [Sco.139, NI.3], although no offence is created unless the order is supported by a traffic regulation order.

When a cyclist is pushing his or her pedal cycle on a pedestrian facility (footway, footpath or pedestrian crossing), case law suggests that he/she is regarded as a pedestrian. If a cyclist is pushing a pedal cycle on a road carriageway, case law suggests that the combination is regarded as a vehicle. A cyclist pushing a pedal cycle on the carriageway the wrong way along a one-way street is therefore likely to be committing an offence.

Pedal cyclists and users of electrically assisted cycles are not exempt from parking restrictions on the highway unless the relevant traffic regulation order is limited to motor vehicles only. However, enforcement may pose problems due to the difficulty in tracing ownership of the offending vehicle.

On carriageways, cycle tracks or bridleways the cyclist is bound by the rules applying to other users of the highway. Although cyclists can be exempted from restrictions applying to motor vehicles, the cyclist must obey mandatory traffic signs applying to the 'way' he/she is using, including traffic signals, and many of the general requirements of road traffic law. If, for instance, a cyclist behaves without reasonable care he/she may be liable for damages in an action for negligence at common law. This is one reason why a cyclist is well advised to take out an insurance policy covering not only loss or damage to the vehicle but also any claims arising out of the use of that vehicle.

Some regulations made under Sections 40 and 66 of the Road Traffic Act 1972 (Ref. 3) [NI.2] affect the construction and use of pedal cycles. These include:

- the Road Vehicles Lighting Regulations 1984 (Ref. 4) [NI.7], which require in the hours of darkness a front position lamp, a rear position lamp, a rear reflector and, in the case of a pedal cycle manufactured on or after 1 October 1985, pedal reflex reflectors;

- the Pedal Cycles (Construction and Use) Regulations 1983 (Ref. 5) [NI.2], which include requirements about brakes and the design and construction of electrically assisted pedal cycles.

As well as the specific offences referred to above, the Road Traffic Act 1972 (Ref. 3) [NI.2] specifies a number of cycling offences which have a level of penalty significantly lower than that applying to the equivalent offence committed by the driver of a motor vehicle. These offences are:

- reckless riding, Section 17 [NI.38];

- careless riding, Section 18 [NI.38];

- riding under the influence of drink, Section 19 [NI.39];

- unauthorised cycle racing on highways, Section 20 [NI.40];

- carrying more than one person (unless on an adapted cycle), Section 21 [NI.41].

25.3 Objectives

The main objectives in providing facilities for cyclists are, as for other road users, improved safety and increased comfort and convenience. Cyclists should not be put at risk or undue inconvenience by other traffic management measures such as long detours, one-way systems or poor siting of signs. Instead, the objectives should be to:

- keep vehicle speeds down where there are significant numbers of cyclists;

- minimise interaction of cycle flows with motor vehicles;

- provide continuous and direct cycle routes away from major roads;

- provide safe crossing points at major roads; and

- recognise the need for cyclists to feel safe as well as being adequately protected.

Roads and cycle tracks need to have well maintained, smooth surfaces with low gradients if they are to provide safe and convenient routes for cyclists.

25.4 Cycle Routes and Facilities

General Points

Cycle facilities have to be selected and designed to meet particular local circumstances and the following general points should be borne in mind:

- it is essential to have a good knowledge of where cyclists want to go and in what numbers, since cycle facilities which do not lie close to cycle desire lines are unlikely to be used;

- in some areas there may be no clear-cut pattern of movement, either because overall demand is low or because destinations and travel paths are well distributed. In these cases there may be little to be gained in implementing specific facilities, unless it can be shown either that there are localised areas of conflict which would be susceptible to spot treatment, or that the provision of a particular designated route will draw cyclists to it, and bring about an overall benefit;

- the objective of each scheme must be to satisfy an observed need and the most important need will be to avoid known danger. Another reliable indication of need is when numerous cyclists use a facility that is not meant for them, such as a footway or footpath, a pedestrian subway or the use of a one-way street in the wrong direction;

- special attention must be paid to the detailed design and implementation of cycle facilities in order to attract as many cyclists as possible to use them;

- great care needs to be taken with the detailed design of cycle facilities to encourage cyclists to use them correctly, thereby minimising inconvenience to, and possible conflict with, other users. This is particularly important where shared use with pedestrians is contemplated; and

- schemes that encourage or condone illegal cycling must be avoided.

Towards a Cycle Route Network

A wide range of measures can be used to provide cycle routes and the ultimate aim should be to link these routes together with cycle crossing points on major traffic routes to form a comprehensive cycle network.

Special Provisions on Busy Roads

On heavily trafficked roads there may be advantages in signing cyclists onto minor roads where these provide an acceptably direct alternative. On major roads, consideration should be given to widening the nearside lane or providing special cycle lanes (see Plate 25.1). Contra-flow cycle lanes and combined bus and cycle lanes and cycle slips can be used to minimise inconvenience to cyclists arising from traffic management measures such as one-way streets or other schemes which significantly lengthen route paths.

Plate 25.2 A shared route for cyclists and pedestrians

Plate 25.1 A cycle lane on a busy dual carriageway

Shared Facilities

Advice on the shared use of facilities by cyclists and pedestrians is given in Ref. 6. Footpaths and footways can be partly or wholly converted for shared use in appropriate circumstances. When part of a footpath or footway is made into a cycle track, separate ways for cyclists and pedestrians should be clearly differentiated by kerbs, railings, verges, markings, surface texture or surface colour. For information on the procedures necessary see Refs. 7 and 8 and associated regulations [Sco.140].

Existing pedestrian subways may also be converted for combined use by pedestrians and cyclists (see also Ref. 9 for the new construction of combined pedestrian and cycle subways) [Sco.141, NI.7].

Special Routes

Cyclists can sometimes be permitted through pedestrianised areas where a distinct carriageway has been retained. Special routes can be provided through parks and open spaces. Bridleways, disused railways and occasionally canal towpaths can be considered for conversion for use by cyclists. Where appropriate in new developments, the construction of cycle routes should be considered at an early stage in the planning process (see also Chapter 31) and when a road is to be closed, it may be possible to retain a through route for cyclists. For examples of shared routes for cyclists and pedestrians see Plate 25.2 and Refs. 6 and 9.

25.5 Junctions and Crossings

Existing Junctions

Existing junctions can be modified to make them safer and more attractive for cyclists to use. A route for cyclists can be clearly defined through a junction by the use of signs and road markings. At junctions with low traffic flows priorities can if necessary be changed to favour the cycle route. Where cyclists must give way or stop, an additional lane might be provided for them.

Crossing Major Roads

To help cyclists cross the carriageway a protected area in the centre of the road can be beneficial and a waiting area provided in front of vehicles can be helpful to assist turns to the right or left.

Where cycle tracks cross major routes away from existing junctions, special crossing facilities can be provided. The cycle track can be treated as a minor road giving way to motor vehicles. Staggered barriers or bollards can be used to control cyclists' approach speeds to the major road. Signs and road markings can be used to highlight the cycle path across the main route. A protected area in the centre of the main road can allow cyclists to cross a wide carriageway in two stages.

Exclusive signal controlled crossings operated by loop detectors in the carriageway can help cyclists cross busy routes. In particular, a 'G-turn' layout with signals can allow cyclists to make a safe right turn. Parallel cycle and pedestrian crossings can also be provided, with possible restrictions on cycle movements (see Figure 25.1 and Plate 25.3).

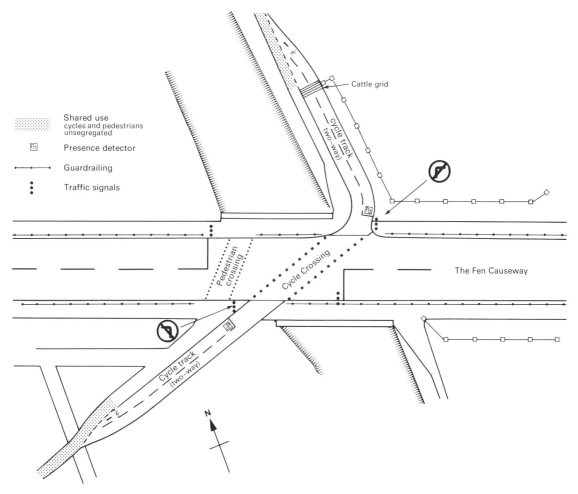

Figure 25.1 Layout of a shared signal controlled crossing for cyclists and pedestrians

Source: TA 5/86 DTp (1986)

Plate 25.3 Shared signal controlled cycle and pedestrian facilities

Source: Avon County Council

Signalised Junctions

At signal controlled junctions, in addition to the above measures, the signal staging can be altered to cater for cyclists. The introduction of a stage where cyclists have right of way, or a stage where they have an early start over other vehicles (if they have their own lane and signals), can improve safety. Intergreen periods can also be extended to give cyclists more time to clear the junction.

Roundabouts

Roundabouts pose particular problems for cyclists. The provision of a cycle lane on a roundabout at the nearside of the carriageway or the conversion of the surrounding footways to joint use by cyclists and pedestrians are possible measures. However, where justified, and subject to space and topography, grade separation can provide a safer alternative. The highway code (1987-Ref. 11) recommends riders to dismount whenever they feel unable to cope with the traffic conditions. For further details on cycle crossing facilities see Ref. 10.

25.6 Cycle Parking

Parking facilities for cyclists should be secure and convenient otherwise they will be underused and cycles will be parked in a haphazard fashion. Devices to support cycles should be designed and located to minimise damage and maximise security against theft and vandalism (see Plates 24.4 and 25.4).

[N.B. Further information on facilities for cyclists is given in the Institution of Highways and Transportation's Guidelines on Providing for the Cyclist (1983) (Ref. 12) and in the Department of Transport's Traffic Advisory Unit Leaflet series.]

Plate 25.4 Cycle parking close to a shopping area

Source: Leicestershire County Council

25.7 References

1. Highway Act 1835, HMSO.   *Text Reference*   (25.2)

2. Town and Country Planning Act 1971, HMSO (1971).   (25.2)

3. Road Traffic Act 1972, HMSO (1972).   (25.2)

4. Road Vehicles Lighting Regulations 1984, Statutory Instrument 1984 No 812, HMSO (1984).   (25.2)

5. Pedal Cycles (Construction and Use) Regulations 1983, Statutory Instrument 1983 No 1176, HMSO (1983).   (25.2)

6. DTp—LTN 2/86, '*Shared use by cyclists and pedestrians*', DTp (1986).   (25.4)

7. Highways Act 1980, HMSO (1980). [Sco.140]   (25.4)

8. Cycle Tracks Act 1984, HMSO (1984).   (25.4)

9. DTp—TD 3/79, '*Combined pedestrian and cycle subways: layout and dimensions*', DTp (1979). [Sco.141]   (25.4)

10. DTp—LTN 1/86, '*Provision for cyclists at junctions and crossings*', DTp (1986)   (25.5)

11. The Highway Code, HMSO (1987).   (25.5)

12. IHT—'*Guidelines for providing for the cyclist*', Institution of Highways and Transportation, London (1983).   (25.5)

25.8 Further Information

13. DTp—Traffic Advisory Unit Leaflets 1/86–15/86, 1/87 (1986/87).

14. DTp—'*Summary of Experimental Cycle Schemes*', DTp (1985).

15. Bevis, P J (DTp)—'*Cycle Facilities in Towns. The Department of Transport's experience*', DTp Velo City Conference (1984).

16. Wall, J F (DTp)—'*National Cycle Policy and Major Cycle Projects in the United Kingdom*', DTp Velo City Conference (1984).

17. Dean, J D—'*Pedestrians and Traffic.*' Planning and Transport Research and Computation Company (PTRC) 10th Summer Annual Meeting. p. 226, PTRC (1982).

18. London Cycling Campaign—'*Guidelines for Shared Use*', LCC.

19. DTp—Leaflet, '*Traffic Signs for Cyclists*', DTp (1983).

18. Bevis, P J (DTp)—'*Three Recent Innovatory Cycle Schemes*', PTRC Summer Annual Meeting, (1983).

19. DTp—LTN 1/83, '*Signs for Cycle Facilities*', DTp (1983).

20. Banister, C and Groom, D—'*Planning for Cycling in the 1980's*', University of Manchester Dept. of Town and Country Planning, (1983).

21. DTp/TRRL—Report LF 972, '*TRRL Research on Cycling*', DTp (1982).

22. DTp/TRRL—Report LF 916, '*Surveys of a Range of Cycleways*', DTp (1982).

23. Hudson, M—'*Bicycle Planning—Policy and Practice*', Architectural Press (1982).

24. DTp—'*Cycling Policy*'—Statement by the Secretary of State for Transport, DTp (1982).

25. Ford, J A (DTp)—'*Development of DTp's Policy on Provision of Facilities for Cyclists*', DTp Velo City Conference (1982).

26. DTp—LTN 1/78, '*Ways of helping cyclists in built-up areas*', DTp (1978).

27. DTp—Traffic Advisory Unit Leaflet, '*Cycling Bibliography*', DTp (Updated Biannually).

26 Measures to Assist Buses

26.1 Introduction

Public transport makes a significant contribution to travel in urban areas and bus services can provide for the movement of large numbers of people while occupying a relatively compact space on the road (see Plate 1.3). They also offer a service to society and contribute to the economic base of an area by providing those who do not have the use of a car with a form of mobility to meet work, social and recreational needs.

The Transport Act 1985

The operation and organisation of public transport in Great Britain was significantly changed by the provisions of the Transport Act 1985 (see Refs. 1 and 2) [Sco.142, NI.2, NI.12]. The main purpose of this Act was to establish a competitive market in the provision of local bus services. To facilitate this Part I of the Act abolished road service licensing outside London and replaced it with a system of registration. Part II retained a licensing system within London. The barriers between bus and taxi operators were also reduced with taxi operators being free to register their vehicles for use as 'local services' (outside London).

The old terminology referring to 'stage carriages', 'express carriages' and 'contract carriages' was replaced by a new twofold definition which established 'local services' and the rest, local services being similar to the previous stage carriage service except that the relevant distance requirement was reduced from 30 to 15 miles. A local service is therefore one carrying passengers at separate fares between points less than 15 miles apart, measured in a straight line.

The Act also provided for the reorganisation and privatisation of the National Bus Company and its subsidiaries and revised the public transport powers and responsibilities of local authorities and Passenger Transport Executives to establish some distance between public transport companies and their parent authorities. The Act requires that local authorities must not inhibit competition between the persons or bodies providing (or seeking to provide) public transport services, or discriminate unfairly in the execution of their powers.

The Act strengthened existing requirements for Public Service Vehicle (PSV) Operator Licences and vehicle maintenance standards. The provisions for driver licensing are unchanged. The Act did, however, make a new provision to enable local traffic authorities to apply to the Commissioner for the determination (under Section 7 of the Transport Act 1985) of traffic regulation conditions in order to prevent danger to road users or to reduce severe traffic congestion (having regard to the interests of those who registered services to operate in the area, the users of such services and the elderly and the disabled). These conditions can affect:

- the routes of bus services;
- the stopping places of bus services;
- the times vehicles may stop and how long; and
- the turning or reversing manoeuvres vehicles may make.

Local highway authorities still retain their wide powers under the Road Traffic Regulation Act 1984 (Ref. 3) to control the use of individual roads and routeing of all classes of vehicle and indeed the exemption from waiting regulations previously afforded to stage carriages (section 3(4) of the 1984 Act) was repealed.

Bus Priority Generally

Many local highway authorities introduce traffic management measures to assist bus operation and give priority to buses over other traffic. Bus priority measures vary in scale and impact from a simple exemption from a maneouvre prohibited to other traffic, to area-wide measures such as priority in urban traffic control schemes.

The main advantages to be obtained from bus priority measures include:

- reduced route mileage, which is likely to save bus operating costs;

- avoidance of delays due to congestion;

- provision of priority access to major traffic generators like shopping centres and transport interchanges;

- improved reliability of services which makes travel by bus more attractive and could increase bus patronage;

- less aggregate delay suffered by travellers if bus journey times are reduced, as vehicle occupancy rates for buses are generally much higher than for private cars; and

- improved services and social benefits for those who do not have use of a car.

Bus priority measures can also have disadvantages in that they can impose restrictions on, or reduce the amount of road space or traffic signal green time available for, other vehicles which may incur additional delay. For these reasons the full costs, benefits and any other effects of each proposal must be carefully assessed to ensure that each scheme provides a net overall benefit to the community as a whole.

Terminology and Signing

A variety of descriptions exist which refer to different types of vehicle and service (eg. bus, coach, taxi, public service vehicle etc.) some of which are defined in legislation whilst others are recognised within the industry (eg. commuter services, hail and ride, extended tours etc.).

Any scheme which seeks to give priority to public transport or conversely to limit access, must recognise the various type of vehicle that may be used to provide public transport and the various types of service provided.

Traffic regulation orders must therefore be worded to reflect the specific intentions of a scheme and traffic signs must also be provided to notify the public of its effects. Since traffic signs must be designed to be easily read and understood, this can limit the complexity of the traffic regulation order and hence the design of the scheme. For this reason signing should be considered during the earliest stages of scheme design.

26.2 Bus Stops

Siting

Bus stops should be located at points where passengers may board and alight safely and conveniently and where disruption to other road users is minimised. Most bus stops will have existed at their present location for many years and should continue to operate satisfactorily unless traffic conditions change. However, the need to provide a new bus stop or to resite an existing one may occur because of a change to services, a new development, or when a specific problem has been identified, such as a road safety hazard in which the bus stop is a contributory factor or where a bus stop is causing unacceptable nuisance to frontage properties. Wherever new stops are proposed by an operator, or an existing stop is to be moved, it will be beneficial if discussions are held between the operator, the local authority and the local police in order to determine the most suitable location.

Ideally, a new bus stop should be located:

● at or near a point where pedestrian routes or paths to or from the generation points of bus trips tend to converge;

● where the stop is unlikely to be detrimental to road safety and where disruption and delay to other traffic will be minimised; and

● away from residential and other sensitive frontages where noise and disturbance are undesirable.

On congested urban roads with continuous frontage development ideal sites may be difficult to find and judgement and compromose will sometimes be necessary to establish the most suitable location.

Frequency of Stops

The frequency of bus stops is typically between 2–3 per kilometre, depending on the density of development. In new residential developments, bus stops should preferably be no more than 300 m apart and arranged to be within 400 m (ie. five minutes' walk) of every individual dwelling. Bus stops on opposite sides of the road should be sited tail-to-tail to be safer for vehicles overtaking and services with a common destination should share the same stop. Walking distances between interchange stops and the need for pedestrians to cross the road to change stops, should be minimised wherever possible. Consideration should also be given to the road surfacing at bus stops to avoid deformation and damage to the surface from the softening effects of fuel and lubricants on bituminous materials.

Footway Treatment

Wherever possible, footways should be sufficiently wide (3.0 m minimum) so that queueing passengers do not obstruct normal pedestrian traffic. Bus shelters will be beneficial at both terminus and boarding stops and can be provided by local authorities, bus operators or commercial advertising companies. This is especially important where the service is infrequent and the stop is particularly exposed to bad weather. Where pedestrian crossing facilities are required they should be provided close to bus stops taking care to ensure that pedestrians are not masked by a standing bus (see Figure 26.1). A bus stop sited close to a pedestrian crossing should preferably be on the exit side of (ie. past) the crossing.

Laybys

Where space permits, bus laybys may be beneficial to reduce the delaying effects of a standing vehicle on routes with heavy traffic. On other roads laybys will not normally be necessary as they are costly to provide and can increase journey times when buses have to wait to re-enter the traffic stream. Where a layby is justified and the full width cannot be provided then a lesser width will still allow a bus to pull over causing less disruption to other traffic (Figure 26.2 gives the standard dimensions for bus laybys of various types).

Parking at Bus Stops

To operate safely and conveniently bus stops must be kept clear of parked vehicles. This can usually be

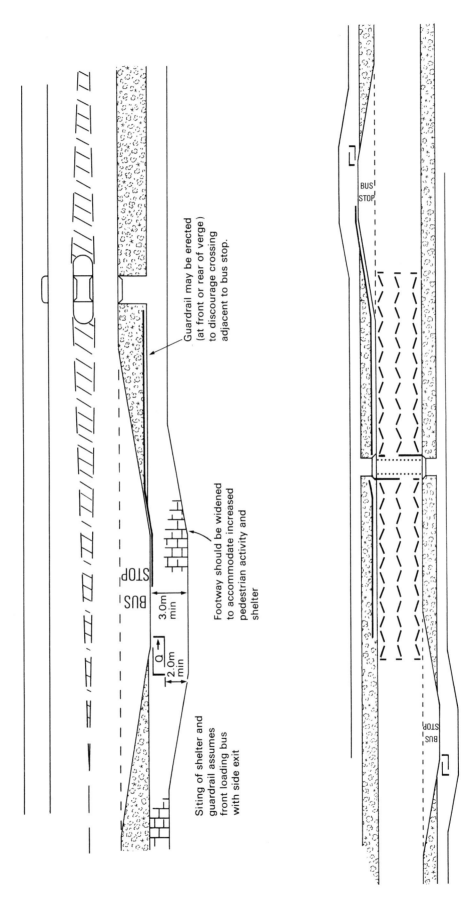

Guardrail may be erected (at front or rear of verge) to discourage crossing adjacent to bus stop.

Footway should be widened to accommodate increased pedestrian activity and shelter

BUS
STOP

3.0m min

Q

2.0m min

Siting of shelter and guardrail assumes front loading bus with side exit

BUS STOP

BUS STOP

Figure 26.1 Pedestrian crossing facilities at bus stop laybys

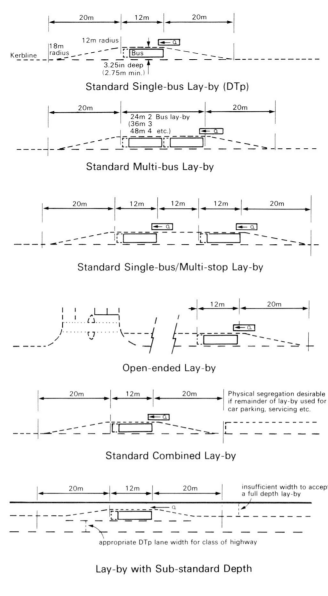

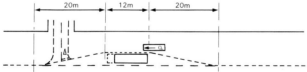

Figure 26.2 Standard dimensions for bus laybys

Source: Urban Planning and Design for Road Public Transport, Confederation of British
Road Passenger Transport (1981)

achieved by providing the prescribed bus stop 'cage' carriageway markings, but where parking demand is high these may be reinforced by an appropriate waiting (and possibly loading) restriction or by introducing a bus stop clearway which has standardised hours of operation set at 7am–7pm (see also the current Traffic Signs Regulations and General Directions—Ref. 4) [Sco.143].

Bus 'Boarders'

At some bus stops in densely parked streets in London, the footway has been extended into the carriageway to provide a 'bus boarder' which discourages parking and permits buses to pull up beside the kerb, assisting people who have difficulty in stepping onto buses from the road surface. (See Figure 26.3 and Plate 26.1.) However, care must be taken to ensure that these features do not create a hazard to moving vehicles when adjacent parking spaces are not occupied.

Bus Terminus and Turning Points

At terminal stops buses may be standing for some time and will usually need to turn round. It is therefore preferable to provide a turning area off the highway

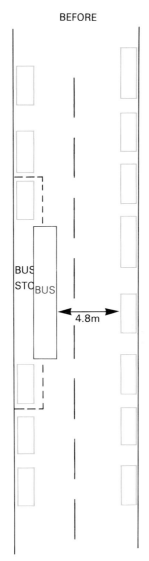

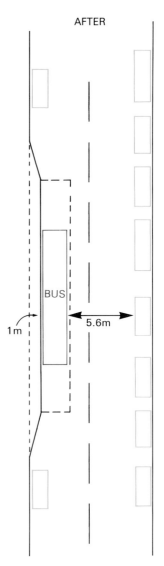

BEFORE

AFTER

BUS STOP BUS

4.8m

BUS

1m   5.6m

Bus stop on typical 11m
two-way road showing
cars parked illegally
at bus stop

Bus stop boarder on typical
11m two-way road

Figure 26.3 Layout for a bus stop 'boarder'   Source: London Borough of Barnet

Plate 26.1 A bus stop 'boarder' in use   Source: S Sexton Esq

unless there is a suitable roundabout or gyratory system which can be used. In residential areas, it is desirable to locate terminals well away from houses. A typical layout for a bus turning area is illustrated in Figure 26.4. Terminal facilities may also be required at large industrial or commercial developments to cater for workers or other special buses (see also Chapter 32).

It is also worth considering the provision of car parking facilities at bus (and rail) terminus points, particularly at out-of-town sites where 'park and ride' schemes can be encouraged to offer travellers a practical alternative to bringing their cars into congested areas.

Bus operators also require places for their vehicles to stand in order to avoid running ahead of the scheduled times and to change crews. Suitable sites should be agreed between the operator, the police and the local

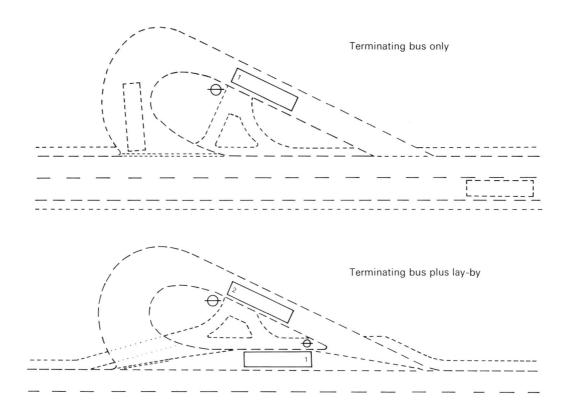

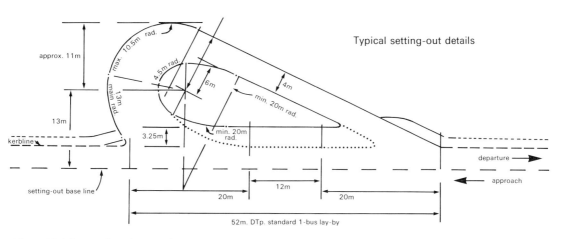

Terminating bus only

Terminating bus plus lay-by

Typical setting-out details

approx. 11m

max. 10.5m rad.

13m main rad.

4.5m rad.

6m

4m

min. 20m rad.

13m

kerbline

3.25m

min. 20m rad.

departure

approach

setting-out base line

20m

12m

20m

52m. DTp. standard 1-bus lay-by

Figure 26.4 Layout for a bus turning area

Source: Urban Planning and Design for Road Public Transport, Confederation of
British Road Passenger Transport (1981)

authority so as to avoid indiscriminate waiting at unsuitable places. Where regular waiting is necessary, off-street facilities should be sought wherever possible and this is particularly important at places of public interest which attract large numbers of vehicles.

26.3 With-flow Bus Lanes

Purpose

A bus lane is created when part of the carriageway is allocated for the use of buses (and other specified categories of vehicle) for all or part of the time. A with-flow bus lane enables buses to pass slow moving or queueing traffic and reduces the delay incurred at bus stops because drivers do not have to wait for a gap to force their way back into the traffic stream. A with-flow bus lane will normally be placed on the nearside of the carriageway (See Figure 26.5 and Plate 26.2) although in certain circumstances, such as within gyratory systems or at approaches to traffic signals where a right turn or straight ahead movement is required, or in one-way streets, the offside might be more appropriate. With-flow bus lanes should be delineated by carriageway markings rather than a physical barrier. They may be emphasised by different surface colouring which tends to assist compliance.

219

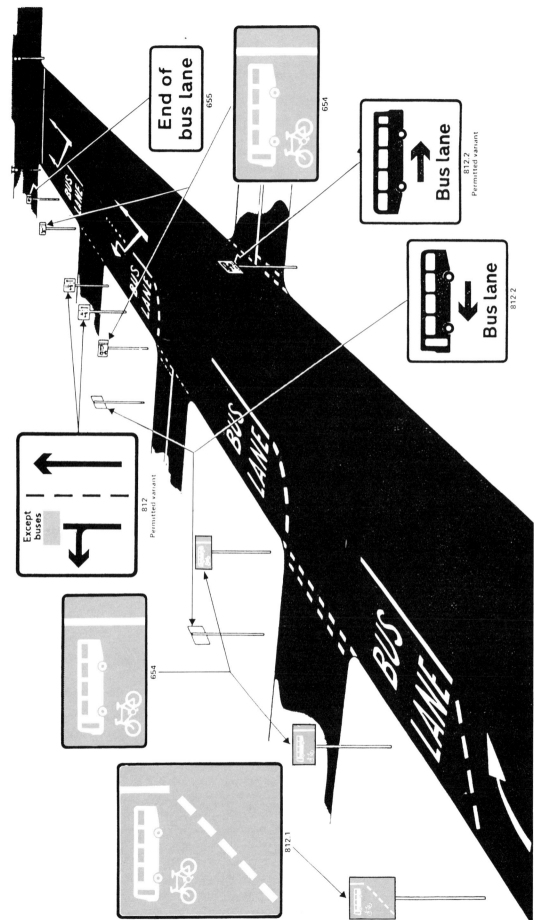

End of bus lane
655

654

Bus lane
812.2
Permitted variant

Bus lane
812.2

Except buses
812
Permitted variant

654

812.1

Figure 26.5 Schematic layout of a with-flow bus lane   [NB. Sign numbers refer to the Traffic Signs and General Directions 1981]

Times of Operation

The priority given to buses over other traffic may only be necessary or justified during peak hours so that kerbside loading may still take place off-peak. When the bus lane is operative throughout the day, loading must be permitted for at least part of that time to ensure reasonable access to frontage properties.

It is useful to standardize operating times for bus lanes in any one area to avoid confusing road users. Peak hours lanes often operate from 7am–10am and/or from 4pm–7pm. All-day lanes often operate between 7am–7pm.

Use by Other Traffic

Cyclists are often permitted to use with-flow bus lanes to avoid their being trapped between a bus on their near-side and another vehicle on their off-side. This provision can sometimes result in slight delays when buses find cyclists difficult to overtake. Consideration should also be given to allowing **taxis, coaches** and **emergency vehicles** to use bus lanes. This can be particularly beneficial where the number of scheduled buses is not very large and the presence of other authorised vehicles can help to enforce the existence of the bus lane, but each scheme should be considered on its merits. **Motorcycles** are not a recommended category of vehicle permitted to use bus lanes since they are capable of keeping up with general traffic and should not be encouraged to weave and overtake on the inside.

Signing of Bus Lanes

The terms of use of bus lanes have to be indicated by traffic signs which must be easy to read and understand at a glance. This can create difficulties for enforcement officers, particularly when permitted classes of vehicle are difficult to distinguish from general traffic (eg. private hire cars). Careful consideration should be given to this aspect of control when deciding which vehicles should be permitted to use bus lanes, but in general all public service vehicles (including taxis operating as local services) should be permitted.

Design of Bus Lanes

A with-flow bus lane should not normally be less than 3.0 m wide, although this may be reduced to 2.8 m over short distances. However, a lane width of 3.5 m is desirable and, if there are significant numbers of cyclists, 3.5 to 4.0 m is preferable. Any reduction below 3.0 m may result in damage to kerbside street furniture and create a serious hazard for pedestrians on adjacent footways because of the overhang of driving mirrors.

At junctions, particularly where traffic other than buses is permitted to go straight ahead or turn left, the end of the bus lane should be set back from the stop line to allow the full width to be used by all traffic and thus maintain full saturation flows at the junction. At traffic signals, for example, an estimate of the setback can be made by allowing 2–3 metres for every second of green time on the approach. The extent of this setback is crucial to the efficiency of the junction.

26.4 Contra-flow Bus Lanes

In many older urban centres complex and sometimes circuitous one-way systems have evolved. It may be possible to allow buses to by-pass some of these systems by the use of contra-flow bus lanes whereby buses are permitted to travel against the general flow of traffic. The introduction of contra-flow bus lanes need particularly careful planning, design and publicity, as pedestrians and other drivers will no longer be accustomed to two-way traffic on what may previously have been a one-way street (see Figures 26.6 and Plate 26.3). It is for this reason that contra-flow lanes tend to have higher accident levels than with-flow lanes.

Contra-flow bus lanes can be delineated by a continuous physical island or by the appropriate carriageway markings supplemented by refuge islands at close intervals. Islands can highlight the particular two-way nature of the road for pedestrians and help them to cross but can give rise to problems for loading vehicles or for overtaking parked or broken down vehicles. They can also intensify wheel tracking of the carriageway surfacing.

Special attention is necessary to the design of entry points to a bus lane where drivers in a one-way street are confronted by an opposing traffic stream. A refuge island with bollards and keep-left roundels will reinforce the associated carriageway markings and road signs. Similarly, pedestrian guardrailing and judiciously located warning signs and carriageway markings will make pedestrians aware of the increased dangers and encourage them to look in the right direction when crossing the road.

Cyclists should not normally be permitted to use contra-flow lanes unless the lane is 4.0 m or more wide so that a bus may safely overtake a cyclist without entering the opposing traffic stream. If cyclists are to use contra-flow bus lanes then there should be adequate provision for them at the entry and exit points and 'Buses and cycles only' signs (WBM 267/267.1) would need to be authorised by the Secretary of State for use at the entry to the lane instead of the diagram 616 'No Entry' signs with exemption plates.

Kerbside Loading

Contra-flow bus lanes can create considerable difficulties where frontage properties require regular servicing from the carriageway. It is not normally

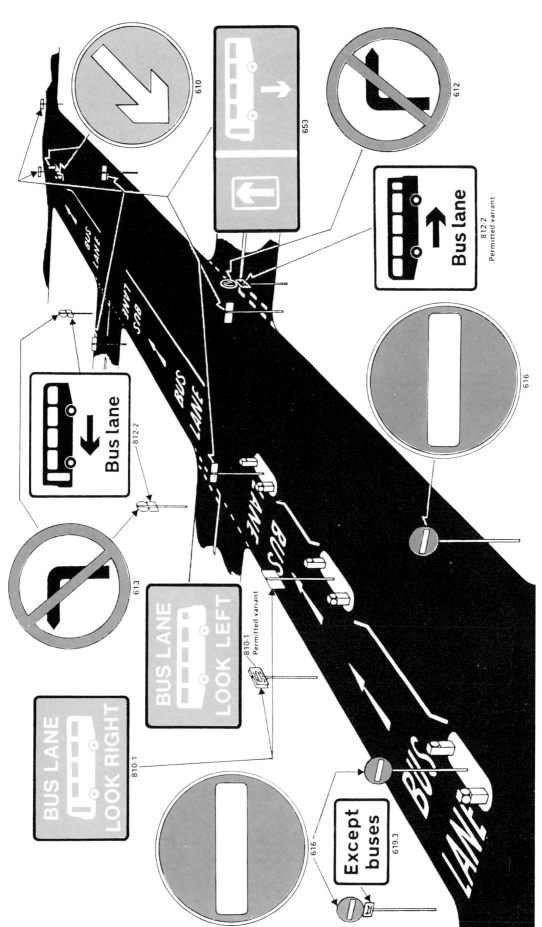

Figure 26.6 Schematic layout of a contra-flow bus lane   [NB. Sign numbers refer to Traffic Signs Regulations and General Directions 1981]

Plate 26.3 A contra-flow bus lane

Source: G Crow Esq

appropriate to allow access vehicles to travel the full
length of the bus lane so they may have to be permitted
to cross the white line to gain access to the kerb. If a
continuous island is used to separate the lane then
loading might be permitted from vehicles parked
alongside it, but this would involve crossing the bus
lane. In addition, contra-flow lanes complicate junction
operations which can have an effect which counteracts
the improved efficiency for which one-way systems are
introduced.

26.5 Evaluation and Assessment of Bus Lanes

No bus lane should be installed without first
undertaking a comparative evaluation of the expected
benefits to buses against the costs of installation and
any estimated disbenefits to other traffic.

Different locations and types of bus lane can be
evaluated for each site. Surveys of the road network
and affected bus routes should determine the journey
times of buses and other traffic, delays experienced on
the routes and at junctions in different traffic conditions
and the walking times of passengers between bus stops
and popular destinations.

Contra-flow bus lanes in particular have been shown
to reduce delays and operating costs for buses and
maintain or improve passengers' access to bus services
(see also Refs. 5 and 6).

Bus lanes should be considered where they:

● give a real advantage to buses;

● do not significantly reduce overall network capacity
  or cause congestion by inducing excessive queues;

● yield a net benefit to the community;

● would have minimal adverse effects on road safety,
  frontagers and on the adjacent environment;

● may assist the flow of other traffic.

Further advice on the evaluation of all types of bus
priority measure is available from the Department of
Transport's Traffic Advisory Unit [Sco.144].

26.6 High Capacity Bus Systems

One of the problems with bus lanes, especially when
they are segregated from general traffic movements, is

223

coping with several services which may run partially on common routes and tend to obstruct one another at bus stops, with the consequence of limiting the capacity of the bus lane.

Two systems have been developed for use in South America to minimise this problem; **bus convoys** and **express trunk lines.**

The **bus convoy system** (see Figure 26.7(a)) allows a group of buses to operate like a train while passing through crowded corridors. Each group of buses stops simultaneously at bus stops and departs together in a convoy. In the example, buses from a number of routes are divided into three groups A, B, C, depending on their general destinations. Bus stops along the route are similarly divided into well marked areas, A, B, C, enabling passengers to board the three buses simultaneously. Such a system operating in Sao Paulo, Brazil has regularly handled 300 buses per hour carrying 12,000 passengers per hour at an overall operating speed of 19 km/h on one traffic lane.

Even higher flows can be achieved adopting an **express trunk line** (see Figure 26.7(b)). With this system conventional buses feed a bus terminal at the start of the trunk line where passengers will transfer to special trunk buses (according to their designations), perhaps trolly buses with higher capacity and more door space to allow rapid loading and unloading. Each line then runs without stops until it reaches the specific section of the corridor it is serving. This approach is beneficial if the extra time required for passengers to transfer is made up by time saved on the trunk route.

Both of these systems required extremely detailed planning which may be difficult to achieve where services are run by more than one operator. In Europe the provision of feeder services timed to coincide with trunk services (usually rail) is quite common.

(a) BUS CONVOY

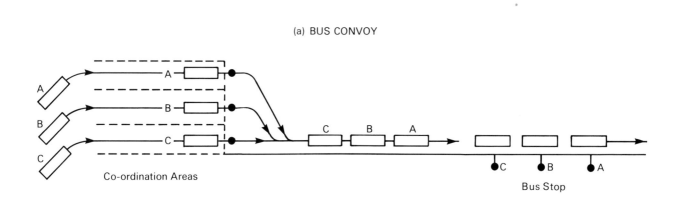

(b) EXPRESS TRUNK LINE

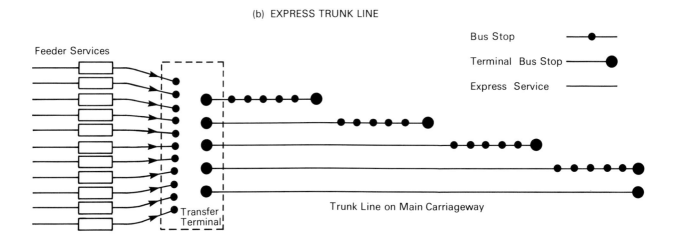

Figure 26.7 High capacity bus systems

26.7 Bus Priority at Junctions

Exemptions from Prohibited Turns

Most of the delay on urban highway networks occurs at junctions. In order to increase junction capacity or reduce the likelihood of accidents it may be beneficial to prohibit some manoeuvres, especially right turns. The resulting reduction in delay will benefit buses, along with other traffic. However, when the prohibited manoeuvre results in increased bus mileage, or interrupts a bus route, consideration might be given to exempting buses from the prohibition. Any decision to do so will need to take into account the number of buses involved and the implications for junction capacity and road safety.

Other Priority Techniques

As explained above, buses can avoid queues on the approach to a junction by using a with-flow bus lane. Other methods of achieving priority for buses at junctions involve the provision of special facilities at signal controlled junction such as:

● extending the green time on bus route approaches or allocating two stages in a cycle to the bus route so that, for example, an existing traffic signal sequence 1, 2, 3, becomes 1, 2, 1, 3, where buses have right of way during stage 1;

● if buses can be provided with an exclusive approach to a signal controlled junction, inductive loops on that stage might give a priority call for, or extension of, an appropriate stage; or

● providing selective vehicle detection tuned to react only to buses (see also Refs. 7 and 8). No exclusive lanes are provided but when a bus is detected there will be a priority call. This is generally only appropriate at junctions which are not saturated.

These techniques are most appropriate when there is only one main bus movement at a junction and therefore only one signal stage to be prioritised.

26.8 Measures to Assist Buses in Environmental Areas

Bus Only Streets

In many town centres some streets are closed to certain classes of vehicle for all or part of the day in order to create a better environment for pedestrians. Buses are often exempted from these restrictions to create in effect a 'bus only' street which facilitates access for buses to the very centre of the shopping or business district, reduces the distance for passengers to walk and makes buses more attractive for trips into the centre (see also Chapter 24.11 which deals with pedestrianisation).

However, the presence of any vehicles in such streets detracts somewhat from a relaxed pedestrian environment and may endanger safety when traffic flows are very light and pedestrians become less aware of the potential danger. This may be aggravated where rear engined buses are used as the front of the vehicle can be 12 m in front of the source of engine noise. In such circumstances the major responsibility rests with drivers to avoid pedestrians and they should be made well aware of this.

On any lightly trafficked road drivers tend to travel faster than is appropriate unless deterred by road geometry and design features. Central area bus only streets should therefore avoid long straight lengths and introduce curves, reinforced by the judicious siting of planting boxes or other street furniture. In an environment where pedestrian activity predominates, kerb faces should be the minimum required to provide a drainage check and in some cases only differences in surfacing may be necessary. However, on the curved alignments of bus only streets and at bus stops within a pedestrian area, a full face kerb will help to prevent vehicle overrun and will also help pedestrians to board the bus.

The choice of an appropriately durable surface for the bus carriageway is important. Whilst its appearance should be sympathetic with that of the street scene generally, it must be structurally adequate for its purpose. Coloured asphalt and small block paving are among the materials currently used but the design specification should be such as to avoid damage and deformation due to vehicle 'tracking' particularly where the carriageway width has been reduced to a single lane.

Bus Links and Gates

A **bus link** consists of a length of bus only road and a **bus gate** enables a bus to pass between two roads where other traffic is prohibited and may or may not involve a physical barrier. While bus gates and links can be useful in town centres they are most commonly used away from central areas.

The constraints imposed on the design of new residential or industrial areas by the desire to achieve low vehicle speeds and discourage extraneous traffic, may make it impossible to provide a suitable route for an efficient bus service (see also Chapter 31 and Ref. 9). As buses will usually be restricted to local distributor roads with a minimum width of 6.7 m, it may be appropriate to link two otherwise self contained road networks with a length of exclusive bus only road (a bus link). There will often be strong pressure from different road user groups (eg. residents or delivery vehicles) to use these links and enforcement may be a problem where the alternative route is circuitous. Emergency vehicles will normally be exempted but

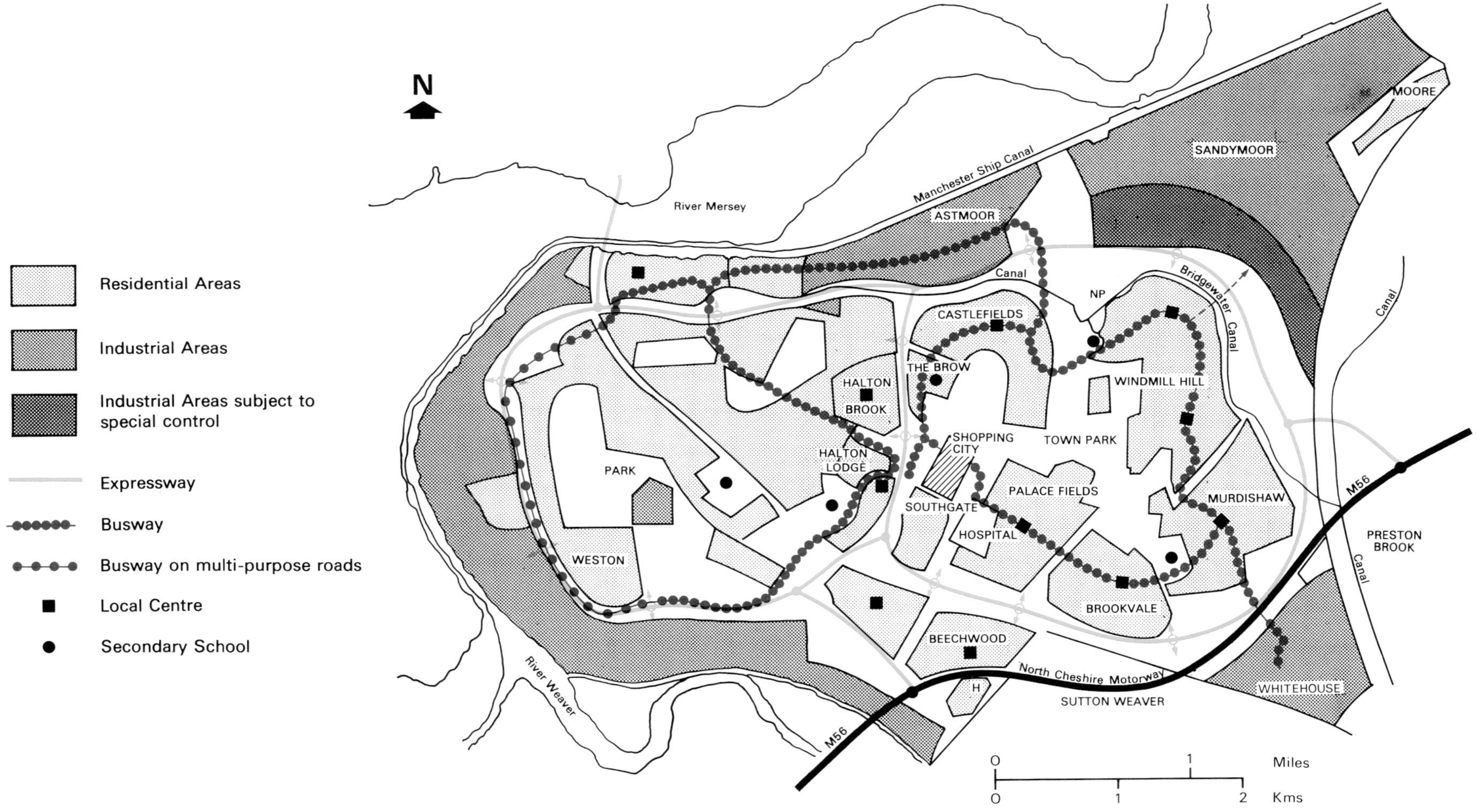

Residential Areas

Industrial Areas

Industrial Areas subject to special control

Expressway

Busway

Busway on multi-purpose roads

Local Centre

Secondary School

N

MOORE

SANDYMOOR

PRESTON BROOK

Canal

M56

WHITEHOUSE

Canal

Bridgewater Canal

MURDISHAW

WINDMILL HILL

NP

TOWN PARK

PALACE FIELDS

BROOKVALE

Manchester Ship Canal

ASTMOOR

Canal

CASTLEFIELDS

THE BROW

SHOPPING CITY

SOUTHGATE

HOSPITAL

BEECHWOOD

H

North Cheshire Motorway

SUTTON WEAVER

River Mersey

HALTON BROOK

HALTON LODGE

PARK

WESTON

River Weaver

M56

Miles

Kms

0 1 2

Figure 26.8 Plan showing the busway in Runcorn New Town (Cheshire)

Source: Runcorn Development Corporation

caution should be applied to admitting any other motor vehicle. Longer bus links may often be preferred to a shorter bus gate because they are easier to enforce.

Regulatory signing of bus gates and links (as well as bus lanes) requires particular consideration. Compliance by other traffic is generally higher when a 'No Entry' sign is erected with the supplementary plate 'Except Buses', rather than the permissive 'Buses Only' type of sign. The current regulations do not permit the signing of an exemption for cyclists to a 'No Entry' sign, so a separate cycle gate must be provided. Alternatively all motor vehicles may be prohibited with an exemption for buses although the general level of compliance by other traffic may be reduced.

The problem of compliance can be overcome by the introduction of a physical barrier employing a system of selective detection, although any hardware failure would cause inconvenience and delay to bus passengers.

Priority for Buses in Traffic Management Schemes

A package of traffic management measures such as co-ordinated traffic signals, limiting the flow of traffic from side roads and banning turns, can be designed specifically to give priority for buses as well as improving conditions for other traffic. To avoid detours from existing bus routes, buses can be exempted from turns banned from the main route and allowed to enter or cross the route where other side road traffic is prevented. Bus lanes, one-way streets and signal settings to favour buses can also be included. The Bitterne Road scheme in Southampton showed that such measures could achieve significant reductions in bus journey times for passengers (Ref. 10).

Busways

In area-wide redevelopment schemes and in new towns, roads may be constructed specifically for the exclusive use of buses. These reserved tracks avoid any delays which might occur on the ordinary road network and can link directly to the most important residential, industrial and shopping areas. An example of this approach is shown in Figure 26.8 and on Plates 26.4 and 26.5. For reasons of financial economy and reduced land requirements, automatically guided or tracked busways may be preferred to other types of busway which rely on manual steering.

Plate 26.4 Aerial view of the Runcorn busway

[NB. The busway is shown with a broken white line]

Source: Warrington and Runcorn Development Corporation

Plate 26.5 A segregated busway (part of the Runcorn system)

Source G Jacobs (TRRL)

26.9 References

Text Reference

1. Transport Act 1985, HMSO 1985. (26.1)

2. DTp—Circular 3/85, *'Transport Act 1985'* DTp (1985). [Sco.142, Wa.37] (26.1)

3. Road Traffic Regulation Act 1984, HMSO (1984). (26.1)

4. Traffic Signs Regulations and General Directions 1981, Statutory Instrument 1981 No 859, HMSO (1981). (26.1)

5. DoE/DTp/TRRL—Report LR 809, *'With flow bus lanes: economic justification using a theoretical model'*, DoE/DTp (1979). (26.5)

6. DoE/DTp/TRRL—Report LR 918, *'Contra-flow bus lanes: economic justification using a theoretical model'*, DoE/ DTp (1979). (26.5)

7. DTp—H2/77, *'Bus priority at traffic signals using selective detection'*, (Corrigendum 25/10/77), DTp (1977). (26.7)

8. Dow, I M—*'The Department of Transport bus detector'*, Traffic Engineering and Control, Vol 18 Nos 1 and 2 (1977). (26.7)

9. DoE—Circular 82/73, *'Bus operation in residential and industrial areas'*, DoE (1973). [Wa.38] (26.8)

10. DoE—*'Working Group on Bus Demonstration Projects, and subsequent Summary Reports 1-9'*, DoE (1970-1976). (26.8)

26.10 Further Information

11. Addenbrooke et al—*'Urban planning and design for road public transport'*, Confederation of British Road Passenger Transport (now the Bus and Coach Council), London (1981).

12. DTp—*'Bus Selective Detection in Swansea'*, Report by Traffic Advisory Unit, DTp (1980).

13. DTp/TRRL—Report LR 925, *'Bus-actuated Traffic Signals: Initial assessment, Part of the Swansea Bus Priority Scheme'*, DTp (1980).

14. National Bus Company—NBC Research Report No 19: *'Bus Priority Schemes'*, NBC (1978).

15. DTp—H6/76, *'Implementation of bus priorities'*, DTp (1976). [Sco.144]

16. DoE/TRRL—*'Bus priority systems, NATO CCMS Report 45'*, DoE (1976).

27 The Management of Heavy Goods Vehicles

27.1 Introduction

The movement of goods is essential to the wealth of the nation and of £23.3 billion spent in the UK on inland freight transport in 1985, over £22.7 billion (or 97.5 per cent) was spent on sending freight by road. This is not surprising as it is the only practical means of delivery to and collection from farms, shops, offices and most factories and warehouses.

The location of warehousing and distribution points near to major urban centres; the necessity for transhipment between rail borne, water borne, air borne and road borne freight to obtain access to centres of industry and commerce located in or close to urban areas; and the need to provide services and delivery access to residential areas, will all continue to ensure that careful management of heavy commercial vehicles will be necessary for the foreseable future to minimise their impact on the environment and the community whilst recognising and providing for their essential functions.

Although the overall number of lorries has remained fairly constant, their size and weight has increased and there is considerable public concern about their effect on the environment, on people and on local communities. Complaints are made about noise and exhaust emissions and pedestrians, cyclists and car drivers sometimes feel that their safety is threatened. These problems are perceived at their worst when lorries use unsuitable roads.

Heavy lorries can also cause severe wear and tear on roads but the propensity to cause wear and deterioration increases very rapidly with axle weight rather than overall vehicle weight; it is therefore not always the heaviest or largest lorries which create the greatest wear. In order to minimise the adverse effects of heavy commercial vehicles, manufacturers are continually working with the Department of Transport to develop improvements in such areas as axle loadings and exhaust emission, noise and other performance characteristics. In addition, the Road Vehicles (Construction and Use) Regulations (1986) lay down stringent design and in-use requirements to limit environmental nuisance.

There are, however, still opportunities to manage the movement of goods vehicles by the use of regulatory controls, traffic management techniques and through voluntary and advisory routeing arrangements. These measures are described below.

27.2 The Effects of Heavy Goods Vehicles

Problems commonly associated with heavy goods vehicles are:

- danger and nuisance to persons (from noise, fumes and visual intrusion) caused by the passage of heavy traffic on unsuitable routes through sensitive areas (eg. residential areas);

- damage to the highway because of high axle loadings;

- intimidation due to close proximity of large vehicles to pedestrians and cyclists;

- damage to footways caused by parking or passage of vehicles;

- danger and inconvenience to other road users, including pedestrians, by parking or unloading in unsuitable places;

- the effects of noise and vibration on buildings; and

- intrusion and noise caused by overnight parking and early morning starting up at unsuitable locations.

See also Chapters 12 and 19 which deal with environmental assessment and protection and Ref. 1.

When area-wide management measures are being planned to control the movement and parking of heavy goods vehicles, local and national operators and their representative bodies should always be consulted to determine their requirements and the extent to which they might be affected by any scheme. The wider effects of all schemes should be assessed beforehand and monitored afterwards to ensure that a localised problem has been truly alleviated and not merely displaced elsewhere. Whenever controls are being considered the evaluation should take account of the adverse effects on vehicle operating costs, time and convenience and these must be weighed against the expected level of benefits to ensure that the measures are worthwhile.

27.3 Non-regulatory Controls

Advisory Routeing

Advisory route signing using the 'white lorry' sign can be beneficial in directing heavy traffic onto suitable routes and discouraging the use of unsuitable ones. It is relatively cheap and quick to provide but may not be sufficient to reroute traffic where a more obvious and direct route is still available. The difficulties of

Plate 27.1 Automatic detection signing for over-height vehicles
[The insert shows the detection device]

Source: Mid-Glamorgan County Council

compliance can be reduced by introducing physical barriers which are self enforcing and by discussing the problems with local operators.

Physical Barriers

The simplest physical measure is a **height barrier** though these are usually only used to give advance warning of physical restrictions ahead (eg. a low bridge). They can, however, be useful when placed at the entrance to a car park, or elsewhere, to physically prevent access by oversized vehicles. An illustration of an automatic warning system provided at a low bridge, is shown in Plate 27.1 (the sign is actuated by a height detector unit).

On the highway it may be possible to narrow the carriageway (under Highway Act 1980 powers) to less than 2.5 m at selected points to prevent the passage of large vehicles (a 2.28 m clear width between posts is often used, see Fig 27.1 which shows a number of typical layouts). The method of construction, using for example bollards or planting boxes, will need to be particularly robust to withstand a certain amount of abuse, especially in the early stages of introduction as drivers who have not seen, or have chosen to ignore,

the associated warning signs may try to squeeze through. It will usually be necessary to locate such a **width restriction** adjacent to an existing junction which can be used as a turning head for those drivers who have not complied with the warning signs.

Width restrictions and other physical barriers are, however, usually supported by traffic regulation orders to introduce a legal sanction against vehicles which disregard the physical control (see Plate 27.2).

Width restrictions can effectively create culs-de-sac without turning space, so that large vehicles can become trapped and may have to reverse for long distances. It is therefore important that they be signed well in advance.

There are a number of problems associated with physical width restrictions as they are inappropriate for bus routes and can be detrimental to normal servicing requirements, particularly refuse vehicles, furniture removal vans and coal and fuel delivery vehicles. Although ambulances will normally be able to pass a width restriction, fire appliances will usually be prevented and the additional distance for emergency

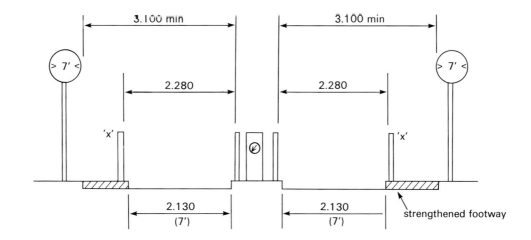

Fig. A: FOR CARRIAGEWAY WIDTH 5.100 – 7.500m

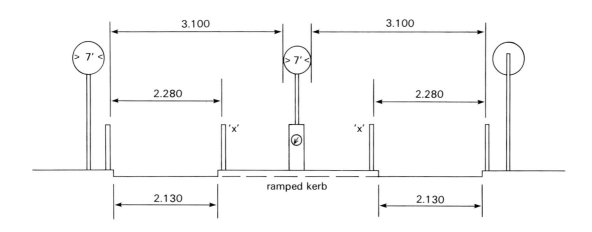

Fig. B: FOR CARRIAGEWAY WIDTH 7.500 – 9.000m

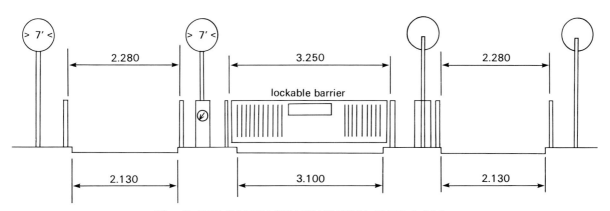

Fig. C: FOR CARRIAGEWAY WIDTH OVER 9.000m

Notes (i)   'x' = removable/collapsible steel bollard

(ii)   A clear width of 2.280m between bollards permits an ambulance to pass without the attendant having to leave a casualty to unlock the barrier.

(iii)   Further details of width instructions are given in the Code of Practice for Local Authorities/Emergency Services available through ALBES.

Figure 27.1 Typical layouts for width restrictions

Source: Highways and Traffic Management in London, ALBES/DTp (1986)

Plate 27.2 A typical width restriction

Source: G Crow Esq

vehicles may have more important consequences than those of cost. It may be possible to provide a lockable barrier or removeable bollards for fire appliances but this will add extra time penalties to the journey. Whenever width restrictions are contemplated discussions should be held with all of the emergency services at the earliest stages (for further information see also Chapter 17 on emergency access).

27.4 Regulatory Controls

Local highway authorities are empowered to make traffic regulation orders to control the movement of heavy goods vehicles as a specified class of traffic under the Road Traffic Regulation Act 1984 (Ref. 2) [NI.42].

Weight, Width and Length Registrictions

For many years local authorities have taken action to protect sensitive or weak parts of the highway infrastructure from the effects of heavy vehicles. For example, prohibiting them from using weak or low bridges using both regulatory and advance warning signs.

In 1973 the legislation was extended by the Heavy Commercial Vehicles (Controls and Regulations) Act 1973 (now incorporated in the Road Traffic Regulation Act 1984) to include environmental considerations and regulatory signs are available to limit the weight, width and (less commonly) the length of vehicles in unsuitable areas.

Where necessary, regulatory controls can be used to reinforce physical measures but the aim should be to achieve compliance by good design and driver understanding and not to rely solely on these controls, which can impose a heavy burden on police manpower.

Parking and Loading Restrictions

The simplest form of restriction to affect heavy vehicles is a prohibition of on-street loading as well as parking, usually introduced to maintain traffic flow on important routes. Where there are consequences for servicing frontage premises, such restrictions are usually only introduced in peak traffic hours. Studies in many European cities have indicated that most deliveries take place in the morning and that only a very small percentage occur in the afternoon. Therefore restrictions should usually be aimed at the morning peak whereas evening peak loading restrictions may be unnecessary.

Restrictions on Access

In many older shopping streets, where rear servicing facilities are not available, conflict often occurs between delivery vehicles and other commercial activities on the street, especially pedestrian movements. This has encouraged many local authorities to restrict access to such streets during certain times of the day, usually mid-morning to late afternoon, to coincide with the highest levels of pedestrian activity. Others have introduced full or partial pedestrianisation (see also Chapter 24).

Although part or full pedestrianisation schemes are beneficial to pedestrians, owners of local businesses sometimes fear an adverse effect on trade, caused by the absence of passing vehicles and less direct vehicular access. However, in practice these fears are usually proved to be groundless and trade often improves, sometimes at the expense of neighbouring areas. There may, however, be adverse consequences for deliveries. It may be relatively easy for an operator to reschedule deliveries to cater for one or two restrictions, but when several shopping centres in the same region have similar schemes then the operator's difficulties become more acute. For such schemes to be successful, full consultation should take place with both traders and operators of delivery vehicles (see also Ref. 3). In some cases it may be necessary to allow limited access for delivery purposes but each scheme must be judged on its merits.

Sometimes existing premises can be adapted to provide loading bays and service yards and rear service ways can sometimes be created with the consent and co-operation of occupiers and owners. For new industrial and town centre developments see also Chapters 32 and 33.

27.5 Area-wide Traffic Management Measures

The intrusion of heavy vehicles is likely to be perceived as being at its worst in residential areas where people might reasonably expect peace and quiet (see also Chapter 19 on environmental protection). Particular aggravation can occur at night or weekend.

There are two main types of area-wide measures that can be applied to minimise environmental intrusion by heavy vehicles:—

Lorry Mangement Schemes

Removing heavy vehicles from residential areas may be achieved in a number of ways, the simplest being to prohibit them from a short length of a street, by reference to 7.5 or 16.5 tonnes maximum gross vehicle weight. This acts as a 'plug' and forces drivers to divert on to another more suitable route (see Figure 27.2). Sufficient advanced warning must be given by erecting signs some distance from the plug, showing the restriction on advance direction signs. Any order which incorporates exemptions, particularly 'except for access'

(with its attendant problems of definition) is likely to reduce compliance and increase enforcement difficulties. It is now more usual to specify 'except for loading', as this is easier to enforce.

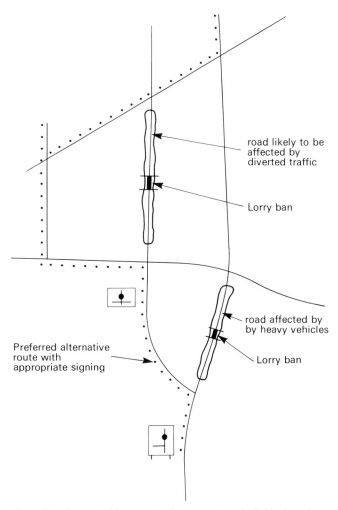

Figure 27.2 Layout of lorry controls to protect an individual road or small area

Lorry controls are notoriously difficult to enforce, especially when applied to a short length of highway. Drivers are often prepared to take the risk of being detected by a police officer to avoid the inconvenience and time penalty of a more circuitous route. To overcome this, several independent regulatory controls, supported by physical measures, might be introduced to protect a series of streets, or planned in conjunction with each other to protect an environmental area (see Fig 27.3).

Lorry Cordons

An alternative to an area lorry ban is the lorry cordon whereby controls are made in one direction only, preventing vehicles from entering an area (but not from leaving it) except on specified routes, or for specified purposes. This measure can be effective in preventing through traffic and can reduce the exposure to heavy vehicle noise for those living in the area, while maintaining reasonable facilities for access and deliveries.

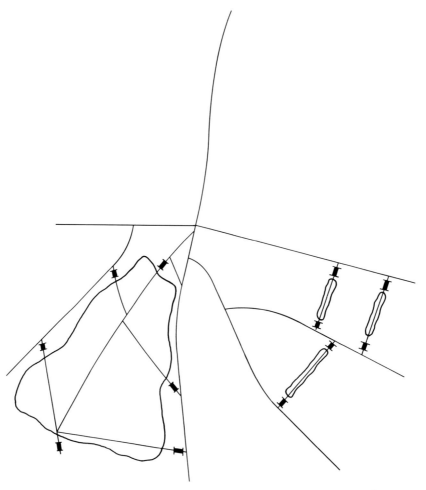

Figure 27.3 Layout of lorry controls to protect an environmental area and adjacent streets

An example of this type of measure is shown in Figure 27.4 (Refs. 4 and 5).

Permit Based Schemes

In some cases lorry control measures have been based on the use of permits issued by the local authority to operators complying with some specified criterion like, for example, need for access or related to the physical characteristics of the vehicle. This approach needs to be treated with caution since it is administratively cumbersome, is vulnerable to misuse and could result in operators having to display a variety of such permits for use in different areas. It may, however, have merit in particular circumstances where a limited number of specific vehicles require exemption from a general control.

27.6 The Evaluation of Lorry Controls

As with other traffic management measures the evaluation of the effects of lorry controls should take account of both the environmental benefits gained by residents of an area and the additional operating costs incurred by the freight transport industry. A method for doing this is described in the ALBES Code of Practice for Highways and Traffic Management in London (Ref. 6), based on assessment of the numbers of people and dwellings affected and the scale of the problem. Further information on assessment techniques is also given in Chapter 12 and in Chapter 19.6 on the evaluation of environmental measures (but see also Ref. 7).

Use of standardised and systematic techniques will be of great value in presenting schemes for decision. Since schemes involving traffic regulation orders may involve public inquiries, the data collected will enable the facts to be presented in a clear and objective way.

27.7 Longer Term Measures

Transfer from Road to Rail

As explained in 27.1 the characteristics of many freight movements will render them inherently unsuitable for transfer from road to rail. However, such transfers are sometimes worthy of consideration and grants are obtainable under Section 8 of the Railways Act 1974. The 'Rail Freight Facilities Grant Scheme', enables grants to be given (by government) towards the capital

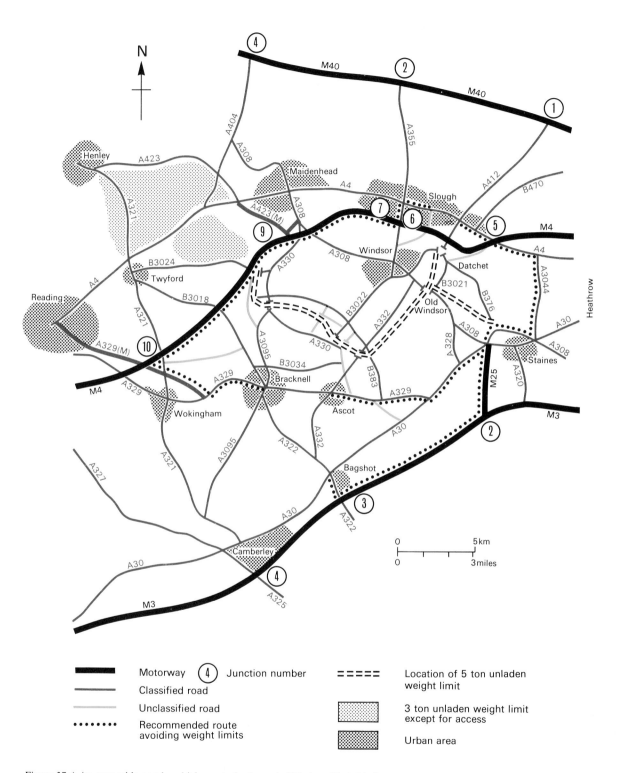

Figure 27.4 An area-wide goods vehicle control scheme in Windsor (Berkshire)

Source: DOE/DTp TRRL Report SR 381 'Review of the result of
lorry planning studies (1978)

cost of new or modernised facilities, especially private sidings, handling equipment and railway wagons. A grant may help to make rail transport competitive with road and lead to a reduction in heavy lorry traffic but to qualify it is necessary to demonstrate that the proposal would not have been commercially viable without the grant.

New Road Construction

The provision of a new alternative route may be justified if there is a particularly severe problem of heavy vehicles passing through, for example, the main street of a local centre.

Development Control

The routeing of heavy vehicles can also be influenced, in the longer term, by development control. The general aim will be to identify land-use areas which might give rise to significant numbers of heavy vehicles and to discourage such developments where they are inappropriate.

Controls on Operator's Licences

An operating centre is defined in Section 52 of the Transport Act 1982 (Ref. 8) [NI.43] as the base or centre at which the vehicle is normally kept. References to an operating centre of the holder of an operator's licence are references to any place which is an operating centre for vehicles authorised under the licence.

The Goods Vehicles (Operators' Licences, Qualifications and Fees) Regulations 1984 as amended by the Goods Vehicles (Operators' Licences, Qualifications and Fees) (Amendment) Regulations 1986 (Ref. 9) [NI.44], set out the environmental considerations and conditions licensing authorities may take into account. This is not a supplement to planning and a licensing authority can only control vehicles authorised on the licence. Local authorities should receive copies of all applications and details free from Traffic Area Offices. These list all applications and give details of operating centres.

There are 21 days [NI.45] in which to object. A local authority, a planning authority, a chief officer of police and a trade union or association can lodge an objection to the granting of an operator's licence with the licensing authority. In addition, representation against the grant or variation of an operator's licence on environmental grounds may be made by any person who owns or occupies land (including buildings) in the vicinity of an operating centre, provided that any adverse effects on environmental conditions arising from the use of the operating centre would be capable of prejudicially affecting the use or enjoyment of that land.

Appeals against a licensing authority's decisions may be made to the Transport Tribunal.

Controls Based on Developments in Communications Technology

Methods using vehicle-to-roadside communications systems are under development in different parts of the world. These offer the prospect of saving police manpower and of recording unauthorised entry of vehicles into banned areas. Demonstration projects are under way in the USA and are being planned in the UK, but it will be some years before these techniques can be widely and effectively employed.

Overnight Lorry Parks

Where the problem is larger and more diverse a suitably located secure lorry park may need to be considered. Any lorry park provided for this purpose should be reasonably close to the area of greatest demand with good access by public transport. It should not be directly adjacent to any residential properties which could suffer nuisance and disturbance. The object is to reduce or solve problems not simply to move them elsewhere.

27.8 Abnormal Indivisible Loads

General

The road layout and structure in most urban areas has been designed, or has evolved, to cater for a certain maximum size and weight of vehicle. The normal size and weight limits are contained in the Road Vehicles (Construction and Use) Regulations 1986 (Ref. 10) [NI.46] and it is unlawful to exceed these. However, some loads are very large and/or heavy and yet indivisible (ie. they cannot reasonably be divided and thereby reduced in size and weight) for road transport purposes. These loads may have to be transported on specialised vehicles which are larger and heavier than normal lorries (see Plate 27.3).

The Motor Vehicles (Authorisation of Special Types) General Order 1979 (the 'STGO') (Ref. 11) [NI.47] authorises the road use of specific kinds of abnormally large and/or heavy vehicles which either laden or unladen exceed the Construction and Use Regulations limits. Such vehicles include abnormal load carriers, mobile cranes, large tipper lorries, etc.

Size

Under the Construction and Use Regulations and the STGO [NI.47], notice of the movement of the following must be sent in advance to the police who may consult the local highway authority for advice on appropriate routes:

Plate 27.3 An abnormal indivisible load

Source: Chief Constable Hampshire

● a load projecting more than 305 mm (12 inches) either side of the vehicle;

● a vehicle or load exceeding 2.9 m (9 feet 6 inches) in width;

● a vehicle or load exceeding 18.3 m (60 feet) rigid length;

● a motor vehicle, trailer and load together exceeding 25.9 m (85 feet) in length;

● a load projecting more than 3.05 m (10 feet) over the front or rear of the vehicle;

● a vehicle or vehicle and load exceeding 76,200 kgs (75 tons), gross weight.

Weight

The STGO authorises the road use of specific kinds of vehicle which either laden or unladen exceeds the Construction and Use axle or gross weight limits provided that all highway and bridge authorities along the route are:

● notified in advance of details of the vehicle and route; and

● indemnified against any damage caused thereby; and

that the vehicle travels at a reduced speed on ordinary roads (not applicable on motorways).

Routeing

The recommended routes for loads of abnormal dimensions will not necessarily be the same for each load but will be constrained by physical features such as bridges under and over the carriageway, restricted junctions and street furniture. For especially large loads, the route may be extremely circuitous in order to avoid these features, but local authorities will be aware of the most appropriate routes for different types and sizes of load. These routes may be designated as especially appropriate for abnormal loads and opportunities may be taken to replace existing street furniture with designs which are easily demountable and, in the longer term, it may be beneficial to amend layouts which regularly present problems.

The informal status of a route set aside for abnormal loads should also be taken into account and not compromised when any junction improvement or maintenance schemes are designed. Loads requiring this type of consideration, although important for local industry, are unlikely to be frequent enough to create long term environmental or road safety problems.

27.9 Hazardous Loads

Definitions

Modern industrial processes increasingly require the transport of hazardous loads not only within and between industrial areas, but also to warehouses, stores and hospitals. The United Nations has a comprehensive system of numbering all hazardous substances, classified under headings such as flammable, explosive, corrosive, toxic and radioactive.

Identification

In Britain, a UK Hazard Information System (UKHIS) has been developed and is designed to give the emergency services all the necessary information in the event of an accident involving spillage. An important part of this is the HAZCHEM 'action' code, incorporated on the orange plates on vehicles, which give instructions for immediate action (see Plate 27.4 and Ref. 17). The system covers the transport of notifiable hazardous wastes (Ref. 12) but does not apply to packaged goods.

Vehicles carrying dangerous (ie. to which the regulations apply Ref. 17) goods in packages should carry a plain orange plate (40 cms × 30 cms) to front and rear. If the vehicle is laden but has less than 500 kg of the substance the plate *may* be displayed but if it has more than 500 kg, it *must* be displayed. If the vehicle is empty the sign should be covered up.

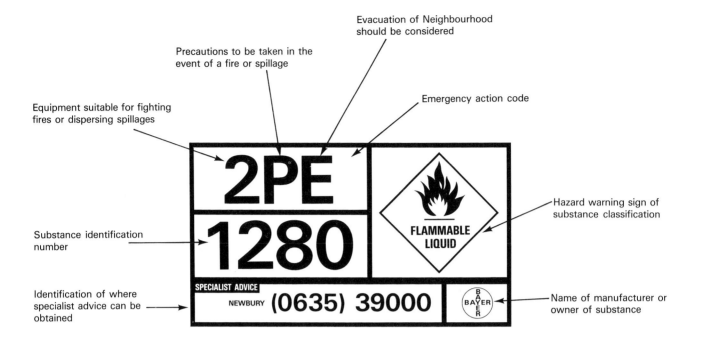

Plate 27.4 A HAZCHEM label for use on commercial vehicles

Source: Bayer UK Ltd

The effectiveness of the UKHIS controls has led to an accident rate for road tank vehicles carrying hazardous loads which is significantly less than that for ordinary goods vehicles (Ref. 13) although the potential for damage and environmental impact, if and when a serious accident does occur, is of course far greater. This suggests that no special provision for routeing hazardous goods vehicles needs to be made other than to encourage them to use major roads away from residential areas, providing this does not add greatly to the mileage travelled. Recent legislation (Ref. 18) covering packaging and labelling of dangerous substances in small quantities (not tanks) and the carriage of those packages (Ref. 19), should help further to decrease the risks of accidents in transit and of failure to deal correctly with any spillages that do occur.

The Department of Transport's Circular Roads 1/82 (Ref. 14) [Sco.145] describes the procedures which highway authorities should adopt to combat the dangers that may arise in the aftermath of a road accident involving hazardous substances.

Accidents

If an incident to a vehicle carrying dangerous goods occurs, the police and fire brigade will normally be informed by the driver, or if he is unable to do so, by someone else at the scene. For bulk loads, the emergency services will obtain technical advice or

assistance, when necessary, from the specialist advice telephone number shown in the hazard information panel. For packaged goods, the name and address of the manufacturer, importer, wholesaler or supplier of the substance will appear on the package and the driver is required to carry information in writing for the non dangerous substances.

Once the immediate emergency is over, a highway authority may be called upon to remove dangerous substances from the highway. The highway authority has a statutory duty under Section 22 of the Control of Pollution Act 1974 (Ref. 15), to remove any spillages from the highway where such removal is necessary for the maintenance of the highway or the safety of traffic. Under Section 149 of the Highways Act 1980 (Ref. 16) [Sco.146] the highway authority also has power to remove anything deposited on a highway which constitutes a nuisance, danger or substantial inconvenience to users of the highway and to recover the cost of removing it from the person responsible.

If a dangerous substance has to be removed from the highway and there is any doubt about the method appropriate and the safeguards to be taken, the highway authority should seek technical advice from the company concerned. Specialist advice telephone numbers are sometimes shown on the hazard information panel or on other markings.

27.10 References

1. DTp/TRRL—Supplementary Report SR 774, '*A national survey of lorry nuisance*', DTp (1983).   (27.2)

2. Road Traffic Regulation Act 1984, HMSO (1984).   (27.4)

3. Freight Transport Association (FTA)—'*Planning for lorries*', FTA (1983).   (27.4)

4. DoE/DTp/TRRL—Report SR 458, '*Effects of lorry controls in the Windsor area*', DoE/DTp (1978).   (27.5)

5. IHE (now IHT)—'*Lorry Management Schemes: Assessment, Procedures, Implementation Guidelines*', Institution of Highways and Transportation (1981).   (27.5)

6. ALBES/DTp—'*Code of Practice for highways and traffic management in London*', HMSO (1986).   (27.6)

7. DoE—Lorry Plans Advice Notes, DoE (1976):   (27.6)
   - Control of Heavy Commercial Vehicles,
   - The Environment and Road Safety
   - Effects of Lorry Plans,
   - Legal Powers,
   - Vehicle Operating Costs for the Evaluation of Lorry Plans,
   - Survey Techniques for Lorry Plans,
   - Signs.

8. Transport Act 1982, HMSO (1982).   (27.7)

9. Goods Vehicles (Operators' licences, qualifications and fees) Regulations (1984), Statutory Instrument 1984 No 176 HMSO (1984) and ditto (amendment) Regulations 1986, Statutory Instrument 1986 No 666, HMSO (1986).   (27.7)

10. Road Vehicles (Construction and Use Regulations) 1986, Statutory Instrument 1986 No 1078, HMSO (1986).   (27.8)

11. Motor Vehicles (Authorisation of Special Types) General Order 1979, Statutory Instrument 1979 No 1198, HMSO (1979).   (27.8)

12. Norton, T, Isaac, P C G and Hills, P J—'*The transport of non-nuclear toxic and dangerous wastes*', Research Report No 61, Transport Operations Research Group, University of Newcastle upon Tyne (1985).   (27.9)

13. Gandham, B and Hills, P J—'*Monitoring the movements of hazardous freight by road*', Research Report No 45, Transport Operations Research Group, University of Newcastle upon Tyne (1982).   (27.9)

Text Reference

14. DTp—Circular Roads 1/82, '*Spillages of Hazardous Substances on the Highway*', DTp (1982). [Sco.145, Wa.39]   (27.9)

15. Control of Pollution Act 1974, HMSO (1974).   (27.9)

16. Highways Act 1980, HMSO (1980). [Sco.147]   (27.9)

17. The Dangerous Substances (Conveyance by Road in Road Tankers and Tank Containers) Regulations 1981, Statutory Instrument 1981, No 1059, HMSO (1981).   (27.9)

18. The Classification; Packaging and Labelling of Dangerous Substances Regulations 1984, Statutory Instrument 1984 No 1244, HMSO (1984).   (27.9)

19. Road Traffic (Carriage of Dangerous Substances in Packages etc.) Regulations 1986, Statutory Instrument 1986 No 1951, HMSO (1986).   (27.9)

27.11 Further Information

20. DTp—Circular 2/82, '*Lorry controls*', DTp (1982). [Wa.40, WA.41]

21. DTp—'*Lorries, people and the environment*', White Paper, (The Armitage Report), HMSO (1981).

22. DTp—Circular Roads 4/78, '*Advisory Link Roads for Goods Vehicles*', DTp (1978). [Sco.148]

23. DoE/DTp/TRRL—report SR 381, '*Review of the results of lorry planning studies*', DoE/DTp (1978).

24. FTA (1978–1985). Freight Facts:
    - 1/78 One-way systems for commercial vehicles
    - 2/78 Five years of lorry management since Dykes
    - 1/79 The case for the heavier lorry
    - 2/79 Lorry bans: a review of three experimental schemes
    - 1/80 Road costs: do lorries pay their way
    - 1/82 Tolls: a case for abolition
    - 2/82 Lorry controls in Paris: an FTA review
    - 1/83 An FTA survey of town centre restrictions
    - 2/83 Designing for heavier lorries
    - 3/83 The signing of lorry bans
    - 1/85 Tolls: are we getting a fair deal

N.B. For additional references for Scotland see Sco.149–152 in Chapter 45.

25. DTp—'*The transport of goods by road in Great Britain*', HMSO (annual).

26. DTp—'*Transport Statistics Great Britain 1972–1982*', HMSO (1983).

27. ECMoT—Round Table 61. '*Foods distribution systems in urban areas*', ECMT (1984).

28. DTp/TRRL—Report LR 1059, '*Goods vehicle trip generation and attraction by industrial and commercial premises*', DTp (1982).

29. Pike, J—'*Major factors influencing modal choice in the UK freight market*', Research Report No 52, University of Newcastle upon Tyne, TORG (1982).

30. CSS—'*Facilities for lorries and their drivers*', County Surveyors' Society (1984).

31. DTp/TRRL–Report LK 1058 '*Dykes Act lorry controls; their use and effects*', DTp (1982).

32. DTp/TRRL—Report SR 746, '*Operational performance of the TRRL quiet heavy vehicle*', DTp (1982).

PART 4 HIGHWAY AND TRAFFIC CONSIDERATIONS FOR NEW DEVELOPMENT

28 Highway and Traffic Aspects of Development Control

28.1 Land Use and its Associated Traffic Patterns

Changes in the use of land often affect the traffic patterns in the surrounding area. Sometimes these effects are such that the existing transport network of roads, footpaths, cycle routes and facilities for public transport and servicing need to be augmented or modified.

In order to quantify and assess the impact of a proposed development on the existing transport network it is necessary to estimate its potential to generate and attract different kinds of traffic and the likely origins and destinations of individual trips. The characteristics and volume of traffic will depend on the type of development and its location and relationship with other existing or projected land uses in the area which, considered as a whole, give rise to a complex pattern of occupational, commercial, shopping, educational and recreational activities.

The highway and traffic aspects of new developments which may need to be identified are:

the demands

- the traffic volumes generated by and attracted to the development by mode and time period;

- the routes taken by that traffic (vehicular and pedestrian) when approaching and leaving the site; and

the facilities

- the adequacy of existing transport facilities to cope with the increased demands;

- the arrangements for access to and from the site; and

- the arrangements within the site for internal circulation, servicing and the parking of vehicles.

New developments should provide satisfactory arrangements for access, circulation and parking and must have regard to safety, operational efficiency and the general environment within which the development is to take place (see also Chapter 29.1 and Table 29.1).

28.2 Application for planning Permission

The basis of the British planning system is that (with some exceptions) all development of land requires the prior consent of the local planning authority [NI.13].

Important exceptions include the maintenance and improvement of the highway within its existing boundaries and changes in the use of land or buildings to a use within the same designated class (Ref. 1).

Applications for planning permission are made to the local planning authority (LPA), which is usually the District, London Borough or Metropolitan District Council [Sco.153]. Standard forms are made available for this purpose and a charge is made which relates to the type and stage of the application.

Applications must include plans at an appropriate scale to show the boundaries of the development, points of access, confirmation of ownership and of notice to the occupier. In the case of so-called 'bad neighbour' developments, or applications in conservation areas or affecting listed buildings, evidence of advertisement of the application must also be included [Sco.154].

Types of Application

Application may be made for **outline permission** where approval in principle is sought prior to the drawing up of detailed proposals. Outline permission cannot be sought for change of use only. When outline permission is granted it will be subject to the imposition of conditions, reserving matters such as internal layout, access and building materials, until the detailed application is received.

Otherwise, the application will be for **full planning permission**. This may be granted unconditionally, or with conditions (including temporary permission), or may be refused. In certain circumstances, where permission is refused or conditions are imposed on the development of land which makes it incapable of beneficial use, the owners may serve notice on the LPA requiring it to purchase their interest in the land.

Planning Appeals

Applicants for planning permission have the right to appeal to the Secretary of State for the Environment (or for Scotland or Wales as appropriate) against any decision by the local planning authority when:

- planning permission has been refused;

- conditions are imposed which the applicant considers unreasonable;

- approval is not given to details of an application which already has outline permission or conditions are imposed which the applicant considers unreasonable; or

● if the local planning authority fails to issue a decision within the time limit of eight weeks [Sco.155] or any extension period which has been mutually agreed in writing.

Any appeal must be made within six months of the day of issue of the LPA's notice of decision and must provide the grounds for the appeal. The Secretary of State then appoints an Inspector from the Planning Inspectorate [Sco.156] to consider the appeal. If the appellant and the local planning authority agree, the appeal may be dealt with by written representations, otherwise a public inquiry will be held.

If he has been given delegated power the Inspector [Sco.157] will give his decision in a letter to the appellant and the local planning authority, otherwise he will report his findings to the Secretary of State who then determines the appeal. Once issued, the decision is final and can only be challenged on legal grounds in the High Court [Sco.158].

Time Period for Planning Consents

Unless a contrary condition is imposed, development must begin within five years of the granting of planning permission, otherwise permission lapses. In cases where development takes place without permission or without complying with any condition imposed, the LPA may serve an enforcement notice requiring the breach to be remedied if it is expedient to do so. In most cases an enforcement notice must be served within five years of the breach occurring.

The Role of County Planning Authorities

Certain types of application, such as those concerned with mineral exploitation and mining or those which conflict with the provisions of a Structure Plan, will be determined by the county planning authority (CPA). In addition, when considering other types of application, the LPA may be required to consult with the CPA and a variety of other bodies [Sco.159]. These consultations are required by the Town and Country Planning (General Development) Order 1977 (GDO) as amended by the Town and Country Planning General Development Amendment Orders (Refs. 1, 2 and 3) [Sco.160].

The Role of Highway Authorities

Articles 11, 12, 13 and 15 of the GDO [NI.50] are particularly relevant from a highway and traffic point of view although the Government propose (1987) to replace local highway authorities' powers of direction in England and Wales with a right to be consulted, as is currently the case in Scotland (Ref. 4 and Chapter 35.2). Until such a change is made:—

Article 11 requires that in the case of an application involving:

● the formation, laying out or alteration of a means of access to any part of a trunk road with a permitted speed above 40 mph or to a special road; or

● a development of land (other than above) within 67 metres from the middle of a proposed trunk or special road or of a proposed improvement to an existing trunk or special road;

the Secretary of State may use his power (in Article 10) to direct the local planning authority to determine or condition the application in a particular manner [Sco.161].

Article 12 requires that in the case of an application involving:

● the formation, laying out or alteration of any means of access to a classified road or to a proposed road the route of which has been adopted by resolution of the local highway authority and notified as such to the local planning authority; or

● any use of land likely to result in a material increase in the volume of traffic entering or leaving a classified or proposed road or to prejudice the improvement or construction of such a road, or likely to result in a material change in the character of traffic entering, leaving or using such a road;

the local highway authority may direct the LPA to determine or condition the application in a particular manner.

Article 13 requires that, in the case of an application involving the laying out or construction of a new street, the local highway authority must be consulted.

Article 15 requires that, in the case of an application involving the formation, laying out or alteration of any means of access to a highway (other than a trunk road) and the local authority concerned are not the highway authority, the highway authority must be consulted. In the case of an application for development likely to create or attract traffic which will result in a material increase in the volume of traffic entering or leaving a trunk road or using a level crossing over a railway, the Secretary of State for Transport must be consulted.

Articles 11, 12, 13 and 15 described above are applicable in those areas where the LPA and the highway authority are different bodies [Sco.162, NI.50]. Where local planning and highway functions are combined, the highway and traffic aspects of a proposed development must still be given proper consideration.

In a limited number of Enterprise Zones where fewer planning controls operate, not all the procedures set out above will necessarily apply. However, appropriate standards of design should be incorporated into the Enterprise Zone scheme by the LPA in order to ensure a satisfactory standard of development. In due course similar standards will need to be applied in Simplified Planning Zones (Ref. 5).

28.3 Agreements Between Developers and Local Authorities

In the discussions which often take place prior to, or during the normal course of consideration of an application for planning permission, local authorities may enter into legally binding agreements with developers on certain matters which are not possible through the normal development control procedure (see also Chapter 3.6). These arrangements are sometimes used to minimise any adverse effects of new developments on the existing infrastructure.

In England and Wales [Sco.163, NI.50] the types of agreement particularly relevant to highway and traffic matters are:

● where a developer agrees with a LPA (currently under the **Town and Country Planning Act 1971 s52**) (Ref. 6) to carry out or finance certain additional works or make some other provision on land either inside or outside the proposed development site;

● where a highway authority agrees with a developer (currently under the **Highways Act 1980 s38**) (Ref. 7) to adopt any roads or footpaths constructed as part of the development as highway maintainable at public expense. It is usual for the local highway authority to require that these roads are built to their approved standards of construction and geometry;

● where a highway authority, proposing to carry out road works, may enter into an agreement (under **Highways Act 1980, s278**) with a developer to incorporate within the proposed works, other road works which will add to or modify the authority's works, or may bring them forward in time in order to minimize the effect of the proposed development on road safety and traffic flows and assist it to proceed. The highway authority may not, however, use its powers to compulsorily acquire land for the purpose of such an agreement; and

● where a developer wishes to erect a building or bridge above a highway the highway authority can specify the vertical clearance required and any other conditions as they see fit and may grant a licence under the powers provided in **Sections 176–178 of the Highways Act 1980**.

Section 111 of the Local Government Act 1972 (Ref. 8) provides a further general power under which developers may be permitted to carry out work on the highway. This is sometimes useful in conjunction with agreements under s38 of the Highways Act 1980. In addition local Acts may make provision for different agreements between local authorities and developers.

28.4 References

Text Reference

1. Town and Country Planning (General Development) Order 1977, Statutory Instrument 1977 No 289, HMSO (1977). [Sco.164] (28.2)

2. Town and Country Planning General Development (Amendment) (No 2) Order 1985, Statutory Instrument 1985 No 1981, HMSO (1985). [Sco.165] (28.2)

3. Town and Country Planning (Local Government Reorganisation) (Miscellaneous Amendments) Order 1986, Statutory Instrument 1986 No 435, HMSO (1986). (28.2)

4. DoE—'*Building Business not Barriers*', Cmnd. 9794, HMSO (1986). (28.2)

5. Housing and Planning Act 1986, HMSO (1986). (28.2)

6. Town and Country Planning Act 1971, HMSO (1971). [Sco.166] (28.3)

7. Highways Act 1980, HMSO (1980). [Sco.167] (28.3)

8. Local Government Act 1972, HMSO (1972). (28.3)

28.5 Further Information

9. DoE—Circular Roads 22/83, '*Town and Country Planning Act 1971—Planning Gain*', DoE (1983). [Wa.42]

29 General Guidelines for the Assessment and Design of New Developments

29.1 Basic Principles

The highway and traffic aspects of new developments were identified in the previous chapter and the general considerations for assessment and design are set out in Table 29.1. There are a number of other matters which might also warrant consideration and examples are given below.

Development proposals will vary greatly in scale and character. Whilst the same basic principles for assessment apply in each case, the amount of work involved in making forecasts should have regard to the size, location and significance of the development. In the case of minor developments a simple schedule of information will often suffice but for large or complex developments a fuller assessment will usually be required.

Developments which by their nature generate or attract large numbers of trips will need particularly careful consideration in respect of such matters as parking provision and the sufficiency of the surrounding road network. Examples of this kind of development include one-stop shopping centres, sports and recreational facilities and some types of commercial undertakings.

Whilst individual developments may not in themselves create significant impacts on their surroundings thought must be given to whether a number of similar developments could in aggregate lead to problems, since it will be more difficult to resist subsequent applications which are similar to those which have already been approved.

These factors should be taken into account when structure, local, and unitary development plans are drawn up (see Chapter 3) since these plans provide the basic framework upon which planning control is based.

To supplement the policies contained in development plans many local authorities have produced their own guidelines to help developers present their applications in a way which makes them easier to process. These guidelines may include such matters as a requirement for a traffic generation assessment and they often set down standards for road geometry and, where not already included in the development plan, for parking provision. (N.B. A substantial guide to traffic generation for various kinds of development was produced by the Greater London Council in 1985 (Ref. 1).)

Provision for Those with a Mobility Handicap

Special consideration for the disabled and those with reduced mobility should be an integral part of the design of every development (Ref. 2). Provision of facilities for the mobility handicapped will often also help the able bodied to move more freely and easily, but for those most directly concerned it may mean the difference between making a trip or staying at home. Facilities incorporated in the initial construction of a development can usually be provided most economically.

Road Safety Audit

As with all highway improvement and traffic management schemes, the layout of each development proposal should be examined to ensure that no road safety hazards are built in to the basic design. This appraisal should include such matters as expected vehicle speeds, curve radii and camber, adequate visibility, traffic signing and road markings and layouts which separate turning movements and conflicts wherever possible.

29.2 Development Related Vehicle Trips

Estimation of the number of vehicle trips generated by or attracted to a proposed development is an important first step in design and assessment and in identifying whether improvements to the existing transport and road network will be necessary.

The number of trips expected by various modes will depend on:

- the policies for movement and transport set out in the development plan (eg. traffic restraint);
- the type and scale of the development;
- the general location of the trip ends remote from the development;
- local levels of car availability; and
- the adequacy of the surrounding public transport services.

The actual origins and destinations of individual trips will depend on the general disposition of other land uses which may change in the longer term as reflected in local and structure plans.

National forecasts for vehicle movements are available based on consideration of future levels of population and industrial/commercial activity. However, in the

HIGHWAY AND TRAFFIC ASPECTS OF NEW DEVELOPMENT WHICH REQUIRE INVESTIGATION	THE INFORMATION AND ASSESSMENTS REQUIRED
TRAFFIC VOLUMES ATTRACTED BY THE DEVELOPMENT, BY MODE AND TIME PERIOD	An estimation of the traffic generated or attracted to the site and its distribution by: (i) time of day/day of week; and (ii) by mode of travel (e.g. private car, bus, HGV, Cycle or pedestrian) is an essential first step in the assessment of any development proposal. It will usually also be necessary to assemble information on traffic volumes currently using the network together with forecasts of future increases. (See also Chapters 10 and 11).
THE ROUTES TAKEN BY ATTRACTED TRAFFIC AND EXAMINATION OF THE ADEQUACY OF THE EXISTING TRANSPORT NETWORK.	Consideration must be given to the likely impact of the development on the different parts of the existing transport network (e.g. roads, footpaths and public transport) with regard to safety, environment and traffic capacity. Special consideration should be given to: (i) suitable locations for the points of access to the site; (ii) effects on existing traffic management arrangements (e.g. one-way systems, banned turns, types of junction control); (iii) the requirement for additional facilities for pedestrians or cyclists (e.g. crossings, footpaths or cycleways) and provision for those with a mobility handicap; and (iv) the requirement for additional public transport facilities (e.g. bus stops, turning facilities or alterations to bus routes).
ACCESS TO THE SITE.	The assessment must consider whether appropriate access arrangements can be provided. An appropriate access should: (i) be sited to take account of the requirements of the existing transport network and the internal circulation system required for the new development; (ii) provide appropriate standards of geometry, visibility and capacity to cater for the numbers and size of vehicles expected to visit the site with the minimum probability of queues forming on the external highway network (including provision for emergency vehicles); (iii) provide appropriate provision for pedestrian access including consideration for those with a mobility handicap. Where appropriate, separate access arrangements for vehicles, cyclists and pedestrians may be beneficial.
THE DEMANDS WITHIN THE SITE FOR INTERNAL CIRCULATION, PARKING AND SERVICING.	A satisfactory system for internal circulation is necessary to provide appropriate standards of safety and operating efficiency. The design for internal circulation should therefore consider: (i) the need to absorb vehicular traffic entering the site with the minimum probability of queues forming on the external highway network even if part of the system is blocked by an accident or maintenance or public utilities works; (ii) the need to cater for pedestrian activity within the development and any special facilities for cyclists or those with a mobility handicap; (iii) any special provisions for servicing and deliveries and the geometry necessary to cope with heavy goods vehicles, buses or emergency vehicles (especially fire appliances) to be agreed with appropriate authorities; and (iv) provision for the parking of different types of vehicles (e.g. private cars, taxis, HGVs) and for different purposes (e.g. residents, employees, visitors and different lengths of stay (e.g. short stay, park and ride, 'kiss and ride'). Consideration should also be given to the level of signing necessary to ensure the satisfactory operation of the internal circulation system. Where possible the circulating systems for vehicles and pedestrians should be segregated.

Table 29.1 General guidelines for the assessment and design of transport facilities resulting from new development

247

248

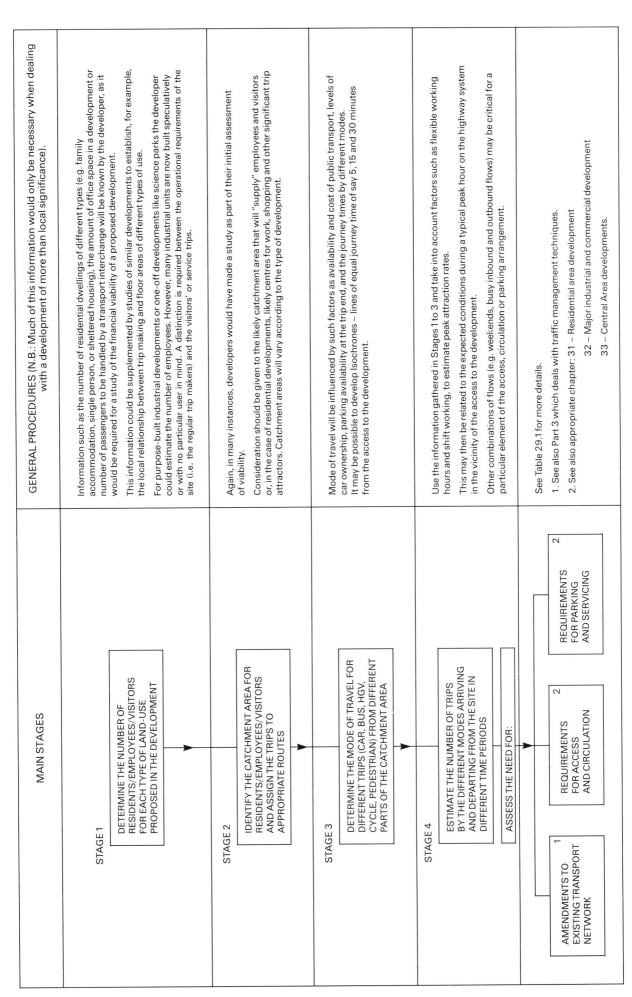

MAIN STAGES

GENERAL PROCEDURES (N.B.: Much of this information would only be necessary when dealing with a development of more than local significance).

STAGE 1

DETERMINE THE NUMBER OF RESIDENTS/EMPLOYEES/VISITORS FOR EACH TYPE OF LAND-USE PROPOSED IN THE DEVELOPMENT

Information such as the number of residential dwellings of different types (e.g. family accommodation, single person, or sheltered housing), the amount of office space in a development or number of passengers to be handled by a transport interchange will be known by the developer, as it would be required for a study of the financial viability of a proposed development.

This information could be supplemented by studies of similar developments to establish, for example, the local relationship between trip making and floor areas of different types of use.

For purpose-built industrial developments or one-off developments like science parks the developer could estimate the number of employees. However, many industrial units are now built speculatively or with no particular user in mind. A distinction is required between the operational requirements of the site (i.e. the regular trip makers) and the visitors' or service trips.

STAGE 2

IDENTIFY THE CATCHMENT AREA FOR RESIDENTS/EMPLOYEES/VISITORS AND ASSIGN THE TRIPS TO APPROPRIATE ROUTES

Again, in many instances, developers would have made a study as part of their initial assessment of viability.

Consideration should be given to the likely catchment area that will "supply" employees and visitors or, in the case of residential developments, likely centres for work, shopping and other significant trip attractors. Catchment areas will vary according to the type of development.

STAGE 3

DETERMINE THE MODE OF TRAVEL FOR DIFFERENT TRIPS (CAR, BUS, HGV, CYCLE, PEDESTRIAN) FROM DIFFERENT PARTS OF THE CATCHMENT AREA

Mode of travel will be influenced by such factors as availability and cost of public transport, levels of car ownership, parking availability at the trip end, and the journey times by different modes.
It may be possible to develop Isochrones – lines of equal journey time of say 5, 15 and 30 minutes from the access to the development.

STAGE 4

ESTIMATE THE NUMBER OF TRIPS BY THE DIFFERENT MODES ARRIVING AND DEPARTING FROM THE SITE IN DIFFERENT TIME PERIODS

Use the information gathered in Stages 1 to 3 and take into account factors such as flexible working hours and shift working, to estimate peak attraction rates.

This may then be related to the expected conditions during a typical peak hour on the highway system in the vicinity of the access to the development.

Other combinations of flows (e.g. weekends, busy inbound and outbound flows) may be critical for a particular element of the access, circulation or parking arrangement.

ASSESS THE NEED FOR:

| AMENDMENTS TO EXISTING TRANSPORT NETWORK | 1 | | REQUIREMENTS FOR ACCESS AND CIRCULATION | 2 | | REQUIREMENTS FOR PARKING AND SERVICING | 2 |

See Table 29.1 for more details.

1. See also Part 3 which deals with traffic management techniques.
2. See also appropriate chapter: 31 – Residential area development
32 – Major industrial and commercial development
33 – Central Area developments.

Table 29.2 General procedures for estimating trip attractions to a new development

assessment of most new developments emphasis should be placed on local forecasts of growth, traffic data collected from the local road network and observations of activity (trip rates and parking demand) at similar developments elsewhere. A more extensive explanation of this process is given in Chapters 10 and 11.

Although it is possible to 'model' the transport network, the number of trips by different modes and their distribution through time, a detailed examination of this kind would be inappropriate for an initial site appraisal or the preliminary assessment of a planning application by a local authority; it may, however, be necessary subsequently for developments which generate high levels of traffic activity.

The general procedures for estimating the number of trips and thereby determining the requirements for access and circulation, parking, servicing and impact on the existing network are set out in Table 29.2. The time and effort required to assemble all the information in column 2 may only be justified when dealing with developments of more than local significance.

29.3 References

Text Reference

1. GLC—'*Traffic Generation: User's Guide and Review of Studies (2nd Edition)*', Greater London Council (1985).   (29.1)

2. IHT—'*Guidelines for Providing for People with a Mobility Handicap*', Institution of Highways and Transportation (1986).   (29.1)

30 Provision for Parking in New Developments

30.1 Demand for Parking Space

Every development results in a demand for parking or loading space to cater for trips made to or from the development using vehicles of one type or another. Different types and intensities of development produce different levels of demand with, for example, very high demands at places which attract large numbers of people (eg. sporting arenas and other public buildings, shopping centres and transport interchanges like railway stations and airports). Other types of development such as residential or industrial buildings also produce a demand for parking space but it can be seen that the nature of these demands is likely to be very different. Major retail developments are becoming increasingly dependent on access and parking for customer's vehicles and so-called hypermarkets and superstores selling food and bulk goods will have particularly high parking requirements which will have a major effect on their locational suitability in respect of neighbouring developments and the highway network.

30.2 The Significance of Location

The location of a development proposal may have an important effect on the modal distribution of trips made and hence the scale and nature of the demand for parking space and the extent to which satisfying these demands is important to transport planning policies. To illustrate this point, levels of car ownership are generally higher in rural areas where the provision of public transport tends to be more dispersed and less frequent. Conversely, in urban areas where there may be a number of optional forms of public transport, the ownership and use of a car may be less important. Futhermore, the traffic levels experienced in certain high activity areas like shopping centres or business areas may mean that the local authority may seek to actively discourage the use of private vehicles and may use its parking control powers as an instrument of this policy (see also Chapter 5.5 on planning and development control and Chapter 7 on alternative transport modes) notwithstanding the demand for high intensity uses in existing urban areas.

30.3 Planning Consent and Parking Provision

Local planning authorities' (LPA) powers [NI.13] to control development include the provision of parking and many authorities have produced their own standards as to the level of provision appropriate for different types of development in different locations. It

can be seen that since the level of provision which is judged to be desirable for a particular type of development is so dependent on location, there can be no standard for the country as a whole and large differences may exist even within a single LPA area.

Tables 30.1 and 30.2 are examples of schedules prepared for different urban areas to illustrate alternative ways in which parking standards are specified for different types of development in different locations. The figures quoted can vary substantially from place to place and a wide range is often provided for a particular type of use. For example, it may be necessary to distinguish between large scale food retailers and other retail outlets since a higher standard of parking is necessary for the former and ease of access for trolleys will also be a consideration. Standards may be precise or may lay down maximum or minimum values depending upon the policies contained in the development plan.

Because each authority will need to determine its own standards according to local circumstances the figures quoted in the Tables should not be regarded as recommendations.

30.4 The Different Types of Parking Space Requirement

Any development will produce different types of parking demand which can be classified in various ways. It is often useful to divide demand into short term and long term requirements. For example, a single residential unit will usually exhibit a need for at least one permanent parking space for the occupier. The level of provision will vary depending upon the type and size of property from zero, for, say, sheltered accommodation for old people, to perhaps 3 spaces for larger units with several occupants. However, all dwellings will need some space for visitors' vehicles but this is usually a short term need so that each visitors' space will serve several individual trips each day. Visitors' space should include provision as appropriate for essential trips like refuse collection, service vehicles and provision for emergency access as well as for business or social visitors.

Commercial properties (which include shops, offices and industrial premises) usually have a need for what is termed 'operational parking space'. This is parking space provided to meet the needs of the business being carried out and can often be associated specifically with a particular occupant. For example, a normal retail shop may need space to be allocated for delivery

TYPE OF DEVELOPMENT	TYPICAL LEVELS OF CAR PARKING REQUIRED IN DIFFERENT DEVELOPMENTS		
	RESIDENT	VISITOR	EMPLOYEE
RESIDENTIAL: Typical Family Accommodation	One space per dwelling – driveways may count towards this provision but it generally excludes garages within the curtilage. This figure may be significantly increased for larger properties.	One space for every two dwellings – usually provided outside the curtilage.	n.a.
Multiple Occupation	One assigned space per dwelling preferably provided within the curtilage.	One space for every two dwellings preferably provided within the curtilage.	n.a.
Sheltered Housing	One space for every four bed spaces to cater for residents and their visitors.		One space for every resident warden.
Old Persons Homes	One space for every ten dwellings to cater for residents and their visitors.		One space for every permanent member of staff.
OFFICE: Central Area Locations	n.a.	Ranges from one space for every 250 square metres of floor area to provision only for operational needs clearly demonstrated by the applicant.	
Non Central Locations	n.a.	One space for every 25-50 square metres of floor area.	
SHOPPING: Central Area Locations	n.a.	Ranges from one space for every 50 square metres of gross floor area (may be expressed in terms of retail sales area) to very restricted provision.	
Non Central Locations	n.a.	Ranges from one space for every 50 square metres to one space for every 10 square metres of gross floor area. (The provision of appropriate levels of customer car parking are critical to the financial viability of some non central shopping developments and the levels provided by developers will often exceed the normal requirements set by the local highway authority.	
INDUSTRIAL:	n.a.	Ranges from one space for every 50 square metres to one space for every 25 square metres of gross floor area.	
HOTELS:	A maximum of one space for every bedroom plus additional spaces for areas open to the general public such as bars and restaurants (see below).		One space for every resident member of staff plus one space for every four non-resident staff employed at peak times.
RESTAURANTS/BARS/ CLUBS:	Treated as for residential accommodation when provided.	One space for every two seats or ranges from one space for every 5 square metres to one space for every 10 square metres of gross floor area.	One space for every resident member of staff plus one space for every three non-resident staff employed at peak times.
MEDICAL CENTRES: Health Centres/Surgeries	Treated as for residential accommodation when provided.	Two spaces for every consulting room.	One space for every doctor plus one space for every two other staff employed at peak times.
Hospitals	Treated as for residential accommodation when provided.	One space for every three beds.	One space for every doctor and senior administrator plus one space for every three other members of staff employed at peak times. Alternatively the floor area may be broken down into its constituent uses and the appropriate rates applied.

Table 30.1 An example of levels of car parking required for different types of development

[NB. See text ref. 30.3—this table gives an indication of the categorisation used to specify parking standards, it is *not* a definitive guide to parking provision.]

LAND USE:

STANDARDS WHICH ARE INDEPENDENT OF FACTORS OTHER THAN LAND-USE

1) RESIDENTIAL:

i) private	1 car space per dwelling unit
ii) municipal	0.8 of a car space per dwelling unit, but initial provision may be reduced according to the size of the development, as follows:– Number of dwelling units: 1-9 10-19 20-99 100+ Car spaces per unit: 0.7 0.6 0.55 0.52
iii) Housing Associations (or co-operatives)	0.9 of a car space per dwelling unit, but initial provision may be reduced
iv) old persons' dwellings	0.1 of a car space per dwelling unit, subject to a minimum provision of 2 car spaces
v) dwellings for physically disabled persons	1 car space per dwelling unit

STANDARDS WHICH ARE DEPENDENT ON PUBLIC TRANSPORT ACCESSIBILITY AND LAND USE

2) SHOPS:

i) customers and/or public use	1 car space per 50m² gross floorspace (minimum standard)					
Accessibility level	(low) 1	2	3	4	5	(high) 6
ii) staff use only Multiple of gross floor area, or part thereof, (in m²) which justifies each car space (maximum standard)	500	500	1000	1000	1500	1500

3) HOTELS:

i) accommodation only Number of bedrooms justifying:						
– each car space:	5	5	10	10	10	10
– each coach space:	100	100	100	100	100	100
ii) where other services (e.g. ballrooms) are provided Multiple of gross floor area, or part thereof, set aside for these services (in m²) which justifies each extra car space in excess of those at (i) above.	10	10	20	20	extra spaces dependent on availability of local off-street parking.	

STANDARDS WHICH ARE ALSO DEPENDENT UPON THE AVAILABILITY OF ON-STREET PARKING CONTROL

			CONTROLLED PARKING ZONE (CPZ) IN OPERATION						REST OF BOROUGH, NOT COVERED BY A CPZ				
Accessibility level:			low 1	2	3	4	5	high 6	low 1	2	3	4	5
4) INDUSTRIAL/ WAREHOUSING:	Multiple of gross floor area, of part thereof, (in m²) which justifies each car space (minimum of 2 spaces in any development)	i) Operational standard	100	100	100	100	100	100	100	100	100	100	100
		ii) Non-operational standard	500	1000	1500	2000	2500	–	250	250	250	500	750
			(maximum standards)						(minimum standards)				
5) OFFICES:		i) Operational standard	200	200	200	300	400	500	200	200	200	300	400
		ii) Non-operational standard	250	500	750	1000	1500	–	60	60	60	80	100
			(maximum standards)						(minimum standards)				

Table 30.2 An example of parking standards included in a local plan

[NB. 1. This table provides a further guide to the way in which parking standards are expressed and may be contrasted with Table 30.1. Here also the standards laid down should not be taken as a definitive guide.

2. The term "Accessibility level" used in this table relates to the ease of access from a site to other places such as business or shopping areas. The scale requires a value judgement, varying from 6 where access by foot and public transport is easy to 1 where it is very difficult.]

vehicles but customer parking will not need to be immediately associated with the shop itself. However, exhaust fitting centres will need operational space for customer' cars. Similarly, certain types of office use need operational space for both employees and business callers. In shopping areas the demand for visitors' (shoppers) spaces will far exceed the requirement for longer term needs.

30.5 Perception of Parking Requirements

Perceptions of parking requirements will vary depending on the viewpoint of, for example, a property developer, a potential building occupant or the local authority.

Different emphases will be placed on different aspects of each development and these are affected by commercial considerations. For example, city centre office developments are much more easily let or sold if some parking space is available for the exclusive use of staff or visitors and a developer may try to achieve as much parking space as possible in areas where parking is notoriously difficult.

Conversely, in other circumstances it may be the local authority which is seeking to ensure that a development includes adequate parking space so that all its needs are provided for within the site without a detrimental spillover into surrounding streets. However, in the immediate vicinity of underground stations or other major public transport interchanges, there may be little justification for providing more than a limited amount of off-street parking unless it is for a 'park and ride' facility.

Occupants of properties usually wish to have sufficient parking space for their own needs, allowing them the option of using private transport if they wish.

In certain special circumstances (eg. where existing property is converted to a new use or is in a conservation area) departures from standards may occasionally be justified for practical reasons or on amenity grounds.

Thus the overall picture is one of competition and changing requirements which vary from area to area.

30.6 The Cost of Off-Street Parking Space

There are three direct cost elements associated with parking space. The first is the value of the land area occupied by the space, the second is the construction cost of providing it and the third is the cost of maintaining and operating the space. The value of the space under some alternative use may also be a relevant consideration.

The relationship between these costs varies with location. In inner city areas land costs will be high and it may be worthwhile to create space underground or above ground, accepting that construction costs will be high. In less intensively developed areas surface level space may be feasible. In some locations, pressure on parking space may be such that intensive security arrangements are required to reserve space for its intended users as well as to provide protection against theft and vandalism. Electronically operated barriers and access control devices may be required. Elsewhere less sophisticated devices may be adequate, such as simple labelling of parking spaces.

30.7 Design Considerations

Where parking space is to be provided the following points should be considered when preparing development plan requirements or in assessing individual planning applications:

accessibility and convenience: the location of parking and loading areas should be sufficiently close to the building or land they serve to reduce the likelihood of drivers parking indiscriminately to avoid walking;

disabled persons: location is particularly important for physically handicapped people and any allocated spaces should be close to the destination, sufficiently large to allow wheel chair access and connected to the destination without steps. Ramps or lifts may be necessary;

vehicle access and safety: geometric standards should be applied which allow reasonably comfortable clearance for the type of vehicles for which the space is provided. Special attention will be necessary at turning points and to give head room and ground clearances at ramps. Good standards of visibility must be maintained at all times and this is particularly important where the car park access joins a main road. It is also necessary to ensure that vehicles waiting for a space do not cause complete blockages of the circulatory system or cause queues to extend out onto the access road;

operation and maintenance: it is essential that car parking spaces are used in the way that is intended and it may be advisable to consider some form of access control. In some places this might extend to fully automatic doors or grills, or even cages for individual vehicles to prevent vandalism. It may also be necessary to employ attendants to ensure that operational and visitors' space is used correctly. Good design can minimise supervision and maintenance and surfaces should be resistant to attack by oil or petrol. Robust and vandal proof light fittings and safety barriers may have to be provided;

	Car	Light Van	Coach (60 seats)	Heavy Goods Vehicle	
				Rigid	Articulated
Vehicle Dimensions (m)	3.8 x 1.7* 5.0 x 2.0*	up to 6.0 x 2.1	up to 12.0 x 2.5**	up to 11.0 x 2.5**	up to 15.5 x 2.5**
Allocated Parking Area (m)	4.8 x 2.3	5.5 x 2.3	14.0 x 3.5	14.0 x 3.5	18.5 x 3.5
Overall Space Per Parked Vehicle (m²) including access and manoeuvering space	20 to 25	20 to 30	100 to 150	100 to 150	150 to 200

* Typical range of dimensions.

** Maximum dimensions normally permitted in UK.

Table 30.3 Typical parking space requirements in surface vehicle parks

impact on the surrounding road network: the number of spaces provided should have regard to the capacity and functions of the surrounding road network and the characteristics of use of the particular development. For example, the provision of large works car parks will often mean that very large numbers of vehicles arrive and leave at the same time and exit and entry arrangements must be designed to cope with these peak flows. It is particularly important to examine the probabilities associated with various queue lengths to determine the likelihood of interference with traffic on the external road system. Adequate queueing space should be provided both outside and within the car park. In some cases traffic signalled entry and exit systems may be necessary for reasons of safety or to provide a positive form of control.

Alternative Provision

The availability of public off-street or controlled on-street parking in the vicinity of the development may strongly influence the scale of provision required within the site.

30.8 Size and Layout of Spaces

Table 30.3 gives the dimensions of some vehicles and the typical space required for parking areas. These may be used as basic reference values but different layouts

(eg. parallel, herring-bone, in-line) will have slightly different overall space requirements and the detailed layout of parking spaces will be site specific. Advice on the general principles of parking layouts for different vehicles and in different types of development is given in subsequent chapters.

30.9 Further Information

1. DoE—Circular Roads 1/85, '*The use of conditions in planning permission*', DoE (1985). [Sco.168, Wa.43]

2. DoE—Circular 22/84, '*Memorandum on Structure and Local Plans*', DoE (1984). [Sco.169, Wa.44]

3. IHT/I Struc E—'*Design recommendations for multi-storey and underground car parks—2nd Edition*', I Struc E, London (1984).

4. DoE—Circular 22/83, '*Town and Country Planning Act 1971—Planning Gain*', DoE (1983). [Wa.45]

5. University of Manchester Institute of Science and Technology—'*Car Parking Standards in Development Control, Conference Proceedings*', UMIST (1983).

6. The British Parking Association will also provide guidance on parking policy, standards and design.

31 New Residential Development

31.1 Introduction

The Significance of Roads in New Developments

The great majority of developments in urban areas are on small infill and redevelopment sites, which will have existing roads on at least one boundary (eg. see Figure 31.1). Restrictions on the use of such roads to give direct access to individual dwellings and parking spaces may determine whether or not a site can be used for housing and there may also be restrictions on the type, spacing and design of junctions which can be provided to connect any new roads required to serve the new development.

Such factors are usually less critical when large sites are being developed. An example of such a site is shown in Figure 31.2. An economical layout of new roads can normally be provided within the site to serve individual dwellings and parking spaces and existing roads can often be extended to provide new points of access. In these circumstances, the principles which govern the layout of new roads are usually at least as important as those which govern access from existing roads.

Roads and traffic issues must be considered as an integral part of the design of residential developments as the layout of roads will play an important part in creating surroundings which are safe, convenient, nuisance free, visually attractive and economical to construct and maintain.

The accommodation to be provided will normally be determined by local planning policies and market demands which together will determine building density, dwelling design, parking provision, open space, landscaping and other design features. Site requirements which affect frontage access and parking arrangements will be important in determining the amount of space in a development that will need to be occupied by roads. Figure 31.3 describes typical types of housing provision which are appropriate to different densities of development.

Scope of this Chapter

This chapter deals particularly with new developments on self-contained sites. It is, however, recognised that in many existing urban areas much development (or re-development) is carried out on a small scale or in locations where existing housing is simply replaced by new dwellings. The scope for adopting the standards suggested in this chapter may be limited in these circumstances but where existing conditions are unsatisfactory (eg. on the grounds of traffic movement, safety or a generally poor environment) there may be other techniques which can achieve some improvement and these are explained in Part 3 which deals with the management of traffic on the existing road network. Where development proposals would simply perpetuate an undesirable situation they may well be in conflict with the adopted structure, local or unitary development plans and have to be rejected by the local planning authority.

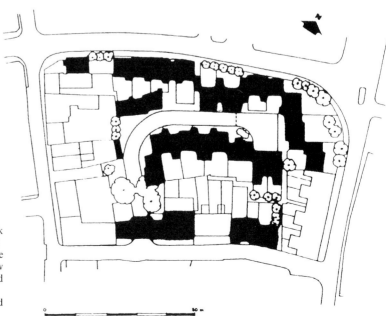

Figure 31.1 A small redevelopment site with limited access
Notes: A small redevelopment site set within a network of heavily trafficked roads. Access can only be gained from a narrow lane along one side and visibility at the entrance is restricted by existing buildings. The narrow frontage terraced houses are arranged formally around one shared surface access road. Parking provision is integral with the dwellings and in grouped garages and hardstandings.

Figure 31.2 A 'green field' development site with good access
Notes: A green-field site set within a network of new local distributor roads. A hierarchy of access roads is served from a roundabout at the entrance to the site and a separated footpath route serves one part of the site. The wide frontage detached houses are mainly grouped around shared surface access roads. Parking provision is mainly within dwelling curtilages.

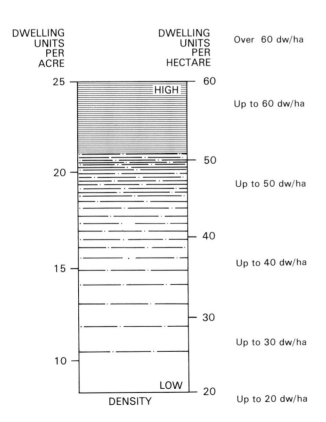

Over 60 dw/ha	Flats. Grouped parking provision and common open space. (Low/middle/high income developments including sheltered accommodation for elderly people).
Up to 60 dw/ha	Narrow frontage terraced houses. Integral and grouped parking provision. (Low-income developments on inner urban and suburban sites and high-income developments on urban sites).
Up to 50 dw/ha	Medium frontage terraced houses. A mixture of within curtilage and grouped parking provision. (The majority of low/middle-income developments).
Up to 40 dw/ha	Semi-detached houses on narrow frontage plots. Parking provision within curtilages. (The majority of middle-income developments).
Up to 30 dw/ha	Detached houses on narrow frontage plots. Parking within curtilages. (Middle/upper-income developments on surburban sites).
Up to 20 dw/ha	Detached houses on medium and wide frontage plots. Parking within curtilages. (High-income developments on surburban and rural sites).

Figure 31.3 Typical housing provision at different densities

Source: The Architects Journal (11th March 1981)

Main soures of design guidance

To assist with the preparation of development plans and supplementary guidance, the Department of the Environment and Department of Transport published (1977) recommended principles for the layout of residential roads and footpaths in Design Bulletin 32 (DB32—Ref. 1) [Sco.170]. The bulletin emphasised that a balance must be struck between highway design standards and other requirements and that engineers, planners, public utilities' representatives, public transport operators, developers and housing designers need to collaborate when local standards are being produced for inclusion in local and unitary development plans, when scheme designs are being prepared and when proposals are being considered during the development control process.

Since DB32 was published most highway authorities [NI.50] have published new or revised standards for the adoption of roads and the majority of these have accepted the bulletin's recommendations (Ref. 2). However, there are still substantial differences between authorities with some adopting standards more onerous than those of the majority.

To help promote DB32, the Department of the Environment produced a film, 'More than just a road' (Ref. 3) and an accompanying brochure which summarised findings from research (Refs. 2, 4 and 5) which has been undertaken since DB32 was published. Also, the Secretaries of State have stated (Ref. 6) that they are not prepared to support any planning or highway authority requiring geometric standards which are higher than those which would result from applying the principles set out in DB32.

A revised version of DB32 is under consideration (1987) to reflect findings from research and the experience gained in the use of the earlier version.

31.2 Highway Adoption Agreements

In England and Wales new highways are usually adopted as highways maintainable at public expense through agreements between developers and highway authorities, normally under Section 38 of the Highways Act 1980 (Ref. 7) (See also Chapter 28.3) [Sco.171, NI.6]. Such agreements ensure that access to services is available in emergencies and for routine maintenance and that powers are available to remove any obstructions that may make access difficult or cause damage to services.

Public Utilities' Requirements

Public utilities normally expect their services to be located along adopted roads and footpaths and this usually restricts the numbers of dwellings that may be served by any unadopted roads that have to be provided. Public utilities usually expect service strips to be demarcated (and other safeguards) when underground services have to be laid in adopted verges within privately maintained gardens (Refs. 8, 9 and 10). Figure 31.14 shows the recommended arrangement of mains in a 2 m footway.

Developers' Requirements

Adoption agreements are normally sought by private sector house-builders because house purchasers seldom wish to be responsible for the maintenance of spaces outside dwelling curtilages once the development is complete. Equally, public sector developers (ie. local housing authorities, housing associations and new town development corporations) do not normally wish to maintain roads even when they are prepared to maintain common open spaces and landscaped areas [Sco.171].

Highway Authorities' Requirements

Requests for adoption agreements are normally welcomed by highway authorities [NI.50] because they can then specify layout and construction standards as a condition for adoption—thereby reducing the likelihood of future demands from residents for the adoption of roads which may be both uneconomical to maintain and costly or difficult to improve.

Authorities normally wish to adopt not only the carriageways, verges and footways but any other land that may be located within visibility splays at junctions and on bends. This is to ensure that vegetation or other obstructions to visibility can be removed or trimmed if necessary. Authorities may also be prepared to adopt grouped parking spaces contiguous with carriageways on payment by the developer of a commuted sum to cover the costs of future maintenance.

31.3 Main Categories of Roads in Residential Developments

Highway authorities normally set separate standards for the two main categories of roads in the hierarchy which are appropriate in residential developments (see also Chapter 5 which describes the roads hierarchy in full); these are:

Local distributor roads, which form the links between access roads and district distributor roads from which direct access to individual dwellings and parking spaces is not normally allowed in areas of new developments. This category includes local roads whose function is to distribute originating and terminating traffic within districts.

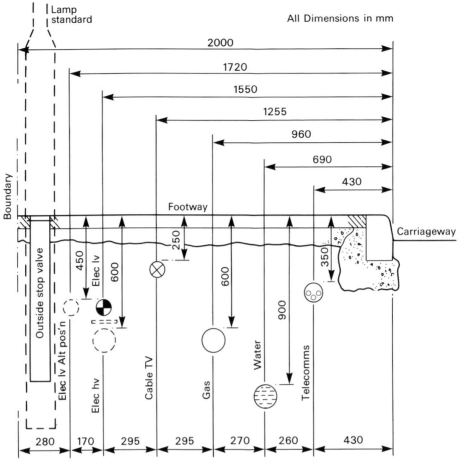

Figure 31.14 Recommended positions for mains in a 2 m footway

Source: NJUG 'Recommended Positioning of Utilities. Mains and Plant for New Works' (1986)

For the purpose of this chapter the definition of a local distributor road includes roads which only distribute access traffic or provide bus routes within large residential developments. Such roads are often also referred to as 'major collector roads' or 'access collector roads' and should have design speeds (see Chapter 34) of 50 kph or less.

Access roads, which form the major part of residential road networks, provide direct access to individual dwellings and parking spaces. This category includes roads with traditional layout and cross-section (ie. with footways separated from the carriageway by kerbs and a change in level, see Plate 31.1). Differences between the numbers of dwellings served by these roads are commonly indicated by the use of terms such as 'major access road' and 'minor access road' but the design speed for all access roads should be less than 30 kph.

This category also includes roads in which the same surface is shared by both pedestrians and vehicles (see Plate 31.2). Such roads are commonly called 'shared surface access roads'. This generic term covers a wide range of different layout arrangements which are sometimes called 'access ways', 'mews courts' and

'housing squares'. When such roads serve not more than a handful of dwellings and they are not to be adopted by the highway authority, they are often called 'shared private drives'.

31.4 Vehicular Access to Development Sites

When a site is being appraised to see whether it would be suitable for residential (or other forms of) development it will be necessary to consider whether the existing roads have the capacity to carry the amount and type of traffic that would be generated by the new development and whether such traffic would cause any existing traffic or safety problems to be exacerbated, or new ones to be created.

Where alternatives are available, the number and location of points of access to a site may be determined by considerations such as the volume, type and destination of vehicular traffic using the existing roads, the volume of vehicular traffic likely to be generated by the scheme and the main directions in which such traffic is likely to go when moving between the dwellings and destinations outside the site.

Plate 31.1 Residential access road with one footway

Source: DOE, Design Bulletin 32

Plate 31.2 A shared surface residential access road

Source: DOE, Design Bulletin 32

It will also be important to consider whether junctions with an appropriate capacity and geometry can be created (see Parts 3 and 5); including, when appropriate, connections to existing roundabouts or signal-controlled junctions. It is sometimes necessary for developers and highway authorities to enter into agreements (see also Chapter 28.3) to finance the improvement of roads or junctions which are outside a proposed development but directly affected by it and developers will need to discuss such constraints and opportunities with local highway and planning authorities before design work is started.

For large developments, they will also need to consult local bus operators about their requirements. The need to make provision for buses will vary according to local public transport objectives and policies (Ref. 11). Provisions might involve amending an existing bus route, relocating existing bus stops or altering existing footways or footpaths to provide improved access to and facilities for bus stops (see also Chapter 26). Access for pedestrians and cyclists must also be considered (see 31.6 below).

31.5 The Layout of Roads and Footpaths

The overall layout of roads and footpaths within a development will depend partly on the location of points of access to roads serving the site and on whether or not links are required with any adjacent footpaths or cycle tracks.

Loops and Links for Public Transport

When an existing bus route needs to be extended into a large site which has only one point of access it will normally be necessary to provide a loop road, or turning and layover facilities if a terminus is needed. With more than one access point, an existing bus service may need to be routed through the site and a bus gate or link may be beneficial to connect one large residential area with another while at the same time preventing that route from being used as a short-cut by through traffic.

Prevention of Through Traffic

To help create surroundings which are safe and free from traffic nuisance, it will normally be necessary to ensure that non-access traffic either cannot use the roads to take a short cut (see Figure 31.4), finds there is no advantage in doing so (see Figure 31.5) or else finds it inconvenient to do so because the route is longer and more tortuous (see Figures 31.6 and 31.7) than the alternative outside the site (see also Chapters 16 and 17).

In large developments it may be necessary to consider limiting the numbers of dwellings which are to be served by each point of access to the site in order to reduce the amount of traffic on roads within the development and to minimise the inconvenience that would be caused if roads were to be blocked because of repairs (see Figure 31.8). When only one point of access is possible in large developments, the main road within the site will, whenever possible, need to form a loop so that access can be gained from either direction (see Figure 31.9).

Security and Crime Prevention

Crime prevention has become an increasingly important consideration in the layout of roads and footpaths in residential developments (Ref. 12), particularly in some inner city areas. Careful design can help to reduce risks. It has, for example, been suggested that the risk of house burglaries may be reduced if access to dwellings is provided from culs-de-sac rather than loop roads and if heads of culs-de-sac are not linked by footpaths. Risk of assault may be reduced if separated footpath routes are kept to a minimum (see also 31.6 below); and risks of car theft and vandalism may be reduced if parking provision is made mostly within dwelling curtilages (see also 31.8 below). Other features such as good street lighting, an absence of concealed places of refuge and the use of vandal proof fittings will all help. Developers should consult the local police force about the need for such measures.

Vehicle/Pedestrian Relationship

Drivers need to be made aware on entry and throughout the site that they are in surroundings where the needs of pedestrians are expected to take precedence over the convenience and free flow of vehicles. In large developments the aim should be to provide a convenient progression from roads where the needs of drivers predominate to those where pedestrians' requirements are of greatest importance. In many residential areas the most important activities will be children playing, pedestrians walking with prams and cycling.

In large developments with a single point of access, a short length of road may be required to provide a transitional link between the road network within the site and that outside. Such links would need to form the stem of a T-junction with the road outside (see Figure 31.10).

The aim of giving priority to the needs of pedestrians in the design of surroundings in the immediate vicinity of homes can normally be achieved by serving as many of the dwellings as possible from roads which carry low volumes of traffic. In large developments, this means locating a majority of dwellings around short culs-de-sac and a minority along roads which connect those culs-de-sac with points of access to the site (see Figure 31.11).

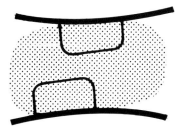

Figure 31.4 Road layout preventing use as a short cut

Figure 31.5 A looped road layout inhibiting diversionary routeing

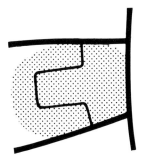

Figure 31.6 Road layout involving a detour when used as a through route

Figure 31.7 Alternative road layout involving a detour for through vehicles

Figure 31.8 Dual points of access to a development

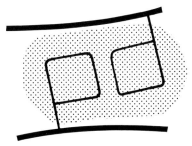

Figure 31.9 Dual looped access roads

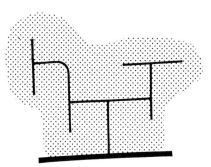

Figure 31.10 Use of a transitional link for a single point of access

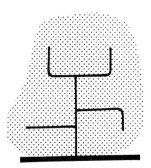

Figure 31.11 Road layout involving short culs-de-sac

Source: DoE/DTp DB 32 (1977)

261

Direct Access to Dwellings and Parking Spaces

The principles set out in DB32 suggest that roads serving more than around 300 dwellings should not normally give direct access to individual dwellings or parking spaces though many existing roads do allow such access. When new frontage development is provided along such roads the aim should be to provide direct access via an access road and ensure that drivers would not have either to park on, or to back-out onto the road outside. This will not always be possible on existing roads (see also Chapter 16.7).

When new community buildings such as churches and shops are part of the development they should be located immediately adjacent to a local distributor road, with direct access being provided via access roads which serve car parks and service entrances.

Vehicle Speeds

Although the most important contributions to safety can be achieved by excluding through traffic and reducing traffic volume, the overall configuration and geometry of road design also can be designed to ensure that drivers keep to speeds of well below 30 mph (50 kph), especially along access roads.

On access roads with footways and traditional cross-sections and visibility standards, research suggests that the use of 90° bends with tight radii and only short lengths of road between junctions or bends can help to bring speeds down to as low as 20 mph (32 kph) (Ref. 5). The research also showed that minor reductions in carriageway width appeared to make little difference to speeds and even more substantial reductions, like those produced by lines of parked cars, had only a limited effect.

The provision of innovative road layouts based on the principles set out in DB32, produced measured speeds well below 20 mph (32 kph). This was probably partly due to changes in road surfacing and the use of planting (see also 31.6 below) as well as the geometric standards employed.

Landscaping

If there are existing trees or shrubs on the site a survey will be needed to establish their position and condition so that the layout of roads and footpaths and underground services can allow for as many as possible of those that are sound to be retained.

Carefully considered hard and soft landscaping will be needed to help distinguish shared surface access roads from other types of road (see also 31.6 below). A flowing alignment of curves and verges with variable widths to accommodate trees and shrubs will be beneficial along the longest roads. It will also be desirable to allocate space to accommodate planting in rectilinear road layouts and in all places where the scene would otherwise be dominated by views of back gardens, garages or screen fences.

Special care will be needed in the selection of pavings, trees and shrubs (Ref. 13) so that maintenance is minimised and vegetation does not obscure sight lines or cause damage to services underground. Whenever possible, trees and shrubs should be located in places that will be maintained by individual householders (ie. usually in gardens within dwelling curtilages).

31.6 Provision for Pedestrians

General Aims

To complement the principles of site access and layout described above, the design of the development as a whole will need to ensure that footways and footpath routes are convenient for residents and visitors to use—especially those who are elderly or disabled. Such routes will also need to be laid out to help strangers to find their way round and be convenient for those who make regular door-to-door collections and deliveries.

The widths and alignment of footways will need to ensure that when passing each other pedestrians do not have to step out onto busy carriageways. It will also be necessary to ensure that the widths and alignment of both footways and footpaths are adequate to meet public utilities' requirements wherever services underground have to be accommodated.

Footways and Verges

Footways will normally need to be provided along both sides of local distributor roads and it will assist pedestrian safety and comfort if footways can be separated from the carriageways by verges along the most heavily trafficked local distributor roads. Footways are normally required along both sides of access roads but it may be safe to omit one footway in places where individual dwellings are not directly served and vehicle flows will not be high.

In some circumstances both footways may be omitted but verges will be needed where underground services have to be accommodated. Vehicle clearance margins will still be required in places where there are no footways or underground services. Footways along local distributor roads should only be omitted when it is certain that pedestrians will use separated footpaths or footways along other roads to reach their destinations.

Shared Surfaces

It is normally safe for both footways to be omitted from access road culs-de-sac, thereby creating shared surface access roads, provided that:

- only small numbers of dwellings are to be served;

- vehicle speeds can be kept very low;

- drivers are warned at the entrance that they are entering a shared surface (eg. by carriageway narrowing or a ramp or rumble strip);

- surface finishes contrast visually with the surfaces of roads with footways (eg. by using a coarse surface dressing, interlocking concrete block paving or brick paviors or setts) [NI.48];

- grouped parking spaces are clearly demarcated from pedestrian and vehicular routes;

- features such as lamp-posts, bollards and planting are located so that they do not cause obstructions or hazards to disabled people when moving between the home and parking spaces; and

- major pedestrian routes do not pass through the shared surface.

The public utilities normally expect markers to be provided to denote the limits of adopted areas when there are services under verges which are contiguous with privately maintained front gardens (eg. the 'Access Way' layout illustrated in Figure 31.12).

Underground services may need to be located beneath carriageways in some shared surface access roads, but the public utilities will normally need to be consulted about their detailed requirements for the location of such services. Services will normally need to be ducted where they must cross or are located beneath the carriageway.

Footpaths

Separated footpaths may be wasteful of land and an unnecessary maintenance burden if pedestrians find it more convenient to walk along roads to reach their destinations or prefer to do so for other reasons (such as the fear of assault). When there are clear benefits to be obtained from the provision of footpaths they will need to be convenient to use, well-lit and not provide potential hiding places or traps for litter.

Cycle Tracks

Special provision for cyclists may be required if a significant number of cycling movements is expected (eg. on routes to schools or recreational centres). Cycle tracks might be provided either contiguous with foot-paths (though separated from them by demarcation—see Plate 25.2) or as an unsegregated route available

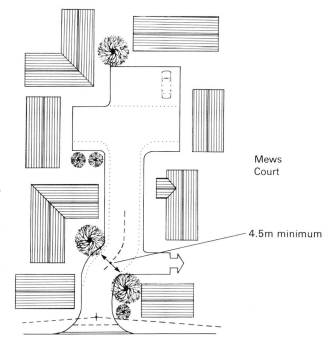

Mews Court

4.5m minimum

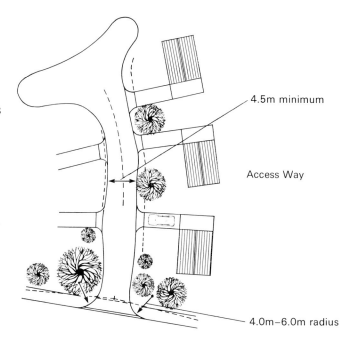

4.5m minimum

Access Way

4.0m–6.0m radius

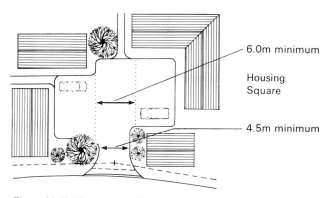

6.0m minimum

Housing Square

4.5m minimum

Figure 31.12 Three types of layout using a shared surface access road

263

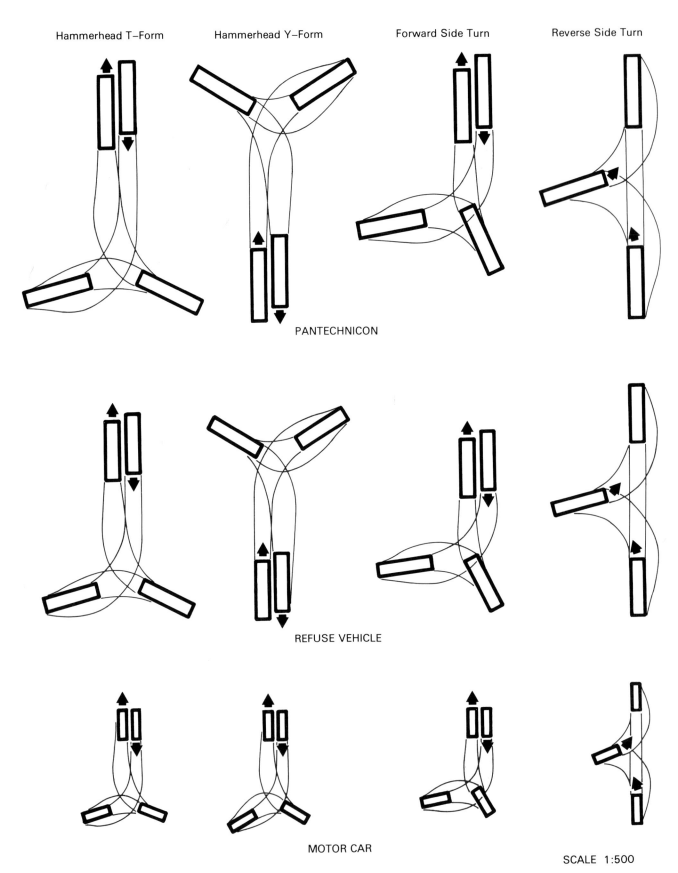

Hammerhead T–Form   Hammerhead Y–Form   Forward Side Turn   Reverse Side Turn

PANTECHNICON

REFUSE VEHICLE

MOTOR CAR

SCALE 1:500

Figure 31.13 Geometric characteristics of turning vehicles

to pedestrian and cyclists. Measures to assist pedestrians and cyclists are considered in Chapters 24 and 25 respectively and the management of pedestrians at different types of junction is described in the appropriate chapters in Part 5.

31.7 Provision for the Movement of Vehicles

Carriageways

The widths and alignment of carriageways provided in a residential development should take account of:

● the adequacy of off-street parking provision (see also 31.8 below);

● the expected speed and volume of traffic;

● the frequency with which cars may need to pass one another; and

● the need for provision for service vehicles to pass one another.

To minimise the risk of accidents it will also be necessary to provide intervisibility between pedestrians and moving vehicles and ensure that visibility on bends and at junctions is sufficient to enable drivers to slow down or stop if necessary to avoid collision.

Widening of carriageways on bends is usually required when the combined 'swept' paths of vehicles likely to pass one another is greater than the width of the straight carriageway.

Turning Areas

The spacing, layout and dimensions of turning areas should be designed to cater for the sizes of vehicles normally expected to use them, avoid the need for vehicles to reverse over long distances and take account of the possibility that vehicles may use turning bays for parking. Examples of the geometric characteristics of turning vehicles are provided in Figure 31.13.

Turning areas capable of accommodating a refuse vehicle will normally need to be provided at the heads of culs-de-sac serving more than a small number of dwellings. Unwanted parking in turning areas will normally be discouraged if the turning areas provide access directly into parking spaces within the curtilages of adjacent dwellings. It may also be possible to design junctions which can accommodate turning vehicles along access roads carrying low volumes of traffic.

Junctions

The spacing, layout and dimensions of junctions should take account of the types and numbers of vehicles that will be likely to use the junction, the likely directions of movement at the junction and the extent to which

delays may be caused by conflicting vehicular movement. Further information on the characteristics of different types of junction and their design requirements is given in Parts 3 and 5.

Priority junctions (ie. with road markings to indicate vehicle priority) will be appropriate for most of the busier locations within residential developments; but where a local distributor road serving a large development joins the existing road network, some other form of control may be necessary and may require a roundabout or use of traffic signals. The design of priority junctions is dealt with in Chapter 39, roundabouts in Chapter 40 and Traffic Signals in Chapter 41.

Visibility at junctions should be sufficient to enable drivers to slow down or stop if necessary to avoid collision and to enable drivers turning into a more heavily trafficked road, such as a local distributor, to make turning movements safely.

Requirements for the spacing of adjacent and opposite junctions, kerb radii and 'x' and 'y' sight line dimensions at junctions (see Chapter 39.2) will depend on the numbers of dwellings being served by the major and minor roads at individual junctions and the expected speeds of the vehicles using them, but minimum standards for safety will always be required.

31.8 Provision for Parking

General Considerations

The numbers of parking spaces provided and their location can make a substantial difference to the width of carriageway required to avoid damage from vehicles parking on footways and verges and to the standard of visibility achieved in practice on the carriageway. Thus the design of roads and parking provision should always be considered together.

Numbers of Parking Spaces

Planning authorities usually provide standards or guidelines for the parking provision appropriate to different types of development (see Chapter 30). These standards should take account of projected saturation levels of car ownership and the mixture of dwelling types and sizes as well as the authorities' transport policies for the area in which the site is located.

The aim will usually be to make each group of dwellings self-sufficient with regard to its parking provision. Experience suggests that few drivers are prepared to use parking spaces more than a short distance away from their destinations. Thus, to help avoid indiscriminate on-street parking, it will be necessary to ensure that:

- off-street parking spaces are provided in sufficient numbers for residents' and visitors' cars and long-stay parking by service vehicles;

- some spaces for short-term parking are provided on or alongside carriageways which give direct access to dwellings; and

- routes between off-street parking spaces and dwelling entrances are short enough to discourage long-stay parking on carriageways.

Location and Assignment of Parking Spaces

To help achieve these aims, parking spaces for residents and their visitors will normally need to be located no further from dwelling entrances than the distances required for service vehicles and conveniently positioned with regard to dwelling entrances, footpaths and footways.

Suggested maximum distances are given in Table 31.1. For convenience and to minimise risks of car theft and vandalism, as many residents' and visitors' parking spaces as possible will need to be located within dwelling curtilages (see Plate 31.3) or else in very close proximity to and within sight of the dwellings they serve (see Plate 31.4).

The smallest number of parking spaces per dwelling will normally be required when provision is made in the form of unassigned grouped hardstandings (ie.

	From entrance to dwelling	From entrance to curtilage
Maximum walking distance to refuse vehicle (m)		25
Maximum distance to refuse vehicle when refuse facilities shared (m) i.e. special handling may be necessary		9
Maximum walking distance to communal parking spaces (m)	50	
Maximum distance for the approach of a fire appliance (m) (when no floors greater than 6m above ground)	45	
Maximum walking distance to bus stop (m)		400 i.e. 5 minutes walk

Note: Specific consideration should be given in sheltered housing developments or special accommodation for the disabled to the need for ambulances or specially adapted vehicles to gain access.

Table 31.1 Typical maximum approach distances for different access requirements

Source: DoE/Welsh Office circular 82/73, DoE/DTp DB32 (1977)

when none of the spaces are to be provided for the sole use of individual households). In this situation the needs of households with above average car ownership can be balanced against those with below average car ownership and the number of spaces required for visitors' and service vehicles is also minimised.

When one or more spaces per dwelling are to be assigned for the sole use of individual households (ie. when the spaces are to be provided within dwelling curtilages or in assigned hardstandings or garages outside curtilages) some additional unassigned spaces will be required for visitors' and service vehicles and to meet the needs of households with more cars than can be accommodated within their assigned spaces.

In some high density developments, typically in central area locations, land costs might justify the construction of a multi-storey or underground car park controlled by issuing passes to residents. If an existing car park is close by or is incorporated in the same comprehensive redevelopment it may be possible for reserved spaces to be allocated to residents on a contractual basis.

31.9 Detailed Design Considerations

Road and Footpath Dimensions

Developers will always need to consult local plans, unitary development plans and highway authorities' [NI.1] design guides for their requirements on matters of detailed design such as the width and alignment of carriageways, footways, verges and footpaths and the provision of adequate visibility on bends and at junctions. Table 31.2 gives an indication of the range of carriageway widths and some other dimensions that might be appropriate depending on the volume and type of traffic carried [NI.49].

It will also be necessary to consult the Fire Service about local requirements for access by fire appliances; and the public utilities about local requirements for the widths of footways and verges and the location and demarcation of services underground.

Traffic Signs and Road Markings

A comprehensive scheme of traffic signs, including street name plates and road markings, will be needed as an integral part of residential road networks, though every effort should be made to keep such features to a minimum to help enhance the visual character of the development and to minimise maintenance costs. All signs and road markings must comply with the current Traffic Signs Regulations and General Directions.

In developments which have access directly from primary or district distributor roads with higher speed

Plate 31.3 Parking within dwelling curtilages

Source: DoE, Design Bulletin 32

Plate 31.4 Parking in a courtyard close by dwellings

Source: DoE, Design Bulletin 32

	Access Roads	Local Distributors
Minimum carriageway width (m)	5.5 / 4.8 / 4.5 / 4.1 / 3.0	6.7 / 6.1
Minimum centre-line radius (m)	30 / 20 / 10	90 / 60
Minimum junction spacing: Adjacent (m) Opposite (m)	40 / 20 20 / 10	90 40
Minimum kerb radii at junctions (m)	6 / 4	10

NB. Dimensional requirements normally vary according to the volume and type of traffic which the road is intended to carry.

Table 31.2 Typical dimensions for residential roads

limits, particular attention will need to be given to the erection of speed restriction signs and it will be essential to ensure that any speed limit or other order making procedures are progressed to coincide with road opening (see Chapter 22.2).

Any orders required to control the movement of traffic or parking can only be made by the appropriate authority and most regulatory traffic signs have no legal status without a traffic regulation order (see also Chapter 15).

Street Lighting

Most developments will need to incorporate a scheme of street lighting in accordance with the British Standard Code of Practice for Road Lighting (BS 5489) (Ref. 14) and this should be designed to complement the style and ambience of the development.

Construction

The construction and drainage of carriageways, footways, verges and footpaths will need to be appropriate to the topography and soil conditions on the site—with adequate forms of edge restraint and cross falls that deal adequately with surface water. Local authorities usually provide their own specifications for the construction of roads which are to be adopted for maintenance at public expense.

To help minimise the risk of damage to footways and verges by over-running vehicles it will normally be necessary to ensure that adequate protection is afforded by robustly constructed kerbs, banks and special features such as bollards.

Maintenance

It will also be necessary to ensure that the differences in carriageway surfacing materials which are required to demarcate shared surface access roads from other types of road will not only remain visually apparent

and provide a safe surface for vehicular movement over many years, but also be economical to maintain and be visually acceptable after repairs have been carried out. These matters should be discussed with the local authority during the design stages.

Parking Space Dimensions and Demarcation

Specially dimensioned and reserved parking spaces will usually need to be provided adjacent to all dwellings designed for occupation by old or disabled persons and access to these dwellings should avoid steps or steep gradients. Requirements for the dimensions of hardstandings, garages and parking forecourts and for the demarcation of hardstandings' will sometimes be found in local plans and unitary development plans or in design guides issued by planning and highway authorities. National guidance on such matters has also been published (Refs. 15, 16 and 17).

Grouped hardstandings may need to be individually demarcated to help avoid the waste of space and obstruction that can be caused by random parking. A change of surface material or use of granite setts are usually best for this purpose, rather than surface markings. Parking spaces contiguous with carriageways can be demarcated with setts laid flush with the road surface.

31.10 References

1. DoE/DTp—Design Bulletin 32, *'Residential roads and footpaths: layout considerations'*, DoE/DTp (1977). (N.B. For the status of this bulletin see DoE Circular 72/77, DTp 5/77, Welsh Office 92/77 *'Residential roads and footpaths'*, DoE/DTp/Welsh Office (1977)). [Sco.170] (31.1)

2. Noble, J—*'Local standards for the layout of residential roads: a review'*, Housing Research Foundation (1983). (31.1)

3. DoE—'*More than just a road*', (film and brochure), DoE (1984). (31.1)

4. Jenks, M—'*Residential roads researched*', The Architects' Journal, Vol 177 No 26 (29 June 1983). (31.1)

5. Bennett, G T—'*Speeds in residential areas*', The Highway Engineer, Vol 30 No 7 (July 1983). (31.1, 31.5)

6. DoE—Circular 13/84, '*Land for Housing*' (Annex A Para 13), DoE (1984). (31.1)

7. Highways Act 1980, HMSO (1980). [Sco.172] (31.2)

8. NJUG—'*Provision of mains and services by public utilities on residential estates*', the National Joint Utilities Group Publication No 2 (1979). (31.2)

9. NJUG—'*Recommended positioning of utilities' mains and plant for new works*', the National Joint Utilities Group Publication No 7 (1986). (31.2)

10. SLASH Study Team—'*Servicing mixed use access layouts: study team report*', prepared by C P Lee, Scottish Local Authorities Special Housing Group (1980). (31.2)

11. DoE/Welsh Office—Circular 82/73 (155/73) '*Bus operation in residential and industrial areas*', DoE/Welsh Office (1973). (31.4)

12. NHBC—'*Guidance on how the security of new houses can be improved*', National House Building Council (1986). (31.5)

13. DoE—Housing Development Note II, '*Landscape of new housing*', DoE (1973). (31.5)

14. BSI—BS 5489 '*Code of Practice for Road Lighting*', British Standards Institute (1973). (31.9)

15. DoE—Housing Development Note VII, '*Parking in new housing schemes: Parts 1 and 2*', DoE (1977). (31.9)

16. Goldsmith, S—'*Designing for the disabled*', Royal Institute of British Architects (1976). (31.9)

17. Noble, J—'*Activities and spaces*', The Architectural Press (1983). (31.9)

31.11 Further Information

18. Local highway authorities' standards for road layout and construction (generally).

19. Local planning authorities' standards for parking provision and aspects of design such as landscaping (generally).

20. Local public utilities' requirements for the provision of services (generally).

21. Noble, J—'*Housing plot developments compared: Part 2 England*', The Architects' Journal (11 March, 1981).

22. BSI—'*Precautions against fire Part 1: Flats and maisonettes (in blocks over two storeys). CP3: Chapter IV*', British Standards Institution (1971).

23. Home Office—Fire Prevention Note 1/70, '*Access for fire appliances*', Home Office Fire Department (1970).

24. GLC—'*An Introduction to Housing Layout*', Architectural Press (–).

32 Major Industrial and Commercial Development

32.1 Introduction

This chapter deals with the general principles of layout and design for major industrial and commercial developments which often attract significant numbers of vehicles. They therefore usually require the provision of large car parks and in many cases a road layout to cater for the manoeuvring characteristics of large or heavy goods vehicles. The most common types of development of this kind are:

'Out of Town' Shopping Centres, where most trips will be made by private car, although bus and pedestrian access will also need to be catered for. The provision of significant levels of car parking and facilities for bulk deliveries and servicing is therefore essential for successful operation.

Industrial Trading Estates, where there may be a need to provide appropriate levels of car parking for employees as well as visitors and where an important design constraint will be the need to cater for the loading, parking and manoeuvring of the significant number of large and heavy goods vehicles likely to visit the site. Larger industrial estates may need to be served directly by public transport, which might be a regular local service or peak hour workers' specials.

Science Parks, which are small industrial estates with a significant high technology or research and development content, probably with sales support, where most employees may wish to travel to work by private car.

Lorry Parks/Transhipment Depots, where overnight parking, possibly with accommodation facilities for drivers, is required for externally based operators en route elsewhere, as well as for local operators.

Exhibition Centres/Theme Parks/Sports Centres and Stadia, where high levels of parking are required as well as comprehensive provision for public transport.

Selection of Suitable Sites

Land intended for these types of development will often have been identified in Development Plans such that most large developments of this kind will be sited on the fringe of urban areas or as reclaimed industrial land which might exist in inner city areas or Enterprise Zones. These sites should be distanced or physically separated from existing or proposed residential areas where the presence of high traffic levels and heavy goods vehicles would be undesirable.

Land used for commercial and industrial activities should be capable of being accessed directly from primary or district distributors (see Plate 32.1).

Provision of Rail Heads

Certain types of bulk freight and loads being hauled over longer distances can sometimes be transported more easily and cheaply by rail. Developments which involve certain industrial processes or the use of bulk raw materials may be attracted to sites with an existing rail terminal or where a new siding could be provided and Government grants may be available to encourage this (Ref. 1).

Control of Vehicle Operating Centres

In addition to controlling land use through development plans and development control, local authorities may also influence the siting of lorry depots by making representations to the Traffic Commissioners responsible for licensing lorries and their operating centres [NI.13]. Powers contained in the Road Traffic Act 1974 (Ref. 2), clarified and amended by the Transport Act 1982 (Ref. 3), control the use of vehicle operating centres with a view to preventing or minimising any adverse environmental effects.

32.2 Access and Internal Circulation

The important factors to be considered for the layout of the access and the internal circulatory systems within new developments are set out in Table 29.1.

Large Single Site Commercial Developments

In order to achieve satisfactory levels of safety and operating efficiency for a major new development it will usually be necessary to provide a new access to the highway or to make significant alterations to an existing point of access. The local highway authority is likely to require the developer to finance these works (see Chapter 28.3) and the type of junction control required will depend on estimates of traffic generation. Road junctions should be designed in accordance with the advice given in Part 5.

The internal circulatory system should be designed to ensure that in normal circumstances no traffic queues form on the external highway network. It is therefore important to provide sufficient queueing space between the access junction and the nearest conflict point within the development. It may be beneficial to provide separate access points for customers' or visitors' cars and service traffic, or to segregate the two types of

Plate 32.1 An example of highway access to a major commercial site from a primary distributor

traffic at the earliest opportunity. This minimises the conflict between vehicle types and permits separate circulatory systems to be designed to the standards required for different types of vehicle (eg. private cars and heavy goods vehicles).

In large developments where more than one car park is provided it is important to ensure that traffic is guided to where it wishes to go. Direction signing and road markings help to achieve this.

The design of road junctions should ensure that traffic leaving the site does not cause entering traffic to queue back onto the external public road network. Any queueing should therefore be contained within the site. Where petrol filling stations are provided as part of the development they should generally be sited on the exit road. Consideration must also be given to access by the emergency services (see Chapter 17) and, where appropriate, to parking and access for disabled people.

Industrial Trading Estates

The layout of individual factories and depots should be designed to assist their operational functions and aim to achieve the most efficient layout commensurate

with road safety. Roads and footpaths, whether private or intended for adoption by the highway authority, should provide a safe and efficient means of access for workers, visitors and the range of service and delivery vehicles which might be anticipated when a number of different industrial processes and commercial activities are grouped together. Estate layouts will vary according to the size and topography of the site, the mix and size of factory units and the points of possible safe access from the existing distributor road network.

In developments likely to generate less than 250 commercial vehicle trips per day (ie. possibly equivalent to about 125,000 m^2 of gross floor area (gfa) or less), access to individual factory units can be from a single industrial access road but a looped arrangement is preferable. A cul-de-sac up to 250 m in length may be acceptable if site conditions require it, subject to the provision of adequate turning facilities.

In larger developments a number of industrial access roads should feed to the main industrial distributor road which should not provide direct access to individual factory units. Again a looped arrangement is preferable so as to prevent the possibility of creating a rat run for main road traffic (see Figure 32.1).

271

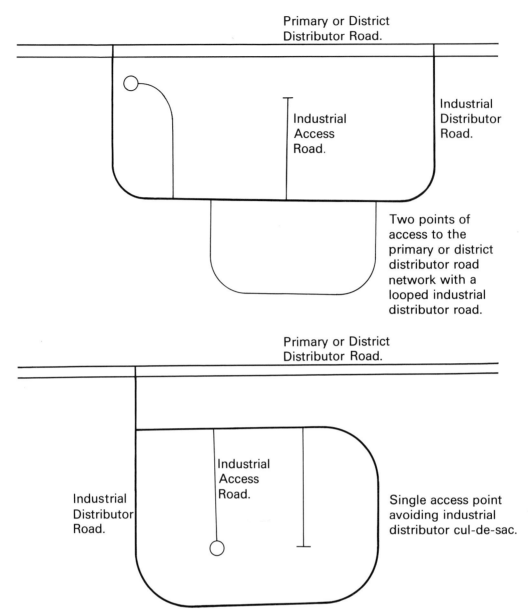

Figure 32.1 Alternative schematic layouts for industrial trading estate roads

The normal maximum permissible width of heavy goods vehicles is 2.5 m (2.58 m for refrigerated vehicles) excluding mirrors (Ref. 4). To permit sufficient clearance to the edge of the carriageway and between opposing traffic flows, all two-way industrial trading estate roads should have a minimum width of 7.3 m with local widening on bends (see Figure 32.2) where necessary. The normal minimum centre line radius is 60 m. Table 32.1 summarises suggested minimum design standards.

A road layout designed to the above standards should cope adequately with the geometric requirements of heavy goods vehicles but designs must also provide sufficient capacity to cope with expected traffic flows (see Part 5 for the design of road junctions).

Any large individual premises (greater than say 25,000 m² in gross floor area) should have its own access at least 6.1 m wide. Any security or gate facilities should be sited at least 20 m from the boundary of the industrial estate road so that administrative formalities can be conducted without disrupting other vehicular or pedestrian traffic.

At the other extreme, individual workshop units may have loading, parking (and the building entrance itself) on a forecourt contiguous with the highway (see Plate 32.2). In these circumstances, care must be taken to avoid indiscriminate use of the forecourt and overspill onto adjacent footway or carriageway areas. Formal marking of the forecourt to identify areas for different activities may overcome these problems but they may

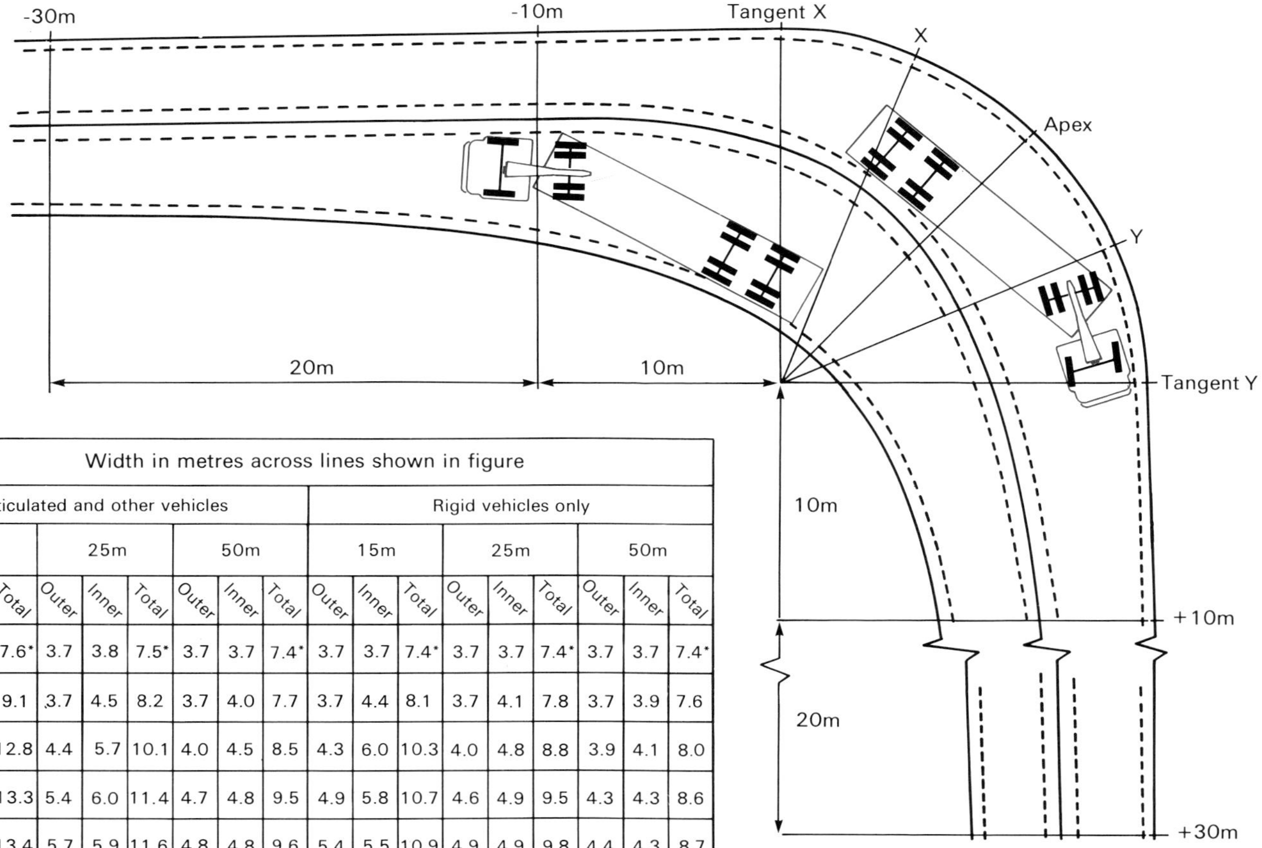

Width in metres across lines shown in figure

Radius of outside curve	Articulated and other vehicles									Rigid vehicles only								
	15m			25m			50m			15m			25m			50m		
Lane	Outer	Inner	Total	Outer	Inner	Total	Outer	Inner	Total	Outer	Inner	Total	Outer	Inner	Total	Outer	Inner	Total
Width at -30m	3.7	3.9	7.6*	3.7	3.8	7.5*	3.7	3.7	7.4*	3.7	3.7	7.4*	3.7	3.7	7.4*	3.7	3.7	7.4*
Width at -10m	3.7	5.4	9.1	3.7	4.5	8.2	3.7	4.0	7.7	3.7	4.4	8.1	3.7	4.1	7.8	3.7	3.9	7.6
Width at Tangent X	5.0	7.8	12.8	4.4	5.7	10.1	4.0	4.5	8.5	4.3	6.0	10.3	4.0	4.8	8.8	3.9	4.1	8.0
Width at X	6.2	7.1	13.3	5.4	6.0	11.4	4.7	4.8	9.5	4.9	5.8	10.7	4.6	4.9	9.5	4.3	4.3	8.6
Width at Apex	6.9	6.5	13.4	5.7	5.9	11.6	4.8	4.8	9.6	5.4	5.5	10.9	4.9	4.9	9.8	4.4	4.3	8.7
Width at Y	7.0	6.2	13.2	5.9	5.3	11.2	4.9	4.6	9.5	5.6	5.0	10.6	4.9	4.6	9.5	4.3	4.3	8.6
Width at Tangent Y	6.4	6.3	12.7	5.3	4.6	9.9	4.6	3.9	8.5	5.3	4.7	10.0	4.6	4.1	8.7	4.2	3.8	8.0
Width at +10m	4.6	4.2	8.8	4.2	4.2	8.4	4.0	3.8	7.8	4.1	3.8	7.9	3.9	3.8	7.7	3.8	3.7	7.5
Width at +30m	3.8	3.7	7.5*	3.8	3.7	7.5*	3.8	3.7	7.5*	3.7	3.7	7.4*	3.7	3.7	7.4*	3.7	3.7	7.4*

* Note for all practical purposes the road width at this point can be assumed to be 7.3m - the standard width.

Figure 32.2 Design standards for local widening on bends in industrial distributor roads

Source: 'Designing for deliveries', © FTA (1983)

ROAD TYPE	Nominal Design Speed (km/h)	Minimum Carriageway width (m)	Minimum Centre Line Radius (m)	Minimum vertical curve length (m)	Minimum Junction Spacing (m)	
					Adjacent	Opposite
Industrial Distributor Road	50	7.3 m	60	30	90	40
Industrial Estate Road	40					

Table 32.1 Recommended minimum design standards for industrial trading estate roads

Plate 32.2 An example of separated parking and loading facilities for individual commercial units

Source: Telford Development Corporation

Plate 32.3 Landscaping to enhance and segregate areas for different uses

Source: Warrington and Runcorn Development Corporation

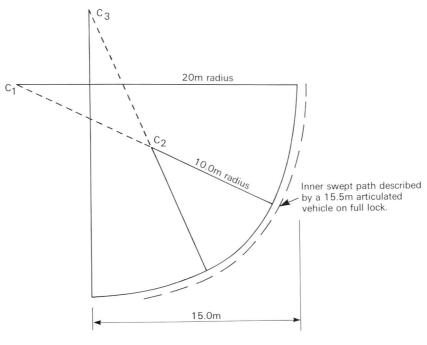

Figure 32.3 A typical compound curve for corners

Source: Greater Manchester Council

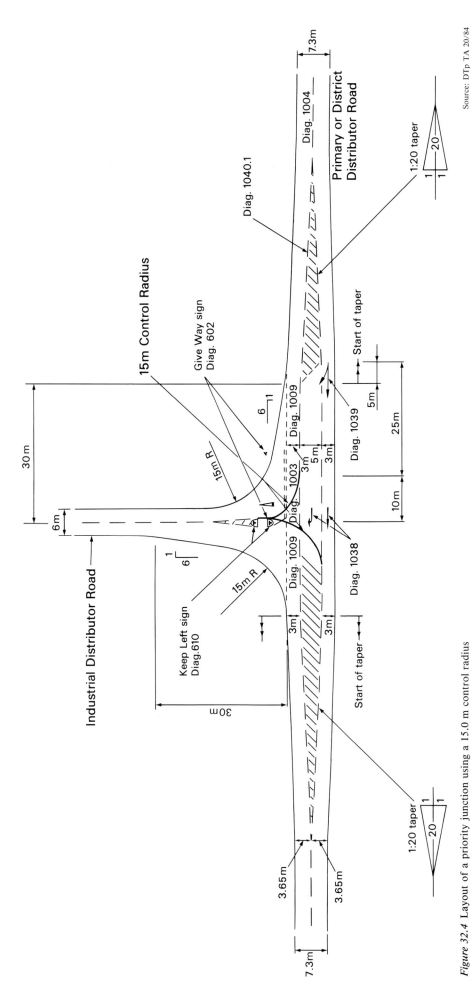

Figure 32.4 Layout of a priority junction using a 15.0 m control radius

Source: DTp TA 20/84

need to be reinforced by carefully sited physical barriers such as bollards or landscaping (see Plate 32.3). The use of different coloured or textured pavements can help to identify pedestrian areas (see also Chapter 33.2).

Junctions Within Industrial Trading Estates

With relatively low traffic volumes within industrial trading estates, priority junctions will usually be adequate. However, where an industrial distributor road serving a large development joins an existing primary or district distributor road network some other form of control may be necessary (eg. roundabout or traffic signals).

The design of priority junctions is dealt with in Chapter 39 (see also Ref. 5) [Sco.173] but particular considerations in industrial areas are:

The **swept path** described by a turning heavy goods vehicle does not follow a simple curve. Compound curves (see Figure 32.3) should therefore be used on corners to assist turning manoeuvres, avoid damage to kerbs and footways by vehicle over-run and remove the need to cross into the opposing traffic stream. At junctions between industrial distributor roads or with the primary or district distributor road network, a channelisation island, which can also act as a pedestrian refuge, may be beneficial if designed with a control radius of at least 15 metres (see Figure 32.4).

The **braking and acceleration performance** of heavy goods vehicles is less than that of cars and at priority junctions visibility 'x' distances (see Chapter 39) should only be reduced below 9 m in exceptional circumstances so that the driver of a heavy vehicle may make an early decision on whether to stop or proceed through the junction. 9 m × 90 m visibility splays should therefore be provided at junctions in industrial and service areas where the distributor road is designed for 50 kph. Exceptions may have to be made in confined underground service areas (eg. beneath shopping precincts) where adherance to these standards would have severe cost penalties. Here the reduction in visibility standards can be ameliorated by the use of mirrors but speeds must be kept very low.

32.3 General Design Requirements for Heavy Goods Vehicles

The manoeuvrability of heavy goods vehicles depends upon their size, whether they are rigid bodied or articulated, the number of axles and the skill and judgement of the driver. Although some manufacturing processes employ specialist vehicles with manoeuvring characteristics that can be translated directly into a design, the majority of industrial estates, factories and distribution depots will involve a range of vehicle types and sizes. The current maximum permitted dimensions of normal heavy goods vehicles are given in Table 32.2.

Vehicle Type	Axles (1) (No)	Max-Weight (2) (tonnes)	Maximum Length (m)	General (4) Maximum Width (m)	Maximum Height (3) (m)
Rigid	2 3 4	17.00 24.39 30.49	11.0	2.5	– – –
Motor Vehicle and Drawbar-trailer (road-train)	4 or more	32.52	18.0	2.5	–
Articulated	3 4 5 or more	24.39 32.52 38.00	15.5	2.5	– – 4.2

Notes: (1) Normal maximum axle weight is 9.20 tonnes which, with wide or twin tyres, may be increased to 10.17 tonnes, or to 10.5 tonnes, for the sole driving axle of 2 axled motor vehicles.

(2) Dependent upon axle spacing.

(3) Not generally specified.

(4) Max. width refrigerated vehicles 2.58 m.

Table 32.2 Current UK maximum permitted dimensions for HGVs

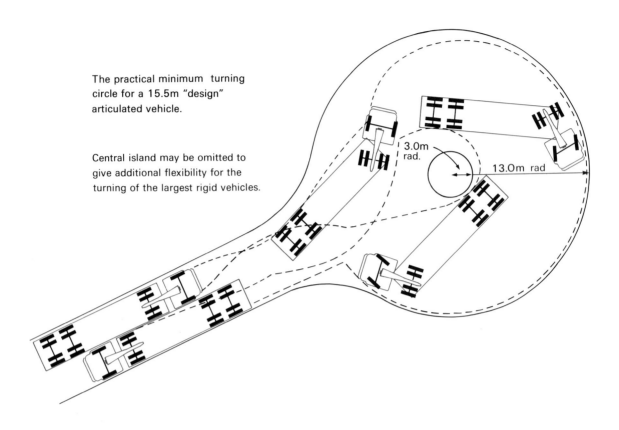

The practical minimum turning circle for a 15.5m "design" articulated vehicle.

Central island may be omitted to give additional flexibility for the turning of the largest rigid vehicles.

3.0m rad.

13.0m rad

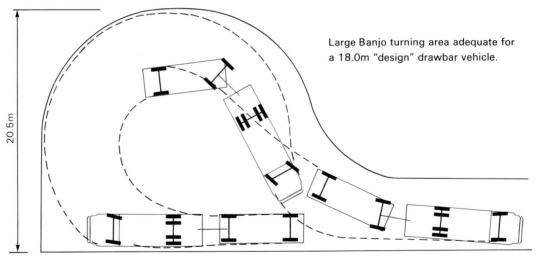

Large Banjo turning area adequate for a 18.0m "design" drawbar vehicle.

20.5m

Figure 32.5 Turning areas for heavy goods vehicles

Source: 'Designing for deliveries', © FTA (1983)

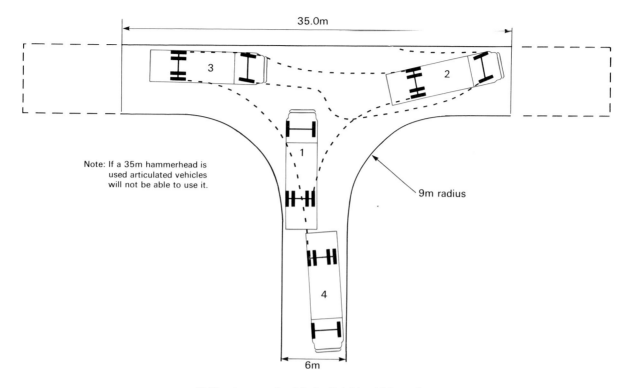

T–Turning area for "design" rigid vehicles only

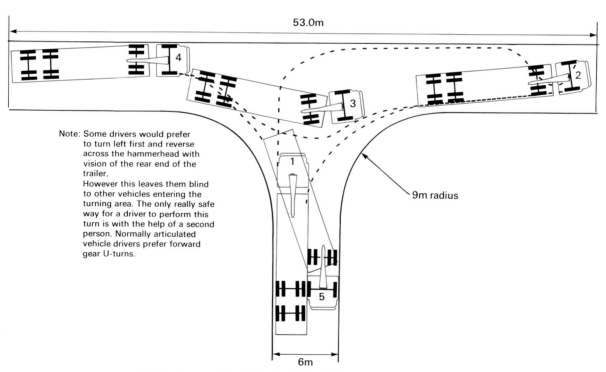

T–Turning area for "design" rigid and "design" articulated vehicles.

Figure 32.6 Turning areas for heavy goods vehicles

Source: 'Designing for deliveries', © FTA (1983)

279

In most aspects of highway design it is seldom practical or economical to provide facilities to cope with the worst of all possible operating conditions (eg. large numbers of the largest vehicles visiting a site in a short space of time). However, designs should be able to cope adequately with the most commonly occurring circumstances, recognising that a small number of the largest vehicles will occasionally experience some degree of difficulty in manoeuvring and that individual vehicle performance varies greatly with axle configuration and spacing.

In practice it will be helpful to use a 'design' vehicle to achieve efficient and uniform layouts and to establish the expected number and distribution through time of all vehicle movements, particularly those of vehicles which exceed the design standard. The Freight Transport Association have developed a specification for design vehicles which approximates to the performance of the 85th percentile vehicle. A small selection of the resulting layouts are reproduced in figures 32.5–32.8. These will accommodate the majority of vehicles with ease.

Most designs will operate satisfactorily if they can cope with the requirements of a 15.5 m long design articulated vehicle and a 10.0 m long design rigid vehicle. Articulated vehicles are often used for the longer, inter-urban (so-called trunking) trips and rigid vehicles for deliveries, (both single and multi-drop) within urban areas. Rigid vehicles will therefore tend to predominate at shopping and similar service areas and articulated vehicles at trunk lorry parks and the depots of large long distance operators. Break bulk, consolidation and similar types of transhipment and distribution depots will have significant numbers of both types of vehicle.

In general, articulated vehicles are more manoeuvrable than the equivalent sized rigid vehicle because the radius of the inner swept path described by the rear axle(s) is much less (Ref. 6).

A computer program is available to predict the paths described by large vehicles as they manoeuvre (Ref. 7).

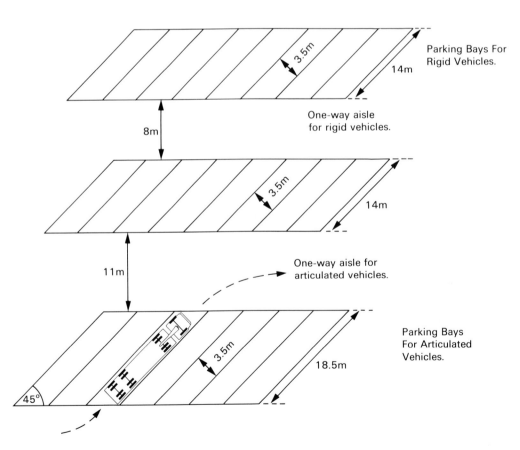

Figure 32.7 Parking areas for heavy goods vehicles

Source: 'Designing for deliveries', © FTA (1983)

280

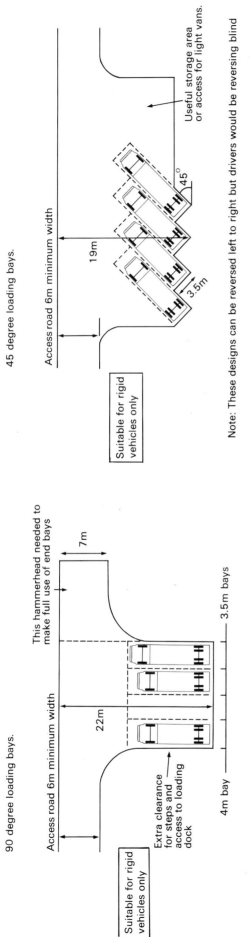

90 degree loading bays.

This hammerhead needed to make full use of end bays

7m

Access road 6m minimum width

22m

3.5m bays

Extra clearance for steps and access to loading dock

4m bay

Suitable for rigid vehicles only

Note: These designs can be reversed left to right but drivers would be reversing in clockwise and blind to obstructions
— a second person would be needed.

45 degree loading bays.

Useful storage area or access for light vans.

Access road 6m minimum width

19m

45°

3.5m

Suitable for rigid vehicles only

Note: These designs can be reversed left to right but drivers would be reversing blind

Other angles can be used (for example 60° or 50°) with proportional increases in the clearance provided.

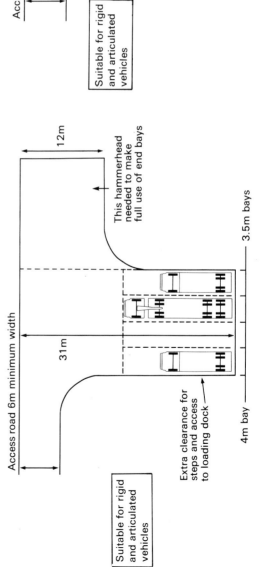

Useful storage area or access for light vans

Access road 6m minimum width

25m

45°

3.5m

Suitable for rigid and articulated vehicles

12m

This hammerhead needed to make full use of end bays

3.5m bays

Access road 6m minimum width

31m

Extra clearance for steps and access to loading dock

4m bay

Suitable for rigid and articulated vehicles

Figure 32.8 Loading bays for heavy goods vehicles

Source: 'Designing for deliveries', © FTA (1983)

281

32.4 Geometric Requirements for Turning, Parking and Loading

Developments which attract numbers of heavy goods vehicles will require areas where they may be turned safely and conveniently, parked securely when not in use and loaded easily and efficiently without disrupting other traffic.

Turning Areas

A turning area must be constructed at the end of every cul-de-sac and at any other location where large vehicles might otherwise be expected to reverse more than a short distance. The severely restricted rearward vision of heavy goods vehicles means that reversing can be a difficult and hazardous manoeuvre. A circular or banjo form of layout is therefore preferable, although on constrained sites, or where a significant number of the largest rigid vehicles is anticipated, a hammerhead may be provided (see Figures 32.5 and 32.6.)

Reductions below these dimensions will result in difficulty for drivers and the likelihood of damage to kerbs, footways and any adjacent street furniture or structures. Tyre scrub on the rear axles can also occur when trailers are turned too sharply. From this it can be seen that reduced construction costs may well result in increased maintenance costs. It is also important to ensure that turning areas are kept free of parked vehicles, trailers, skips and pallets and the other paraphenalia associated with manufacturing, storage and distribution. This is best achieved by providing more convenient and attractive locations for these activities.

Parking Areas

A secure and convenient parking area is important to any freight or haulage site where vehicles or empty trailers are likely to be left for long periods. Variable lengths and manoeuvrability affect the layout and size of individual bays which should be grouped together according to length (Ref. 5).

Bays should be 3.5 m wide and angled at approximately 45° towards the point of egress (see Figure 32.7). This layout permits reduced aisle widths to be used. Using this configuration approximately 72 rigid vehicles or 48 articulated vehicles (or different combinations) can be accommodated on one hectare of land, although this is also dependent upon the shape of the site and the location of the points of access.

Loading Areas

Well designed loading areas located away from the highway will overcome problems associated with loading on-street and make the task easier and more efficient to perform. They should therefore be incorporated in all new shopping, industrial and freight handling developments. As with parking facilities, it is important to encourage their use by making them more attractive and convenient to use than the adjacent highway. Figure 32.8 provides some alternative loading bay layouts. Most vehicles will be loaded from the rear although some vehicles have side entry facilities as well. If suitable loading docks are not provided or a fork lift truck is likely to be employed, a 3.0 m (minimum) wide working area will be required adjacent to the vehicle.

Loading bays should be 3.5 m wide and 16.0 m long for articulated vehicles and 12.0 m long for rigid vehicles. It may be unnecessary to require a small development of small workshop units to incorporate facilities for the largest vehicles. Individual units of 150 m^2 gfa or less should, however, incorporate a 6.0 m × 3.5 m loading area, suitable for light delivery vans. Groups of these units with a total gfa of 450 m^2 or more should have access to at least one 12.0 m bay.

Headroom

Some developments will be undercover and the service areas of some split level shopping developments may be below ground or underneath the main shopping level. The maximum height of vehicle likely to be encountered in such a situation is 4.2 m (ie. a standard container on a suitable flatbed vehicle). Minimum headroom provided should therefore be 4.65 m exclusive of any additional space required for lighting units and service pipes or ducts. Additional clearance will be required if there is a possible requirement for a surface overlay in the future. Changes in gradient may also reduce the effective headroom for long vehicles (see Figure 32.9). Consideration should be given to the provision of an alarm or warning device for drivers of oversized vehicles and the headroom provided should be indicated on warning signs.

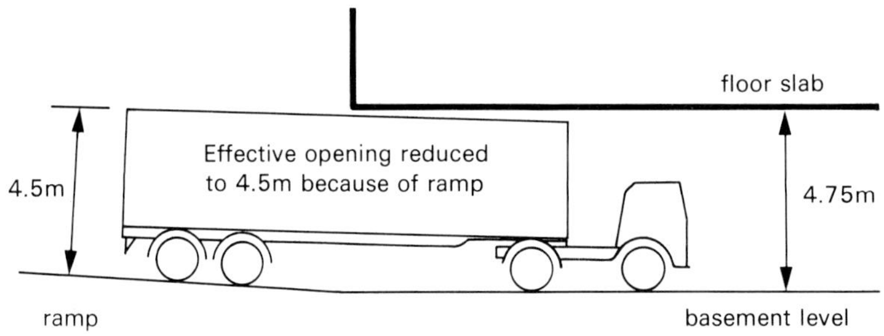

Extra headroom is needed at the foot of ramps.

Figure 32.9 Effect on headroom of a change in gradient

Source: 'Designing for deliveries', © FTA (1983)

32.5 Layout of Single Level Car Parking

Because of the generally lower land values away from town centre locations and the cost of constructing multi-storey car parks, car parking provided with new industrial or commercial developments will often be at ground level. Occasionally, the construction of a multi-storey car park may be justified at out-of-town sites either because sufficient land is not available, to reduce walking distances or on economic grounds.

Access and Internal Distribution

The type of access required to a car park will depend on the scale of the development. For example, the car park at the National Exhibition Centre in Birmingham has access directly from a motorway junction, but such arrangements are rare and are generally only suited to premises of national significance. Access to a car park should be available from all directions and where there are restrictions, either at entry or exit, adequate signing will be required.

The design of the main entry road should help the transition from the higher speed external road network to the parking area where pedestrian activity and low speed manoeuvring should predominate. An entry road with a curved alignment of sufficient length to minimise the probability of queues forming on the external road network will often be suitable (see Plate 32.4).

The internal distribution system should be designed so that:

● a vehicle arriving from any entry point can reach any parking bay and, on exit, can visit any internal facility such as pick-up points or petrol filling stations (ie. secondary movements); and

● conflicts between different users (eg. pedestrians, cars, delivery vehicles and, where appropriate, public transport) are minimised. Consideration should be given to segregated circulatory systems wherever possible.

Road markings should establish the circulation pattern supplemented by appropriate traffic signs as road markings can be obscured when vehicles are travelling close to one another. Adequate lighting should be provided to help pedestrians and drivers and as an aid to security. Individual operators may have specific security requirements which the design should take into account and consultation in advance may be helpful.

Plate 32.4 An example of road access and car park layout to a commercial office development
Source: Telford Development Corporation

Very large single level car parks should be subdivided by walkways and landscaping into smaller areas of about 800 spaces. These areas can be given a unique identity to help drivers to find their cars on their return. Letters or numbers are often used but pictorial signs such as animals or flowers may be easier to remember (see Figure 32.10). Walkways may be identified by different coloured or textured paving or a small, but abrupt change of level. Gaps for pedestrians should be provided between bays at appropriate intervals and car parks associated with large supermarkets should have areas set aside for customers to deposit shopping trolleys (see also Chapter 33.6). Special facilities should be provided for disabled persons to minimise walking distances and provide sufficient width for wheelchair access. Ramps or lifts may be necessary at changes in level.

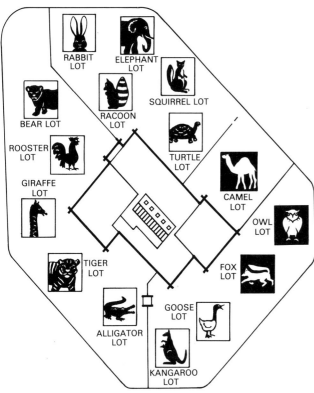

Figure 32.10 Symbolic signing applied to different parts of a large single-level car park

Parking Aisles and Bays

Traffic aisles provide access to the parking bays. The length of an aisle should relate to the turnover of spaces so that in relatively short stay car parks (eg. associated with shopping) 250 m (which will provide access to approximately 200 spaces where bays are on both sides) is a general maximum for a through aisle (ie. accessible from both ends). In longer stay car parks for employees or commuters, aisles may be extended up to 500 m. If the aisle forms a cul-de-sac the length should be reduced to that at which a passing motorist can establish whether there are any vacant spaces without having to enter the aisle. This is usually less than 30 m. Aisles are generally 6.0 m wide for one-way operation and 6.75 m for two-way. Landscaping and areas for storing shopping trolleys should be protected by kerbs or other physical barriers.

Parking bays are usually positioned at 90 degrees to the access aisles although other angles may be used to fill awkwardly shaped sites. Alternatively it may be better to use any residual space for motorcycle parking or for landscaping in order to provide a regular set of clearly marked car parking bays and to improve the environment. Bays are normally 4.75 m long to give a 'bin width' (ie. bay + aisle + bay) of 15.5 m for one-way operation. The width of a parking bay should relate to its purpose eg:

- long stay (employees, commuters' parking): 2.3 m;
- general parking: 2.4 m;
- short stay (shoppers' parking): 2.5 m;
- parking for the disabled: minimum 3.2 m
                        (3.6 m preferred).

Increased bay width permits easier and quicker manoeuvring into and out of the bay and makes getting into and out of the vehicle more convenient, especially with parcels and shopping. Depending on the shape of the site, it is generally possible to provide 300 to 400 spaces per hectare.

Other aspects of car park layout and design such as capacity and entry/exit controls are dealt with in Chapter 33.6—Multi-Storey Car Parks.

32.6 Facilities for Pedestrians, Cyclists and Public Transport

The process of design and assessment of any new development, but particularly those attracting large numbers of people (such as shopping, exhibition and sports centres) should include consideration of the needs of pedestrians and cyclists and for public transport. Detailed advice on the types of facilities which might be provided is given in Chapters 24 and 25 respectively as well as in Chapters 31 and 33.

32.7 Environmental Design Considerations

The parking and access requirements of major developments will often result in large areas being allocated for the exclusive use of moving or standing vehicles. Whilst this may be unavoidable for the operating efficiency of the development, the potentially adverse visual effects of such layouts should be borne in mind and, wherever possible, hard and soft landscaping features should be included in the design to relieve these effects and help to humanise their overall scale.

32.8 References

1. Railways Act 1974, HMSO (1974).   (32.1)

2. Road Traffic Act 1974, HMSO (1974).   (32.1)

3. Transport Act 1982, HMSO (1982).   (32.1)

4. The Road Vehicles (Construction and Use) Regulations 1986, Statutory Instrument 1986 No 1078, HMSO (1986).   (32.2)

5. DTp—TA 20/84, *'Layout of Major/ Minor Junctions'*, DTp (1984). [Sco.173]   (32.2)

6. Freight Transport Association—*'Designing For Deliveries'*, FTA (1983).   (32.3)

7. Savoy Computing—*'TRACK: Library of vehicle swept paths'*, Savoy Software Sciences Ltd., London (1983).   (32.3)

32.9 Further Information

8. Freight Transport Association—Freight Facts 2/83, *'Designing For Heavier Lorries'*, FTA (1983).

9. Howarth, S L and Hilton, I C—*'Car Parking Standards and the Urban Economy'*, Traffic Engineering and Control, Vol 23 No 11 (1982).

10. Leake, G R and Turner, D J—*'Shopper and vehicle characteristics at large retail shopping centres'*, Traffic Engineering and Control, Vol 23 No 1 (1982).

11. Lilley, A A and Walter, B J—*'Concrete block paving for heavily trafficked roads and paved areas'*, Cement and Concrete Association (1978).

12. Duffell, J R et al—*'Parking in relation to recreational needs'*, report of the British Parking Association Regional Seminar, Stoneleigh (1977).

13. DoE—Circular 82/73, *'Bus operation in residential and industrial areas'*, DoE (1973). [Wa.46]

14. Cliff Tandy—*'Handbook of Urban Landscape'*, Architectural Press (1972).

33 Central Area Development

33.1 Introduction

Despite the general trend towards decentralisation described in Part 1, town centre areas are still very important for shopping, business and commerce and often provide facilities for a wide range of cultural and leisure activities requiring good accessibility for workers, shoppers, tourists and other visitors and for servicing. The balance between public and private transport will be determined by local policies and objectives (see Chapter 8), but it will usually be necessary to have well designed, easy to use public transport facilities and interchanges, as well as convenient parking and loading facilities. The high land values which often exist in central areas generally result in more dense developments and require more economy in the use of space.

The following types of development and transport facilities are common in town centre areas:

Pedestrian Malls, Precincts and Concourses, which are somewhat loosely defined terms (see below) used to describe purpose-built pedestrian areas which often form the core of major developments such as shopping centres, transport interchanges or exhibition complexes. They are sometimes based on the conversion of existing streets to pedestrian use only but may also be totally enclosed within a development (the pedestrianisation of existing streets is considered in more detail in Chapter 24).

Pedestrian Mover Systems are sometimes provided where there is a need to move large numbers of pedestrians between fixed points or to a different level such as at an airport terminal or underground station.

Public Transport Interchanges will be necessary to facilitate easy and efficient interchange between the different modes of transport in central areas.

Multi-Storey Car Parks are often necessary to provide parking space in areas where the availability or cost of land precludes the provision of single level parking.

33.2 Pedestrian Malls, Precincts and Concourses

As well as providing pedestrian routes these areas may also perform other functions such as a place for meeting, sitting, waiting or eating, or for window shopping, entertainment or for presenting information and displays. A guide to the space requirements appropriate for these activities is indicated in Table 33.1.

Pedestrian Malls are covered streets generally within a shopping centre (see Colour Plate 33.1). The basic

Activity in Pedestrian Concourses	Recommended Area Per Person (Sq metres)
(a) General circulation areas	
Overall allowance for public areas in public buildings.	2.30 to 2.80
Waiting areas, with 50 per cent seating and 50 per cent standing without baggage, also allowing for cross-flows (e.g. airport lounge).	1.10 to 1.40
Waiting areas, with 25 per cent seating and 75 per cent standing, without cross-flows (e.g. waiting rooms, single access).	0.65 to 0.90
Waiting areas, with 100 per cent standing and no cross-flows (e.g. lift lobby).	0.50 to 0.65
People standing in very crowded conditions – acceptable only for temporary periods.	0.20
(b) Corridors	
General design purposes.	0.80
People moving at 1.3m/s (good walking pace) or more.	3.70
People moving at 0.4m/s to 0.9m/s (shuffle).	0.27 to 0.37
People at standstill due to an obstruction.	0.20
(c) Lifts	
4-person car.	0.20
More than 4 person car/up to 30 person car.	0.30

Table 33.1 Recommended areas per person for various circulation areas

Source: Greater Manchester PTE

elements of a single mall will probably be major stores at either end to act as attractions to shoppers and to generate pedestrian movements to ensure that the shops between are not isolated. Most shopping centres will have more than one mall with the major attractors located in appropriate places. The width of a mall will depend on the anticipated level of pedestrian activity but will generally be between 5 and 12 metres (typically 8 m) wide. Side malls which provide access to car parks and other streets outside the centre, may be narrower. A focal point is often provided within a mall. This may be a fountain, a sculpture or an area of planting, probably with seating and refreshment facilities and space for exhibitions and displays to create an informal amenity area.

The term **pedestrian precinct** is used to describe a linear pedestrian area usually resulting from prohibiting vehicular traffic from an existing street and therefore open to the sky.

Pedestrian concourses are paved areas of open space generally surrounded by and integrated within a development.

The design of purpose-built pedestrian areas requires a variety of specialist skills to ensure that such matters as commercial success, satisfactory servicing and access, convenience and personal security and a pleasant environment are all created. Early discussions are advisable between developers, the public authorities involved and, where appropriate, local residents.

Design Capacities for Pedestrian Areas

The width appropriate for pedestrian walkways, footways, footpaths and shopping malls, will depend on the predicted number of pedestrians and intended level of service to be provided (see also Chapter 34.2). A typical walking speed under free flow conditions is 1.3 m per second but this will reduce with density. Walking speed is also affected by gradient, temperature and the purpose of the trip (Ref. 1). Walking speeds for shopping or leisure purposes are generally lower than for journeys to work. The maximum pedestrian flow rates for a typical walkway will therefore vary throughout the day.

Empirical studies of walkway capacities have indicated a range of values. However, an average flow rate of between 50 and 60 pedestrians per metre width per minute will serve for most situations. An allowance of up to 1 metre must be made for frictional effects resulting from the 'dead' width at the kerb edge and any side wall to the footway (see also Refs. 2, 3 and 4).

Use of Coloured or Textured Surfacing

The use of different coloured or textured surface treatments has two significant advantages over traditional paving materials:

- they can be used to create a more interesting and visually attractive environment, especially in areas where pedestrian activity predominates (see Colour Plates 24.4 and 24.5); and

- they can be used to convey information and give visual clues to road users about the nature of the area, especially where there is a mix of pedestrian and vehicular activity. They cannot, however, be used instead of prescribed road markings to indicate legal restrictions on use of sections of the highway without authorisation by the Secretary of State.

A range of materials is available which can be used to reduce large areas of paving to a more human scale. The planting of trees, careful design of street furniture and sensitive landscaping will all help create more attractive areas for people to meet, shop, stroll or simply enjoy for its own sake. Materials should therefore be chosen which are in sympathy and in character with the area and surrounding buildings. Particular care is necessary in the vicinity of any historic or other imposing building which may act as a focus for pedestrian activity, especially in conservation areas.

Several colours may be used within the same scheme to distinguish between areas to be used for different activities or functions such as places reserved entirely for pedestrians, places where vehicles and pedestrians share space or areas provided especially for loading or parking. Drivers and pedestrians should be made aware of the different functions by changes in the surface treatment without the need for traditional kerbs and the more formal distinction between carriageway and footway. Particular care should be taken to provide tactile clues for the visually handicapped.

Examples of places where the use of different coloured or textured surfaces may be advantageous are where it is desirable:

- to distinguish between uses within the same paved areas (eg. pedestrians only, loading and shared use), although prescribed signs and markings must also be used to indicate any legal requirements or restrictions;

- to indicate to drivers where pedestrians are likely to be encountered (eg. informal pedestrian crossing points in vehicle circulation areas, at the entrance to and within shared surface residential access roads, across junctions where vehicle flows are light and pedestrian activity is relatively high (see Chapter 24);

- to distinguish between parts of the carriageway reserved for particular vehicles, such as bus or cycle lanes (although the prescribed lane markings must also be used to indicate the boundary of the lane); and

● to inform visually handicapped pedestrians that they have reached a pedestrian crossing, or that they are approaching a hazard, by the use of tactile surfaces which are detectable under foot. The paving used at the approaches to pedestrian crossings must comply with the criteria in Department of Transport Circular DU 1/86 (Ref. 5) and as it comes within the definition of a traffic sign, it must be specially authorised by the Secretary of State until such time as it can be prescribed in the traffic signs regulations. However, before kerbs are removed, consideration should be given to the fact that guide dogs are trained to recognise and halt at kerbs (Ref. 6).

The choice of material for a particular location should take account of:

● the degree to which any special skills required to lay the material are available (many well intentioned schemes have failed because of poor attention to the detail of design and incorrect laying);

● the load bearing properties where there is a likelihood of vehicular traffic and (especially in areas intended for heavy commercial vehicles and buses) the

resistance to the solvent effects of dripped fuel and lubricants; and

● the consequences for future maintenance of using special materials which may not be readily available in the future (requiring stocks to be retained for long periods).

33.3 Pedestrian Mover Systems

In some types of development it may be desirable to provide mechanical devices to assist pedestrian movements particularly where:

● distances are significant (100 m or more);

● most pedestrians have heavy luggage (eg. at airport terminals and other transport interchanges); and

● a change of level is necessary (eg. at underground systems or multi-level shopping centres).

Pedestrian Conveyors are moving walkway systems generally running flat or with gentle gradients up to 12 degrees (see Plate 33.2). Speeds generally range from

Plate 33.2 A pedestrian conveyor (moving walkway) system

Source: 'The Surveyor'

0.6 m to 1.0 m per second, higher speeds may create difficulties for disabled pedestrians. Capacities up to 4000 pedestrians per hour per metre width have been obtained on these systems.

Escalators are moving stairways generally operating at an angle of 30 degrees. Capacities up to 2500 pedestrians per hour per metre width can be achieved but they can create difficulties for the mobility handicapped and for those with pushchairs or heavy luggage. Where escalators give access to a development, lifts should also be provided.

Lifts are most appropriate where there is a substantial difference in the levels of a pedestrian circulatory system and where access is required for people with a mobility handicap. Lifts should normally be provided in buildings to which the public have access where there is a climb of more than two storeys. Separate systems may be provided for goods and pedestrians. Typical speed for an eight person lift is 0.6 m per second although this may be increased in the tallest developments depending on floor heights and the location of busy floors (see also Table 33.1).

Other mechanical pedestrian mover systems may be introduced to solve particular problems. Where distances greater than 300 metres are involved separate vehicle systems may be desirable such as those introduced at Gatwick and Birmingham airports (see Plate 33.3).

It should be noted that mechanical pedestrian mover systems are relatively expensive to install and can be expensive to maintain if they prove unreliable in service or are subject to vandalism.

33.4 Public Transport Systems Involving Shared Use of Highways

Most urban public transport in Britain is provided by conventional motor vehicles or by segregated tracked rail systems such as conventional suburban railways or light rapid transit (eg. Tyneside Metro, London Docklands Light Railway) the design of which lies outside the scope of this document.

Plate 33.3 The 'Maglev' link between Birmingham airport and railway station

Source: New Civil Engineer

Plate 33.4 The Lille tramway system in France

Source: G Crow Esq

However, light rail systems operating wholly or partially within the highway may also be worthy of consideration and many such systems operate in other countries particularly in North America but also in Europe (see Plate 33.4). Design standards for dual or shared use of the carriageway and for signalling and signing would need to be developed for British practice.

Specified areas for consideration would be:

● the safety of overhead electric catenary cables and supporting columns;

● the safety of pedestrians, especially at crossing points and on streets with low traffic flow where pedestrian activity predominates;

● the safety of cyclists, especially in relation to grooved tracks; and

● the treatment of junctions and the establishment of general rules of priority over other vehicles.

33.5 Public Transport Interchanges

Siting

The precise location of any public transport interchange must take account of the needs of passengers, the requirements of transport operators and the land available. Historically, transport interchanges have been located in the central core of an urban area but this may not always be necessary, especially for interchanges catering for long haul trips which might be sited on the fringe of the central area. Interchanges which cater mostly for local journeys are generally best sited along transport corridors in order to intercept with work, shopping and leisure trips.

Access and Internal Circulation

The important considerations for access and internal circulation are set out in Table 29.1 but the following points are particularly important:

● an adequate standard of access to the external highway network is necessary to cope with peak volumes of each type of traffic, including pedestrians, likely to visit the site; and

● the segregation of pedestrians from vehicles and the segregation of different activities within the site. A one-way circulatory system will usually be beneficial.

Each interchange may need to provide:

● an unloading and storage (layover) area for arriving vehicles;

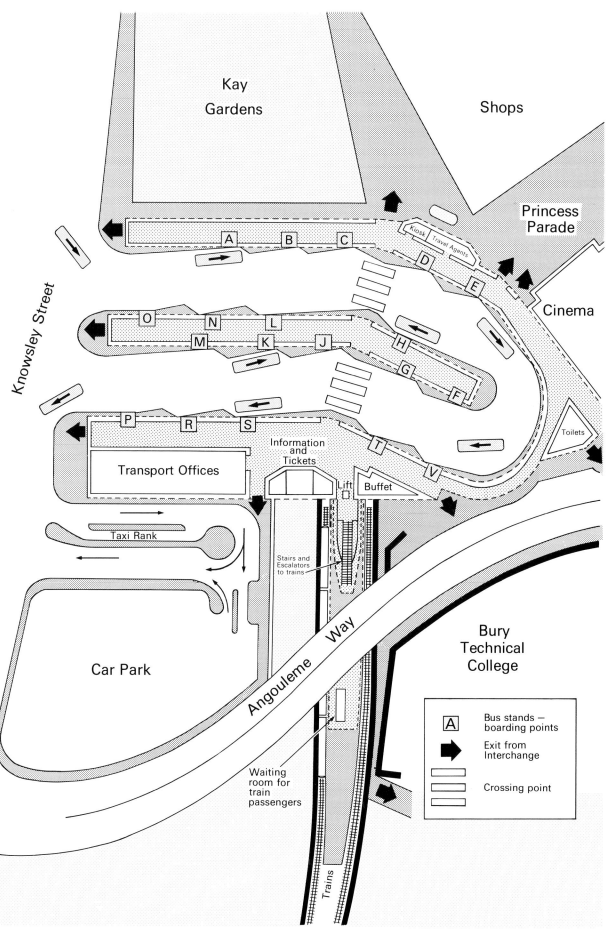

Figure 33.1 An example of the layout for a public transport interchange

Plate 33.5 A public transport interchange at Portsmouth, Hampshire

Source: Hampshire County Council

● buildings for activities such as ticket sales, passenger information, refreshments, and operations administration;

● passenger loading areas for the different types of transit vehicle; and

● depending on the nature of the interchange, an appropriate level of car parking.

Particular activities which may need to be catered for within the site are described below. Typical layouts for transport interchanges are shown in Figure 33.1 and in Plate 33.5.

Taxis—taxi ranks should be located close to the entrance to any terminal building and space should be provided for queueing. Secondary queueing could be available close-by during peak demand periods. Taxi ranks should be clearly marked to discourage use by other vehicles.

'Kiss and Ride'—a kiss and ride facility allows for picking up and setting down of passengers and their luggage and also needs to be located close to the entrance to any terminal building. To help ensure that the area is not misused it may be beneficial to provide

a short stay parking area close-by for drivers waiting to pick up arriving passengers who may have been delayed. A clockwise circulatory system will allow the passenger door to be positioned nearest to the kerb. A canopy could be provided to give some weather protection.

'Park and Ride'—a park and ride facility allows drivers to leave their vehicles for longer periods to make use of buses, trains or aeroplanes. The majority of park and ride interchanges are at commuter stations well away from central areas. Major interchanges (eg. airports) may include very long stay parking for drivers on extended trips. Sufficient space should be provided to avoid overspill parking in adjacent streets. The turnover of cars at park and ride facilities is usually low because they cater mostly for all day work trips. Because of this bay widths may be reduced to 2.3 m (see also Chapter 32.5). It will also be necessary to provide adequate security arrangements for vehicles parked for long periods, including cycles and motorcycles.

Buses and Coaches—most transport interchanges will provide some facilities for buses and coaches. It is important to involve bus operators during the design

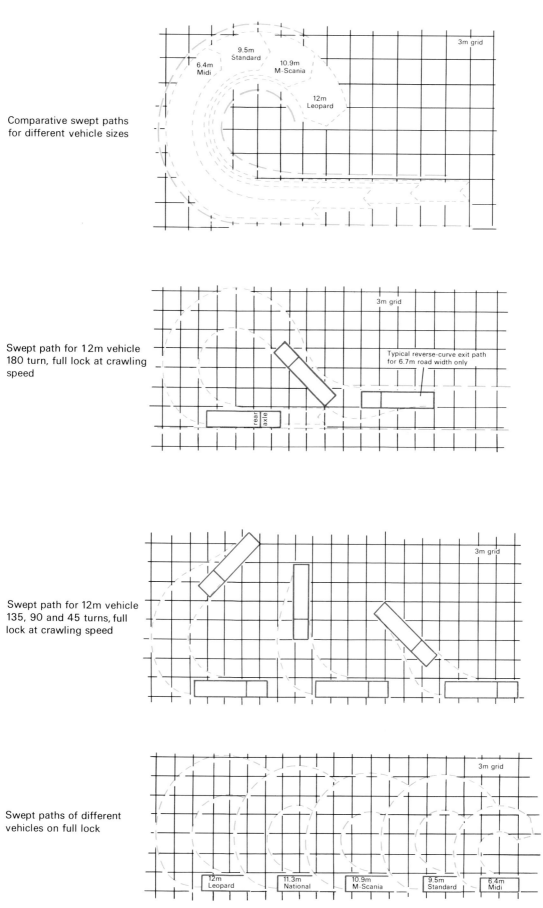

Comparative swept paths for different vehicle sizes

Swept path for 12m vehicle 180 turn, full lock at crawling speed

Swept path for 12m vehicle 135, 90 and 45 turns, full lock at crawling speed

Swept paths of different vehicles on full lock

Figure 33.2 Geometric requirements for buses turning

Source: 'Planning and design for Road Public Transport, (now the Bus and Coach Council)' Confederation of British Road Passenger Transport (1981)

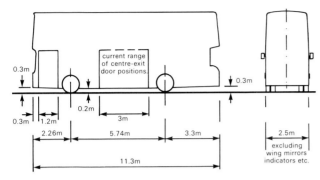

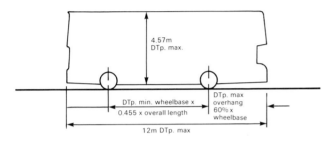

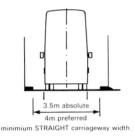

Horizontal and vertical clearances

Figure 33.3 Typical bus dimensions and appropriate clearances

Source: 'Planning and design for Road Public Transport', Confederation of British Road Passenger Transport (1981)

process to ensure that the layout conforms with their operational requirements.

Design Standards

All interchanges should take account of the manoeuvring characteristics of the different vehicles likely to use them. A comparison of swept paths for different types of buses is given in Figure 33.2 and Figure 33.3 illustrates the horizontal and vertical clearances necessary for safe operation. All bus and coach facilities should be capable of accommodating the largest type of vehicle likely to be used regularly. Although vehicle dimensions are unlikely to increase significantly, consideration might be given to providing for the introduction of longer articulated buses and increasing vertical clearances to accommodate trolley buses.

Types of Layout

The two principal types of bus station platform layout are 'drive through' and 'forward in/reverse out' as shown in Figure 33.4. Drive-through layouts may be either linear or shallow 'saw-tooth' with one-way or two-way carriageways. Generally, drive-through layouts are more appropriate for high frequency services particularly where one-person-operated (OPO) vehicles are used. Reversing layouts may be either at right angles or at some other angle and enable a central passenger concourse with greater segregation for passengers and vehicles to be used. This is more appropriate for low frequency longer distance services (Ref. 7).

Pedestrian Facilities

Pedestrians need special consideration at transport interchanges with the aim of segregating them from vehicles and minimising walking distances. Crossing points can be emphasised using coloured or textured surfaces to reinforce the implied preference for pedestrian movement. Well designed signing and passenger information systems should be provided together with lifts or ramps where there are significant changes of level. All passenger movements should preferably be protected from the weather.

The construction and surfacing of vehicle operating areas should be selected to avoid deformation of the surface and resist damage from dripped fuel and lubricants. Dark coloured block paving is widely used to meet these requirements (see Plate 33.6).

33.6 Multi-storey Car Parks

All public car parks in town centres should preferably be accessed directly from a primary or district distributor road. They may be on the periphery of the town centre but should be within reasonable walking distance. Short stay town centre car parks should be not more than 400 m (ie. five minutes walk) from the main central area activities they are planned to serve. Close proximity is less important for long stay parking.

Multi-storey car parks permit a more intensive use of space in areas where land is in short supply and values are particularly high. However, construction, maintenance and operating costs will be significantly greater than with single-level car parks; although it may not be necessary to justify the cost of construction independently if a multi-storey car park is being provided as an integral part of some other development such as high density housing, a sports centre or a prestige public building where the costs of the car park will be recovered elsewhere.

Because of their utilitarian purpose and the wish to minimise costs many multi-storey car parks are unattractive structures. This need not be so as Colour Plate 33.7 illustrates.

A) SINGLE-BUS, DRIVE-THROUGH, LINEAR STANDS

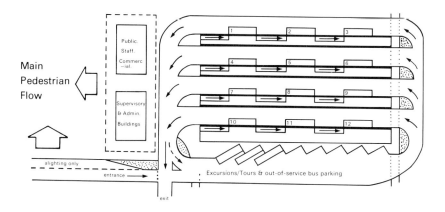

B) SINGLE-BUS, DRIVE-THROUGH, SHALLOW SAWTOOTH STANDS

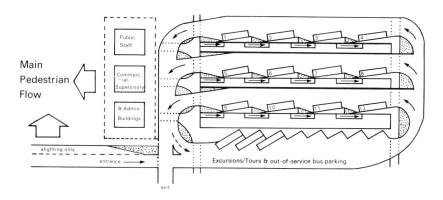

C) SINGLE-BUS, RIGHT ANGLE FORWARD IN/REVERSE OUT

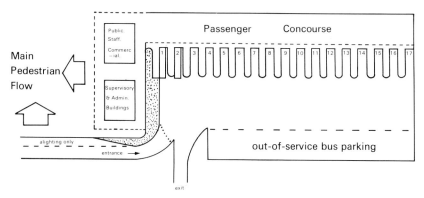

Figure 33.4 Elements of typical bus station layouts

Source: 'Planning and design for Road Public Transport', Confederation of
British Road Passenger Transport (1981)

Size and Layout

Because of the need to provide ramps between floors there is an absolute minimum practical size of site suitable for a multi-storey car park and this is generally accepted to be 35 m square. The number of spaces provided in any single facility will be determined by:

● the amount of land available;

● forecasts of parking demand in relation to supply in the area and the likely net income (from any charges which will be imposed after deduction of the annual costs of construction, maintenance and operation);

● the impact of the car park on the external road network. Short stay, usually higher priced, parking in the most central locations will have a greater

Plate 33.6 Use of block paving at a bus station in Cardiff

Source: 'The Surveyor'

turnover for a given level of occupancy and will therefore attract more traffic throughout the day. Long stay parking, especially when directly associated with a particular place of work, will only produce flows of traffic in the morning and evening peak periods;

● the generally accepted maximum capacity of an integrated car park with several aisles accessed directly by ramps is 1600 spaces. A single search path should not exceed 500 spaces;

● there will be a limit on the number of parking levels acceptable for a particular site on planning and environmental grounds, imposed by the local planning authority—and the costs of underground construction are likely to be significantly greater than those above ground.

Although these comments are concerned specifically with multi-storey car parks, much of the advice is equally applicable to the design and assessment of single-level car parks.

Capacity

The total number of spaces available in a car park is termed the **static capacity**; however, it is generally more important to consider the **dynamic capacity**. The dynamic capacity relates to the maximum in-flow or out-flow of vehicles from the whole car park (Ref. 8). The most important constraint on dynamic capacity is usually the type of control employed at entry and exit, which includes the method of collecting any charges.

With minimal formalities on entry or exit the dynamic capacity is determined by the capacity of the circulatory aisles, generally 800–900 vehicles per hour for most layouts. As a general rule, the dynamic capacity should be sufficient to permit 20–25 per cent of the static capacity to enter or leave the car park within 15 minutes (ie. 100% in an hour).

The practical capacity is likely to be lower than the theoretical static capacity, particularly where there are no marked out bays or staff to insist on disciplined parking. In addition, since cars are arriving and departing simultaneously, newly vacated spaces may be missed by those already in the car park searching for a space. Where entry is controlled, deliberate undercapacity margins (of about 5% depending on size and turnover) are sometimes introduced to overcome this problem. Where parking discipline is particularly weak and spaces between columns badly designed, actual capacities can be as much as 50% below the

Plate 33.8 Use of a lifting arm barrier to a multi-storey car park

Source: Newcastle City Council

theoretical maximum. Conversely, in some small private parking areas where drivers are known to one another and parking is even tolerated in circulation areas, actual capacity may be up to 125% of static capacity.

Entry and Exit Controls and Payment Systems

The type of control, if any, to be used on entry and exit is most important and usually determines, or will be determined by, the method of collecting any charges. In general, entry to a car park should not be permitted unless a space is available. Entry may be controlled by a lifting arm (see Plate 33.8) or a rising step barrier. Rising step barriers should be supplemented by traffic signals which show red when the barrier is raised in order to reduce the chance of damage either by equipment malfunction or driver error. Exits may be controlled in a similar way or by using collapsible plates hinged on their leading edge to ensure that vehicles can only pass over them in one direction. Where parking is free, or where payment is made on entry or using a pay-and-display system, exits need not be controlled.

There are a variety of payment systems in common use including:

Fixed Charge—where payment of a fixed charge is made to a cashier or using an automatic machine on entry to or exit from the car park;

Pay-and-Display—where, after a space has been found, a ticket is purchased from a machine within the car park and displayed on the vehicle. Where parking is permitted for more than one fixed period the driver must decide how much time to purchase before he leaves his vehicle;

Variable or Graduated Charge—where a ticket is issued on entry and payment is made to a cashier or automatic machine on exit according to the scale of charges and the time spent in the car park. When automatic machines are in use the failure of a driver to have the correct change or mechanical breakdown of the system can result in serious congestion. Equipment is available which allows for payment by an electronic device such as a charge card;

Ticket on entry and pay-and-walk—where a ticket is issued on entry and payment is made to a cashier or automatic machine on departure but before the driver returns to his vehicle.

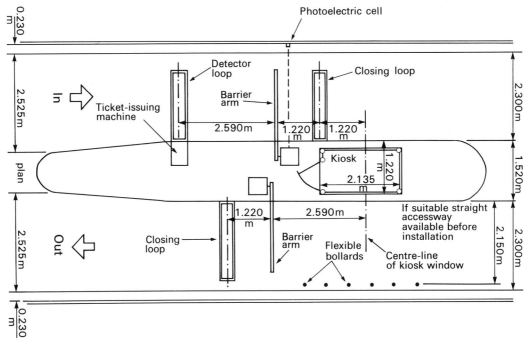

Figure 33.5 Typical layout for a car park entry/exit system

Source: 'Design Recommendations for Multi-Storey and Underground Car Parks', IHT/1 Struc. E (second edition 1984)

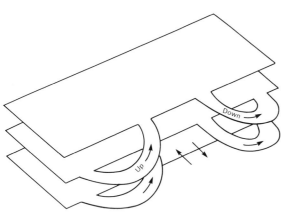

(a) Flat deck car park with external ramps.

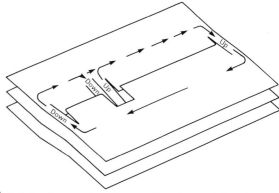

(b) Split level car park with separate entry, and departure circulation and short down (departure) ramp system.

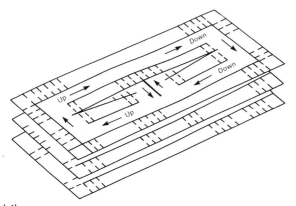

(d) Warped slab car park.

(c) Ramped floor car park with separate entry and departure parking ramps.

Figure 33.6 Structural layouts used in multi-storey car parks

Source: 'Design Recommendations for Multi-Storey and Underground Car Parks', IHT/1 Struc. E (second edition 1984)

Access and Circulation

To prevent queueing at the point of entry, the entry capacity should be equal to or greater than the maximum anticipated arrival rate. An access road should provide a queueing reservoir for those occasions when the car park is operating at or near its dynamic capacity and it should be designed to assist the transition from higher speed travel on the external road network to the parking area. A curved alignment is often appropriate (see also Chapter 21). Access roads should be used exclusively for entry into the car park so that other traffic is not unnecessarily delayed.

The rate of discharge from the car park should not exceed the reserve capacity of the road on to which it discharges and priority must be retained on the external road system so that any queueing takes place within the car park. A typical layout for entry/exit is provided in Figure 33.5.

Floor Levels and Ramp Arrangements

The circulation system within the multi-storey car park will depend upon the type of structure (Ref. 9). There are four main types (see Figure 33.6):

Flat Deck—where the parking levels are flat and the decks are linked by curved or straight ramps (Figure 33.6(a));

Split Level—where the rise between flat deck and parking levels is half the floor to floor height (Figure 33.6(b));

Ramped Floor—where the circulation aisle also acts as a ramp (Figure 33.6(c)); and

Warped Slab—where the floor slabs are flat at the edges but fall internally to provide a ramp system (Figure 33.6(d)).

Ramps may be used solely to distribute traffic between levels (clearway ramps) or may also act as parking aisles (ie. giving direct access to parking bays). Ramps may be one-way or two-way, although the latter generally require higher design standards for visibility and clearance to structures.

Aisles give direct access to individual parking bays. The minimum recommended width for a one-way aisle is 6 m (6.95 m for two-way operation) although this may be reduced if parking bays are angled. Parking bay width will depend on the use made of the parking facility (see Chapter 32.5).

Increased bay width permits easier and quicker manoeuvring into and out of the bay and therefore assists aisle capacity and makes getting into and out of vehicles more convenient. The additional width for disabled parkers may be shared between two adjacent bays.

Signing

It is important that public car parks be adequately signed to assist and direct drivers unfamiliar with the area. This will help to avoid congestion and reduce the amount of time and fuel wasted while searching for a place to park. Where a choice of car parks is available, signs should direct drivers to the most appropriate one for their purpose (eg. long stay or short stay or parking provided in conjunction with a particular event). In larger towns consideration might be given to introducing a more sophisticated system of direction signing employing variable message signs linked to entry or exit controls to indicate which car parks have spaces and what options are available (see also Chapter 21 and Plate 20.1). Direction signs to car parks should not be used as a means of advertising for the benefit of the operator, whether public or private.

The rates imposed for parking should be clearly displayed at the entrance and an escape route provided for drivers who choose not to use the car park.

A comprehensive system of signing and road marking should be provided on the routes within the car park to assist circulation around what might be a complex layout and to achieve the most appropriate search path and the quickest exit. Where several search paths are available it may be helpful to indicate which levels have spaces.

Mechanical Car Parks

A number of different mechanical devices have been developed for parking and storing cars (Ref. 10). These range from simple devices for placing one car above another to complex systems usually requiring the cars to be placed on pallets or plates which are then closely stacked using a combination of lifts and rollers. The need for circulation ramps and aisles is therefore reduced or dispensed with. Mechanical car parks have not been widely adopted in Britain. The disadvantages of these devices are the increased costs of maintenance and particularly the delay in parking and recovering vehicles, especially at peak times, as people must wait for an attendant to operate the machinery.

Pedestrian Facilities in Multi-Storey Car Parks

As with all new developments, a new car park may affect existing pedestrian routes and there may be a need for replacement or additional footpaths, pedestrian crossings and signing for pedestrian routes.

Within the car park, ticket machines and entrances to lifts and stairways should be demarcated from parking areas. Signs should direct pedestrians to the appropriate exit and each level should be given a unique identity to help drivers to find their cars on their return. Letters or numbers are often used but pictorial signs such as animals or flowers may be easier to remember (see Figure 32.10).

The holders of Orange Badges for the disabled (see Chapter 15.6) should have the most convenient spaces in a car park reserved for their use. Care must be taken to ensure that mobility handicapped people can leave the car park, preferably without using lifts as these may occasionally be out of order.

33.7 References

Text Reference

1. Elkington, J et al—'*The pedestrian—planning and research*', Transport & Environment Studies (TEST), London (1976). (33.2)

2. Pushkarev, B S and Zupan, J M—'*Urban Space for Pedestrians*' MIT Press, Cambridge, Mass. and London, (1975). (33.2)

3. O'Flaherty, C A and Parkinson, M H—'*Movement on a city centre footway*', Traffic Engineering and Control, Vol 14 No 6 (1972). (33.2)

4. Older, A J—'*Movement of Pedestrians on Footways in Shopping Streets*', Traffic Engineering & Control, Vol 10 No 4, (1968). (33.2)

5. DTp—Circular DU 1/86, '*Textured Footway Surfaces at Pedestrian Crossings*', DTp (1986). [Wa.47] (33.2)

6. IHT—'*Guidelines for Providing for People with a Mobility Handicap*', Institution of Highways and Transportation, London (1986). (33.2)

7. Addenbrooke et al—'*Urban planning and design for road public transport—2nd edition*', Confederation of British Road Passenger Transport (CBRPT), London (1986). (33.5)

8. DoE/DTp/TRRL—Report LR 221, '*Parking: Dynamic capacities of car parks*', DoE/DTp (1969). (33.6)

9. IHT/Institution of Structural Engineers—'*Design recommendations for multi-storey and underground car parks*' (2nd edition), IHT/I Struct E (1984). (33.6)

10. Brierley, J—'*Parking of Motor Vehicles*' (2nd edition), Applied Science Publishers, London (1972). (33.6)

33.8 Further Information

11. Prideaux, J D C A—'*Rail/Road Interchanges*', The Journal of the Institution of Highways and Transportation (April 1984).

12. Design Council—'*Street Furniture*', Design Council, London (1983).

13. Lyon, R R—'*Providing for the disabled highway user*', Municipal Engineer (April 1985).

14. Feeney, P J—'*Problems of the High Street: Needs of the Handicapped*', Proceedings of PTRC Summer Meeting PTRC (1981).

15. Cliff Tandy—'*Handbook of Urban Landscape*', Architectural Press (1972).

16. Lilley, A A and Knapton, J—'*Concrete block paving for lightly trafficked roads and paved areas*', Cement and Concrete Association (1978).

17. Blythe, K R G et al—'*Multi-storey car parks in shopping centres and office blocks*', report from a British Parking Association Seminar, London (1980).

18. Lilley, A A—'*Concrete block paving for specialised traffic—a design method*', Cement and Concrete Association (1978).

19. DoE—'*Lorry Parking—The report of the working party on the parking of lorries*', HMSO (1971).

20. Bloom, E K et al—'*Off-street Parking*', A report from a British Parking Association Seminar, London (1970).

21. Ministry of Housing and Local Government/Ministry of Transport/SDD/Welsh Office—'*Parking in Town Centres*', HMSO (1965).

PART 5 THE DEVELOPMENT AND DESIGN OF MAJOR HIGHWAY SCHEMES

34 Design Concepts

34.1 Introduction

This part of the manual deals with general principles relating to the design of major roads in urban areas which normally comprise the primary and district distributor network. The main function of these roads is to cater for the main radial and circumferential distribution of traffic as well as through movements. Primary distributors will generally have principal or trunk road status (see Tables 5.1 and 5.4).

The layout and planning of minor roads (ie. local distributors and access roads) is covered in Part 4. Since the design of local distributors is governed by design speed (normally 50 kph); this Part (5) will apply to local distributors as well as to major roads, whenever it is appropriate. It should be noted that much of the content of Part 5 is based on the standards and advice provided by the Department of Transport [Sco.174] and these documents should be referred to whenever a fuller understanding is required.

The design of all trunk roads is based on the Department's standards which are usually also applied to the design of other major roads in Britain. It may sometimes be necessary to depart from these standards where this is justified by special circumstances but this should not be allowed to result in a significant lowering of road safety standards. Any departure from the Department's standards on trunk roads requires authorisation by the Department [Sco.174].

34.2 Level of Service

Level of service describes the different operating conditions which can occur on a road at different times and the way they affect the amenity enjoyed by road users in terms of speed, safety, drivers' comfort and vehicle operating costs. Generally speaking, as traffic speeds increase design standards need to be more generous in order to retain a given level of service.

The level of service concept for design purposes is applied to design standards in the United States (see Ref. 1) but has not been adopted in Great Britain. Nevertheless, in Britain, level of service is normally deemed to be taken into account in the Department of Transport's COBA [Sco.175] method of economic assessment where higher levels of service, operating speeds and comfort are traded off against the additional costs involved. However, COBA was not designed specifically for use in urban areas and a full explanation of demand modelling, economic and environmental appraisal techniques is therefore provided in Chapters 11 and 12.

34.3 Estimation of Future Traffic Demands

Estimating future traffic demand for major urban roads involves establishing existing demand and applying a range of factors to produce design flows. There are a variety of models and techniques available to assist this process ranging from conventional, serial (four step) models for major schemes to models suited for more detailed localised study (eg. SATURN, CONTRAM and TRAFFICQ). A full explanation of the role and suitability of these models is provided in Chapter 11.

A design based solely on maximum peak hour travel demand may result in a scheme which is unacceptable because of its cost and the severe environmental impact that it may have in an urban area. A decision has therefore to be made between an increase in delay and a poorer level of service that may be experienced during peak periods by adopting lesser design standards; and the cost and other adverse effects incurred by providing for the highest levels of demand.

It should be noted that British practice has always been to design for traffic flow rates achievable in fair weather daylight conditions. Smaller traffic flows will occur when conditions are less favourable.

Uncertainty

Establishing a reliable local growth factor can be extremely difficult. The factor will almost certainly change with time where, for example, new policies involving traffic restraint are imposed or new traffic management measures are reduced and as new development or changes in land use take place, sometimes as a reaction to the provision of an improved road facility.

It is sometimes useful to estimate the probability of a future traffic demand being realised and to establish a range of design flows based on varying levels of probability. Each design flow should then be tested to assess how sensitive the scale of the project is to varying traffic demand.

Flexibility

Flexible designs will minimise the consequences of errors and uncertainties in estimating traffic demand. However, flexibility generally involves additional construction costs and a judgement will be required. Flexibility can be achieved by making provision for future changes such as the construction of additional carriageway width or alterations to the size or type of control employed at junctions.

34.4 Design Speed

Drivers regulate their speed in accordance with the road layout and their perception of prevailing road conditions. Apart from the amount of traffic on the road, weather and daylight conditions, the main factors that influence speed are visibility, curvature, width, surface conditions, the presence of junctions and accesses and speed limits. The so-called 'speed value' of individual curves is therefore no real guide as to what the actual vehicle speeds over a length of road might be.

In selecting the design speed for a new road, account needs to be taken of the wide range of vehicle speeds that obtain in practice. To design for the fastest drivers would be unnecessarily expensive and often environmentally unacceptable; to design for the much slower driver could be unsafe for the faster drivers. The general practice is therefore to design for the 85th percentile speed (the speed up to which 85% of vehicles travel, or may be expected to travel, in free flow conditions).

Once a best estimate of the 85th percentile speed has been made (see Chapter 37), this identifies a range of speed distribution and the dynamic parameters that result from this choice should be such that acceptably safe conditions prevail throughout the speed range. The selected design speed should thus be used as the basis for the coordination of all the various elements of geometric design and the design should aim to create an operating environment that encourages drivers to conform to the chosen design speed.

34.5 Design Standards

The design of roads of national significance forming part of the trunk road network is carried out in accordance with the requirements of the Department of Transport. Although its own 'Highways Manual' is only available within the Department [Sco.174], the Department publishes a wide range of Circulars, Technical Standards and Advice Notes covering all aspects of highway design, for general application (Ref. 2).

Detailed references are included as appropriate in subsequent Chapters which cover the various aspects of design.

Choice of Road Layout

The standard of layout chosen for a major urban road needs to be a carefully balanced compromise between meeting the intended function of the road, in terms of its operating efficiency and safety, whilst being realistic about the constraints imposed by the urban environment and the capital resources which are likely to be available.

Factors which might influence the estimates of future traffic demand should be monitored carefully and the final design adjusted to meet any such changes in traffic demand.

Identification of Land Requirements

The alignment of a new urban road or major improvement to an existing road is normally constrained to a corridor of opportunity which is determined by the extent of land which can realistically be acquired. Throughout the planning stages advantage should be taken of sites that become available within the identified corridor taking into account;

● the need to minimise blight (see also Chapter 35); and

● the responsibility on the acquiring authority to maintain and manage the property, if required to do so.

Wherever possible, major roads should avoid severing environmental areas so as to minimise disruption to existing communities and local traffic routes.

Geometric Standards

The alignment for a new urban road should, whenever possible, be so designed that the various geometric elements such as curvature, superelevation, sight distances etc., provide at least the minimum values consistent with the estimated design speed of the road.

However, the severe constraints on road alignments frequently encountered in urban areas will often result in the appropriate design standard for a particular geometric design element not being achievable within the previously defined corridor of opportunity without unacceptable cost or environmental damage. It may not be possible therefore, to justify even the lowest levels of the design parameters given in the Department of Transport's [Sco.174] standards for layout design. In these cases it may be possible to achieve sufficient advantage to justify a departure from the usual standards.

The design parameters are not, therefore, sacrosanct in all circumstances. Where it is considered appropriate, departures should be assessed in terms of their economic worth, the environment and the safety of the road user.

Choice of Junction Type

The standard of junction design to be adopted will be determined by the hierarchical types of road involved (see also Chapter 5), estimates of future traffic demand and the physical characteristics of the site.

34.6 Frequency of Intersections

The frequency with which junctions should be provided along a new road will depend on its role in the road hierarchy (see also Chapter 5). The most important routes (ie. primary distributor routes) should have intersections provided only to roads of the same or immediately lower order. Existing routes crossing these roads may therefore need to be diverted under or over the new road or be closed to traffic. Roads lower in the hierarchy with important distribution functions can have more closely spaced junctions to permit greater use by local traffic and it will be essential to maintain access to existing land and property. In urban situations the requirements of access will have a major influence on scheme design.

34.7 Provision for Pedestrians

Wherever it is practical to do so, pedestrians should be discouraged from using major vehicular traffic routes. However, it will always be necessary to make safe and convenient paths available for pedestrians where there is sufficient demand and this must be determined during the earliest stages of design (see also Chapters 33 and 36).

On primary distributors schemes involving new construction should aim to segregate pedestrian routes from the carriageway and subways or footbridges should be provided at crossing points. On district distributor roads, especially those with bus routes, significant pedestrian flows should be anticipated in the vicinity of bus stops but elsewhere it may be acceptable to provide only the minimum width of footway. However, in established urban areas, district distributors may also be major pedestrian corridors. In these cases safety measures such as guardrails to channelise movements and controlled crossings may be required at appropriate locations and pelican crossings or provision for pedestrians at signal-controlled junctions may also be required (see also Chapters 24 and 41).

34.8 Staged Construction

Fluctuations in the pace of urban development and the availability of investment capital may sometimes make it preferable that a major new road be constructed in a number of discrete stages. For example, only one carriageway or only the roundabout section of a grade separated junction might be constructed initially (see also Chapter 40.2). Care will be necessary to minimise long term blight and uncertainty on property lying within the area of possible future extensions (see also Chapter 35.2).

In urban schemes, particularly at junctions where the predicted hourly flows are uncertain, the cost of being wrong should be borne in mind. Inevitably, development to the highway boundary will take place, making costly, if not virtually precluding, future improvement. Where there is a choice the higher standard should be incorporated initially if it can be economically justified (see Chapter 6.2).

Where staged construction is envisaged each stage should demonstrate worthwhile benefits but avoid design features which may increase the risk of accidents. As an example, the provision of a single carriageway designed to eventually be one half of a dual facility, should not give drivers the false impression of actually being a dual carriageway.

34.9 Minimizing Impact on the Environment

The impact of any new road scheme on the environment can be minimized if care is taken during the initial design stages and by sensitive landscaping and civic design. The intention should be to make the new road blend with its surroundings and close attention to levels and profiles and sympathetic design will help to achieve this.

Steps should be taken to avoid leaving existing development scarred by the construction of the new route. Wherever it is possible to arrange it, the concurrent redevelopment of areas adjacent to the route will help to ensure a continuous and integrated townscape. If it is necessary to leave existing property close to the road, accommodation works must be sympathetically designed. Special care must be taken in restoring the existing form of any buildings divided by a new route. For example, the way that a truncated terrace of houses is treated can have a significant effect on the way a new road is seen to fit into the environment. Sensitive re-instatement of walls, building facades and appropriate choice of materials and street furniture can make a positive contribution towards blending a new road into the existing scene, thereby reducing adverse public reaction.

The planting of grass, shrubs and trees is generally preferable to large areas of hard landscaping but sight lines and other considerations of road safety (eg. clearances), must be preserved. An example of the softening effect of vegetation is shown in Colour Plate 34.1.

Where large paved areas are essential, the use of different coloured or textured treatments will make them more visually attractive.

Vegetation softens the outline of road surfaces and structures and is generally pleasing to the eye. However, 'hard' landscaping may well be more appropriate to smaller areas within major built-up areas, particularly where maintenance considerations are important. Where planting is carried out, safe and convenient access for maintenance staff and machinery must be provided.

34.10 Maintenance Considerations

The general maintenance of the highway and of associated street furniture, traffic signs and street lights should be considered during the design process. The closure of a carriageway, or even a traffic lane, to accommodate a maintenance vehicle or to provide a safety margin for workmen, can impose large additional operating costs on other road users. Traffic delays can be caused, particularly during peak hours, and consideration should be given to increasing design standards to provide flexibility for these occasions. For example, a wide central reserve could be provided to accommodate a tower wagon carrying out maintenance

of lighting, without disrupting traffic. The use of an additional depth of carriageway construction for a longer design life may also be cost-effective to defer the costs involved with strengthening the pavement at a later stage.

34.11 References

Text Reference

1. Transportation Research Board—Special Report 209, '*Highway Capacity Manual*', US Transportation Research Board (1985). (34.2)

2. DTp—'*Departmental Standards, Advice Notes and Technical Memoranda—Index of current titles*', DTp (1986). [Sco.176] (34.5)

34.12 Further Information

3. DTp—A new technical advice note dealing with the treatment of roadside features is in the course of preparation (1987).

35 Procedures for the Planning and Approval of Road Schemes

35.1 Initial Steps

Structure plans and Part I of unitary development plans (see Chapter 3 and Ref. 1) should define the primary road network for an area and should set out general proposals for any major improvements to it which it is intended to commence within the timescale of the plan. Local plans and Part II of unitary development plans should elaborate the proposals for the improvement of the primary network and indicate other proposed new roads and improvements [Sco.177, NI.8, NI.13].

Each proposal should be based upon a design brief which sets out broad objectives for the scheme which are compatible with the development plan, together with an indication of target costs and date for completion. The brief will also contain forecasts of traffic flows, the standard of the more important design elements (eg. carriageway width and type of junction control) and a description of the corridor within which it is intended that the road be constructed.

Schemes not already included in the development plan should be appraised and evaluated against, and compatible with, the objectives drawn from the plan to ensure that they are properly integrated and compatible with the planning of transport and land use matters (see Chapter 12). Where applications for planning permission are made for new roads not included in the development plan, it will normally be necessary for these to be treated as 'departures' from the plan (Ref. 2) [Sco.178].

Planning permission will normally be required for a highway authority's new road proposals. Highway authorities may obtain deemed permission for such schemes by following the procedures set out in the Town and Country Planning General Regulations 1976 (Ref. 3, see also 35.5 below) [Sco.179]. These require notification, consultation and publicity for the proposals comparable with the procedures applied to private applications.

Planning permission for improvement works to existing highways is granted by Article XIV of the 1977 General Development Order (Ref. 4), being works carried out on land outside but abutting the boundary of the highway. Such improvements may, however, be included as proposals in development plans and be subject to development plan procedures for consultation, objection, approval and adoption (see Chapter 3). Improvement works carried out entirely within the existing highway boundary do not require planning permission.

35.2 Protecting the Land Required and Avoiding Planning Blight

Once a decision in principle has been made to introduce a new road or improve an existing one, it will be desirable to include the proposal in the development plan as soon as possible. Local plans and Part II of unitary development plans should only include firm road schemes on which the highway authority intend to commence work within about 10 years (Ref. 1) [NI.8, NI.13].

It would be wrong to allow land or buildings to be blighted or lie idle for a considerable period because of a potential road scheme. Therefore, safeguarding powers should only be used when a particular road proposal is included in the development plan and in the case of trunk roads, is also included in the current Roads White Paper [Sco.180].

The lines of some road proposals, intended to be carried out only as sites are redeveloped, have in the past been safeguarded by some authorities on an 'as and when' basis, although no firm proposals existed. Such safeguarding can affect the redevelopment potential of sites and cause unnecessary blight. As a consequence, the use of 'as and when' safeguarding is no longer generally pursued.

The formal protection of the corridor of land required for a road scheme is currently effected under the General Development Order (GDO) 1977 as amended (see Chapter 28). Under Article 12 of the GDO, a local highway authority may, in respect of proposed, or existing but to be improved classified roads, direct a local planning authority to refuse consent to a planning application or to attach conditions (which may include temporary consent) to any consent to be given. Alternatively, a development application may be amended to take account of the road proposal (see also Chapter 3) [Sco.181].

Under Articles 10 and 11 of the GDO the Secretary of State has similar powers to control development alongside trunk and special roads (see Chapter 28). He too, may direct a local planning authority to refuse consent or to attach conditions to any consent to be given in respect of any development of land within 67 metres of the middle of an existing but to be improved, or proposed, trunk or special road [Sco.182].

(N.B. The Secretary of State for Transport intends (Ref. 5) that local highway authorities' powers of direction under Article 12 should be replaced with an expanded right to be consulted under Article 15.

Legislation to give effect to this change has been enacted in the Housing and Planning Act 1986 (Ref. 6). The change is to be made in a new General Development Order. The effect of such an amendment to the GDO would be that local highway authorities would no longer be able to direct local planning authorities to take certain decisions but, instead, would be able to give advice.)

If a road proposal included in a draft or approved development plan or alteration gives rise to blight notices then the local highway authority, or the Department of Transport [Sco.183], whichever is responsible for the scheme, will be the appropriate authority under S.205 of the Town and Country Planning Act 1971 (Ref. 7) [Sco.184], provided that the proposal has been included in the plan with their consent. If a local planning authority includes a road proposal without the relevant highway authority's consent it may be that the local planning authority will be held to be the appropriate authority under S.205(2)(a) of the 1971 Act [Sco.184].

35.3 Land Acquisition

The wide variety of land uses, land owners and occupiers in urban areas can make the acquisition of land for a road difficult. When land cannot be purchased by agreement between the owner and the highway authority, it may be acquired compulsorily using powers currently provided by the Highways Act 1980, S.239 (Ref. 8) [Sco.185, NI.50]. Guidance on the making and submission for approval, of compulsory purchase orders under the Act is given in DoE and DTp Circulars (Refs. 9 and 10) [Sco.186]. These draw attention to the need to provide a planning backing to justify compulsory purchase and to the importance of identifying related matters (eg. development plan proposals, planning applications and appeals) on which it may be desirable to arrange for a concurrent or joint inquiry with the highway compulsory purchase order on the grounds of speed and efficiency. The acquisition of areas of special category land such as public open space, allotments and common land can involve additional procedures which usually require replacement land to be provided (Ref. 11).

35.4 Land Compensation

The Land Compensation Act 1973 (Ref. 12) [NI.52] provides a right to compensation for depreciation of value of interests in land caused by the use of highways, aerodromes and other public works. The Act gave highway authorities powers and duties to mitigate the injurious effect of such works on their surroundings and amended the law relating to compulsory purchase and planning blight.

As a result of this legislation designers of road schemes must give careful consideration to the following:

● that compensation can be claimed (under Part 1 of the Act) by owners of property where its value is depreciated by noise and other specified physical factors arising from the use of a new or altered highway (the period during which claims can be made is six years starting one year after the first opening of the new or altered highway but intensification of existing use by traffic is specifically excluded as a valid reason for making a claim);

● that the Noise Insulation (Mandatory) Regulations 1975 [NI.53] (made under Section 20 of the Act) require the highway authority to make offers of noise insulation or grant to occupiers of dwellings subjected to additional noise at or above the specified level due to the use of a new highway or a highway to which a new carriageway has been added (the noise insulation package includes the provision of double glazed windows, venetian blinds, double or insulated doors and supplementary ventilation—eligible rooms are living rooms and bedrooms only; halls, landings, kitchens, bathrooms, etc. cannot qualify);

● that these Regulations also give certain powers to a highway authority to make similar (discretionary) offers of noise insulation or grant where dwellings are subjected to additional noise at or above the specified level due to the use of an altered highway other than by resurfacing. There are also powers to enable offers of noise insulation to be made to occupiers of properties adjacent to the site of roadworks if it is felt that the works will give rise to noise at such level that it will seriously affect the enjoyment of a dwelling for a substantial period of time.

35.5 Public Consultation

The procedures for the planning and approval of road schemes provide several opportunities for public consultation [N.I.50]. These include development plans, planning applications, line orders, side road orders, traffic regulation orders and compulsory purchase orders. Nowadays most highway authorities will carry out a large scale, non-statutory public consultation exercise using the techniques described in Chapter 13. (See also Chapter 10.)

35.6 Public Inquiries

Trunk Roads

Where the road is a proposed trunk road the Secretary of State for Transport [Sco.187] may decide that a

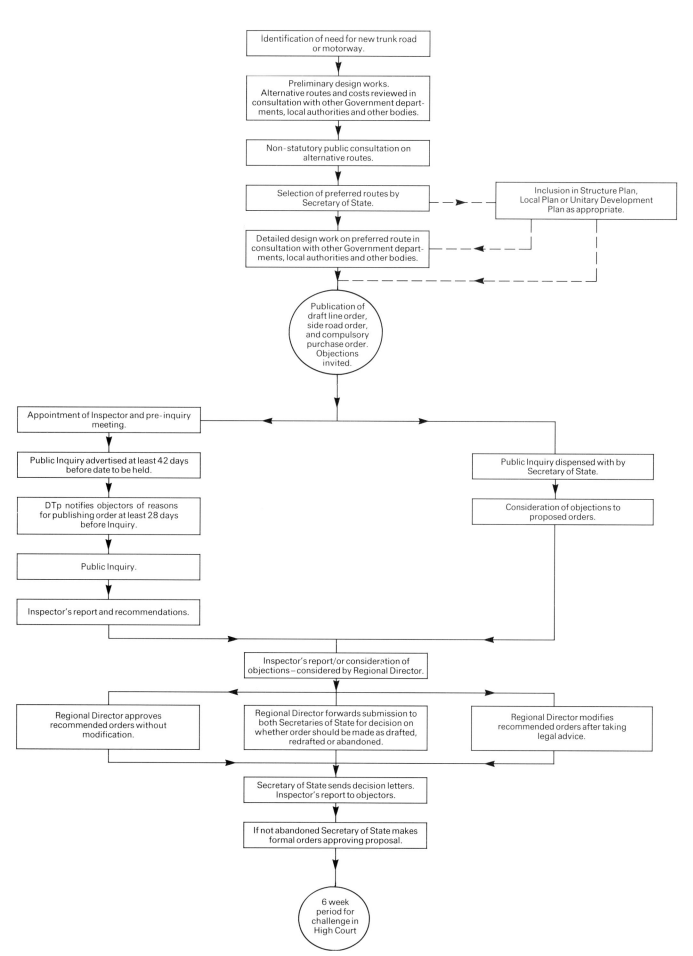

Figure 35.1 Procedures followed by DTp for the planning and approval of a new trunk road (under the Highways Act 1980) [Sco.188]

309

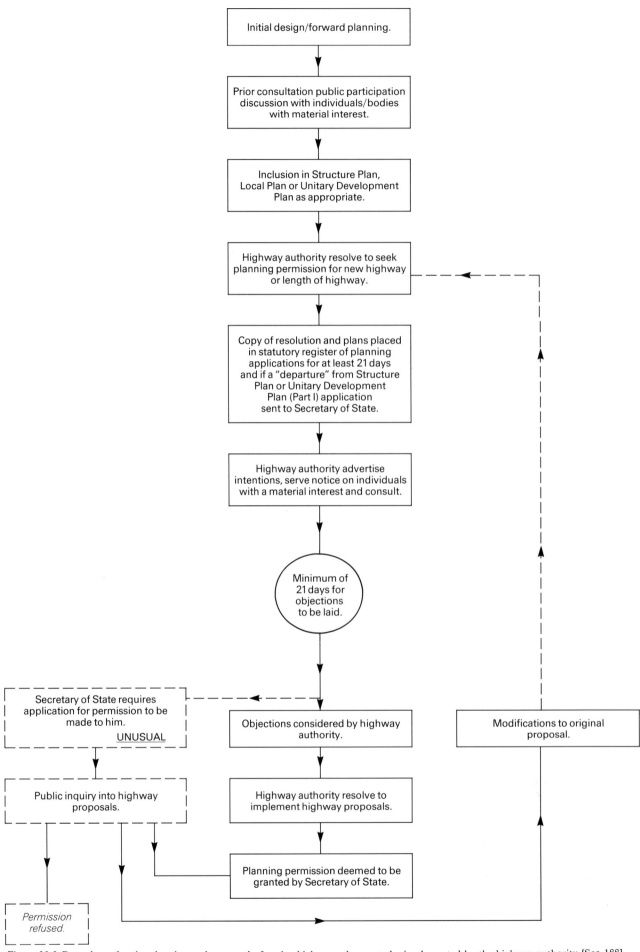

Initial design/forward planning.

Prior consultation public participation discussion with individuals/bodies with material interest.

Inclusion in Structure Plan, Local Plan or Unitary Development Plan as appropriate.

Highway authority resolve to seek planning permission for new highway or length of highway.

Copy of resolution and plans placed in statutory register of planning applications for at least 21 days and if a "departure" from Structure Plan or Unitary Development Plan (Part I) application sent to Secretary of State.

Highway authority advertise intentions, serve notice on individuals with a material interest and consult.

Minimum of 21 days for objections to be laid.

Secretary of State requires application for permission to be made to him.
UNUSUAL

Objections considered by highway authority.

Modifications to original proposal.

Public inquiry into highway proposals.

Highway authority resolve to implement highway proposals.

Planning permission deemed to be granted by Secretary of State.

Permission refused.

Figure 35.2 Procedures for the planning and approval of major highway schemes to be implemented by the highway authority [Sco.188]

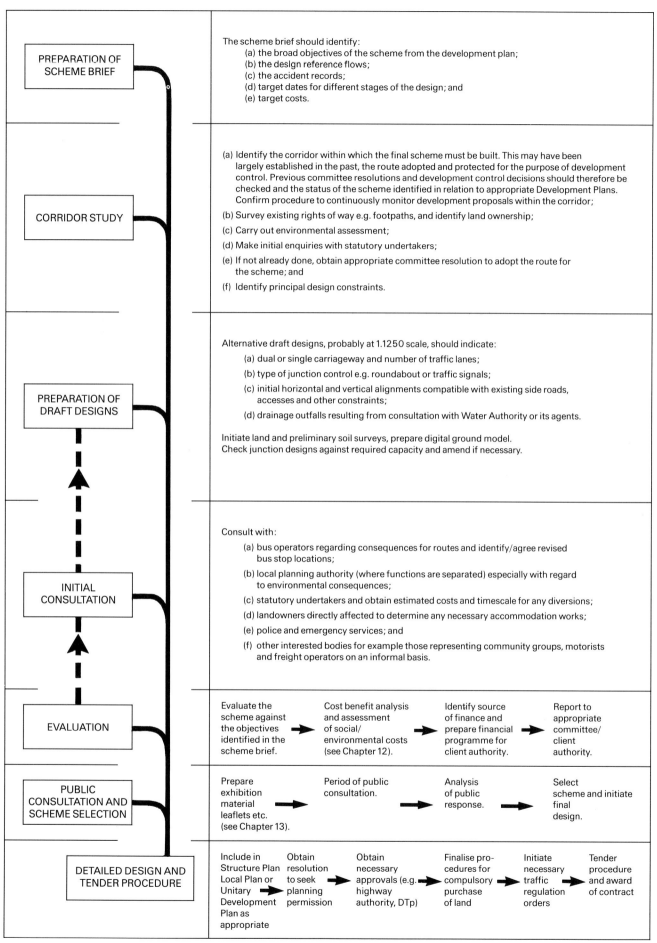

Figure 35.3 Main stages in the preparation of a non-trunk major highway scheme, by a local highway or authority [Sco.188]

public inquiry under the Highways Act 1980 is appropriate because the scheme is contentious. There are statutory rights under the Highways Act for objections to be made to line orders, side roads orders and to any compulsory purchase orders necessary for a trunk road scheme to proceed [NI.50]. The procedures for the conduct of public inquiries are described in Chapter 13.

The main procedural stages followed by the Department of Transport for the planning and approval of trunk roads under the Highways Act 1980 are set out in Figure 35.1 [Sco.188]. Trunk road proposals should also be included as proposals in structure plans, local plans and unitary development plans when they are included in the current Roads White Paper. Where an order under the Highways Act, as specified in Section 16 of the Town and Country Planning Act 1971, has already been made on a particular trunk road scheme, the Secretary of State for the Environment and the local planning authority have discretionary power to disregard objections to the inclusion of the scheme in the development plan.

Local Authority Roads

The procedures followed by the local highway authorities in seeking planning approval for non-trunk roads are set out in Figure 35.2 and Figure 35.3 sets out the main steps which local authorities follow in developing a highway scheme from initial design brief to tender stage [Sco.188].

35.7 References

Text Reference

1. DoE—Circular 22/84, '*Memorandum on structure and local plans*', DoE (1984). [Sco.177, Wa.48] (35.1, 35.2)

2. DoE—Circular 2/81, '*Development Plans Direction*', DoE (1981). [Sco.178, Wa.49] (35.1)

3. Town and Country Planning General Regulations 1976—Statutory Instrument 1976 No 1419, HMSO (1976). [Sco.189] (35.1)

4. Town and Country Planning General Development Order 1977—Statutory Instrument 1977 No 289, HMSO (1977) [Sco.190], and Town and Country Planning General Development (Amendment) (No 2) Order 1985—Statutory Instrument 1985 No 1981, HMSO (1985). [Sco.191] (35.1)

5. DoE—'*Building Businesses not Barriers*', Cmnd. 9794, HMSO (1986). (35.2)

6. Housing and Planning Act 1986, HMSO (1986). (35.2)

7. Town and Country Planning Act 1971, HMSO (1971). [Sco.184] (35.1)

8. Highways Act 1980, HMSO (1980). [Sco.192] (35.3)
    PART II—S14 to 18. Powers to make orders for highways
    PART III—S24. Powers to construct new highways
    PART XII—S239 to 241. Powers to acquire land for the construction and improvement of highways.

9. DoE—Circular 6/85, '*Compulsory Purchase Orders Procedures*', DoE (1985). [Sco.186, Sco.194, Sco.195, Wa.50] (35.3)

10. DTp—Circular Roads 1/81 '*Notes on the operation of compulsory purchase orders for highway schemes*', DTp (1981). [Wa.51] (35.3)

11. Acquisition of Land Act 1981, HMSO (1981). (35.3)

12. Land Compensation Act 1973, HMSO (1973). [Sco.193] (35.4)

35.8 Further Information

13. DoE—'*Compulsory Purchase Orders: A guide to procedure*', HMSO (1978) (Addendum 1981).

14. DTp Leaflets:
    '*Public Inquiries into Road Proposals—What you need to know*', HMSO (1981).
    '*Trunk Road Planning and the Public*', HMSO (1981). [Sco.196, Wa.52]

15. DoE Pamphlets—'*Land Compensation—your rights explained*':
    Booklet 1—'*Your home and compulsory purchase*', HMSO (1981)
    Booklet 2—'*Your home and nuisance from public development*', HMSO (1980)
    Booklet 3—'*Your business and public development*', HMSO (1986)
    Booklet 4—'*The farmer and public development*', HMSO (1986)
    Booklet 5—'*Insulation against traffic noise*', HMSO (1980)
(available free from local Councils, DoE/DTp Regional Offices, Citizens Advice Bureaux and the Welsh Office).

36   The Highway in Cross-section

36.1 Lane Width and Carriageway Width

The width of a highway link between junctions must be sufficient for its intended function in the road hierarchy (see Chapter 5) and to achieve acceptable levels of safety and operating efficiency. The Department of Transport's procedures for estimating carriageway width are given in TD 20/85 (Ref. 1) and TA 46/85 (Ref. 2). Whilst the accent in these is on rural roads there is also some discussion of application in urban areas.

Where demand is sufficient to justify four or more traffic lanes dual carriageways may be provided. Typical design flows for different widths and types of carriageway are given in Table 36.1 [Sco.197] and illustrations of a variety of urban dual carriageway schemes are shown in Plates 36.1, 36.2 and 36.3.

Speed/Flow Relationships

Typical relationships between vehicle flow and speed for different carriageway widths are shown in Figure 11.4 (see also Ref. 1). The heavier the traffic flow the lower the operating speed in general but the lines merely indicate the averaging of a large number of individual cases. Apart from geometric factors speed/flow is a function of vehicle/driver type, weather and daylight/darkness conditions. Therefore the graphs are at best only an indication of the relative performances of differing road types.

High vehicle speeds can be safely maintained only where traffic flows are relatively light. Heavy traffic flows generally result in lower operating speeds (as shown in figure 11.4).

Typical Road Widths

Typical cross-sections for single and dual carriageway roads are given in Figures 36.1, 36.2 and 36.3 although the verge widths shown exceed Department of Transport [Sco.198] practice and could only be achieved where sufficient land can be obtained without disproportionate cost (see also Ref. 3).

The standard width for a single two-way, two lane carriageway in Great Britain is 7.3 metres, divided by centre line markings into two 3.65 metre lanes, one for each direction of flow. In rural areas there are additional one metre edge strips but these are usually replaced by kerbs in urban areas.

Use of Narrower Lane Widths

Lanes on standard dual or multi-lane carriageways are normally multiples of 3.65 m but lower widths can be used on local distributor roads. A width of 6.7 m is often used on local distributors and widths down to 6.1 m for two-way roads have been found to operate satisfactorily and are often suitable for local distributor roads if kerb-side parking is restricted.

On primary and district distributor roads, the narrowest widths should only be considered at pinch points to overcome a particular local problem or where significant cost savings can be achieved over short distances, such as on bridges or in tunnels. In these circumstances operating speeds should be kept below 65 kph by a consistent reduction in the other elements of design and this may be reinforced by a regulatory speed limit.

On multi-lane roads lane widths down to 3.25 m can be used to help provide an extra lane where space is restricted. On major schemes the Department of Transport's CIDEL (Calculation of Incident Delay) program can be used to make an economic assessment of sites with a restricted width (Ref. 1).

Narrow carriageways are inappropriate where significant numbers of cyclists or large vehicles are anticipated and can result in tracking, (ie. rutting and uneven wear of the road surface) on narrow straight carriageways.

Lane widening is required on small radius curves as shown in Table 36.2 [Sco.199].

Use of Wider Lane Width

Extra wide lanes (ie. greater than 3.65 m), or surfaced strips at the edge of the carriageway delineated by a solid white line, may be provided to improve conditions for cyclists and allow additional margins for large vehicles. This greater width will also improve the flow of traffic past stopped vehicles or during maintenance of the verge at the edge of the carriageway.

On multi-lane single carriageways and dual carriageways the width of the nearside lane may be increased, even at the expense of other lanes, to improve conditions for cyclists and to allow more space for large vehicles.

36.2 Tidal Flow

In situations where traffic flow in opposing directions is unbalanced at different times of the day, consideration can be given to the provision of an odd number of lanes to enable the direction of flow on the

DESIGN FLOWS FOR TWO WAY URBAN ROADS

Road Type	2 lane carriageway					Undivided carriageway				Dual carriageway		
	Peak hourly flow veh/hour, both directions of flow+					Peak hourly flow veh/hour, one direction of flow				Peak hourly flow veh/hour, one direction of flow		
						4 lane			6 lane	Dual 2 lane		Dual 3 lane
	6.1 ■	6.75 ■	7.3 ■	9 ■	10 ■	12.3 ■	13.5 ■	14.6 ■	18 ■	Dual 6.75 ■	Dual 7.3 ■	Dual 11 ■
A Urban motorway											3600	5700
B All purpose road no frontage crossings, no standing vehicles, negligible cross traffic.			2000		3000	2550	2800	3050		*2950	*3200	*4800
C All purpose road frontage development, side roads, pedestrian crossings, bus stops, waiting restrictions throughout day, loading restrictions at peak hours.	1100	1400	1700	2200	2500	1700	1900	2100	2700			

+ 60/40 directional split can be assumed.

* Includes division by line of refuges as well as central reservation; effective carriageway width excluding refuge width is used.

HEAVY VEHICLE CONTENT

The recommended flows allow for a proportion of heavy vehicles equal to 15%. No allowance will need to be made for lower proportions of heavy vehicles; the peak hourly flows at the year under consideration should be reduced when the expected proportion exceeds 15% by:–

Heavy vehicle content	Total reduction in flow level (vehs/h)		
	Motorway and Dual carriageway all purpose road	10m wide and above Single carriageway road	Below 10m wide Single carriageway road
	per lane	per carriageway	per carriageway
15-20% 20-25%	100 150	150 225	100 150

Table 36.1 Design flows for two-way urban roads   (NB. all carriageway widths are in metres)

Source: TD 20/85 DTp (1985)

Plate 36.1 A primary distributor entering an urban area

Plate 36.2 A district distributor in a suburban area

Plate 36.3 A primary distributor in an inner city area

Source: DoE Northern Ireland

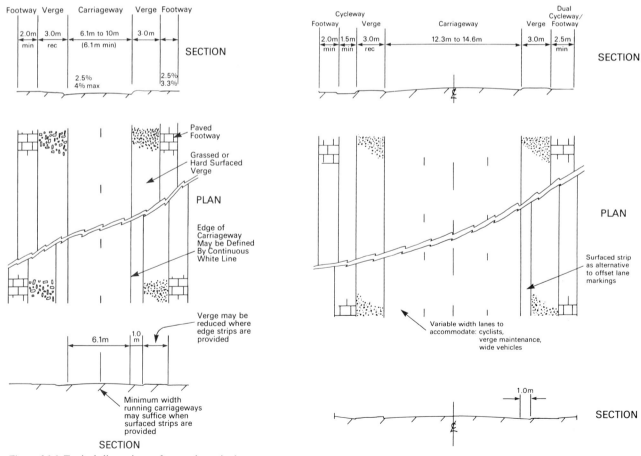

Figure 36.1 Typical dimensions of a two-lane single carriageway

Figure 36.2 Typical dimensions of a four-lane single carriageway

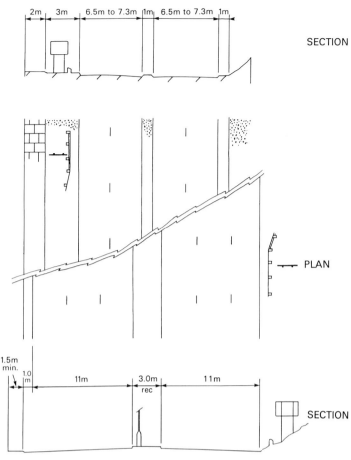

2m | 3m | 6.5m to 7.3m | 1m | 6.5m to 7.3m | 1m

SECTION

PLAN

1.5m min. | 1.0m | 11m | 3.0m rec | 11m

SECTION

Figure 36.3 Typical dimensions of a dual-carriageway

LANE WIDTH \ Radius	<150m	150-300m	300-400m
3.65m	0.3m per lane	NOT REQUIRED	NOT REQUIRED
<3.65m	0.6m per lane	0.5 per lane	0.3 per lane

Table 36.2 Road widening on curves

Source: TD 9/81 DTp (1981)

centre lane(s) to be altered for fixed periods of time to suit traffic conditions. Care must be taken to ensure that opposing flows are adequately signed and separated. This is usually achieved by symbolic variable message signs on overhead gantries (see Plate 36.4), often reinforced by the use of different coloured surfacing on the tidal lane(s). Provision for tidal flow is particularly appropriate for major commuter routes and purpose-built radial roads and at places where the carriageway cannot be widened (eg. bridges, tunnels and frontage development), but the signing equipment can be visually intrusive.

36.3 Edges of the Carriageway

The edge of carriageways on urban roads will normally be kerbed. Kerbs retain the structure of the carriageway, protect adjacent areas from encroachment by vehicles and assist drainage. Kerb faces on major roads should be about 100 mm high except, for example, at pedestrian crossing points where dropped kerbs should be provided to assist prams and wheelchair users. Where footways are provided or street furniture is placed adjacent to the carriageway then half-battered or bullnosed kerbs are commonly used. Elsewhere 45° splay kerbs may be preferred as they assist the removal of immobilized vehicles from the carriageway at times of emergency and tend to improve highlighting of the carriageway edge by headlight beams. Where hard shoulders or surfaced edge strips to the carriageway are provided extruded asphalt kerbs will form a drainage check, but they are not usually appropriate in built-up areas.

36.4 Footways

Ideally, pedestrian movements should be segregated from vehicular traffic but this is often not a practical proposition in urban areas and a paved footway at least 2.0 m in width should be provided (1.8 m as the absolute minimum) to permit prams or wheelchairs to pass in comfort. These are minimum values and should be increased wherever large pedestrian flows are expected (see also Chapter 33), or where more space is available as wider footpaths can provide more distance

317

Plate 36.4 A tidal flow scheme in Lincoln

Canwick Road (A15), Lincoln is a single carriageway road linking a two lane dual carriageway to the north and two single carriageway primary routes to the south. Considerable delays occured in the peak hours. As an alternative to constructing a new length of dual carriageway (estimated cost £4.5 million) the existing carriageway was widened to 9.3 metres to provide three lanes, the centre lane being tidal so that in the morning peak there are two lanes northbound and one lane southbound. This is reversed in the evening peak. Control is maintained within a UTC system by fibre optic lane signals mounted on overhead gantries.

The scheme was introduced in 1986 at a cost of £500,000. Peak hour journey times on this length of Canwick Road were reduced by 50 per cent.

Source: 'The Surveyor'

from passing traffic and give pedestrians a greater feeling of safety.

36.5 Verges

Where footways are located beside carriageways they should preferably be separated from the carriageway by a 3.0 m wide verge, but this is seldom possible in established urban areas. Verge widths may be reduced where hard shoulders, surfaced edge strips or pedestrian guardrails are provided. Wherever possible, public utilities' apparatus should be located in the verge to avoid disruption to carriageways or footways during maintenance work. Verges should be discontinued at bus stops, where a bus layby may be constructed and at pedestrian crossing points. Verges may be hard surfaced or grassed. A hard surface should be in a different material from the adjacent footway and textured in a way that discourages use by pedestrians (eg. cobbles). Grass may be more attractive but the implications for maintenance should be considered.

Where structures such as retaining walls or bridge parapets run parallel with the carriageway, kerbed marginal strips should be provided to reduce the potential for collisions. On bridge decks these should be hard surfaced. Widths will depend on the design speed of the road, the crossfall and on whether any street furniture, such as safety barriers or lamp columns are provided but should always give at least 0.45 m clearance (see Figure 36.4 and also Ref. 3).

36.6 Central Reserves

To Improve Safety

On existing multi-lane roads, where space permits, central reserves may be constructed to segregate opposing flows and create dual carriageways which offer higher levels of safety. Central reserves would normally be appropriate on multi-lane roads where speed limits are greater than 40 mph. Exceptions may need to be made where tidal flow systems are used or

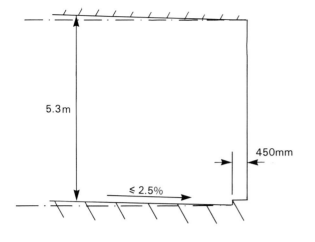

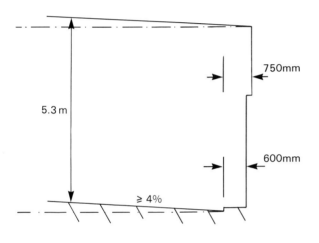

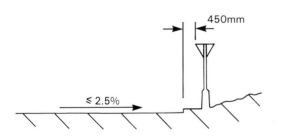

NOTE: ABSOLUTE MAX. SUPERELEVATION 5%

Figure 36.4 Clearances for 50 kph design speed

where economic arguments are strong (eg. on long or very expensive structures).

To Accommodate Street Furniture

Central reserves provide useful areas to accommodate road furniture such as traffic signs, street lighting columns and the legs of sign gantries. Widths must be sufficient to enable clearance to be obtained to these structures and may need to be protected by safety barriers to reduce the chance and effect of vehicle impact. Such facilities will, however, require routine

maintenance which may involve closing a traffic lane with its potential for creating additional delays (Refs. 4 and 5).

Vehicular Crossing Points

Vehicular crossing points should be provided at regular intervals to assist temporary diversions during maintenance works or other incidents. These places should be closed by removable barriers to prevent 'U' turns during normal operation. It should be noted that emergency crossing points are not suitable for major maintenance works and further advice on layout and dimensions is available in Ref. 6.

The location of vehicle crossing points will depend on the particular road layout and the configuration of any grade separated junctions. The most useful points will probably be:

● close to junctions near the end of the dual carriageway;

● either side of all other junctions; and

● approximately mid-way between junctions.

Width

Narrow central reserves should be kerbed and hard surfaced unless they are used as open (French) drains. If pedestrian crossing facilities are provided a minimum width of 2.5 m is required to permit a pedestrian pushing a pram or wheelchair to wait in safety. The normal minimum recommended width of a central reserve is 1.0 m but 3.0 m is preferred where space permits.

36.7 Crossfall (or Camber)

Carriageways

Except on curves where superelevation (see Chapter 37.5) or elimination of adverse crossfall or camber may be required, carriageways should normally have a crossfall of 2.5% from the crown, or central reservation, outwards towards the side of the road.

Excessive crossfall or camber is a source of danger to drivers and cyclists and should be avoided. It may cause loads to be displaced or lead to vehicles slipping sideways in icy conditions. Crossfalls can increase as a result of successive re-surfacing as drainage channels may be kept at their original level. Crossfalls should not exceed 5% in urban areas.

Footways

A maximum crossfall of 4% is recommended for footways and verges.

319

36.8 Other Aspects of Design

Headroom Clearance

There is no general limit on the height of vehicles in Britain although certain regulations apply in specific instances (eg. the Construction and Use Regulations set a height limit for buses and some semi-trailers). It is generally accepted that an absolute minimum headroom of 5.1 m should be provided at the most critical places after taking account of gradient and crossfall; but where a future surface overlay is likely to be required, a headroom of 5.3 m should be provided (see Figure 36.4). The headroom provided under footbridges and gantries is usually 5.7 m. For further information see Refs. 3 and 4.

Obstructions beside the Kerb

Lane capacity can be reduced when obstructions are sited near to the edge of the carriageway and a minimum clearance must be maintained to allow for overhanging loads and the tilting of vehicles towards the obstruction. Figure 36.4 gives recommended clearances for a design speed of 50 kph.

Longitudinal Construction Joints

As far as possible, longitudinal construction joints in the pavement should coincide with the division of the carriageway into traffic lanes. This helps to avoid confusion when driving in poor light or when the road surface is wet.

Location of Manholes

Where service manholes (for drains or utility plant) have to be located within the carriageway, every effort should be made to site the manhole away from the wheel tracks which suffer the worst wear. It is always preferable to locate manholes in verges, footways or on traffic islands to make maintenance work safer and reduce delays to traffic.

Bus Laybys

A major consideration in urban highway design is the provision of facilities for public transport and bus laybys should be located at appropriate places. Further information on the location and layout of bus laybys can be found in Chapter 26.

36.9 References

Text
Reference

1. DTp—TD 20/85, 'Traffic flows and carriageway width assessment', DTp (1985). [Sco.197]   (36.1)

2. DTp—TA 46/85 'Traffic Flows and Carriageway Width Assessment for Rural Roads', DTp (1985).   (36.1)

3. DTp (forthcoming publication), 'Highway construction details'.   (36.1)

4. DTp—TD 27/86, 'Cross Sections and Headrooms', DTp (1987).   (36.5, 36.6)

5. DTp—TD 19/85, 'Safety Fences and Barriers', DTp (1985). [Sco.200]   (36.6)

6. DTp—TA 45/85, 'Treatment of gaps in central reserve safety fences', DTp (1985).   (36.6)

36.10 Further Information

7. DTp—TA 43/84, 'Highway Link Design', DTp (1984). [Sco.197]

8. DTp—TD 9/81, 'Road layout and geometry: highway link design, (Amendment 1)', DTp (1984). [Sco.199]

9. DTp—COBA 9 Manual and subsequent amendments, DTp (1984). [Sco.201]

10. Simpson, D and Baker, D J—'New highway design flow thresholds', IHT Journal No 5 Vol 34 (May 1987).

37 Link Design

37.1 Design Speed

The Department of Transport's Technical Standard TD 9/81 (with Amendment No 1) and Advice Note TA 43/84, (Refs. 1 and 2) [Sco.202] provide guidance on establishing the design speed for road links.

These publications stress that the so-called 'speed value' of individual curves or other geometric elements, is *not* an indicator of an appropriate design speed, which should instead be selected according to the procedures set down in Ref. 1 as the designer's best estimate of likely vehicle speeds (see also Chapter 34.4).

For roads not subject to speed limits other than national maxima, the method of estimating design speed is to some degree iterative to take account of constraints on layout and alignment.

For most urban roads, however, with lesser speed limits and where there are frequent breaks in the regime of flow, design speed can only be estimated using the designer's own judgement, taking account of the mandatory speed limits. The speed limit policy for the road should always be known at the design stage. Measurements of existing 85th percentile approach speeds, or in the case of new links, measurements of speeds on other similar road configurations, can help the designer estimate likely vehicle speeds.

In the absence of more detailed information, Table 37.1 provides a useful guide to the relationship between the mandatory speed limit for a road and suggested design speed. The increments in design speed may be too large for some aspects of design and so each also has an upper or lower limit shown (ie. the A or B category).

SPEED LIMIT		DESIGN SPEED
mph (miles/h)	kph (Km/h)	kph (Km/h)
30	48	60B
40	64	70A
50	80	85A
60	96	100A

Table 37.1 Relationship between speed limits and design speeds for single level urban roads

When the speed limit policy and type of road to be constructed has been established, appropriate standards for curvature, superelevation and visibility can be determined to suit the estimated design speed of the road.

37.2 Stopping Sight Distance (SSD)

The stopping sight distance (SSD) is the theoretical sight distance required by a driver to stop a vehicle when faced with an unexpected obstruction in the carriageway. The SSD has two elements;

the perception-reaction distance, which is the distance travelled from the time the driver sees the obstruction to the time it is realised that the vehicle must stop; and

the braking distance, which is the distance travelled while the vehicle decelerates from the assumed design speed to stop just short of the obstruction.

Drivers' perception and reaction times can vary greatly and are affected by age, fatigue and conflicting stimuli or distractions (eg. bright lights or noise). For safety and comfort, a reaction time of 2 seconds is generally recommended. The braking distance will depend on vehicle performance and the condition of the road surface. Severe braking causes discomfort for passengers and the maximum comfortable deceleration is about 0.25 g, although 0.375 g (absolute maximum) can be achieved on wet, textured, surfaces without loss of control. These are the values used for road design purposes and approximate to average driver behaviour in wet conditions. They do not relate to the times and distances which can be achieved by good drivers in emergency braking conditions on dry roads (viz. Highway Code—shortest stopping distances, Ref. 3). Table 37.2 [Sco.202] provides values for the desirable and absolute minimum SSD to be used for design purposes.

Height of Vision

A drivers forward visibility requires an uninterrupted view between the driver's eye and any obstruction in the carriageway. 95 per cent of drivers of private vehicles have eye heights of 1.05 m or more above the road surface and this figure is used as the lower limit for design purposes. The upper limit for eye height is taken to be 2.0 m to represent drivers of large vehicles.

The height of the obstruction is assumed to be between 0.26 m (low object height) and 2.0 m. Forward visibility should be provided in both horizontal and vertical planes between points in the centre of the lane nearest the inside of the curve (see Figure 37.1).

37.3 Full Overtaking Sight Distance (FOSD)

On single carriageway roads, overtaking vehicles need to use the opposing traffic lane. To do so safely they

DESIGN PARAMETER \ DESIGN SPEED (km/h)	120	100	85	70	60	50
A. STOPPING SIGHT DISTANCE (m)						
A1 Desirable Minimum	295	215	160	120	90	70
A2 Absolute Minimum	215	160	120	90	70	50
B. HORIZONTAL RADII (m)						
B1 Minimum R *without elimination of Adverse Camber and Transitions	2880	2040	1440	1020	720	510
B2 Minimum R *with Superelevation of 2.5%	2040	1440	1020	720	510	360
B3 Minimum R *with Superelevation of 3.5%	1440	1020	720	510	360	255
B4 Desirable Minimum R *with Superelevation of 5%	1020	720	510	360	255	180
B5 Absolute Minimum R *with Superelevation of 7%	720	510	360	255	180	127
B6 Limiting Radius *with Superelevation of 7% at sites of special difficulty (Category B Design Speeds only)	510	360	255	180	127	90
C. VERTICAL CURVATURE (m)						
C1 FOSD Overtaking Crest K Value	*	400	285	200	142	100
C2 Desirable Minimum *Crest K Value	182	100	55	30	17	10
C3 Absolute Minimum *Crest K Value	100	55	30	17	10	6.5
C4 Absolute Minimum Sag K Value	37	26	20	20	13	9
D. OVERTAKING SIGHT DISTANCE (m)						
D1 Full Overtaking Sight Distance FOSD	*	580	490	410	345	290

* Not recommended for use in the design of single carriageways.

Table 37.2 Recommended geometric design standards

Source: TD 9/81 DTp (1981)

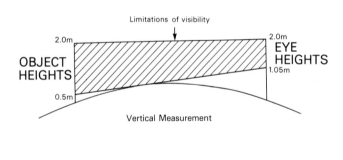

Figure 37.1 Measurement of stopping sight distance

Horizontal Measurement

require adequate sight distances. The Department of Transport's Technical Standard TD 9/81 (Ref. 1) [Sco.202] provides a complex design methodology for the coordinated design of single carriageway roads, for use mainly in rural areas, that uses the concept of Full Overtaking Sight Distance (FOSD), climbing lanes and sections of four lane road (to facilitate overtaking) to achieve minimum prescribed Overtaking Values for a route. The design methodology also results in the use of certain ranges of horizontal radii being not recommended for use in single carriageway design.

The constraints normally associated with urban areas will, however, rarely permit the flexibility of alignment required for such coordinated design. Furthermore, new urban single carriageway roads are likely to be only modest projects in an area where traffic management may already have been carried out on the existing network and the new road is required to extend or improve that management. It is unlikely, therefore, that coordinated design principles for single carriageways will be relevant for urban roads unless a substantial length of grade separated or access free carriageway is envisaged. Opportunities to provide FOSD will therefore be rare. Nevertheless, a brief description of FOSD is given below:

Full Overtaking Sight Distance (FOSD)

The sight distance required to permit drivers to complete a normal overtaking manoeuvre in the face of an oncoming vehicle consists of four elements (see Figure 37.2):

the perception/reaction distance, which is the distance travelled by the vehicle while the driver decides whether or not to overtake;

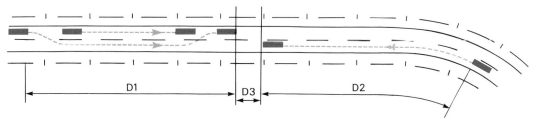

Figure 37.2 Full overtaking sight distance on a single carriageway road

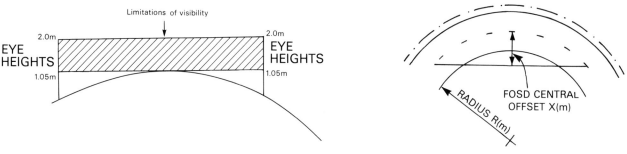

Figure 37.3 Measurement of full overtaking sight distance

the overtaking distance, which is the distance travelled by the vehicle to complete the overtaking manoeuvre (D1);

the closing distance, which is the distance travelled by the oncoming vehicle while the actual overtaking manoeuvre is taking place (D2); and

the safety distance, which is the distance required for clearance between the overtaking vehicle and the oncoming vehicle at the instant the overtaking vehicle has returned to its own lane (D3).

The time taken to complete an overtaking manoeuvre depends on the relative speeds of the vehicles involved, but in practice 85 per cent of manoeuvres take less than 10 seconds to complete. Table 37.2 indicates typical values for FOSD.

To provide an uninterrupted forward view between the overtaking driver's eye and the vehicle to be overtaken and the oncoming vehicle, FOSD should be available between points 1.05 m and 2.00 m above the centre of the carriageway forming an envelope of visibility as shown in Figure 37.3. FOSD should be checked in both the horizontal and vertical planes.

37.4 Interruptions to Lines of Sight

Crests on hills, uncut grass, safety fences and occasionally bridge soffits, can interrupt the driver's line of site. The interruption to lines of sight caused by safety fences in the central reservation of a dual carriageway poses a particular problem in urban design. Urban road alignments are often so constrained that full visibility requirements can only be achieved at a very high cost in financial or environmental terms. In such circumstances the required widening of the central reserve can rarely be justified in urban areas and the use of absolute minimum visibility and departures from standards will often need to be considered.

37.5 Horizontal Curvature

The geometric parameters used in design are normally related to design speed (see also Chapter 36). Table 37.2 shows typical desirable and absolute minimum values for horizontal and vertical curvature and there is an additional lower level designated 'limiting radius' for horizontal radius of curvature.

Designs for new or improved roads should normally aim to achieve the desirable values for each design parameter. However, a relaxation of these standards, down to absolute minimum values, can be made safely wherever substantial construction cost or environmental cost savings can be achieved.

Limiting horizontal radii may also be considered at particularly difficult sites and where the 85th percentile speed is expected to be in the lower half of the design speed band.

DTp Technical Standard TD 9/81 (Ref. 1) [Sco.202] advises that in the design of new roads, the use of radii tighter than the limiting values is undesirable and not recommended. However, as explained in 37.3

above, coordinated single carriageway design is often not feasible in urban areas and circumstances could arise when, on balance, a departure from these standards may nevertheless be justified.

Superelevation

As a vehicle moves round a curve it is subject to centrifugal force which causes it to try to slide outwards or to overturn. Side friction between the wheels and the road surface is generated to counter this force but the carriageway can also be superelevated to reduce the overturning effect when $\frac{V^2}{R}$ is greater than 7 ('V' = Velocity, 'R' = Radius of curvature).

The percentage superelevation (or crossfall), 'S', required, is found from the equation;

$$S = \frac{V^2}{2.828 \, R}$$

where V is measured in km/hr and R is measured in metres.

On horizontal curves, adverse camber should be replaced by a favourable crossfall of 2.5 per cent when the value of $\frac{V^2}{R}$ is greater than 5 and less than 7.

Studies of driver behaviour on curves have shown that whilst superelevation provides a desirable contribution to driver comfort and safety, it need not be applied too rigidly. Thus, for sharp curves in urban areas with at-grade junctions and side accesses, superelevation should be limited to 5%, even though absolute minimum or even limiting radii may still be used in difficult circumstances (Ref. 4).

Transition Curves

Superelevation, or removal of adverse camber, should be achieved progressively over the transition curve which introduces the horizontal curvature.

The basic length of transition curve 'L', can be derived from the equation:

$$L = \frac{V^3}{46.7 \, q \, R}$$

where L = length of transition curve (m)
    V = design speed (km/h)
    q = rate of increase of radial acceleration (m/sec³)
    R = Radius of curve (m).

NB: q should normally be less than 0.3 m/sec³ for unrestricted design although in urban areas it will frequently be necessary to increase it to 0.6 m/sec³ or even higher for sharp curves in tight locations.

37.6 Vertical Alignment

Gradients

Vertical gradients slow vehicles, particularly heavy commercial vehicles, and impose additional running costs as well as increasing the likelihood of accidents as drivers attempt to overtake the slowest traffic. Steep gradients are particularly hazardous in adverse weather conditions and the desirable maximum gradient for various categories of road should be:

Type of Road	Desirable Max. Grade
Urban motorways	3%
All purpose dual carriageways	4%
All purpose single carriageways	6%

Steeper gradients may be justified in hilly terrain but should be avoided if possible where traffic flows are high and a maximum of 5% is suggested for primary distributors. A gradient greater than 0.5 per cent should be maintained wherever possible to assist drainage of the carriageway surface. In flat areas, kerbside drainage channels may have to rise and fall to provide adequate falls to clear surface water.

Vertical Curves

It is necessary to limit the severity of vertical curves because of visibility considerations on the brow of hills and for the comfort of vehicle occupants.

Vertical curves should be parabolic because this form provides a constant rate of change of curvature. It is convenient to determine the length of a vertical sag or crest curve using a 'K' value. The length of the curve can be obtained from the equation:

$$L = KA$$

where L = curve length (m)
    K = design speed related coefficient (chosen from Table 37.2)
    A = algebraic difference in grades (%).

37.7 Coordination of Horizontal and Vertical Alignments

It will be beneficial to coordinate the horizontal and vertical alignments of a road as this will avoid optical illusions on the curvature of bends when the scheme is constructed. This can be achieved by making all the points where horizontal and vertical curvatures change, coincide with one another. Where this is not possible and the curves cannot be separated entirely, the vertical curves should be either contained wholly within, or wholly outside the horizontal curves. Where curves are allowed to overlap, the resulting optical illusions are damaging to the appearance of the road and in extreme cases may contribute to accidents.

37.8 Climbing Lanes (or Crawler Lanes)

Climbing lanes should be provided to assist heavy commercial traffic where gradients are steep and the construction costs can be economically justified. They can be formed by widening a carriageway or re-allocating the existing width to provide an additional lane (further details may be found in Ref. 1).

37.9 References

Text Reference

1. DTp—TD 9/81, '*Road Layout and Geometry: Highway Link Design, and (Amendment No 1)*' DTp (1984). [Sco.202]   (37.3, 37.5)

2. DTp—TA 43/84, '*Highway Link Design*', DTp (1984). [Sco.202]   (37.3)

3. DTp—Highway Code, HMSO (1987).   (37.2)

4. Southampton University—'*The effect of road curvature on vehicle/driver behaviour*', Southampton University (for DTp) (1984).   (37.5)

37.10 Further Information

5. Kerman, J et al—'*Do vehicles slow down at bends?*', report to PTRC annual summer meeting, PTRC (1982).

6. Simpson, D—'*System development and monitoring designs*', paper to ICE conference 6th June 1985 (1985).

38 Junction Design: General Considerations

38.1 Introduction

The capacity of an urban road network usually depends on the operation of its junctions. The need for good junction design is further emphasized by the fact that about two thirds of the fatal and serious injury road traffic accidents which occur in urban areas do so at junctions. The difficulty of reconciling the interests of pedestrians with those of vehicular road users is greatest at junctions, and the desire to provide maximum vehicular capacity must be set against the special needs of cyclists and pedestrians.

Sight Lines and Visibility

In order to assist road safety and maximize capacity it is important that good visibility is available on the approaches to and within all junctions. Where a junction is located on a bend, in a cutting, at or near the summit of a hill, or near a bridge; it may be difficult to achieve the required visibility and special care will be necessary to achieve the best possible standards within the limitations of the site (see also Chapter 39.2).

Telephone kiosks, signs, shrubs, lighting columns and other obstructions should not be placed where they would restrict visibility.

Approaches to junctions should be limited to a gradient of 5 percent. Easing the gradients on approaches will also improve visibility and facilitate stopping and starting, particularly in icy weather.

38.2 Provision and Spacing of Junctions

The frequency and precise location of junctions to be provided along a new distributor road will depend upon its level in the road hierarchy (see Chapter 5) and the proportion of non-local through traffic, which it is intended to carry.

If the number and importance of existing cross-routes would require too many junctions it may be possible to combine two or more side-roads before they reach the main road giving benefits for road safety and junction capacity on the main road.

Junctions should be spaced at regular intervals and the absolute minimum spacing should exceed the stopping sight distance appropriate for the 85th percentile speed of the major road. Greater distance should be provided wherever possible and particular care will be necessary when providing access to sites which generate large numbers of trips.

The location and spacing between all major points of access should be carefully considered to ensure safety and adequate speed/flow characteristics along the major route. Major points of access may be necessary to provide links with public transport interchanges, high density office and residential accommodation, shopping centres and multi-storey car parks.

38.3 Types of Junction

The various types of junction provide a hierarchy of alternative layouts which cater for increasing levels of traffic flow, as follows;

- junctions without any designated priority,
- priority junctions (see Plate 38.1),
- priority junctions with channelisation,
- roundabouts (see Plate 38.2) or traffic signal control (see Plate 38.3), and
- grade separated junctions (see Plate 38.4).

Figure 38.1 gives an approximate guide to the magnitudes of major and minor road traffic that can be accommodated by particular types of junction and further information is available in Department of Transport publications (see Refs. 1 and 2) [Sco.203, Sco.204].

Alternative Solutions

The uncertainties associated with forecasting future levels of urban traffic flow suggest that it is sensible to test a range of design reference flows against the costs and benefits associated with a range of alternative layouts (see also Chapter 11 which deals with the estimation of traffic flows). This process should include varying the proportions of turning traffic which can influence the type and scale of the junction proposed. This type of analysis can identify a range of proposals which offer varying levels of service and other strengths and weaknesses.

To facilitate the decisions involved in junction choice and design, the Department of Transport (TRRL) has developed three computer programs for modelling isolated intersections. ARCADY2 (Assessment and Roundabout CApacity and DelaY) and PICADY2 (Priority Intersection CApacity and DelaY) deal respectively with roundabouts and major/minor priority junctions. OSCADY (Optimised Signals CApacity and DelaY) deals with traffic signalled junctions. All of the programs operate on the same principles—given demand flows and turning movements

Plate 38.1 A priority junction at the intersection of a local access road with a district distributor

Source: S Sexton Esq

Plate 38.2 A roundabout junction at the intersection of two district distributors

Source: Leicestershire County Council

327

Plate 38.3 Traffic signal control at a primary/district distributor intersection

Source: Ferra Computer Systems Ltd

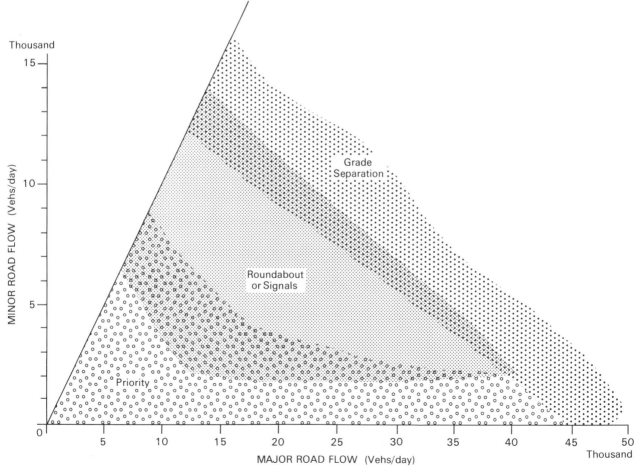

Figure 38.1 Type of junction appropriate for different traffic flows

Plate 38.4 A grade separated junction on a primary distributor

Source: British Road Federation

for typical peak hours and the junction geometry, they predict where queues will form, how long they will last and when and for how long vehicles will be delayed (Refs. 3, 4, 5, 6 and 7).

Other Constraints

Selection of the most suitable type of junction may also depend on other considerations such as:

● where the major road is intended to offer a high level of service, a high standard of provision may be appropriate for all junctions along the route even though the design reference flows would not normally justify such provision for all junctions;

● if the junction is within an existing or proposed UTC area, the use of traffic signal control may be preferred (see also Chapter 20 which deals with UTC);

● traffic signals will also be necessary when a positive form of control is required;

● if there are significant numbers of cyclists at a grade separated junction, roundabouts may not be suitable and grade separation can leave cyclists exposed to fast moving traffic. The requirements of cyclists, pedestrians or public transport can sometimes be crucial to junction design;

● the physical characteristics of the site may help determine which form of junction is most suitable. For example, conventional roundabouts usually require more space than signalled junctions to provide sufficient space to separate junction entry points;

● where traffic speeds are high, roundabouts may be appropriate and they may also be preferred to encourage free flowing traffic conditions, particularly at off-peak times;

● roundabouts are also useful where a route changes in character from a fast flowing district distributor to a more congested urban situation and where a U-turning facility is required.

From this it can be seen that each site must be considered on its merits and no hard and fast rules should be applied.

38.4 Design Principles

Where the type of junction to be designed is not predetermined by other factors, estimates of delay and resource costs can be used to assist in the choice of the best design. Evaluation of alternative proposals should cover the identification of junctions which are critical to the operation of the network and should examine the effects of capacity overloads causing queueing and possible re-routing through unsuitable roads. Cost benefit studies will require the use of appropriate values of time for the people and vehicles

involved and reference should be made to the Department of Transport's COBA 9 Manual [Sco.205] and subsequent amendments (see Ref. 8 and also Chapter 12 which deals with the appraisal of road and traffic schemes).

Delay

Vehicles usually experience some level of delay when negotiating junctions. The exceptions are straight-ahead traffic on the major road at priority junctions and traffic provided with an uninterrupted path by grade-separation.

Delays occur from two sources; those caused by the presence of other traffic, sometimes resulting in queueing (queueing delays), and those arising from the need to change speed and depart from the most direct path, even when no other traffic is present (called geometric delays).

Queueing Delays

For each traffic stream approaching a junction the queueing delay depends on the ratio of the arrival rate of traffic in that stream to the capacity of the junction to pass traffic on that stream under the prevailing traffic conditions; and on the arrival rate itself. The arrival rate is the average rate (vehs/hour) at which traffic approaches the junction, measured upsteam of any queue, and the prevailing capacity is the average rate at which traffic can enter the junction on the arm in question. Each of these quantities may change quite rapidly, especially during peak periods. Where it is practicable to do so, the design of the junction should provide sufficient capacity to keep the ratio of arrival rate to capacity well below unity (eg. below 0.9 or better still below 0.8) for each traffic stream. If this can be done, the length of the queue and the corresponding queuing delay will fluctuate around an equilibrium value which can be estimated from the arrival rate and capacity for each traffic stream.

Where insufficient capacity is available and the ratio of arrival rate to capacity is greater than, or only just less, than unity (perhaps only during peak periods) there will be no equilibrium and queue length (and delay) will grow progressively throughout the peak period until the rate of arriving traffic declines sufficiently to bring the ratio well below unity. Then the queue will progressively decrease towards a new equilibrium value and, with further reductions in traffic, eventually disappear. The growth and decline of queues and the corresponding delays incurred can be estimated from the variation over time in the arrival rate and capacity for each stream at each type of junction.

Analysis of queueing delay is important to junction design and requires that the various streams of traffic be identified. A stream may comprise traffic in more than one adjacent traffic lane and any given lane may include vehicles making different manoeuvres at the junction. As a general rule, traffic in adjacent lanes is part of the same stream where it can be regarded as forming a single queue. The design of a junction will affect both the total amount of queueing delay and also its distribution amongst the various streams of traffic. This can be used to effect given objectives for the movement and distribution of traffic. The DTp/TRRL computer programs referred to in 38.3 above provide a ready method of carrying out this analysis and optimising junction design.

Delays due to Junction Geometry

The geometric delay is dependent on the geometry of the junction and on the speeds of a vehicle as it decelerates on the approach, negotiates the junction and accelerates again on exit. The total geometric delay for any pattern of flow could be obtained by multiplying the delay per vehicle in each stream by the corresponding flow and summing for all the streams. Good junction design should aim to minimize this type of delay as far as possible.

Vehicle Operating Costs at Junctions

In addition to costs arising from delay, costs will also be incurred for each of the separate manoeuvres performed at a junction. Vehicle operating costs depend on the speed, type of manoeuvre and the distance travelled by each vehicle. These costs include the additional cost of fuel, oil, tyres, maintenance and depreciation caused by the layout of a junction and the changes in speed and direction of the vehicles travelling through it.

Generalised Cost

The generalised cost of 'operating' a junction will comprise;

● the costs of time (delays),
● the costs of vehicle operation, and
● the costs of accidents.

Although these are usually studied separately for different purposes, the true optimisation of junction design should aim to minimise all of these costs, discounted over the anticipated life of the junction, in comparison with the capital cost of improving it (see also Chapter 12 which deals with economic assessment and Chapter 6.2 on economic capacity).

38.5 References   *Text Reference*

1. DTp—TD 22/86 and TA 48/86, *'Layout of Grade Separated Junctions'*, DTp (1986).   (38.3)

2. DTp—TA 23/81, *'Junctions and accesses: determination of the size of roundabouts and major/minor junctions'*, DTp (1981). [Sco.203, Sco.204]   (38.3)

3. DTp/TRRL—Report RR35, *'ARCADY2. An enhanced program to model capacities, queues and delays at roundabouts'*, DTp (1985).   (38.3)

4. DTp—HECB/R/30, ARCADY2 User Manual DTp (1985).   (38.3)

5. DTp/TRRL—Report RR36, *'PICADY2, An enhanced program to model capacities, queues and delays at major/minor priority junctions'*, DTp (1985).   (38.3)

6. DTp—HECB/R/31, PICADY2 User Manual, DTp (1985).   (38.3)

7. Burrow, I J and Willoughby, P J— *'OSCADY, A computer program to aid the design of isolated signal junctions'*, Seminar N, PTRC 13th Summer Annual Meeting, University of Sussex (1985).   (38.3)

8. DTp—COBA 9 Manual and subsequent amendments, DTp (1981). [Sco.205]   (38.4)

38.6 Further Information

9. DTp/TRRL—Leaflet LF 1011, *'TRRL Computer Programs for use in junction choice and design'*, DTp (1986).

10. DTp—Local Transport Note 1/86, *'Cyclists at Road Crossings and Junctions'*, DTp (1986).

11. DTp—TA 44/85, *'Capacities, Queues and Delays at Road Junctions Computer Programs HCSLIR/30-31 (ARCADY2 and PICARDY2)'* DTp (1985).

12. DTp/TRRL—Report SR 810, *'Geometric delay at non-signalised intersections'*, DoE/DTp (1984).

13. DTp—TA 20/84, *'Layout of Major/Minor Junctions'*, DTp (1984). [Sco.206]

14. DTp—TA 42/84, *'Geometric Design of Roundabouts'*, DTp (1984).

15. DTp—TD 16/84, *'Geometric Design of Roundabouts'*, DTp (1984).

16. DTp—TA 30/82, *'Choice between options for trunk road schemes'*, DTp (1982).

17. DTp/TRRL—Report LR 909, *'Traffic queues and delays at road junctions'*, DoE/DTp (1979).

39 Priority Junctions

39.1 Geometric Requirements

Priority junctions (see Plate 39.1) are the most common type of junction in urban areas and are appropriate where traffic flows on the minor roads and overall numbers of turning movements are relatively light. More heavily trafficked junctions will require other types of control because as traffic volumes increase, the risk of accidents at priority junctions becomes greater. This is because as delays increase on the minor road drivers attempt to use unsuitable gaps to break into the major traffic stream.

Plate 39.1 A typical priority junction

Signs and Road Markings

Priority (major/minor) junctions are generally controlled by 'Give Way' road markings supplemented by 'Give Way' signs at the busier sites. 'Stop' signs and markings will be necessary where visibility is severely restricted but the Secretary of State's approval to their use is required (Ref. 1).

The three main forms of priority junction are (see Figure 39.1);

- 'T' junctions,
- staggered junctions, and
- crossroads.

Design Considerations

Right-left staggers are preferred because this layout reduces the number of vehicles turning right off the major road. Priority should be given to the route carrying, or expected to carry, the heavier traffic flow. This route will normally be the higher category of road in the hierarchy.

At some sites higher flow rates may occur on the minor arm for short periods. For example, at an exit from a sports stadium or near to a major work complex. This should not alter the allocation of priority but if excessive delays are caused regularly, some other form of control should be considered (eg. traffic signals). The road markings should be designed to give a clear indication of priority and the routes to be taken through the junction by different traffic streams.

The layout of a priority junction should take account of;

- the speed and volume of traffic on the major road,
- the magnitude of the turning traffic,
- the types of vehicle (and pedestrians) likely to use the junction, and
- the required level of carriageway provision.

More detailed information is given in the Department of Transport's Advice Note TA 20/84 [Sco.207] on the layout of major/minor junctions (Ref. 2).

Design Speed

The design speed for the major road is normally taken to be the 85th percentile of the actual vehicle speed for an existing road, or the relevant design speed for a new road.

Turning Radii

The swept path of an 18.0 m drawbar (articulated) trailer (see also Chapter 32 and Figure 32.5), the largest vehicle in common use, may be used as a design parameter where no other design constraints exist. However, in urban areas less accommodating designs are frequently used, particularly when there is little likelihood or intention for the minor road to cater for such large vehicles.

Junction layouts should allow larger vehicles (particularly buses) to complete their manoeuvres without encroaching on adjacent verges or footways. At the busiest junctions, compound curves (eg. three-centred curves, see Fig. 39.1 and also Fig. 32.4) should be used as they more closely represent the path described by a turning vehicle.

Carriageway Widening

Where large radii cannot be achieved it may be possible to take account of the 'overhang' and 'cut-in' associated with large articulated vehicles by widening the carriageway at the junction. However, this may

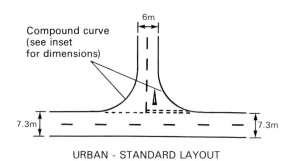

Compound curve
(see inset
for dimensions)

6m

7.3m   7.3m

URBAN - STANDARD LAYOUT

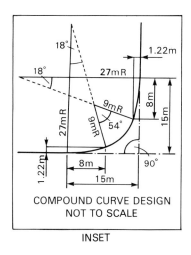

18°

18°

27mR

1.22m

9mR

27mR   9mR

9mR   54°

8m

15m

1.22m

8m

90°

15m

COMPOUND CURVE DESIGN
NOT TO SCALE

INSET

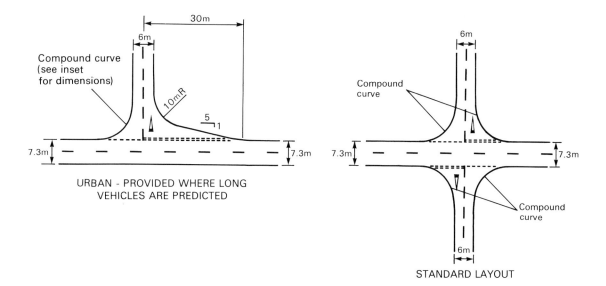

30m

6m

Compound curve
(see inset
for dimensions)

10mR

5
    1

7.3m   7.3m

URBAN - PROVIDED WHERE LONG
VEHICLES ARE PREDICTED

6m

Compound
curve

7.3m   7.3m

Compound
curve

6m

STANDARD LAYOUT

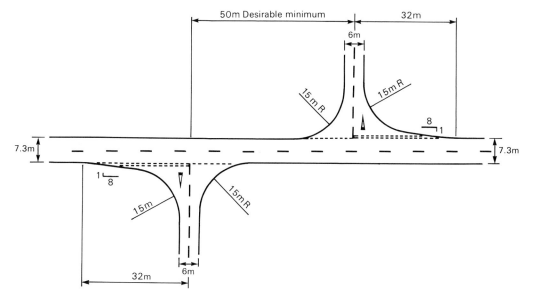

50m Desirable minimum   32m

6m

15m R   15m R

8
    1

7.3m   7.3m

1
  8

15m   15m R

32m   6m

Figure 39.1 Typical priority junction layouts

Source: TA 20/84 DTp (1984)

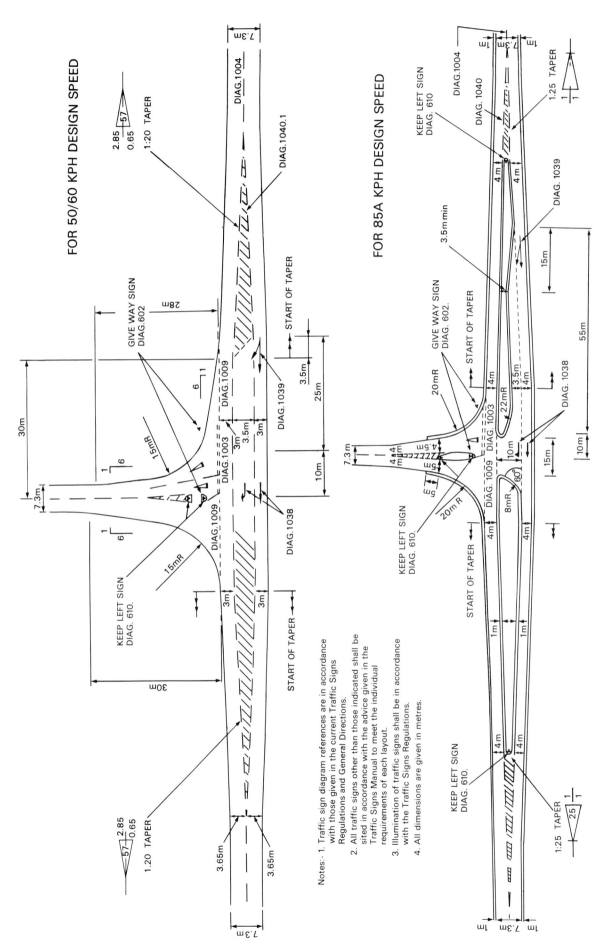

Figure 39.2 Typical 'T' junction layouts for 50/60 kph and 85A kph design speeds

FOR 50/60 KPH DESIGN SPEED

FOR 85A KPH DESIGN SPEED

Source: TA 20/84 DTp (1984)

Notes:- 1. Traffic sign diagram references are in accordance
with those given in the current Traffic Signs
Regulations and General Directions.

2. All traffic signs other than those indicated shall be
sited in accordance with the advice given in the
Traffic Signs Manual to meet the individual
requirements of each layout.

3. Illumination of traffic signs shall be in accordance
with the Traffic Signs Regulations.

4. All dimensions are given in metres.

not be appropriate for access roads in residential areas (see also Chapter 31.4) as it creates a greater width of carriageway for pedestrians to cross.

When significant numbers of large vehicles are expected to use a junction (eg. near a major distribution point) it may be beneficial to provide a flared widening on the exit side of the junction to avoid any encroachment on opposing traffic.

Use of Minimum Radii

The minimum radius which could be used at minor priority junctions on major urban roads is 6.0 m. Vehicular and pedestrian requirements should be considered in every design. Where pedestrian volumes are high the use of a small radius curve will cause the minimum diversion to the footpath alignment and reduce the width of carriageway to be crossed. The use of traffic islands to separate traffic flows and provide a refuge for pedestrians is often helpful (see Figure 39.4).

Merging and Diverging Lanes

On primary distributors where speeds may be high, diverging lanes can be provided so that through traffic is not impeded by turning vehicles as they slow down on the approach to a junction. Diverging lanes may be provided on the offside of dual carriageways within the central reserve where they can provide a reservoir for right turning traffic to queue in safety.

Merging lanes can help minor road traffic to accelerate to main road speed and accept smaller gaps in the main road traffic. However, where major road flows are high they can cause difficulties since they narrow the angle of vision for emerging traffic and this can adversely affect road safety.

The ability of merging and diverging lanes to work effectively requires successful control of parking.

Two examples of layouts for merging and diverging lanes are shown in Figure 39.2.

39.2 Visibility Requirements ('x' and 'y' Distances)

Drivers emerging from the minor road of a priority junction must have adequate visibility to left and right along a single carriageway major road. If the major road is a dual carriageway and there is sufficient space in the gap in the central reserve for minor road vehicles to wait there before entering or crossing the far carriageway, then visibility considerations from the minor road need only apply to the right.

N.B. The Department of Transport's Advice Note TA 20/84 (Ref. 2) gives various recommended values for sight distances and there are also criteria laid down in the Traffic Signs Regulations and General Directions (Ref. 1) for the use of 'Give Way' and 'Stop' signs.

Sight Distance (y) and Speed

The sight distance requirement is determined by the speed of main road traffic which must have sufficient forward visibility to stop if required. This distance, known as the 'y' distance, is measured in both directions (ie. left and right for single carriageway roads) from the centre line of the minor road along the near edge of the running carriageway (see Figure 39.3). The 'y' distances for different main road traffic speeds are given in Figure 39.3.

Visibility Set Back (x)

The view of the driver on the minor road will be from a point set back from the 'Give Way' or 'Stop' line. This distance (known as the 'x' distance, see Fig. 39.3) should be a minimum of 9.0 m at junctions on major roads (primary and district distributor roads), so that drivers on the minor road can see approaching traffic as they move towards the 'Give Way' line.

At physically constrained sites and where junctions have only light traffic flows the 'x' distance may be reduced to 4.5 m but a 'Stop' sign may be required.

Under no circumstances should the 'x' distance be less than 2.4 m. Conversely, increasing 'x' beyond 15.0 m can encourage excessive entry speeds from the side road as well as increasing the land used, which might involve additional capital costs and maintenance expenditure besides creating a rather open and naked appearance.

Driver's Eye Height

The splay of visibility should be uninterrupted at the typical driver's eye height of 1.05 m. It is generally easier to achieve these standards on level ground or at the low point in sag curves, and junctions near the crests of hills can create difficulties.

Other Visibility Considerations

On curved alignments where the splay would otherwise lie within the major carriageway, it should be made tangential to the nearside edge (see Figure 39.3).

On dual carriageways, the distance of clear visibility to the left should be provided within the central reserve.

Lamp columns, or sign poles can be located within the visibility splay but larger obstructions should be avoided as they could result in a reduced level of safety and cause extra delay. As visibility 'envelopes' at junctions should remain free from obstruction, they should lie within the curtilage of the highway to ensure

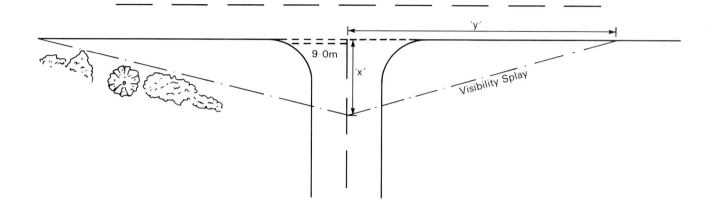

Design speed of major road (Km/h)	100	85	70	60	50
'y' distance (m)	215	160	120	90	70

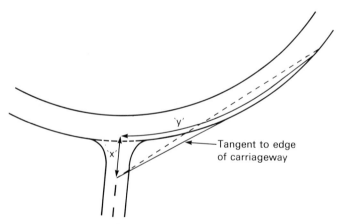

Figure 39.3 Visibility requirements for a priority junction

Source: TA 20/84 DTp (1984)

that regular maintenance can be carried out (see also Ref. 2) [Sco.207].

39.3 Channelisation

Traffic islands can be provided to:

● direct or guide vehicles to take a specific path and segregate opposing traffic streams;

● provide a refuge for pedestrians crossing the road and for vehicles waiting to turn right; and

● provide a convenient location for essential street furniture such as traffic signs, street lighting and manholes and inspection chambers.

Use of Dual Carriageways

Single lane dual carriageway roads are rarely appropriate in urban areas. However, it is sometimes beneficial to provide a length of single lane dual carriageway at a priority junction on a single carriageway road to deter excessive speed and prevent overtaking. Short lengths of two lane dual carriageway at junctions on otherwise single carriageway roads should, however, be avoided as they may result in reduced safety as drivers attempt to overtake in the vicinity of turning traffic.

Central Reserves

Central reserves should be wide enough to accommodate and protect right turning vehicles if the turning flows justify it when considered against site constraints and the costs involved. Where significant numbers of large vehicles are expected, lane widths should be increased to allow for them.

Where kerbed islands cannot be provided, segregation can be achieved by what are commonly known as, 'ghost islands', indicated by hatched road markings and road studs, to give additional warning to drivers. Ghost islands should be 3.5 m wide (ie. a full traffic lane width) and may be up to 5.0 m wide but can be reduced to 3.0 m if necessary because of site limitations. At severely constrained sites an absolute minimum island width of 2.5 m will still provide some protection for right turning traffic but should be carefully monitored in use to ensure that it does not increase the risk of accidents (see also Ref. 2) [Sco.207].

39.4 Provision for Pedestrians

At priority junctions on primary routes where traffic is fast and dense, known pedestrian routes should preferably be provided with grade separated crossings (see also Chapter 42). Where traffic is less dense and speeds are slower, at-grade crossings may be provided using either the formal pelican or zebra types, or refuge islands. The type of treatments that should be considered will depend on anticipated flows both of vehicles and of pedestrians (see also Chapter 24 which deals with pedestrian facilities in more detail).

Location of Crossing Points

Crossing points at a junction on a minor road should be set back at least 10 m from the 'Give Way' or 'Stop' line so that pedestrians cross the minimum width of carriageway and are not directly involved with turning vehicles (see Figure 39.4). Crossing points should not be positioned so far from the junction that an inconvenient detour is created which results in pedestrians crossing away from the safer place. Lowered kerbs should be provided at all crossing points (as explained in Chapter 24).

Guard Railing

Guardrails should be used only where significant pedestrian activity takes place and it is necessary to channelise pedestrians to the most appropriate crossing

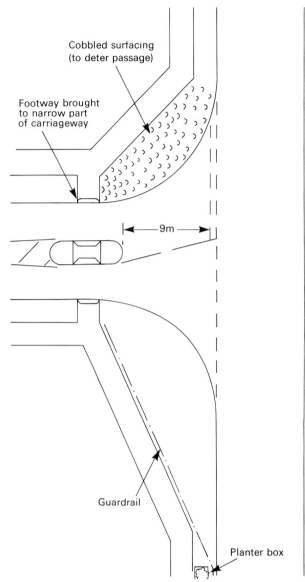

Figure 39.4 Footway layout at a priority junction

points. Care should be taken to ensure that guardrails do not interrupt visibility for drivers and consideration should be given to the use of types of barrier designed especially for this purpose (see Plates 24.10 and 24.11).

39.5 Traffic Capacity and Delay

Priority junctions should only be considered where the capacity of the major road is adequate for the expected traffic flows. Where this is not the case another form of control should be considered.

Capacity

The capacity provided for traffic on the minor road (and, for traffic turning right from the major road) is determined by two factors;

● the proportion of gaps occurring in the major traffic streams that can be used by traffic entering or crossing from the minor road (and by traffic turning right from the major road across the opposing traffic stream),

● the characteristics of the junction layout, such as lane-widths and visibility distances, turning radii etc.

Empirical relationships have been developed to estimate the capacity available for each of the traffic streams that must give way to the major route, as a linear function of the through traffic flows and the proportion of traffic turning left from the major road (see also Figure 38.1). The operating parameters for these relationships must take account of visibility distances.

Delay

The **queueing delay** occurring in each of the traffic steams that have to give way depends mainly upon the ratio of the arrival rate of traffic in each of those streams to the capacity available for them to enter the junction (see also Chapter 38).

Computer programs are available to estimate how queue-lengths and delay can be expected to vary during a day for any given layout and given traffic variations (ie. volumes of traffic making different movements through the junction).

As well as calculating the acceptable design flows for any given layout, these programs can also be used to examine the sensitivity of queue-lengths and delay in the different streams to:

● particular aspects of the layout which are constrained;

● increases in traffic in the streams that must give way;

● increases in traffic on the major road; and

● general growth in traffic, which is likely to affect both the major and the minor road.

The computer program PICADY2 (see Refs. 3, 4 and 5) assesses a junction from a knowledge of the **demand flows** and the **geometry of the layout**. The program uses empirical and theoretical relationships to predict queues and delays by modelling periods of peak traffic flow.

The **geometric delay** (see also Chapter 38) at a priority junction is determined mainly by the curvature of the paths that turning traffic is required to negotiate and the dimensions of any stagger between priority junctions on opposite sides of the major road. The above mentioned computer programs have not, so far, incorporated the effect of geometric layout on vehicle operating costs.

Capacity calculations will be required for the **non-priority** traffic streams which have to give way and thus have limited capacity and incur delay (accepting that the major road traffic flows will have to be accommodated and should not incur delays).

Input to PICADY2 requires:

● reference information (such as a title and the date);

● time information (the start and the end of the period to be modelled and the duration of each time segment);

● geometric details of the junction (including lane widths and visibility distances);

● traffic flow data (including vehicle composition and turning movements);

● if there is a flare on the minor road, the number of vehicles from the give way line to where the flaring begins;

● if there is a pedestrian crossing, its geometric features (eg. length, position) and pedestrian flows;

● if geometric delay is to be calculated, the approach and departure speeds and entry and exit radii; and

● if local observations of capacities have been made, the flows observed.

39.6 References

Text Reference

1. Traffic Signs Regulations and General Directions, Statutory Instrument 1981 No 859 HMSO (1981). [Sco.208, Wa.53]   (39.1)

2. DTp—TA 20/84, *'Junctions and accesses: the layout of major/minor junctions'*, DTp (1984). [Sco.207]   (39.1, 39.2, 39.4)

3. DTp/TRRL—Report RR 36, *'PICADY 2: an enhanced program to model capacities, queues and delays at major/minor junctions'*, DTp (1985).   (39.5)

4. DTp/TRRL—Report SR 582, *'The traffic capacity of major/minor priority junctions'*, DoE/DTp (1980). [Sco.209]   (39.5)

5. DTp—HECB/R/31, *'PICADY 2 User manual,'* DTp (1985)   (39.5)

39.7 Further Information

6. DTp—TA 23/81, *'Junctions and accesses: determination of the size of roundabouts and major/minor junctions'*, DTp (1981).

40   Roundabouts

40.1 Introduction

A roundabout junction operates as a one-way circulatory system around a central island where entry is controlled by 'Give Way' markings and priority must be given to traffic approaching from the right. The operating efficiency of this type of junction depends on the ability of drivers to respond to safe opportunities to join the stream of circulating vehicles already in the junction.

Roundabouts can perform satisfactorily at junctions with many approach arms if they are well designed and the traffic demand is reasonably well balanced between the arms; although four arm roundabouts are generally preferred. Although the initial construction costs may be greater than for other types of junction because of the larger land area required, maintenance and vehicle operating costs are likely to be less as roundabouts permit a free flow of traffic when demand is light and are self-regulating. The ability of roundabouts to cope with U-turn manoeuvres can be particularly useful where one or more of the approach carriageways is divided or where U-turns would otherwise be awkward or disruptive.

During uncongested off-peak periods roundabouts will generally result in less delay than with signal control. However, they are not generally compatible with urban traffic control systems as they cannot respond to positive control commands. They may also be unsatisfactory where there are significant numbers of cyclists or pedestrians and special provisions may be required (eg. grade or mode separation) which can be expensive.

The various types of roundabout layout currently in use are described in Table 40.1 and illustrated in Figures 40.1 and 40.2 and in Plates 40.1 to 40.4.

Accident rates and severity at roundabouts can be 40%–90% lower than those at signal controlled junctions of equivalent capacity. The most common problem affecting safety is excessive speed, mainly on entry but also within the roundabout. Cyclists are particularly at risk, especially at normal roundabouts (see 40.5 over) where they are over 14 times more likely to be involved in an accident than a motorised vehicle (see also Refs. 1, 2 and 3) [Sco.210].

40.2 The Geometric Features of Roundabout Design

The terminology used to describe the geometry of roundabout design is given in Figure 40.3. The main features are:

Entry Path Curvature—To achieve the desired levels of safety and capacity, vehicle approach speeds should be regulated to appropriate levels. This can be achieved by deflecting the vehicle entry path at the junction approach using suitably positioned traffic islands on the approaches and by staggering the entry arms, as shown in Figure 40.4. Entry path curvature should not exceed 100 m radius otherwise high accident rates are likely to occur.

Where mini roundabouts are being created at existing junctions where a 30 mph speed limit applies, an appropriate entry angle can be achieved by small traffic deflection islands or, less effectively, by road markings.

Inscribed Circle Diameter (ICD)—The relationship between the central island diameter and the inscribed circle diameter (see figure 40.3 (a)) is the most important consideration for the passage of large vehicles at small roundabouts where, for example, an 18 m central island diameter requires a minimum ICD of 36 m to prevent over-running. For 'mini' type roundabouts, the ICD should not be greater than 28 m.

Visibility—It is essential that drivers have sufficient visibility of the roundabout they are approaching to be able to stop safely if it is necessary to do so. The requirements for unobstructed stopping sight distance are shown in Figure 40.5. In order to enter and proceed safely through the roundabout, drivers should have adequate forward and circulatory visibility and visibility to the right, as shown in Figure 40.6.

Segregation for Left Turning Traffic—Segregated lanes for left turning traffic (see Plate 40.5) may be adopted where around 50% or more of vehicles entering the junction leave at the first exit and sufficient space is available (see Refs. 4 and 5).

40.3 The Principles for Estimating Capacity and Delay

Except where a segregated left-turn lane is provided, all traffic entering a roundabout from any one approach road will usually be regarded as a single stream for the purpose of analysing capacity and delay. If a segregated left-turn lane is provided, the traffic using it is directed to form a separate stream, with a capacity dependent on the width and curvature of the lane. Otherwise capacity depends on:

● the occurrence of suitable gaps in circulating traffic to enable traffic on the approach arms to enter the roundabout;

340

Type	Description	Use
Normal	• Kerbed central island with diameter greater than or equal to 4m. • Flared approaches to allow multiple entry lanes. • See Figure 40.1.	• New developments and construction. • Junctions within or at the end of dual carriageways. • To change direction of a new road at a junction.
Mini	• Flush or slightly raised central island less than 4m in diameter. • Road markings indicate pattern of movement. • With or without flared approaches. • No street furniture on central island in order to allow long vehicles to overrun. • See Figure 40.1.	• To improve the performance of existing urban junctions where space is severely constrained. • Not used in new construction but in conversions from other roundabout and junction types. • Use at sites subject to a 30 miles/h speed limit.
Double	• Two normal or mini roundabouts are placed within the same junction or at two adjacent junctions connected by a short link road. • See Figure 40.1.	• Useful for controlling unusual or asymmetric approaches. • Useful at approaches with heavy opposing right turning movements, staggered approaches and at sites with more than four arms.
Grade separated	• At least one traffic movement passes through the junction without interruption while the remainder are brought to one or more roundabouts at a different level. • Compact designs are favoured. • See Figure 40.2. • For pedestrians and cyclists: the roundabout is elevated to allow for a pedestrian and cycle network below.	• Urban motorways and dual carriageways. • High capacity road and those with high approach speeds of traffic. • New construction where there are high vehicle and pedestrian flows.
Ring junctions	• A large two-way circulatory system where each approach is provided either with 3-arm roundabouts (normally minis) or with traffic signals. • See Figure 40.2.	• Useful at some special sites to solve particular local problems. • Conversion from very large roundabouts which have entry problems. • Would not be recommended for a new facility.
Signalised	• Traffic entering the roundabout from one or more arms is signal-controlled for all or part of the day. • See Figure 40.2.	• Can increase the capacity under certain operating conditions.
Gyratory systems	• Small one-way systems where normal land use activities can be maintained on the central island.	• Urban areas, especially town centres. • Safe access to the island must be ensured for pedestrians, cyclists and possibly vehicles.

Table 40.1 Types of roundabout (the main characteristics)

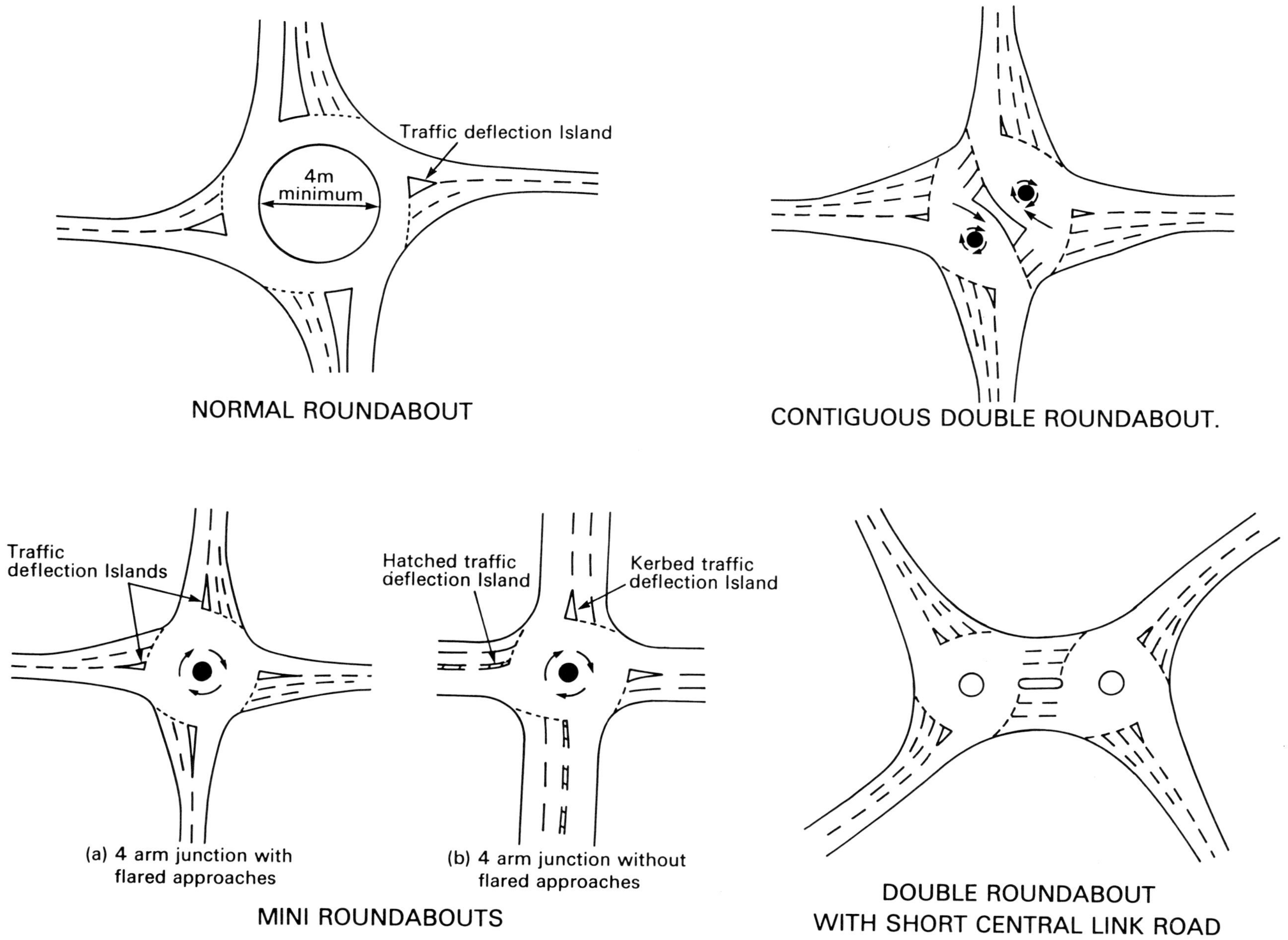

CONTIGUOUS DOUBLE ROUNDABOUT.

DOUBLE ROUNDABOUT
WITH SHORT CENTRAL LINK ROAD

Traffic deflection Island

4m minimum

NORMAL ROUNDABOUT

Kerbed traffic
deflection Island

Hatched traffic
deflection Island

(b) 4 arm junction without
flared approaches

Traffic
deflection Islands

(a) 4 arm junction with
flared approaches

MINI ROUNDABOUTS

Figure 40.1 Types of roundabout (mini type)

Source: TA 23/84 DTp (1984)

341

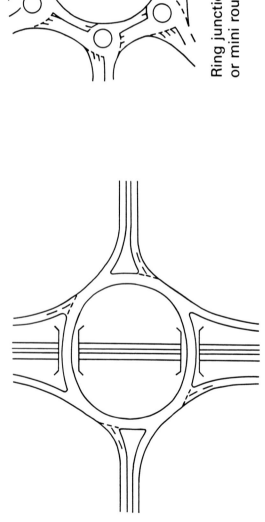

Ring junction layout with small normal or mini roundabouts.

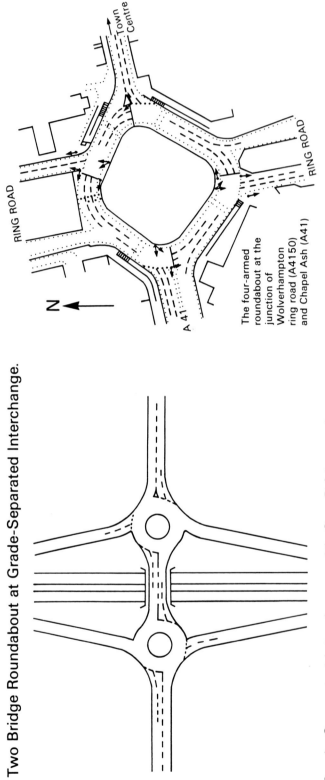

RING ROAD

RING ROAD

A 41

Town Centre

N

The four-armed roundabout at the junction of Wolverhampton ring road (A4150) and Chapel Ash (A41)

Signal-controlled roundabout

Two Bridge Roundabout at Grade-Separated Interchange.

Grade-Separated Interchange with One Bridge and Two Roundabouts-'Dumbell' Interchange.

Figure 40.2 Types of roundabout (signalled and grade separated)

Plate 40.1 A mini roundabout giving equal priority to three local distributors

Plate 40.2 A double-mini roundabout

Plate 40.3 Part-time signal control at a roundabout

In April 1986 part-time, morning and evening peak hour, traffic signals were introduced at the Catedown Roundabout in Plymouth. The objectives were to increase the entry capacity on different arms of the roundabout and to discourage traffic from using unsuitable roads in the area by adjusting relative priorities.

As a result, entry flow from the desired arm has increased by eleven per cent in the morning peak hour while flow on the unsuitable roads has decreased by 30 per cent. In the evening peak hour main road flows have increased by at least ten per cent with a consequent improvement on journey times.

Source: Devon County Council

Plate 40.4 A ring junction

Source: JMP Consultants

344

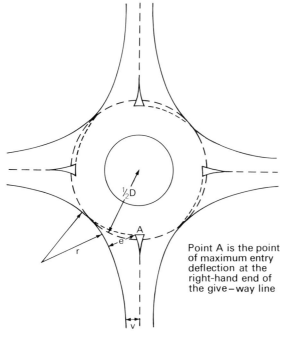

Point A is the point
of maximum entry
deflection at the
right-hand end of
the give–way line

FIGURE 40.3(a)

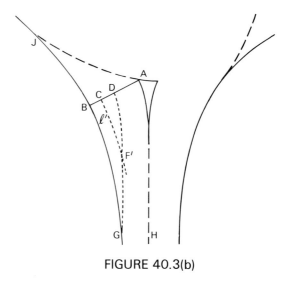

FIGURE 40.3(b)

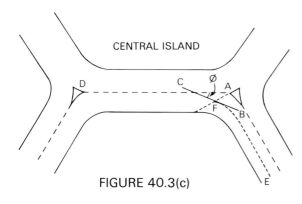

FIGURE 40.3(c)

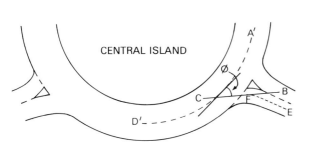

FIGURE 40.3(d)

Figure 40.3 Geometric parameters of roundabout design

Geometric parameter	Definition
Entry width (e)	The width of the entry arm into the junction measured from point A along the normal to the nearside kerb. See Figure 40.3(a).
Approach half-width (v)	The width of the entry arm upstream of the flare measured from the median line to the nearside kerb along a normal. See Figure 40.3(a).
Average length of flare (l')	In Figure 40.3(b) l' is defined by l' = CF' where the line CF' is parallel to BG and distance (e – v)/2 from it. Usually CF' is curved and its length measured along the curve to get l'.
Sharpness of flare (S)	A measure of the rate at which extra width is developed in the entry flare. It is defined by the relationship $S = 1.6(e - v)/l'$.
Entry radius (r)	Measured as the minimum radius of curvature of the nearside kerbline at entry. See Figure 40.3(a).
Entry angle (ø)	The angle between the circulating traffic and that entering the junction. Figures 40.3(c) and (d) show ø for well defined conventional roundabouts. For other types see TA 23/81 DTp (1981).
Inscribed circle diameter (D)	The diameter of the largest circle that can be inserted within the junction outline. Where the outline is asymmetric, the local value in the region of entry is used. See Figure 40.3(a).

Source: TA 23/81 DTp (1981)

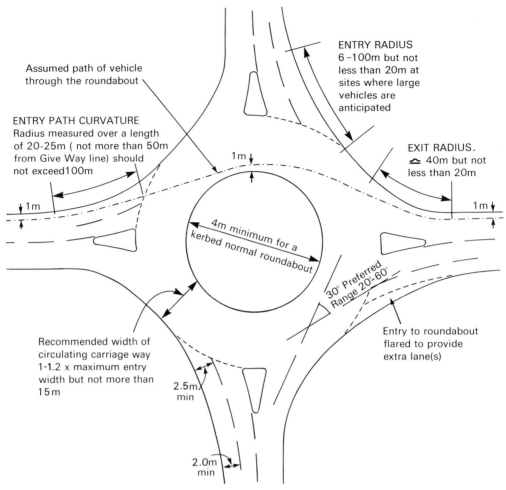

Figure 40.4 Typical roundabout layout showing entry layout

Plate 40.5 A segregated left turn lane in use at a roundabout

Source: Devon County Council

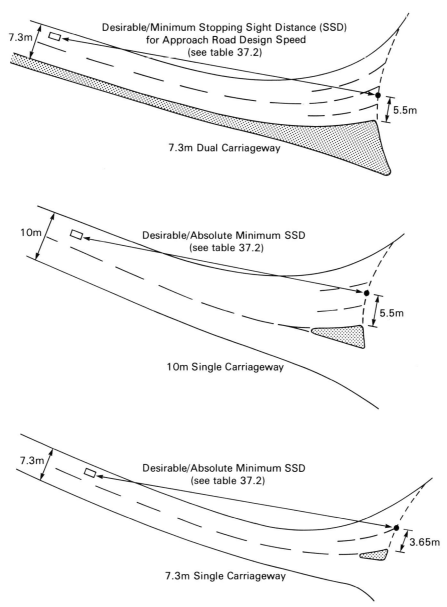

Figure 40.5 Measurement of stopping sight distance Source: TD 9/81 TD 16/84 DTp (1981, 1984)

● the geometric layout of each entry point and of the circulating area (as described in 40.2 above).

Entry Capacity

An empirical relationship has been established which estimates the entry capacity as a linear function of the circulation flow. The parameters of this relationship can be estimated from the geometry of the layout (see Refs. 6 and 7.).

Capacity Calculations

Computer programs are available to estimate how queue lengths and delays may be expected to vary over the day. As well as making calculations for the design flows, the designer may wish to use such programs or other methods of calculation (a manual method is described in Ref. 1), to examine the sensitivity of queue lengths and delay on different approach roads to:

● variation in the layout;

● changes in turning proportions or increases in traffic in particular streams; and

● general increases in traffic over the design period which are likely to affect traffic in all streams.

In particular, the empirical relationships for entry capacity can be used to determine on which entry, or entries, the ratio of arrival rate to capacity will first reach any specified limiting value (eg. 0.9), and which traffic from other entries will cause it to do so.

More information on calculating the capacity of queues and delays at junctions is available in Ref. 8, which explains the ARCADY2 and PICADY2 computer programs, and from Refs. 9 and 10.

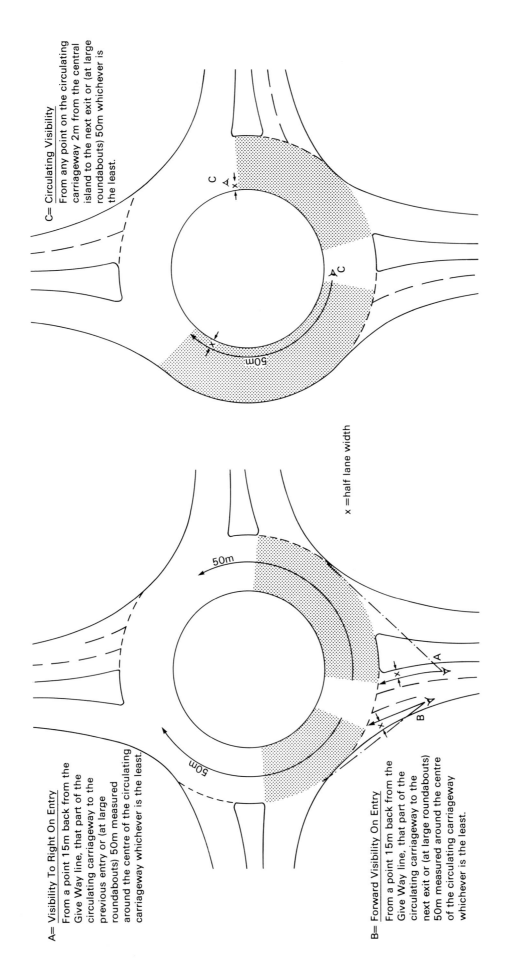

C= Circulating Visibility
From any point on the circulating carriageway 2m from the central island to the next exit or (at large roundabouts) 50m whichever is the least.

A= Visibility To Right On Entry
From a point 15m back from the Give Way line, that part of the circulating carriageway to the previous entry or (at large roundabouts) 50m measured around the centre of the circulating carriageway whichever is the least.

B= Forward Visibility On Entry
From a point 15m back from the Give Way line, that part of the circulating carriageway to the next exit or (at large roundabouts) 50m measured around the centre of the circulating carriageway whichever is the least.

x = half lane width

(In addition for many small diameter and mini roundabouts to operate successfully and for drivers to accept appropriate gaps in the circulating traffic stream some visibility is also required along the other arms of the junction)

Figure 40.6 Visibility requirements at roundabouts

Source: TA 42/84 DTp (1984)

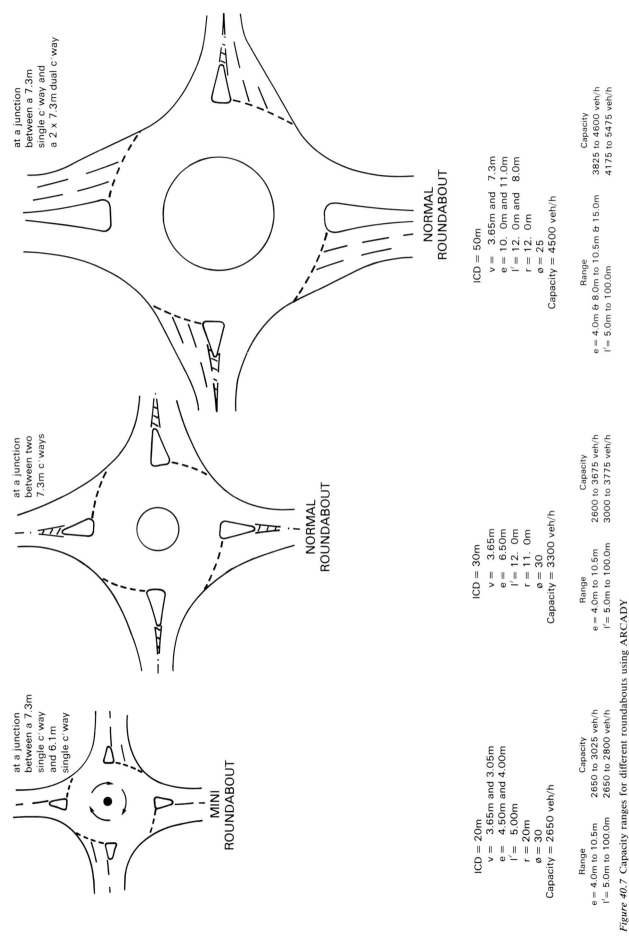

at a junction
between a 7.3m
single c'way and
a 2 x 7.3m dual c'way

**NORMAL
ROUNDABOUT**

ICD = 50m
v = 3.65m and 7.3m
e = 10. 0m and 11.0m
l' = 12. 0m and 8.0m
r = 12. 0m
ø = 25
Capacity = 4500 veh/h

Range
e = 4.0m & 8.0m to 10.5m & 15.0m
l'= 5.0m to 100.0m

Capacity
3825 to 4600 veh/h
4175 to 5475 veh/h

at a junction
between two
7.3m c'ways

**NORMAL
ROUNDABOUT**

ICD = 30m
v = 3.65m
e = 6.50m
l' = 12. 0m
r = 11. 0m
ø = 30
Capacity = 3300 veh/h

Range
e = 4.0m to 10.5m
l'= 5.0m to 100.0m

Capacity
2600 to 3675 veh/h
3000 to 3775 veh/h

at a junction
between a 7.3m
single c'way
and 6.1m
single c'way

**MINI
ROUNDABOUT**

ICD = 20m
v = 3.65m and 3.05m
e = 4.50m and 4.00m
l' = 5.00m
r = 20m
ø = 30
Capacity = 2650 veh/h

Range
e = 4.0m to 10.5m
l'= 5.0m to 100.0m

Capacity
2650 to 3025 veh/h
2650 to 2800 veh/h

Figure 40.7 Capacity ranges for different roundabouts using ARCADY

A range of capacities for typical roundabout layouts derived from the ARCADY2 program is shown in Figure 40.7.

Geometric Delay

The geometric delay at a roundabout is determined by the overall layout and especially by the deflection of the paths that vehicles are required to negotiate and the detour imposed upon them compared with a hypothetical direct path through the junction. The corresponding additional vehicle operating costs can also be determined taking account of the effects of layout and speed for each type of vehicle (see Refs. 11 and 12.)

Queueing Delay

The queueing delay for each of the entering traffic streams depends mainly upon the ratio of arrival rate of traffic in the stream to the prevailing entry capacity (see also Chapter 38).

40.4 Provision for Pedestrians

As a general rule pedestrians should be discouraged from crossing the carriageway on roundabouts and gyratory systems. Guardrails may be required to channel pedestrian movements away from the roundabout to safer crossing points but these should not be so far away that the detour involved discourages their use and leads to dangerous practices like climbing over the guardrails.

Provision should be made for pedestrians to cross the entry and exit arms of roundabouts through a gap in each deflection island. Lowered kerbs should be provided on each of the footways and the crossing points should preferably be set back at least 10 m from the give-way line to minimise the conflict between pedestrians and drivers concentrating their attentions on the circulating traffic stream. On wide multi-lane carriageways, it may be necessary to provide supplementary refuges between traffic lanes on the flared approaches.

At sites with high vehicle and pedestrian flows and especially on primary distributors with high speeds at off-peak times, subways or footbridges may be preferable. At some sites, the topography may lend itself to the provision of an open network of pedestrian routes at a lower, or higher, level to the carriageway.

40.5 Provision for Cyclists

Cyclists are particularly vulnerable at larger roundabouts and gyratories and consideration should be given to providing either:

● a separate and distinct cycle route away from other traffic, possibly with shared use of a pedestrian subway system;

● a signposted alternative route away from the roundabout with crossing facilities on a nearby link; or

● where there are significant numbers of cyclists and no satisfactory way of providing for them, an alternative form of junction control may be necessary.

For further information see also Chapter 25 which deals with the provision of facilities for cyclists.

40.6 References

Text Reference

1. DTp—TA 23/81, *'Junctions and accesses: determination of size of roundabouts and major/minor junctions'*, DTp (1981). [Sco.210]   (40.1, 40.3)

2. DTp/TRRL—Report LR 774, *'Accidents at off-side priority roundabouts with mini or small islands'*, DoE/DTp (1977).   (40.1)

3. DTp/TRRL—Report LR 1120, *'Accidents at 4-arm roundabouts'*, DoE/DTp (1984).   (40.1)

4. DTp—TD 16/84, *'The geometric design of roundabouts'*, DTp (1984). [Sco.210]   (40.2)

5. DTp—TA 42/84, *'The geometric design of roundabouts'*, DTp (1984). [Sco.210]   (40.2)

6. DTp/TRRL—Report LR 942, *'The traffic capacity of roundabouts'*, DoE/DTp (1980).   (40.3)

7. DTp/TRRL—Report RR 35, *'ARCADY2: an enhanced program to model capacities, queues and delays at roundabouts'*, DTp (1986).   (40.3)

8. DTp—TA 44/85, *'Capacities, queues and delays at road junctions (ARCADY2 and PICADY2)'*, DTp (1985).   (40.3)

9. DTp—HECB/R/30, *'ARCADY2 User Manual'*, DTp (1986).   (40.3)

10. DTp/TRRL—Report LR 940. *'ARCADY: a computer program to model capacities, queues and delays at roundabouts'*, DoE/DTp (1980).   (40.3)

11. DTp/TRRL—Report SR810, *'Geometric delay at non-signalised intersections'*, DTp (1984).   (40.3)

12. Kimber, R M, Summersgill, I and Burrow, I J, *'Delay processes at unsignalised junctions; the interrelation between geometric and queueing delay'*, Transportation Research 208 (6) pp 457–476 (1986). (40.3)

40.7 Further Information

13. Layfield, R E and Maycock, G—*'Pedal Cyclists at Roundabouts'*, Traffic Engineering and Control, Vol 27 No 6 (1986).

14. IHT—*'Guidelines on providing for the cyclist'*, IHT (1983).

15. DTp/TRRL—Report SR 72F, *'The effect of zebra crossings on junction entry capacities'*, DoE/DTp (1982).

16. DTp—TD 9/81, *'Road layout and geometry: highway link design'*, DTp (1981) and Amendment No. 1 (1985). [Sco.211]

17. DTp/TRRL—Report SR 721, *'The capacity of some grade-separated roundabout entries'*, DoE/DTp (1981).

18. DTp/TRRL—Report LR 1010, *'Yellow bar experimental carriageway markings—accident study'*, DTp (1981).

19. DTp—Circular 8/78, *'Conversion of large conventional roundabouts to small and mini layouts'*, DTp (1978). [Wa.54]

41 Traffic Signal Control

41.1 Introduction

The use of traffic signals to control traffic movement can bring about major reductions in congestion, improve road safety and enable specific strategies which regulate the use of the road network to be introduced. Examples of such strategies might be:

● to reinforce the designated route hierarchy;

● to give priority to public transport;

● to provide crossing facilities for pedestrians and cyclists, or;

● to maximise traffic flow.

Traffic signals can be introduced at existing uncontrolled junctions, sometimes requiring the layout to be modified to provide traffic islands to channelise turning movements (see Colour Plate 41.1 which shows linked signal control in use on a gyratory system).

Traffic signalled junctions are usually more economical in their use of road space than roundabouts providing equivalent capacity and can allow more flexibility in layout and land take to avoid key areas (eg. historic buildings or public utility equipment).

With all of these advantages it is not surprising that traffic signals and urban traffic control systems (see Chapter 20) are widely and increasingly used in urban areas throughout the world.

41.2 Control Principles

Conflicts occuring between different traffic streams and categories of road user decrease the operational efficiency of junctions and increase the likelihood of accidents. Traffic signals can reduce such conflicts by separating movements in time and regulating their position on the road in a way which allows traffic performance to be maximised in safety.

However, at many sites in congested urban areas there will be little scope for major revisions to junction layout and designs will be restricted to existing highway boundaries. In these instances it may be impossible to achieve a reserve capacity and designs must be aimed at achieving an appropriate balance between provision for traffic movement and the needs of pedestrians, cyclists and public transport. The level of priority afforded to each of these aspects will be a matter for local judgement but on primary distributors traffic needs will often predominate.

41.3 Legislative Background and Design Standards

In Britain, traffic signals are provided under powers contained in the Road Traffic Regulation Act 1984 (Ref. 1) [NI.7] and they must comply with current directions issued by the Department of Transport which include:

● regulations covering the details of prescribed traffic signs (which include traffic signals), currently The Traffic Signs Regulations and General Directions 1981 (Ref. 2) [NI.34];

● standards issued by the British Standards Institute; and

● various specifications relating to traffic signal equipment issued by the Department of Transport (eg. Ref. 3) [Sco.212, Wa.55].

In addition, the Department of Transport issues Technical Standards, Advice Notes and Technical Specifications dealing with the operational aspects of signals and a list of these is provided in 41.14 below (Refs. 3-12) [Sco.213—Sco.220].

41.4 Assessing Site Suitability for Traffic Signal Control

There is no generally accepted rule or threshold level of traffic flows for justifying the installation of traffic signals at new or existing sites. Decisions are based on a number of factors considered together:

● the expected traffic speeds and levels of traffic and pedestrian flows;

● accident records (numbers and characteristics) and how they relate to local patterns;

● the feasibility of alternative types and layouts for the junction (ie. priority, roundabout, grade separated—see also Chapter 38);

● whether there is a need to introduce a control strategy which cannot be achieved by other means; and,

● whether the junction is within a UTC area and its proximity to other junctions (see also Chapter 20).

Advantages of Traffic Signal Control

These include:

● minimising the space required, particularly at constrained sites where physical restrictions could make other types of control costly and difficult to provide;

● the flexibility to assist specific approach arms or categories of road user and to respond to different traffic conditions;

● the ability to link and coordinate with other adjacent signalled junctions (see also Chapter 20 on Urban Traffic Control systems) to influence the pattern and speed of traffic progression;

● relatively low cost; capital costs are usually less than for normal roundabouts or grade separation.

Disadvantages of Traffic Signal Control

These include:

● increased delay and operating costs in uncongested conditions (eg. at off-peak times) when signals may impose more delay and operating costs on traffic than is necessary to resolve conflicts safely;

● some increased risk of certain types of traffic accident (eg. front to rear collision under braking);

● maintenance costs of signal equipment with the additional requirement to continuously monitor signal operations and to update signal settings under fixed time control; and

● no provision for U-turning manoeuvres.

41.5 Traffic Signal Equipment and Operation

A traffic signal installation at an individual location requires:

● a traffic signal controller (ie. the operating 'brain' of the installation);

● signal heads (lights), poles and any associated regulatory signs;

● vehicle detectors and associated cabling to the controller;

● pedestrian push buttons and ancillary equipment.

Detailed specifications for micro-processor controlled traffic signals are given in Department of Transport Specification MCE 0141 (1983) (Ref. 3).

The Traffic Signal Controller

Signal controllers manufactured until recently (many are still in use) used electronic timing to determine the length of the signal stages and electro-mechanical interlocking relays to switch the signals on and off in the required sequence without signal conflicts. With this type of controller the various time periods can be adjusted by signals from vehicle detectors, remote computers or nearby linked controllers, or varied

according to the time of day or traffic density. Controllers in current production contain microprocessors which use digital timing and solid state switching to perform similar tasks with greater reliability and flexibility.

Controllers are programmed to operate the various signal aspects in a number of ways. Modern controllers can function in the following ways:

● under vehicle actuation (ie. responding to direct demands);

● to pre-determined fixed timings;

● as a fully integrated part of an urban traffic control system (see also Chapter 20);

● to coordinate with a neighbouring junction or pelican crossing using cableless or hard wired linking;

● to respond to a 'hurry' call—where a priority demand is entered for a particular stage to ensure that a green signal is given promptly to certain vehicles (eg. fire service vehicles, or buses); or

● under manual control (for emergency use only).

The design of each controller requires that these facilities be allocated a specified order of priority with built-in constraints to govern a change of operation, the circumstances under which the method of operation is overridden and other safety features such as guaranteed minimum green times.

Whenever manual control is provided as an option, the controller should be sited so that all approaches to the junction are visible to the operator.

Signal Phases, Stages and Cycles

A traffic signal controller allocates right-of-way among the various movements at a junction by showing a green signal to different sets of movements so that conflicting ones do not receive a green signal simultaneously, with some exceptions for turning traffic.

The movements are divided into separate sets so that all the movements in each set always receive identical signal indications.

The word **phase** is used to describe a set of movements which can take place simultaneously or the sequence of signal indications received by such a set of movements. In each signal controller there is a normal sequence in which the various phases receive green and one repetition of this sequence is called a **cycle.**

A **stage** is that part of the cycle during which a particular set of phases receives green. These terms are illustrated in Figure 41.1.

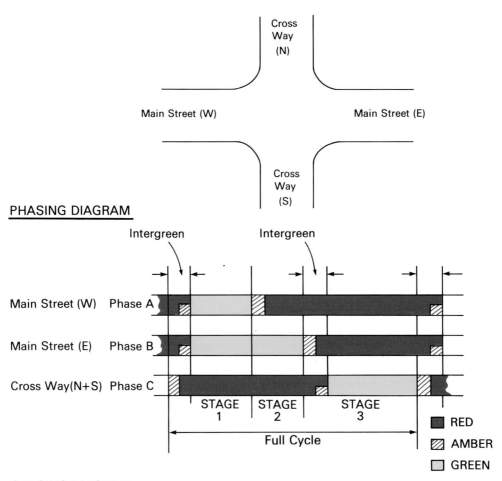

PHASING DIAGRAM

STAGING DIAGRAM

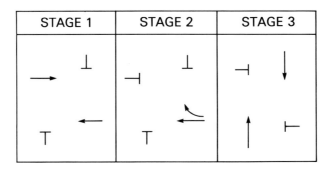

Phasing is denoted by letters, staging by numbers.

Figure 41.1 A typical phasing and staging diagram

Intergreen Period

The period between the end of the green for one phase and the start of the green for another phase gaining right of way at the same change of stage is known as the **intergreen** period between these phases. In the United Kingdom, this period includes an amber for one phase, which lasts three seconds and a red-and-amber period for the next phase, which lasts two seconds. These may overlap by up to one second, run consecutively, or be separated by an all-red period during which both phases receive red signals.

At more complicated changes of stage the intergreen periods between phases may not all coincide. If they do not, the period from the beginning of the first of them to the end of the last is called the **interstage** or intergreen period between the two stages. Because the next stage to which the signals are to change is determined in the controller at the beginning of the preceding intergreen between stages, this intergreen period may be regarded as part of the next stage.

Vehicle Actuation

Traffic signals working under vehicle actuation give green signals for time periods which are affected by traffic demands. Traffic demands are measured by vehicle detectors which are installed on the approaches to the signals. For each phase there will be a **minimum green period** which is the minimum amount of time required by any vehicles waiting between the nearest detectors and the stopline to pass through the junction.

For each phase showing a red signal the first vehicle to cross a detector on an approach in that phase will register a demand for a following stage in which that phase has a green signal. This demand will also initiate a preset **maximum green period** for each phase already displaying a green signal and for which such a period has not already begun.

If detectors on an approach already showing a green signal detect a vehicle moving towards it, the green signal may be extended by a preset **vehicle extension period** and this can be repeated until the maximum green period has been used up.

In the absence of demands for other stages, the stage which is running will continue indefinitely.

Vehicle Detectors

Vehicle detectors are used to:

● demand and/or extend the green period for a phase;

● extend an all-red period;

● demand and/or extend a green for a particular category of vehicle (eg. buses, see also Chapter 26);

● introduce a 'hurry' call; and,

● provide vehicle flow data for use in urban traffic control systems.

The old type of detector which used a **pneumatic tube** has now been superseded by detectors of the **inductive loop** type which are buried in the carriageway and the configuration of detector loops depends on the facilities that are required. Although not approved for use at junctions **microwave** detection may also be suitable in certain instances and is available for pelican pedestrian crossings and portable traffic signals. Vehicle detection can provide information on direction, flow rate, speed and type of vehicle.

Pedestrian Facilities

Pedestrian crossing facilities are often necessary at traffic signals in urban areas (see also Chapter 24) and can be actuated on demand using a push button.

Fixed Time Operation

Traffic signals can operate to a predetermined stage order and duration of green periods. This arrangement is known as fixed time operation and does not generally respond to changes in traffic demand. However, it is possible to incorporate demand-dependent stages, such as a pedestrian stage. An automatic timing device can

be used to implement different predetermined fixed time settings for the different traffic conditions expected at different times of the day. Each set of timings is known as a **signal plan** and the whole process as **multiplan** operation. Fixed time operation is now normally used only within UTC schemes in the United Kingdom (see Chapter 20).

Signal Aspects

Signal heads facing drivers have three signal aspects— red, amber and green. A green arrow may be fitted in place of the full green aspects and further green arrows can be added to assist traffic direction and control when used in conjunction with the appropriate regulatory signs and road markings. Some signs can only be used in conjunction with a Traffic Regulation Order (see the current Traffic Signs Regulations and General Directions).

Where signal heads are provided specifically for cyclists, green and amber cycle symbols on a black background should replace the full amber and green aspects subject to authorisation by the Department of Transport [Sco.212] (see Plate 41.2).

Plate 41.2 Traffic signals for cyclists

Source: TRRL

For pedestrians, each signal head has two aspects—a red and green man.

Signal heads are usually mounted on poles but can also be mounted on mast arms, gantries and catenary cables to provide better visibility at difficult sites and on high speed roads.

41.6 The Layout of Signal Controlled Junctions

Location of the Primary Signal

Arrangements for the layout of traffic signals at existing junctions are generally constrained by features such as buildings and highway boundaries as well as by the

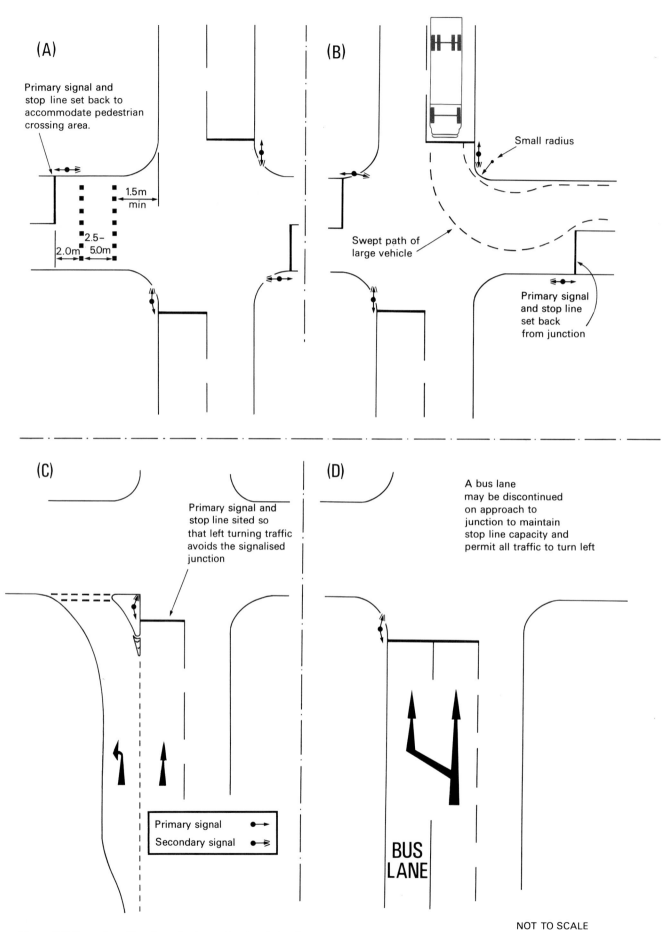

(A)

Primary signal and
stop line set back to
accommodate pedestrian
crossing area.

1.5m
min

2.5–
5.0m

2.0m

(B)

Small radius

Swept path of
large vehicle

Primary signal
and stop line
set back
from junction

(C)

Primary signal and
stop line sited so
that left turning traffic
avoids the signalised
junction

| Primary signal | ●→ |
| Secondary signal | ●⇒ |

(D)

A bus lane
may be discontinued
on approach to
junction to maintain
stop line capacity and
permit all traffic to turn left

BUS
LANE

NOT TO SCALE

Figure 41.2 Examples of location of primary signal and stop line

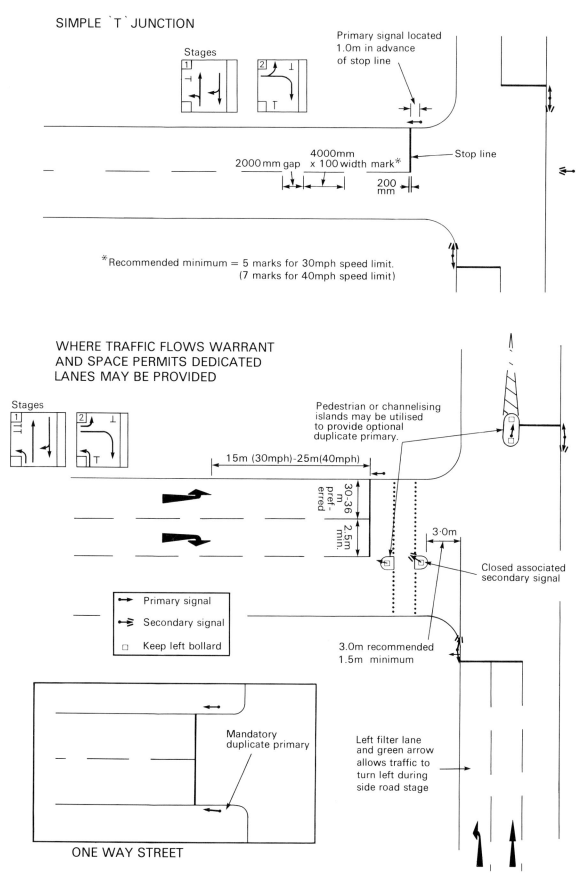

SIMPLE `T` JUNCTION

Stages

Primary signal located
1.0m in advance
of stop line

Stop line

4000mm
x 100 width mark*

2000mm gap

200
mm

*Recommended minimum = 5 marks for 30mph speed limit.
(7 marks for 40mph speed limit)

WHERE TRAFFIC FLOWS WARRANT
AND SPACE PERMITS DEDICATED
LANES MAY BE PROVIDED

Stages

Pedestrian or channelising
islands may be utilised
to provide optional
duplicate primary.

15m (30mph)-25m(40mph)

30-36 m preferred

2.5m min.

3.0m

Closed associated
secondary signal

→ Primary signal

→ Secondary signal

□ Keep left bollard

3.0m recommended
1.5m minimum

Mandatory
duplicate primary

Left filter lane
and green arrow
allows traffic to
turn left during
side road stage

ONE WAY STREET

Figure 41.3 Typical layouts at signal controlled junctions ('T' junctions)

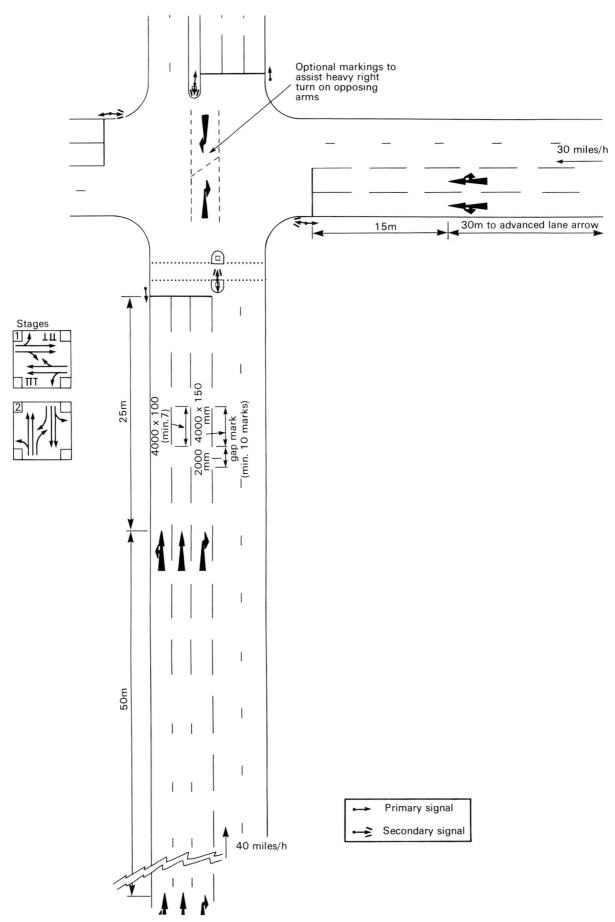

Figure 41.4 Typical layout at signal controlled junctions ('X' roads)

pattern of traffic movements. The aim should be to keep clearance times between conflicting streams as short as possible without adversely affecting safety.

There are some particular points that affect the location of the primary signal:

- the needs of pedestrians (Ref. 5) [Sco.214];

- clearance for turning paths of vehicles from other approaches;

- any unsignalled movements, such as left turns;

- bus stopping and bus lane requirements (see also Chapter 26); and,

- the needs of cyclists (see also Chapter 25).

Examples of various arrangements are shown in Figure 41.2 (a)–(d).

Duplicate Primary and Secondary Signals

There should be at least two signals visible from each approach, usually comprising one primary and one secondary signal. Duplicate primary signals may be required on the off-side of a wide approach or when visibility of the nearside primary signal is restricted and are recommended on all high speed approaches. On two way roads duplicate primary signals should always be placed on a central refuge and not on the offside of the carriageway. On one way roads, however, their placement on the offside of the road is mandatory.

Additional signals are normally sited beyond the junction and are known as **secondary** signals. They must always display the same information as the primary but may give additional information (such as a green arrow aspect) that does not conflict with that shown on the primary. In certain circumstances, it may be undesirable or impractical to position the secondary signal beyond the junction (see Figure 41.3 which shows a closely associated secondary signal) and this arrangement is sometimes used to prevent pedestrians relying on watching the traffic signals, rather than the traffic, when judging whether it is safe to cross the road.

Various devices such as hoods and slats can minimise the possibility of drivers and pedestrians seeing inappropriate signals; for example, where a pelican crossing is sited only a short distance away from a signalled junction. Secondary signals usually have deeper hoods so that they are only visible from the appropriate approach.

Some examples of layouts showing the location of traffic signals and their associated carriageway markings are shown in Figures 41.3 and 41.4. Further details on junction layout are provided in the relevant Department of Transport Advice Notes (Refs. 5, 6 and 7) [Sco.213, Sco.214].

The Stopline

The stopline is located on the approach to the primary signal and one or two metres from it.

41.7 Facilities for Pedestrians and Cyclists

Pedestrians may sometimes need an exclusive signal stage and these should be considered where:

- the pedestrian flow across any one arm is 300 pedestrians per hour or more; or,

- the turning traffic into any arm has an average headway of less than 5 seconds during its green time and is conflicting with a flow of more than 50 pedestrians per hour; or,

- there are special circumstances such as significant numbers of elderly, infirm or disabled pedestrians.

Pedestrian facilities may also be justified on safety grounds (see also Table 41.1, which lists various types of pedestrian facility and Ref. 5). However, an exclusive pedestrian phase may become counterproductive if, in order to provide adequate time for vehicles to clear and pedestrians to cross, the cycle time becomes so extended that pedestrians are tempted to seek earlier opportunities to cross. Some examples of alternative ways of locating pedestrian signals are shown in Figures 41.5 and 41.6, 41.7 and 41.8.

Information on how cyclists can be provided for at traffic signals is given in Chapter 25 (see also the IHT Guidelines—Ref. 13.)

41.8 Other Applications of Signal Control

WIG-WAG Signals

Flashing signals known as WIG-WAGs can be used to stop traffic at railway level crossings, swing bridges, sites near airfields and at fire and ambulance stations. They consist of two red aspects arranged horizontally and flashing alternately and a steady amber aspect placed centrally between the red lamps and displayed before the flashing red lights begin to operate. They remain switched off until control is required and may be activated automatically or manually.

Traffic Signals for Incident and Lane Control

On high capacity roads (eg. motorways) special lane control and other informatory signals can be used to stop traffic in the event of an incident and direct it to change lanes, reduce speed, warn of hazards or direct it to take the next exit from a motorway. These signals are sited either at the side of the road or as lane specific signals placed above the carriageway on gantries, the

Type of facility	Characteristics
No pedestrian signal	● Traffic signals,even without signals for pedestrians,can help pedestrians to cross by creating gaps in traffic streams. ● Especially applicable where there are refuges and on one-way streets.
Full pedestrian stage	● All traffic is stopped. ● Demanded from push buttons. ● More delay to vehicles than combined vehicle/pedestrian stages. ● See Figure 41.5.
Parallel pedestrian stage	● Combined vehicle/pedestrian stage often accompanied by banned vehicle movements. ● Useful across one-way streets. ● See Figure 41.6.
Staggered pedestrian facility	● Pedestrians cross one half of the carriageway at a time. ● Large storage area in the centre of the carriageway required. ● Stagger preferably to face on-coming traffic. ● See Figure 41.7.
Displaced pedestrian facility	● For junctions close to capacity. ● The crossing point is situated away from the junction but within 50m. ● Normal staging arrangements as above apply. ● See Figure 41.8.

Table 41.1 Types of pedestrian facility at signal controlled junctions

latter arrangement being common for tidal flow schemes.

Portable Traffic Signals

At roadworks, portable signals are often necessary to control traffic. Usually this is to implement a one-way system or a single lane past the obstruction. Further information on the use of traffic signals at roadworks is given in Refs. 11 and 12 [Sco.216].

41.9 Traffic Signal Design

The aim in designing a traffic signal installation, is usually to maximise the traffic capacity (the throughput of vehicles, vehicle occupants and pedestrians) whilst reducing vehicular delay and waiting time for pedestrians and maintaining a high degree of safety and a balance between the requirements of traffic in different streams. Queue management techniques may sometimes be necessary to store excess traffic demands at appropriate locations where the required level of capacity cannot be achieved. The following steps should be used as guidelines when designing a signal-controlled junction:

Traffic Flows

It is necessary to determine the traffic flows for all proposed operating conditions, particularly during the four busiest hours. For existing junctions these data should come from up-to-date classified turning counts and may be in the form of vehicles or passenger car units per hour (Refs. 14–17). For proposed junctions, an estimate will be required and appropriate traffic estimation and assignment techniques should be applied (see Chapter 11). As flow data are normally in the form of an average value (eg. averaged over the peak hour), fluctuations of vehicle flow rates within the time period being considered should be taken into account. The peak fifteen minutes is sometimes used at critical junctions.

Lane Allocation

The layout of the junction should reflect traffic volumes and patterns as well as pedestrian needs. Traffic lanes should ideally be allocated for each of the vehicular movements allowed but lane sharing will often be necessary at restricted sites.

An **approach** is one or more lanes where traffic can be regarded as forming a single queue. A traffic **stream** comprises traffic on an approach, all of whch usually receives right-of-way for the same period. Each approach should, as far as is practicable, be capable of carrying the maximum predicted flow for that approach.

Saturation Flows

The saturation flows need to be determined for each stream. The **saturation flow** is the maximum flow rate that can be sustained by traffic from a queue on the approach used by the stream and depends mainly on:

● the number and width of lanes available to that stream and the effects of parked vehicles and bus stops etc. on lane width;

● the proportion of turning traffic and radius of turn; and

● the gradient of the approach.

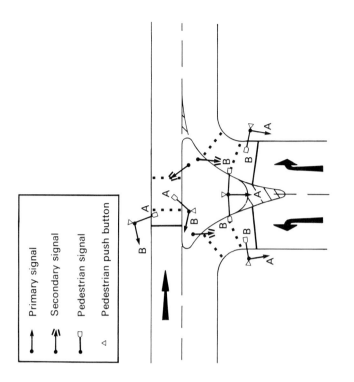

Additional push buttons may
be required on centre refuges

Primary signal

Secondary signal

Pedestrian signal

Pedestrian push button

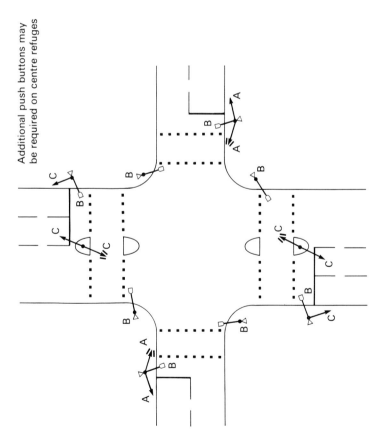

STAGES

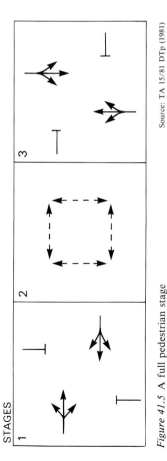

Source: TA 15/81 DTp (1981)

Figure 41.5 A full pedestrian stage

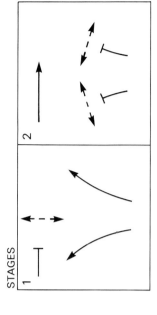

STAGES

Source: TA 15/81 DTp (1981)

Figure 41.6 A parallel pedestrian stage
(one-way street arrangement)

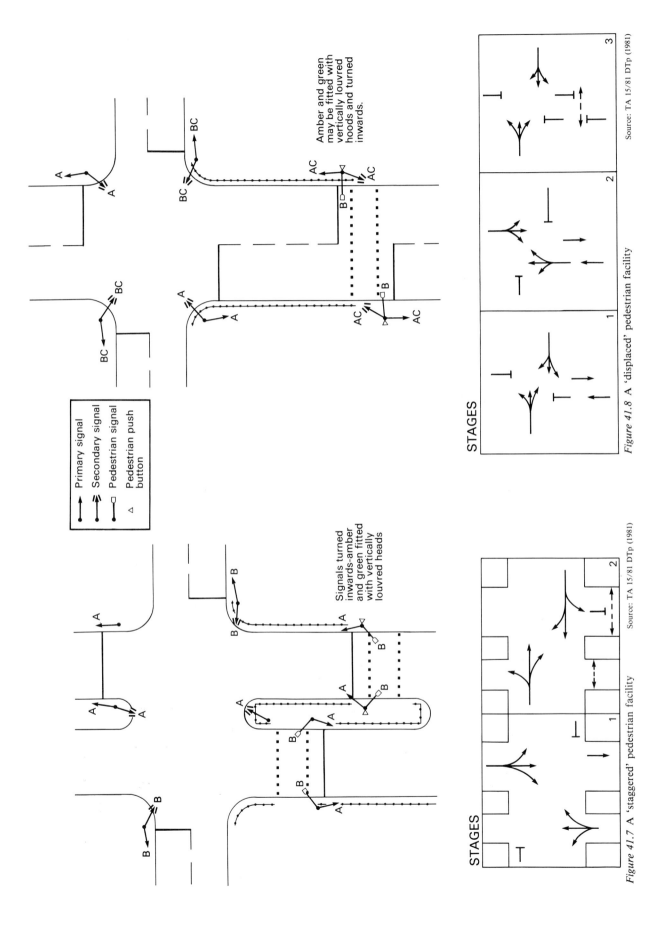

Primary signal
Secondary signal
Pedestrian signal
Pedestrian push button

Signals turned inwards-amber and green fitted with vertically louvred heads

Amber and green may be fitted with vertically louvred hoods and turned inwards.

STAGES

Figure 41.8 A 'displaced' pedestrian facility

Source: TA 15/81 DTp (1981)

STAGES

Figure 41.7 A 'staggered' pedestrian facility

Source: TA 15/81 DTp (1981)

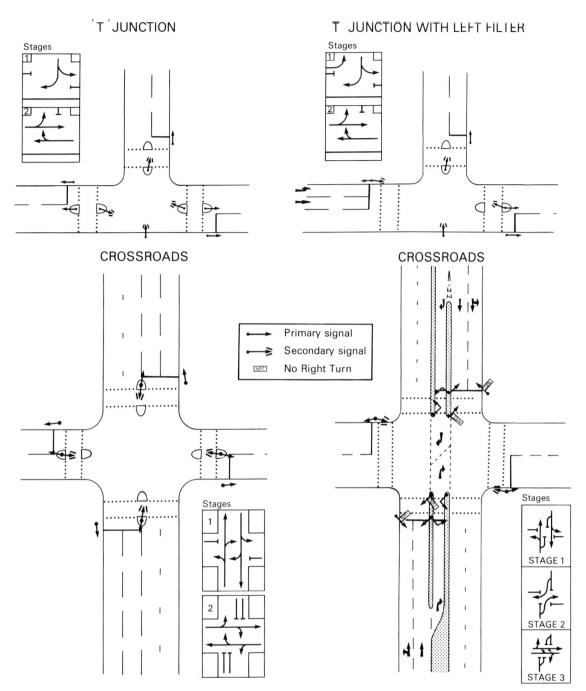

Figure 41.9 Diagrammatic layout of different staging conditions

Source: TA 18/81 DTp (1981)

Traffic composition also affects saturation flows but is taken into account by calculating flows in passenger car units (PCUs) rather than in numbers of vehicles (ie. each vehicle is given an equivalent PCU value).

A stream may have more than one saturation flow value where different movements discharge from it under different signal conditions in the cycle.

For existing junctions direct observation is always the best method for determining saturation flow (Refs. 14 and 15). However, in many cases saturation flow has to be estimated from relationships based on geometric and other characteristics of the site (Ref. 16).

Stage Order

The sets of streams which should run together must be determined together with the order in which those sets receive green signals. For a particular junction, there will usually be several options for controlling traffic.

Signal **phasing** requires cable connections to signal heads and must be decided before installation. Signal **staging**, however, is related to the switching of the wired phases and can therefore be more easily altered within the controller after installation provided that the required options have been allowed for.

Conceptually, every vehicle and pedestrian movement can be allocated its own particular phase. An examination of these potential phases will indicate which streams should receive green together and which should not. Thus, an optimum number of stages and the order in which they run can be chosen having regard to safety and the maximum green time for the phases that need it most. Some examples of options are given in Figures 41.9 and 41.10.

Where sufficient space exists (as for example in Fig. 41.9), consideration should also be given to the introduction of additional signal stop lines between the component elements of an overall junction. The localised system of signals thus created can enable the capacity of the overall junction to be enhanced, often at reduced cycle-times. This can be achieved by the effective reduction in lost time which can be afforded by the additional stop lines (see Refs. 18 and 19). Such systems of junctions can sometimes lend themselves to control by separate streams of stages for each component signal, rather than utilising a single serial stage stream for the junction as a whole.

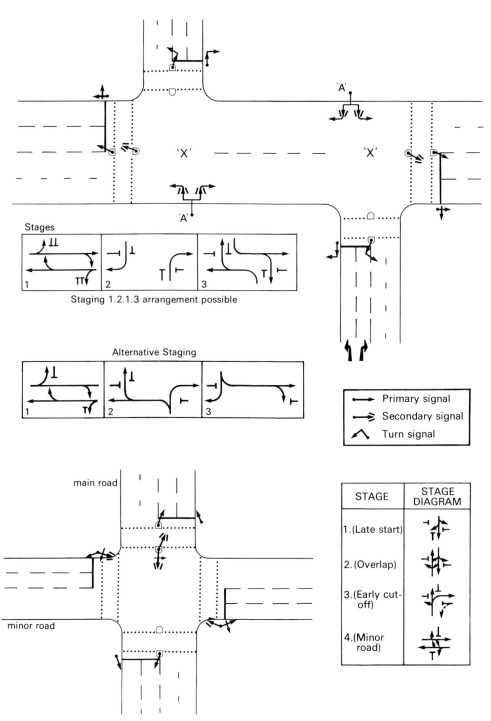

Figure 41.10 Diagrammatic layout of different staging conditions

Source: TA 18/81 DTp (1981)

Signal Timings

Signal timings for installations under isolated control can be calculated using the techniques for manual calculations described in RRL Technical Paper 56 (Ref. 17). Alternatively, computer programs are available to perform these calculations (see 41.12 below). The design of UTC systems is referred to in Chapter 20.

A suggested procedure is as follows:

● determine the intergreen times which will provide safe clearance times between conflicting streams;

● determine the lost time (see below) for each traffic stream; and

● calculate the cycle time and the duration of the green periods in each phase and thus the duration of each stage, usually to optimise some aspect of traffic performance as discussed below.

(NB. The formulae to calculate cycle time and green times are contained in TP56.)

In these calculations, the combined green and amber period for a stream is treated as **effective green time** and **lost time**. The 'lost time' is sometimes known as the starting and stopping losses for each stream. Thus:

effective green time = green + amber − lost time

This is illustrated in Figure 41.11 from which it can be seen that, in this example, traffic experiences a 1 second starting delay but runs on through the amber period. However, lost time may also occur at the end of the green + amber period where the flow ceases more rapidly. The lost time for a stream is best determined from observation but if this is not possible then a value of 2 seconds can be assumed. In calculating the cycle time and the duration of green periods, the total lost time for a junction should be determined from the intergreen times between critical phases and the starting and stopping losses for the traffic streams.

Such calculations are often performed as part of an iterative process of junction design in which the results for a particular proposal are assessed using a measure of traffic performance (see 41.11 below) and recalculations are then carried out using modified junction layouts or stage order.

41.10 Design Techniques

There are usually a number of ways in which traffic movements can be arranged to take advantage of site layout or particular traffic demands. The following features should be considered:

● **accepting a conflicting move** such as a certain amount of right turning traffic opposed by oncoming traffic where the degree of conflict is acceptable and movements can be performed safely;

● **restricting movements** such as banning right turns or creating one-way streets away from the junction. Care must be taken to ensure that such measures do not create other problems elsewhere;

● allowing right turners unopposed right-of-way by giving an **early cut-off** to opposing traffic. This is sometimes proposed as a means of reducing right turning accidents but its effect on pedestrians should

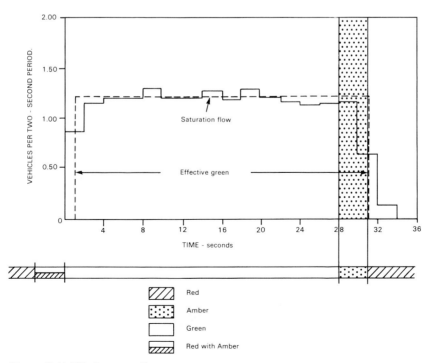

Figure 41.11 Effective green time

365

also be considered. An alternative is to give a **late start** to opposing traffic and these methods are illustrated in Fig. 41.10;

- choosing signal stages which provide **unopposed right turns** to improve lane occupancy and give a definite indication for priority movements;

- allowing **simultaneous non-hooking right turns**;

- **separating left turn movements** with an exit lane controlled only by a 'give way' priority;

- providing **two separate green periods** in a cycle (repeated greens) for important movements;

- **flaring approaches or increasing the number of entry lanes** by making each lane narrower as long as minimum lane widths are provided. Both measures increase the number of vehicles that can wait at the stop line;

- **providing extra lanes for turning traffic** and relating signal timings to their length;

- **combining the green period for vehicles and pedestrians** where this can be achieved safely;

- considering **different stage sequences for different times of the day**;

- **linking to adjacent signals** and pelicans; and,

- **linking within an urban traffic control system** (see Chapter 19).

See also Ref. 6 on the general principles of control by traffic signals.

41.11 Measures of Performance and Signal Timings

Signal-controlled junctions can be assessed and compared by examining various measures of traffic performance including safety (which is discussed in Chapter 18).

Degree of Saturation

The ratios of arrival rate to capacity for the various traffic streams is important in the assessment of traffic flow performance. For a signal-controlled stream, this ratio is known as the **degree of saturation** and can be expressed as:

$$x = \frac{qc}{gs}$$

where q = average arrival rate
     s = saturation flow in the same units as q
     c = cycle time
and g = effective green time in the same units as c

This expression shows how the degree of saturation for a stream depends on the signal timings.

Capacity

For any one signal-controlled stream, the traffic capacity of the approach is **sg/c** but in practice it is desirable for the degree of saturation to remain appreciably less than unity. A largest acceptable value may therefore be specified, typically this is taken as 0.9. With this upper limit, the practical capacity of the approach can be regarded as **psg/c**, where p is the largest acceptable value.

For all approaches at the junction to be operating within their practical capacity, the signal timings must be chosen so that q is less than psg/c for every approach. With any such timings, the amount by which q could be increased without exceeding the practical capacity of the approach is called the **reserve capacity** of the approach.

If q exceeds psg/c, the amount by which it does so is called the **overload** on the approach. The amounts of reserve capacity and overload on different approaches can be influenced by adjusting the signal timings, for example, to equalise the percentage reserve capacity or percentage overload on the most heavily loaded approaches. If this is done, there will usually be more spare capacity (or at least less overload) on some other approaches (ie. on non-critical approaches).

One way of deciding what value of p to specify for design purposes is to decide on the level of delay that should be exceeded with only a given probability (eg. once every 10 cycles).

Vehicular Delay

A commonly used method of assessing performance is to estimate the amount of vehicular delay incurred by traffic. For streams which have a reserve capacity on the approach, equilibrium values of delay can be estimated using, for example, 'Webster's formula' (Ref. 16). For streams on overloaded approaches it is necessary to know how the arrival rate varies over time in order to apply a sheared delay formula (Ref. 17).

Two measures of vehicular delay often used are **average delay** per vehicle and **rate of delay** per unit time (ie. the rate at which delay is incurred per unit time).

The average delay per vehicle is the difference between the average journey time through the junction and the average journey time that would apply if the vehicle were not impeded by the signals.

The rate of delay is normally expressed as the difference between the average number of vehicles within the zone of influence of the junction at a typical instant and the number that would be there if the same flow of traffic were unimpeded by the signals.

Either measure can be applied to an individual stream but only the rate of delay is additive over streams to give a measure of performance for the junction as a whole.

Passenger Delay

The concept of passenger delay could be used as an alternative measure of performance in urban areas where vehicle occupancy can vary significantly, particularly on heavily patronised public transport routes. Where this is done, estimates should also be made of pedestrian delays (suitably weighted) due to the signal control.

Signal Timings

When a junction is overloaded, the timings that equalise and minimise the percentage overload on the most heavily loaded approaches will often provide suitable maxima for vehicle-actuated operation. When a junction has reserve capacity, timings can be calculated which would minimize the estimated rate of delay for the whole junction if it operated on fixed-timings. The resulting green times provide suitable maxima for vehicle-actuated operation.

In either case, practical constraints on green times and cycle times should be respected and, in the overload case, it may be necessary to have regard to the lengths attained by queues in different streams, especially if there are other junctions nearby which may become blocked by excessive queues. In these circumstances green times should be adjusted to limit queueing on the critical approaches.

41.12 Computer Programs

The process of calculating timings to minimise vehicular delay or percentage overload for given traffic flows at isolated junctions can be carried out at least approximately by hand in simple cases. However, computer programs like SIGCAP (Ref. 22) SIGSET, (Ref. 21) and LINSIG (Ref. 23) are available and can deal equally well with more complicated junctions and provide better approximations for timings to minimise delay than do manual methods. Such programs also provide other useful design information. A more comprehensive TRRL program called OSCADY, models the operation of a signal-controlled junction as demand varies over the day (Ref. 24). The TRANSYT program can also be used to model a single junction and to optimise its timings (although it is primarily designed to optimise signal networks). The use of computer programs in the design of UTC systems is dealt with in Chapter 20.

41.13 Other Design Considerations

As with priority junctions and roundabouts, the methods of calculation referred to in 41.12 above can be used to estimate how capacity, queue-lengths and delay would be affected by:

● changes in layout and sequence of stages in the cycle;

● changes in the amount of traffic in particular streams; and,

● general increases in traffic over the years which is likely to affect traffic in all streams.

It must also be borne in mind that traffic conditions vary continuously and the appraisal of alternative designs should include the scope which exists to adjust signal timings to suit varying needs and the overall performance achieved for a variety of circumstances.

41.14 References

Text Reference

1. Road Traffic Regulation Act 1984, HMSO (1984). (41.3)

2. Traffic Signs Regulations and General Directions, Statutory Instrument 1981 No 859 as amended, HMSO (1981). (41.3)

3. DTp—MCE 0141, *'Microprocessor-based traffic signal controller for isolated linked and urban traffic control installations'*, DTp (1983). (41.3)

4. DTp—Circular Roads 5/73, *'Criteria for traffic signals at junctions'*, DTp (1973). [Sco.213, Wa.56] (41.3)

5. DTp—TA 15/81, *'Pedestrian facilities at traffic signal installations'*, DTp (1981). [Sco.214] (41.3, 41.6)

6. DTp—TA 16/81. *'General principles of control by traffic signals'*, DTp (1981). (41.3, 41.6, 41.10)

7. DTp—TA 18/81, *'Junction layout for control by traffic signals'*, DTp (1981). (41.3, 41.6)

8. DTp—TA 14/81, *'Procedures for the installation of traffic signals and associated control equipment'*, DTp (1981). (41.3)

9. DTp—TA 13/81, *'Requirements for the installation of traffic signals and associated control equipment'*, DTp (1981). (41.3)

10. DTp—TA 12/81, *'Traffic signals on high speed roads'*, DTp (1981). [Sco.215] (41.3, 41.8)

11. DTp—TD 21/85, *'Portable traffic signals at roadworks on single carriageway roads'*, DTp (1985). (41.3, 41.8)

12. DTp—Circular Roads 49/75, '*Portable traffic signals for use at roadworks*', DTp (1975). [Sco.216, Wa.57]   (41.3, 41.8)

13. IHT—'*Guidelines on providing for the cyclist*', Institution of Highways and Transportation (1983).   (41.7)

14. MoT/RRL—Road Note 34, '*A method for measuring saturation flow at traffic signals*', MoT (1963).   (41.9)

15. Wood, K—'*Measuring saturation flows at traffic signals using a hand held microcomputer*', Traffic Engineering and Control, Vol 27 No 4, (April 1986).   (41.9)

16. DTp/TRRL—Research Report No 67, '*The prediction of saturation flows for road junctions controlled by traffic signals*', DTp (1986).   (41.9, 41.11)

17. MoT/RRL—Technical Paper 56, '*Traffic Signals*', MoT (1966).   (41.9, 41.11)

18. Hallworth, M S—'*High capacity signal design*', Traffic Engineering and Control, Vol 21, No 2 (Feb. 1980).   (41.9)

19. Hallworth, M S—'*The Sheepscar signal system; an alternative approach to major intersection design*', Traffic Engineering and Control, Vol 24 No 8 (Aug. 1983).   (41.9)

20. DoE/DTp/TRRL—Report LR 909, '*Traffic queues and delays at road junctions*', DTp (1979).   (41.11)

21. Allsop, R E—'*SIGSET: a computer program for calculating traffic signal settings*', Traffic Engineering and Control, Vol 13 No 2 (1971).   (41.12)

22. Allsop, R E—'*SIGCAP: a computer program for assessing the traffic capacity of signal-controlled road junctions*', Traffic Engineering and Control, Vol 17 No's 8/9, (1976).   (41.12)

23. Simmonite, B F—'*LINSIG: A program to assist traffic signal design and assessment*', Traffic Engineering and Control, Vol 26 No 6 (June 1985).   (41.12)

24. Burrow, I J and Willoughby, P J, '*OSCADY: a computer program to aid the design of isolated signal junctions*', PTRC Summer School. Seminar N, PTRC (1985).   (41.12)

41.15 Further Information

25. DTp/TRRL—Report LR 1063, '*Traffic signalled junctions: a track appraisal of conventional and novel designs*', DTp (1982). [Sco.217–Sco.221]

42 Grade Separated Junctions

42.1 Basic Principles

The complexity and conflict between traffic movements at the intersection of two or more major roads (usually primary distributors) can be reduced by providing for traffic on several different levels. This 'grade separation' of traffic allows the heaviest traffic flows to pass unhindered through the intersection whilst the lighter flows, including all the turning movements, are dealt with on separate levels above or below (or both). In general, unless site conditions preclude it, the heaviest flows should be routed through at the lowest level for the most economic and least environmentally intrusive design (see 42.3 below).

Low cost grade separation may be justified economically at design flows of about 20,000 AADF (see Ref. 1). Grade separation by means of overbridges for light vehicles only may be considered as a low cost facility but it is suggested that substandard underpasses (which usually have only 2.5 m headroom—quite common in France) be used only where there are substantial environmental grounds.

The main through road(s) should maintain the same design characteristics as the links which they connect. The slip-roads, acting either as entry ramps or exit ramps, should be designed for slower speed turning traffic entering or leaving the main stream. Where these slip-roads exceed 0.75 km in length, they should be designed to the higher standards of link roads.

Where there are major physical constraints, it may be possible to adopt lower design standards if traffic is compliant with the use of appropriate speed limits and

Plate 42.1 An example of grade separation at a physically constrained site

Source: Telford Development Corporation

Notes: The 'Greyhound' Interchange at Telford is an example of how the component parts of the standard forms of junction can be adapted and amalgamated to permit a satisfactory layout to be provided at a constrained location.
The junction provides a connection between the primary distributor road and the original A5 Trunk Road and was built in two stages. Initially, the primary road in the foreground converged on to a two-way slip road and terminated at the roundabout. Later, the remainder of the layout was constructed, including the remaining slip roads and loops to provide full grade separation. The large factory complex was originally to be demolished to make way for the junction but to avoid sacrificing the jobs that would have been lost, it was retained. The slip roads and loops were therefore redesigned on the other side of the A5 on a confined site in very close proximity to the railway and tunnel portal in the foreground.
The primary distributor road was generally designed to urban motorway standards, with a design speed of 80 kph. The curves at this point on the through alignment are of 540 metres radius, and the slip loops have a gradient of twelve per cent.

warning signs. Plate 42.1 shows an example of grade separation in which a major physical constraint was imposed by the wish to preserve a commercial complex.

Minor flows and turning movements will usually be handled by one or more at-grade junctions, using priority, traffic signal or roundabout arrangements. The design for these should be the same as for the corresponding single level intersection (see 42.4 below).

In the more elaborate arrangements, slip-roads provide direct connections for each turning movement separately but in doing so three or four different levels may be required for the interchange. This type of arrangement is sometimes known as a 'braided' interchange.

42.2 Justification

Except where the topography is favourable, grade separation usually involves a high capital cost and great care should be exercised during the planning stages to ensure that it can be justified as a solution. Where the level of future traffic flows is uncertain there may be a case for staged construction. Alternatively, it may be possible to induce some of the traffic flow away from the junction and avoid the need for grade separation altogether.

Nevertheless, by removing one or more of the potential conflicts to traffic movement, grade separation can increase junction capacity substantially and can also reduce delays and operating costs and enhance road safety.

Disbenefits arise from the significantly greater costs of construction for earthworks and structures and the environmental consequences of increased land-take and visual impact, which can be substantial in built-up areas. In addition, the slip and link roads associated with grade separated junctions could be hazardous to cyclists who may require separate facilities or re-routeing.

For these reasons major grade separation is unlikely to be justified in urban areas unless:

● traffic flows through the junction are such that an appropriate sized roundabout or signal controlled junction would not operate satisfactorily (ie. substantially greater than 30,000 AADF); or

● a significant proportion of the major road traffic is non-local through traffic (eg. where one of the roads is an urban motorway); or

● all other junctions on this and similar category roads in the area are grade separated so that consistency needs to be maintained; or

● the site conditions preclude a roundabout of sufficient size.

At least one of the roads entering a grade separated junction is likely to be a high standard dual carriageway and at junctions between two primary distributor roads consideration may need to be given to providing a three-level roundabout or even a fully-braided interchange. Low standard grade separation may be considered for all purpose roads where economic justification may be made at design flows of about 20,000 AADF. Signing and road markings must reflect the lower standard of junction. A comparative example is given in Figure 1 of DTp Technical Advice Note TA 48/86 (Ref. 1), reproduced here as Figure 42.1.

42.3 Alternative Layouts

The various layouts for grade separated interchanges are listed below to form a hierarchy for increasing levels of traffic flow:

● a diamond and half cloverleaf with either priority or signal-control of minor road flows;

● a dumb-bell roundabout;

● a two-bridge roundabout;

● a three-level roundabout; and,

● a fully-braided interchange (also known as a free-flow interchange).

Figure 42.2 gives details of the different layouts but 3-level roundabouts and fully braided interchanges are seldom likely to be justified in urban areas. The design of each at-grade junction within a grade separated junction should accord with the advice given in Chapters 38 to 40.

The type of grade separation which is most appropriate for any particular junction will depend on the amount and shape of the land which is available and the expected future volumes and relative proportions of turning traffic. In urban areas, the existing road network is usually predetermined and the designs will aim for economic optimisation.

Ideally, the lowest physical level of a multi-level intersection should be used by the heaviest through traffic flow. This should, therefore, pass under the minor flow so that:

● with the heaviest traffic flow in cutting, the visual impact, the effect of noise on the local community, the disruption to local vehicle and pedestrian routes and the severance effects are all minimised;

● high speed traffic leaving the major road is slowed naturally by the up-grade of the exit slip roads or ramps;

● the acceleration of traffic joining the major road is assisted by the down grade of the entry slip roads or ramps; and,

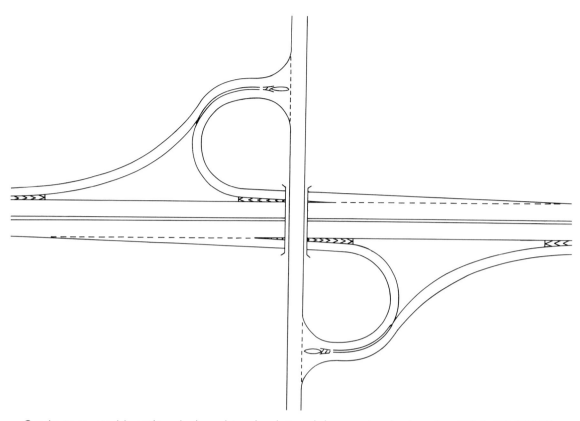

Grade separated junction designed to absolute minimum standards using DTp's TD 22/86

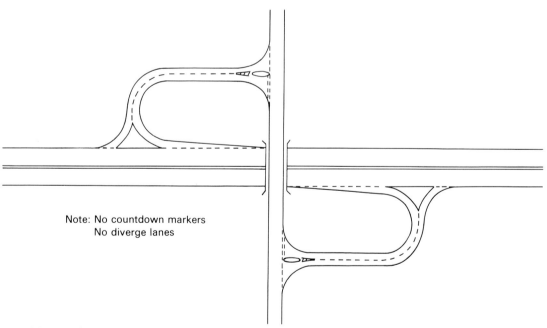

Note: No countdown markers
No diverge lanes

Major/minor junction incorporating a grade separated facility using DTp's TD 20/84

[NB. This type of layout provides a lower standard facility and would not be suitable on some roads]

Figure 42.1 A comparative example of grade separated layouts using different design standards and Road Markings

Source: TA 48/86 DTp (1986)

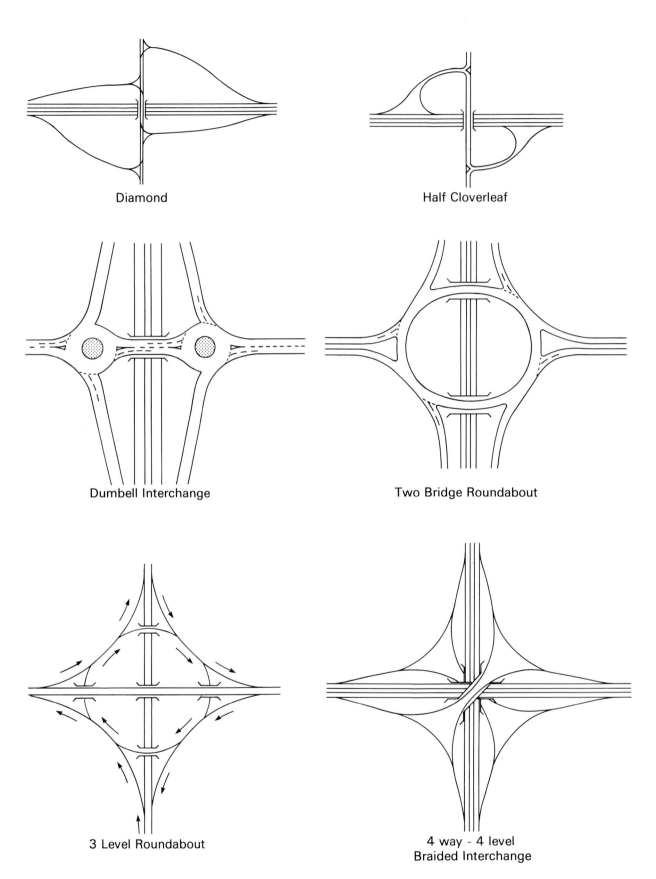

Diamond

Half Cloverleaf

Dumbell Interchange

Two Bridge Roundabout

3 Level Roundabout

4 way - 4 level
Braided Interchange

Figure 42.2 Different layouts for grade separated junctions

Source: TA 48/86 DTp (1986)

• the bridge structures will normally be less elaborate and less costly.

There are disadvantages when constructing roads below ground level which include drainage problems and disruption to services. However, such construction may still be justified when economic optimisation is examined.

Special consideration should be given to the design and siting of informatory road signs and carriageway markings to assist road traffic and pedestrians through grade separated junctions.

Diamond (with or without signal-control)

One of the simplest forms of grade separation is the 'diamond', which requires less space than most other grade separated layouts and the construction of only one bridge. The major road may pass over the minor road, depending on local topography, but preferably underneath it and turning movements take place where the slip roads join the minor road. Plate 42.2 illustrates the preferred arrangement. The at-grade junctions may be of the priority, roundabout (ie. a dumb-bell) or traffic signal type.

The capacity of the slip road/minor road junctions should be sufficient to ensure that queueing vehicles do not tail back onto the main through carriageway. If demand for certain turning movements is low, one or more slip roads may be omitted providing that a convenient alternative route is available.

Half Cloverleaf

This type of layout might be convenient when land is not available in all quadrants. The junction is not as compact as a diamond junction and the loops which form two of the slip roads may have a reduced capacity and an inferior safety record where limiting radii are used (see Chapter 37).

Dumb-bell Roundabout

This is basically a diamond type grade separated junction with roundabouts where the slip roads meet the minor road. If the flow on the minor road is nearing junction capacity, it may be necessary to incorporate traffic signal control at the slip road/minor road junctions as this should reduce the risk of queues forming in the slip roads and conflicting with the through movement of traffic on the major road. A check is advisable to ensure that queues from each roundabout do not extend on the minor road to interfere with the other roundabout.

Plate 42.2 A 'diamond' interchange between a primary and a district distributor

Source: British Road Federation

373

Two-bridge Roundabout

Two-bridge roundabouts are similar in layout to a normal roundabout but generally require slightly more land area and the construction of two bridges. In addition, the long detours which can occur around large roundabouts can result in reduced performance in terms of vehicle operating costs and safety as vehicle speeds tend to build up on the longer arms of roundabouts. This type of layout can be particularly useful when more than two roads intersect.

Three-level Roundabout

A three-level roundabout might be considered where two major roads intersect. The roundabout would normally be sited at ground level with one major road above and the other major road below the level of the roundabout. Through traffic on both major roads would be uninterrupted while turning movements would be achieved using slip roads and the roundabout.

Fully-braided Interchange

A fully-braided interchange provides uninterrupted movement for vehicles moving from one main road to another by the use of link roads with a succession of diverging and merging manoeuvres. They are usually only considered for roads forming part of the national (trunk) road network (see Plate 38.4). Good design should aim to reduce traffic conflict to a minimum, paying particular attention to merging arrangements, and ensuring that the paths between routes are easily understood by drivers. Effective direction signing and road marking will be required.

42.4 Geometric Design

The design of a grade separated junction can be divided into the following elements:

● the single level junctions with a minor road;

● the link and slip roads; and,

● the speed-change lanes that link a grade separated junction with a major road.

Advice on the design of single level junctions can be found in Chapters 38 to 41 while speed-change lanes are discussed in 42.5 below. The design of link and slip roads should follow the recommendations made in Chapter 37. The social and capital costs associated with the construction of an urban grade separated junction may constrain the choice of design speed requiring speed limits to be applied. An absolute minimum design speed of 50 kph is envisaged for slip roads and a value greater than 50 kph for a link road where it can be economically justified within a fully braided interchange.

Where loops form part of the grade separated junction, it may be necessary to introduce advisory speed limits to warn the driver of the safe negotiating speed. The minimum loop radius within an urban motorway junction should be 75 m but for all-purpose roads this minimum radius may be reduced to 50 m for vehicles leaving major roads and 30 m for vehicles joining major roads.

The gradients of link and slip roads should be limited to 6% but this may be increased to 8% where low turning traffic volumes are anticipated.

42.5 Merging, Diverging and Weaving

The detailed geometric layout for the merging, diverging and weaving sections of a grade separated interchange will depend on the maximum hourly flow level that can be achieved per lane. Typical hourly flow values are given in Table 42.1 for use in their design.

	Maximum hourly flow (Veh/h/lane)	
Road class	Main road, two lane links & slip roads (⩾6m wide).	Signal lane links & slip roads (⩽5m wide).
All purpose	1600	1200
Motorway	1800	1350

Table 42.1 Hourly flows for use in merging, diverging and weaving designs

The geometric parameters applicable to merging and diverging lanes are shown in Tables 42.2 and 42.3 respectively while Figures 42.3 and 42.4 illustrate their use in typical layouts.

Spacing between Merging and Diverging Sections

The minimum spacing between the noses of successive merging and diverging sections within a junction should be 3.75 V metres (where V is the design speed in kph of the major road) subject to the minimum distance necessary for effective signing, which may be greater.

The following procedure should be adopted when designing merging and diverging lanes:

● select the 30th highest combination of predicted hourly flows expected in the 15th year of operation;

● adjust the predicted hourly flows to allow for the effects of gradient and the proportion of heavy goods vehicles in the traffic stream. Appropriate correction factors can be found in Table 42.4 which should then be used to gross-up each of the predicted hourly flows. The main road gradient should be measured over 1 km (0.5 km from either side of the merge nose) and the average gradient determined;

Class of urban road	Single lane entry taper (1)	Two lane entry taper (2)	Minimum nose taper (3)	Nose length (4) (m)	Min. parallel lane length (5) (m)	Parallel lane taper (6)
60 miles/h speed limit 50 miles/h speed limit or less	1 : 25 1 : 20	1 : 20 1 : 15	1 : 15 1 : 12	50 40	125 100	1 : 10 1 : 10

Note: The numbers in brackets refer to Figure 42. 3

Table 42.2 Geometric parameters for merging lanes

Class of urban road	Single lane entry taper (1)	Two lane entry taper (2)	Minimum nose taper (3)	Nose length (4) (m)	Min. parallel lane length (5) (m)	Parallel lane taper (6)
60 miles/h speed limit 50 miles/h speed limit or less	1 : 25 1 : 20	1 : 15 1 : 12	1 : 15 1 : 12	50 40	125 100	1 : 10 1 : 10

Note: The numbers in brackets refer to Figure 42. 4

Table 42.3 Geometric parameters for diverging lanes

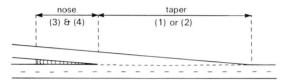

A. Normal merge

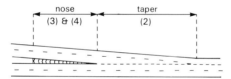

B. Main line lane addition at normal merge

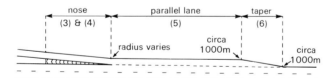

C. Parallel lane merge

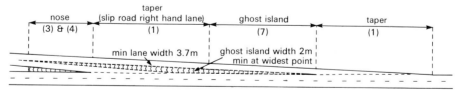

D. Ghost island merge

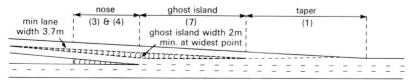

E. Main line addition at ghost island merge

NB: Figures in brackets refer to columns in table 42.2

Figure 42.3 Merging lane layouts for use with Table 42.2

Source: TD 22/86 DTp (1986)

375

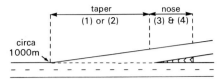

A. Normal diverge

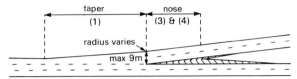

B. Main line lane drop at normal diverge

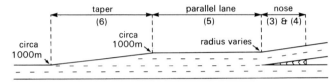

C. Parallel lane diverge

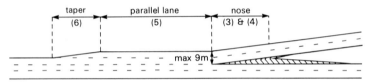

D. Main line lane drop at parallel lane diverge

NB: Figures in brackets refer to columns in table 42.3

Figure 42.4 Diverging lane layouts for use with table 42.3

Source: TD 22/86 DTp (1986)

Proportion of HGVs (%)	Main Road Gradient	
	⩽ 2%	> 2%
5	—	1.10
10	—	1.15
15	—	1.20
20	1.05	1.25

Table 42.4: Correction factors to allow for gradient

- using the corrected predicted hourly flows, select the 'flow region' for the merging lane from Figure 42.5 or for the diverging lane from Figure 42.6; and,

- using the selected flow region, identify the merging lane type from Tables 42.5 and 42.6 or the diverging lane type from Tables 42.7 and 42.8.

Further information on the layout of grade separated junctions is given in Refs. 1 and 2.

The Design of Weaving Areas

The following procedure should be adopted to design a weaving area:

- select the 30th highest hourly value of total weaving flow expected in the 15th year of operation;

- adjust the total weaving flow and the associated non-weaving flows to allow for the effects of gradient and the proportion of heavy goods vehicles in the traffic stream. Appropriate correction factors can be found in Table 42.4 where the main road gradient is measured over 1 km (0.5 km from either side of the merge nose) and the average gradient determined;

- using the adjusted total weaving flow determine the minimum length of weaving section (L_{min}) from Figure 42.7;

- compare L_{min} with the design speed related absolute minimum length of weaving section in Figure 42.7. The greater of the two lengths should be taken as L_{min}, subject to meeting the minimum sight distance requirements; and then

376

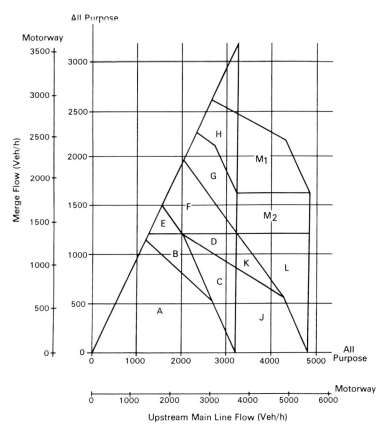

Figure 42.5 Merging diagram (for flow regions)   Source: TD 22/86 DTp (1986)

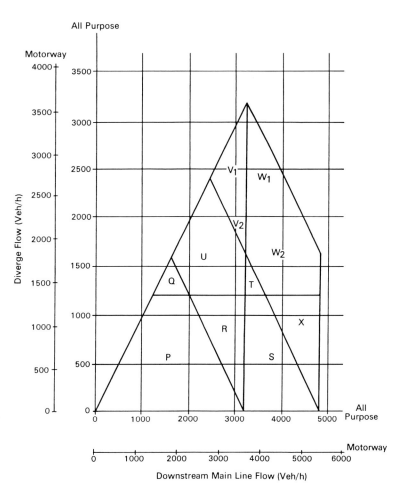

Figure 42.6 Diverging diagram (for flow regions)   Source: TD 22/86 DTp (1986)

377

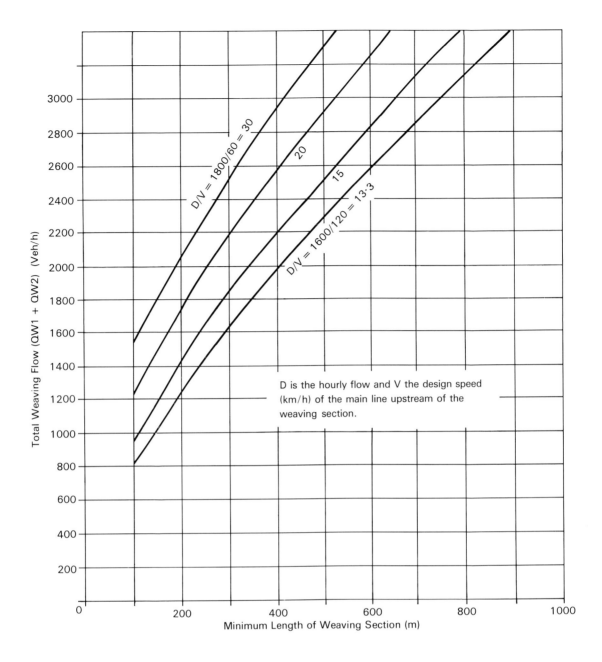

D is the hourly flow and V the design speed (km/h) of the main line upstream of the weaving section.

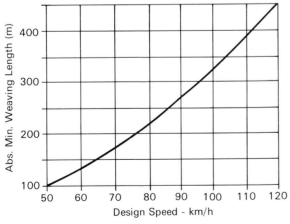

To determine the minimum length of weaving section (Lmin) for insertion within the formula in Paragraph 42.5.

1. For known total weaving flow and chosen D/V value read off the minimum length of weaving section from the graph above.

2. Check the absolute minimum weaving length allowable for chosen design speed from the graph on the left.

3. Select the greater of the two lengths

Figure 42.7 Weaving lengths for grade separated junctions

Source: TD 22/86 DTp (1986)

Merging lane type		1	2	3	4	5	6	7	8
Number of lanes	Upstream main line	2	2	2	2	3	3	3	3
	Link	1	1	2	2	1	1	2	2
	Entry	(1)	(2)	(2)	(2)	(1)	(2)	(2)	(2)
	Downstream main line	2	2	2	3	3	3	3	4
Flow Region	A	✓	✓	✓	✓	✓	✓	✓	✓
	B	–	✓	✓	✓	✓	✓	✓	✓
	C	–	–	–	✓	✓	✓	✓	✓
	D	–	–	–	✓	–	✓	✓	✓
	E	–	–	✓	✓	–	–	✓	✓
	F	–	–	–	✓	–	–	–	✓
	G	–	–	–	✓	–	–	–	✓
	H	–	–	–	–	–	–	–	✓
	I	–	–	–	–	–	–	–	–
	J	–	–	–	–	✓	✓	✓	✓
	K	–	–	–	–	–	✓	✓	✓
	L	–	–	–	–	–	–	–	✓
	M	–	–	–	–	–	–	–	✓

Notes: ✓ Indicates merging lane type acceptable

Table 42.5 Merging lane types (applicable to flow regions in Fig 42.5)

Source: TD 22/86 DTp (1986)

Merging lane type	Fig. number	Layout
1, 3 and 5	A	Direct taper
	C	Parallel lane
2, 6 and 7	D	Direct taper with ghost island
4 and 8	B	Direct taper
	E	Direct taper with ghost island

Table 42.6 Merging lane types (related to Figure 42.3)

Source: TD 22/86 DTp (1986)

Diverging lane type		1	2	3	4	5	6
Number of lanes	Upstream main line	2	2	3	3	3	4
	Link	1	2	1	2	2	2
	Downstream main line	2	2	3	2	3	3
Flow Region	P	✓	✓	✓	✓	✓	✓
	Q	–	✓	–	✓	✓	✓
	R	–	–	✓	✓	✓	✓
	S	–	–	✓	–	✓	✓
	T	–	–	–	–	✓	✓
	U	–	–	–	✓	✓	✓
	V	–	–	–	–	–	✓
	W	–	–	–	–	–	✓
	X	–	–	–	–	–	✓

Notes: ✓ Indicates diverging lane type acceptable

Table 42.7 Diverging lane types (applicable to flow regions in Fig 42.6)

Source: TD 22/86 DTp (1986)

Diverging lane type	Fig. number	Layout
1, 2 3 and 5	A	Direct taper
	C	Parallel lane
4 and 6	B	Direct taper
	D	Parallel lane

Table 42.8 Diverging lane types (related to Figure 42.4)

Source: TD 22/86 DTp (1986)

estimate the number of traffic lanes required using the following relationship:

$$N = \frac{Q_{nw} + Q_{w1}}{D} + \left(\frac{2 \times L_{min}}{Lact} + 1\right)\frac{Q_{w2}}{D}$$

where N = Number of traffic lanes
Q_{nw} = Total non-weaving flow (veh/h)
Q_{w1} = Major weaving flow (veh/h)
Q_{w2} = Minor weaving flow (veh/h)
D = Maximum main road flow from Table 42.1 (veh/h)
L_{min} = Minimum weaving length (m) from Fig 42.7
Lact = Actual weaving length available (m)

See also Refs. 1 and 2 and 42.8 below.

42.6 Facilities for Cyclists

If traffic flows are sufficient to justify the provision of a grade separated junction, then it may also be necessary to provide a segregated cycle network. However, where this is not feasible schemes should be developed to guide and assist cyclists in the areas where they are likely to be most vulnerable (ie. in the merge and diverge areas—see also Chapter 25 which deals with provision for cyclists).

42.7 Bus Stops

Bus stops may be located in laybys on the slip roads of grade separated junctions, preferably on the exit ramps where vehicles are already slowing for the approaching junctions. It is advisable to ensure that adequate stopping sight distance to the layby is provided commensurate with the traffic speed of approach on the exit ramp. The curved ramps of half cloverleafs or more complex layouts may be unsuitable for the location of bus stops due to the problem of forward visibility.

42.8 References

Text Reference

1. DTp—TA 48/86, '*Layout of Grade Separated Junctions*', DTp (1986). (42.5)

2. DTp—TD 22/86, '*Layout of Grade Separated Junctions*', DTp (1986). (42.5)

42.9 Further Information

3. DTp/TRRL—Report SR 721, '*The capacity of some grade-separated roundabout entries*', DTp (1982).

43 Traffic Signs

43.1 Principles of Signing

Traffic signing is effected by the use of road markings, road studs, traffic signals, lamps, cones, cylinders and beacons as well as various types of upright signs (see also Sections 64 to 80 of the Road Traffic Regulation Act 1984) (Ref. 1) [NI.51].

Careful provision of the prescribed signs and markings can make a considerable contribution to the safe and efficient operation of the highway network. Traffic signs must convey clear and unambiguous messages to road users so that they can be understood quickly and easily.

Signing Rules and Standards

The circumstances in which each of the devices referred to above is permitted or required to be used, and a detailed specification for each, are contained in the current Traffic Signs Regulations and General Directions (TSRGD) (Ref. 2) [NI.2]. Advice on the use and design of signs is given in the Traffic Signs Manual (Ref. 3) supplemented by Department of Transport Circulars, Advice Notes and Standards [Sco.221, Wa.58].

Generally speaking, all traffic signs used on the highway must conform to the Regulations, which are periodically updated, but special signs can be individually authorised by the Secretary of State in appropriate circumstances. A list of the relevant Department of Transport publications concerned with traffic signing is provided in 43.7 and 43.8 below [Sco.225-237].

Siting of Traffic Signs

Signs must be sited so that the information is given to road users when they need it; not too soon, lest it be forgotten before it is needed and not too late for the safe performance of any consequent maneuvre. Subject to the siting constraints for different types of sign they should not be placed so as to be environmentally intrusive and cause sign clutter. Further information on the size, design and mounting of traffic signs is given in Ref. 4.

Signs which do not conform to the appropriate regulations or are unauthorised signs or advertisements may distract the attention of road users to the detriment of road safety (see also Ref. 5).

43.2 Categories of Traffic Signs

Apart from traffic signals, which are discussed in Chapters 20 and 41, traffic signs may be divided into three broad categories:

- upright signs—which are themselves divisible into warning, regulatory and informatory signs (Schedule 1 of TSRGD);
- road markings (Schedule 2 of TSRGD); and
- miscellaneous signs (Part 1, Section V of TSRGD).

Warning Signs

These signs give warning of hazards ahead. Warning signs are usually either triangular (black symbol within a red border) or rectangular (white legend on a red background). The latter are used for temporary warnings.

A variety of supplementary plates giving further information are available for use with certain prescribed warning or regulatory signs.

Regulatory Signs

Regulatory signs give notice of restrictions or prohibitions on the speed, movement and waiting times of vehicles. They are mostly circular (red border indicating a negative instruction, blue background indicating a positive instruction). The exceptions are a 'Stop' sign (octagonal) and a 'Give way' sign (inverted triangular). Waiting restriction and zonal restriction signs are rectangular. Most regulatory signs may only be used if an appropriate traffic regulation order has previously been made by the highway authority (see also Chapter 15) but some can be used without an order (eg. Stop, Give Way, Keep Left or Right). Supplementary plates may also be used (see above) and must accord with any associated traffic order (eg. except for access, except for loading).

Informatory Signs

These give information about routes, places and facilities of particular value and interest to road users. Directional signs fall within this category. Informatory signs are either rectangular or 'flag' type (ie. pointed at one end). The colours used depend on the road on which they are used and the information they give (see 43.3 below).

Road Markings

Road markings are provided to convey a warning, a requirement or information. Except where associated with waiting or loading restrictions (in which case they are yellow in colour), they are usually white and may be permitted or required to be of reflecting material. Studs incorporating reflectors may be provided or required to supplement road markings. Reflectors are usually white in colour but red, green or amber studs may also be used depending on their location on the carriageway.

Miscellaneous Signs

Apart from traffic signals these include:

- signs placed temporarily on or near a road to warn, inform or regulate traffic;

- flashing beacons (amber or, in the case of police, blue in colour) warning drivers to take special care;

- red flags advising drivers to stop;

- cones used to define routes round obstructions or road works;

- cylinders indicating the temporary division of a carriageway;

- indicator lamps at refuges to warn drivers of their presence;

- school crossing patrol signs and warning lights; and

- amber road danger lamps to define the extent of a temporary obstruction.

43.3 Direction Signing

General Principles

Direction signing is used to guide traffic to its destination. The broad approach adopted in Britain is first to guide traffic towards a general destination then, at the appropriate point, to direct it to more specific areas and finally to local destinations which may be simply street name plates (though street name plates and house numbers are not classed as traffic signs) or could, in the case of important traffic attractors, be an individual building or car park. Signing therefore becomes increasingly specific moving down a hierarchy of destinations as decision points are reached.

Hierarchy of Destinations

The hierarchy of destinations used is as follows:

- **Super-Primary** destinations, such as towns and cities of regional significance and geographical areas such as 'The North' and 'The South West';

- **Primary** destinations such as towns and cities which are important destinations for traffic;

- **Non-Primary** destinations (ie. towns and cities on non-primary routes of less importance to traffic);

- **Local** destinations such as small settlements, city suburbs, environmental areas, industrial estates and destinations such as transport interchanges or other public buildings which may be significant attractors of traffic;

- **Tourist attractions**. Attractions with over 150,000 visitors [Sco.222] a year (and which meet certain other criteria) may be signed from the nearest motorway junction(s) within 20 miles. On all-purpose roads tourist signing should be in accordance with criteria set by the local highway authority (see Ref. 6 for more details) [Sco.222].

Route Hierarchy and Sign Colours

The colours used in direction signs depend upon the status of the traffic route on which they are placed and the type of information given. A multi-tier system is used in Britain as follows:

On Motorways:
Blue background, white border, symbol, legend and route number—main destinations.

On the Primary Route Network:
Green background, white border, symbol, legend and yellow route number—NB. the primary route network (PRN) is not a road classification as such but rather a network of all purpose roads (ie. not motorways) defined for direction signing purposes.

On Non-Primary Routes:
White background, black border, symbol, legend and route number—these signs should be used on main roads which are not part of the primary route network.

Local Destinations:
Local destinations should be signed using a **white background, blue border, black symbol, legend and mileage**. These may also appear on primary or non-primary routes independently from green background and white background/black border signs.

Tourist Attractions:
Brown background, white border, symbol, legend, route number and mileage. Approved symbols may be used to denote the type of attraction. These signs can be used on all classes of road (see Ref. 6) [Sco.224] including Motorways where the attraction receives over 150,000 visitors a year [Sco.223].

Traffic Diversions:
Signs using a **yellow background, black border, symbol and legend** are for temporary use, most commonly in connection with a diversion caused by road works or when used by a motoring organisation, subject to the approval of the highway authority, in connection with a specific event. Temporary signs can also bear a blue legend on a white background or a white legend on a blue background (see Regulation 27 of TSRGD).

Other Special Themes

In addition to the above signs for general traffic, there are a number of other colours used for specific themes such as lorry routes (black background with a white lorry symbol), pedestrians (blue background with a white symbol of a walking man) and cyclists (blue background with a white cycle symbol) see Traffic Signs Regulations and General Directions (Ref. 2) for further information.

Types of Direction Sign

There are three types of direction sign and their use depends upon where they are sited in relation to the junction.

An **Advance Direction Sign** (ADS) is placed before a junction is reached to give drivers advance information about their route choice. On high speed roads a Forward ADS may be provided some distance ahead of the ADS and on motorways signs are provided one mile and half a mile ahead of, as well as at, the exit itself. (Tourist signs on motorways may be provided if necessary $\frac{3}{4}$ mile and $\frac{1}{4}$ mile in advance of the exit.) Advance direction signs may be mounted overhead on bridges or gantries, or by the side of the carriageway.

The layout of individual advance direction signs may be of the **map type** where the layout of the junction is represented diagrammatically. These are especially appropriate at roundabouts and may display other indications to traffic by incorporating certain warning or regulatory signs. They may also be of the **stack type**, where the individual destinations are stacked above each other on the sign face; or the **lane destination type**, where the carriageway is clearly marked into traffic lanes which are appropriate for different destinations.

A **Direction Sign (DS)** repeats the information on the ADS but is placed at the junction where the turning manoeuvre is actually to be made. Direction signs are normally of the **flag type** but may incorporate an arrow, depending on the type of junction.

A **Route Confirmatory Sign** is placed after the junction to give confirmation of the route number and the destinations ahead.

Design of Direction Signs

The precise layout, design and siting requirements for the different types of direction signs are given in the Department of Transport's Traffic Signs Manual (Ref. 3) and in Ref. 4 but the following general points should be followed so far as possible:

- once a destination has been signed, all relevant signs along that route must indicate that destination until it is reached;

- the number of destinations shown on any one sign should not exceed six (four on motorways);

- not more than two destinations should be signed in each direction on any one sign. Exceptionally, a third destination may be used in certain areas but only if considered absolutely necessary;

- destinations of any category should not be signed beyond a destination of greater significance;

- mileages to destinations should not be shown on ADSs but should generally be shown on DSs within junctions;

- route numbers should appear on both ADSs and DSs other than those of purely local significance.

43.4 Variable Message Traffic Signs

Variable message traffic signs (VMS) have been used for many years but the introduction of microprocessor control and dot matrix displays has provided greater opportunities for their use in the management of traffic. The Traffic Signs Regulation and General Directions require that all variable message signs be approved by, or on behalf of, the Secretary of State before being placed on or near any road.

There are two broad types:—

- **Mechanical or electromechanical signs**; on which the messages are displayed or changed by moving parts. The moving parts may be either flexible (eg. roller blind), rigid (eg. prisms) or rotating laminae to which messages are fixed which when selectively rotated reveal a fluorescent/reflective material to create a range of symbols and messages. The simplest form of mechanical VMS is the flap type sign. An illustration of a car park sign with rotating prism elements is shown at Plate 20.1.

- **Wholly electrical (or electronic) signs**; on which the messages are revealed when an internal light source is switched on and where there is no mechanical movement within the sign. This class also includes matrix signs where a selection of elements from an array of light sources can be illuminated to create a range of symbols and messages, or can alternatively show no message at all.

VMS can be beneficial in a variety of situations where a message is either not required to be displayed permanently or several alternative messages which are not interdependent are required at the same site under different circumstances. The following are given as examples:—

Regulatory signs; (time dependent, tidal and peak hour schemes):
- banned turns,
- no entry,
- restricted access (eg. pedestrian zones),

- one-way traffic,
- bus lanes,
- lane controls,
- warning signs,
- two-way traffic,
- animals crossing,
- aircraft noise,
- overheight vehicles (in conjunction with diversion signs),
- gate(s) closed,
- weather related (eg. flood, fog, ice/snow, wind).

Informatory signs:
- direction signs (destination in conjunction with diversion for any reason),
- diversions,
- facilities/services (eg. closed),
- lane controls,
- motorway services, petrol price signs.

Warning signs:
- detection of overheight vehicles approaching a low bridge.

43.5 Environmental Impact of Direction Signs

The number and size of direction signs should be kept to a minimum commensurate with the need to provide adequate information for drivers. The location of direction signs should take account of other prohibitory signs, traffic signals, street name plates and other street furniture (see Ref. 4). Sign supports should also be designed with care to avoid ugly and overlarge structures. In dense urban areas it is sometimes difficult to find suitable locations for signs, especially where footways are narrow and it may be necessary to compromise on the number of signs provided. In these cases primary and local signs should take precedence over other informatory signs but not over regulatory signs.

43.6 Illumination of Traffic Signs

The requirements for the illumination of signs (whether internal, direct external or by reflectorisation) are contained in Regulations 15–19 of the current Traffic Signs Regulations and General Directions and are conveniently summarised in Ref. 7 which also gives guidance on the use of different types of reflective material. The illumination requirements for direction signs are related to whether or not a system of street lighting (as defined in Regulation 15(1) (c)) is present within 50 metres of the sign. In general, all motorway direction signs should be directly lit in areas with street lighting and this also applies to green background advance direction and gantry signs on primary routes.

The only white background direction signs which must be directly lit are gantry mounted signs located in areas of street lighting. All other direction signs must be reflectorised, if not directly lit, except for pedestrian, MOD and tourist attraction signs where reflectorisation is not required by the regulations but is nevertheless generally recommended.

43.7 References

Text Reference

1. Road Traffic Regulation Act 1984, HMSO (1984). (43.1)

2. Traffic Signs Regulations and General Directions 1981 (Statutory Instruments 1981 No 859), as amended, HMSO. [Wa.59] (43.1, 43.3)

3. DTp—The Traffic Signs Manual, HMSO (1977). [Wa.60] Chapters available separately. (43.1, 43.3)
   - Chapter 1 Introduction, HMSO (1982)
   - Chapter 2 Informatory Signs, HMSO (New edition due)
   - Chapter 3 Regulatory Signs, HMSO (1986)
   - Chapter 4 Warning Signs, HMSO (1986)
   - Chapter 5 Road Markings, HMSO (1985)
   - Chapter 6 Motorway Signs (including road markings), HMSO (New edition due)
   - Chapter 7 Temporary Signs, HMSO (New edition due)
   - Chapter 8 Traffic Safety Measures for Road Works, HMSO (1974)
   - Chapter 9 Signs for Speed Restrictions, HMSO (New edition due)
   - Chapter 10 Miscellaneous (including bollards, school crossings, traffic control signals and level crossings), HMSO (New edition due)
   - Chapter 11 Illumination of Signs, HMSO (New edition due)
   - Chapter 12 Maintenance, HMSO (New edition due)
   - Chapter 13 Sign Construction and Materials, HMSO (New edition due)
   - Chapter 14 Miscellaneous (including Administration and Procedure), HMSO (1977).

4. DTp—Circular Roads 7/75, '*Size, design and mounting of traffic signs*', DTp (1975). [Sco.225, Wa.61] (43.1, 43.5)

5. DoE—Circular 11/84, '*Town and Country Planning (Control of Advertisements) Regulations 1984*', DoE (1984). [Sco.226, Wa.62]   (43.1)

6. DTp—Circular Roads 3/86, '*Tourist Attraction Signing*', DTp (1986). [Sco.227, Sco.228, Sco.229, Wa.63]   (43.3)

7. DTp—TA19/81, '*The Reflectorisation of Traffic Signs*', DTp (1981). [Sco.230]   (43.6)

43.8 Further Information

8. DTp—Circular Roads 35/77, '*Street Name Plates and Numbering of Premises*', DTp (1975). [Sco.237, Wa.67]

9. DTp—H1/78, '*Design Criteria for Sign/Signal Gantries*', DTp (1978). [Sco.236]

10. DTp—TA 6/80, '*Traffic Signs and Safety Measures for Minor Works and on Minor Roads (Addendum)*', DTp (1980). [Sco.235]

11. DTp—Circular Roads 3/81, '*Revision of Traffic Signs Regulations and General Directions*', DTp (1981). [Sco.234]

12. DTp—TA 24/81, '*Road Safety during Installation and Maintenance of Permanent Traffic Signals and Related Equipment on All-Purpose Roads*' and Amendment, DTp (1981).

13. DTp—'*Systematic Place Name Selection for Road Signs Computer Program System*', HECB/R/28 (SIGNPOST), DTp (1981).

14. DTp—Circular Roads 1/83, '*The Traffic Signs (Amendment) Regulation and General Directions 1982*', DTp (1983). [Sco.233, Wa.65]

15. DTp—'*Traffic Signs for Cyclists*', (Leaflet), DTp (1983).

16. DTp—TD 14/83, '*Signing for Traffic Management of Certain Major Road Work Sites*' and Amendment, DTp (1983).

17. DTp—Circular Roads 3/84, '*The Traffic Signs (Amendment) Regulations and General Directions*', DTp, (1984). [Sco.232, Wa.66]

18. DTp—Circular Roads 7/84, '*Reflecting Road Studs*', DTp (1984). [Sco.231, Wa.64]

19. Colby, F J M—'*Variable message traffic signs.*' Highways and Transportation (July 1984).

20. DTp—'*Know Your Traffic Signs*', HMSO (1985).

21. DTp—TD 18/85, '*Criteria for the Use of Gantries for Traffic Signs and Matrix Traffic Signals on Trunk Roads and Motorways*', DTp (1985).

PART 6 APPLICATION IN NORTHERN IRELAND, SCOTLAND AND WALES

44 Application in Northern Ireland

44.1 Introduction

The general principles described in this manual concerning the consideration of problems and the development and design of alternative highway and traffic management solutions are appropriate to practice in Northern Ireland, but there are a number of differences in the legislative framework.

The Department of the Environment for Northern Ireland have provided a detailed annotation of the text indicating where particular legislation, responsibilities or procedures do not apply in Northern Ireland.

These annotations are shown as [NI.1] [NI.2] etc. and an outline of what is appropriate for Northern Ireland

is given in 44.2 below. More detailed information can be obtained through direct contact with:

The Department of the Environment for Northern Ireland
Roads Services Headquarters
Commonwealth House
35 Castle Street
Belfast
BT1 1GU
Telephone: Belfast 221212

Annotations NI.1, NI.2 and NI.7 are used quite frequently and relate to the system of local government in Northern Ireland, to the fact that a particular point is not applicable to Northern Ireland and to the Road Traffic (NI) Order 1981, respectively. Most of the other references relate to individual items in the main text.

44.2 List of Detailed References

Annotation No	Comment for Northern Ireland	Main Text Chapter Reference(s)	
NI.1	In 1973 a major re-organisation of Local Government was carried out in Northern Ireland. The Transfer of Functions (NI) Order 1973 transferred responsibility for the mainstream functions such as Planning, Water, Sewerage and Roads to Central Government. The Department of the Environment for Northern Ireland has responsibility for these functions. The Department consults with the Local Authorities on matters within their respective areas.	3.1 4.1 12.1 15.7 21.2 21.11 31.9	
NI.2	Not applicable to Northern Ireland.	3.2 3.4 3.5 3.6 4.1 4.3 12.1 14.3 15.5	15.6 15.10 19.5 Table 21.1 21.11 24.7 25.2 26.1 43.1
NI.3	Planning (NI) Order 1972 (as amended).	3.2 14.3 15.4	24.11 25.2
NI.4	The Planning (Development Plan) Regulations (NI) 1973.	3.2 3.3	
NI.5	The Roads (NI) Order 1980.	3.2 14.3	

Annotation No	Comment for Northern Ireland	Main Text Chapter Reference(s)	
NI.6	The Private Streets (NI) Order 1980.	3.2	
		31.2	
NI.7	The Road Traffic (NI) Order 1981.	3.2	21.11
		14.3	24.11
		15.1	25.2
		15.3	25.4
		15.7	41.3
		15.10	
NI.8	Structure Plans and Unitary Development Plans are not used in Northern Ireland. Development Plans are prepared by the Department of the Environment for Northern Ireland in accordance with The Planning (NI) Order 1972 and The Planning (Development Plan) Regulations (NI) 1973.	3.3 35.1 35.2	
NI.9	The Acts, Regulations and Orders given in Table 3.1 do not apply in Northern Ireland. The following is a list of the Acts, Regulations and Orders with important considerations for roads and traffic in Northern Ireland: Land Clauses Consolidation Act 1845 Land Acquisition and Compensation (NI) Order 1973 Land Compensation (NI) Order 1982 Planning (NI) Order 1972 Planning (Development Plan) Regulations (NI) 1973 Planning Blight (Compensation) (NI) Order 1981 Roads (NI) Order 1980 Road Traffic (NI) Order 1981 Private Streets (NI) Order 1980 Planning (Use Classes) Order (NI) 1973 Planning (General Development) Order (NI) 1973 (as amended)	Table 3.1	
NI.10	FUNDING OF ROADS Funds for the range of Road Service functions are voted directly by Parliament in Annual Appropriation legislation. In estimating the funds necessary for roads, account is taken of other public expenditure priorities within Northern Ireland. Roads Service finance is administered by a central headquarters which disburses money in accordance with agreed policy objectives. The primary aim is to maintain the existing road network to prevent unnecessary deterioration which would be costly to remedy at a later date. The maintenance programme is complemented by substantial investment in major and minor capital projects. This ensures the continued development of the road network in response to both local need and the strategic requirement of the province as a whole. OTHER SOURCES OF FINANCE 1. European Community assistance is obtained for selected roads projects under various regulations. Generally, the revenue has no public expenditure implications and does not impact upon the roads vote.	4.2	

Annotation No	Comment for Northern Ireland	Main Text Chapter Reference(s)
	2. Developers who construct new residential and industrial estate roads and/or agree to finance highway related works on roads outside their development but adversely affected by it.	
	3. Other revenue such as parking charges and tolls.	
NI.11	Interpretation is given in Article 2(2) of the Roads (NI) Order 1980.	Table 5.3 Table 5.4
NI.12	Public transport in Northern Ireland is provided by both state owned and private companies. Although the Northern Ireland system is broadly similar to that of Great Britain, Northern Ireland has built up its own independent system over the years with differences suited to local requirements.	8.1 9.1 26.1
	In the publicly owned sector, operating responsibility for the individual services lies with a number of separate companies—Northern Ireland, Railways, Ulsterbus, Citybus and Northern Ireland Airports—which are subsidiaries of the Northern Ireland Transport Holding Company.	
	The Department of the Environment for Northern Ireland is responsible for transport policy and legislation and maintains close liaison with the Holding Company and the operating subsidiary companies.	
	The structure of separate operating companies allows for coordination while still permitting the separate companies to act in a commercial manner and to concentrate on their own field of operation.	
	The governing legislation is contained in the Transport Act (NI) 1967 and the Transport (NI) Order 1977.	
NI.13	In Northern Ireland the Department of the Environment for Northern Ireland, Town and Country Planning Service is the sole authority in dealing with planning matters.	13.1 28.2 30.3 32.1
	While procedures generally follow the basic principles described in the text, the operation of these procedures is carried out under different legislation. The main items of legislation are given in ref NI.9 above.	35.1 35.2
	Further advice on planning matters may be obtained from:	
	The Department of the Environment for Northern Ireland Town & Country Planning Service Commonwealth House 35 Castle Street BELFAST BT1 1GU	
NI.14	Article 23A of The Road Traffic (NI) Order 1981 as amended by The Road Traffic, Transport and Roads (NI) Order 1984.	14.4

Annotation No	Comment for Northern Ireland	Main Text Chapter Reference(s)
NI.15	There is no Northern Ireland equivalent to the various Traffic Orders (Procedures) Regulations quoted. However procedures for consultation, notices, public inquiries (discretionary power exercisable by the Department of the Environment for NI), objections, making of orders, validity of orders, duration of traffic orders, police powers and exemptions are broadly comparable.	15.2
NI.16	Motor Vehicle (Construction and Use) Regulations (NI) 1976 (as amended).	15.4
NI.17	The Road Traffic (NI) Order does not allow for exemptions by reference to the issue of permits to a particular person.	15.4
NI.18	The Road Traffic (NI) Order does not allow for restriction on certain classes of vehicles for environmental reasons alone.	15.4
NI.19	Section 14 of the Chronically Sick and Disabled Persons (Northern Ireland) Act 1978.	15.6
NI.20	Article 40 of the Roads (NI) Order 1980 provides for the making of orders to abandon or stop-up roads either wholly or to such extent as may be specified.	15.8
NI.21	Article 79 of the Planning (NI) Order 1972 provides that the Department of the Environment for Northern Ireland may by order extinguish any public right of way where it is satisfied that such extinguishment is necessary for the proper development of land.	15.8
NI.22	The Planning (NI) Order 1972 provides that the Department of the Environment for Northern Ireland may for the purpose of improving the amenity of an area, by order, provide for the extinguishment of the right to use vehicles on a road.	15.9
NI.23	The Department of the Environment for Northern Ireland has powers under the Road Traffic (NI) Order 1981 to provide on-street parking places which may include the designation of paying parking spaces.	15.10
NI.24	There is no specific statutory provision in Northern Ireland equivalent to Sections 19 and 38 of the Road Traffic Regulation Act 1984. The Department of the Environment for Northern Ireland engages in consultative arrangements with bus operators for the provision and siting of stands and the selection of routes.	15.10
NI.25	The Department of the Environment for Northern Ireland has powers to designate parking places for 'hackney carriages', to licence taxis and appoint taxi ranks in accordance with bye-laws made under Article 65(1) of the Road Traffic (NI) Order 1981.	15.10
NI.26	The Department of the Environment for Northern Ireland may make bye-laws under the provision of Article 105 of the Road Traffic (NI) Order 1981 as to the use of parking places, the vehicles or classes of vehicles entitled to use them and the charges to be paid. It may enter into arrangements for car parks to be operated by others on the Department's behalf.	15.10

Annotation No	Comment for Northern Ireland	Main Text Chapter Reference(s)
NI.27	There is no specific power in Northern Ireland road legislation prohibiting the riding of a bicycle on a footway. Article 62 of the Road Traffic (NI) Order makes it an offence for any pedal cyclist through his own negligence on a road (which includes a footway) to endanger his own safety or that of any other person.	15.11 25.2
NI.28	Statutory Rule of Northern Ireland 1984 No 135, The Motor Vehicles (Variation of Speed Limits) Regulations (NI) 1984.	15.12
NI.29	The Department of Environment is the sole authority for setting speed limits on public roads in Northern Ireland.	15.12
NI.30	In Northern Ireland a restricted road is one where on 1 October 1956 a system of street lighting furnished by means of lamps placed not more than 200 yards apart was provided or where there is in force an order made under the provision of Article 50(4)(c) of the Road Traffic (NI) Order 1981.	15.12
NI.31	Article 158 of the Road Traffic (NI) Order 1981.	17.3
NI.32	Articles 21 and 107 of the Road Traffic (NI) Order 1981.	21.3
NI.33	Northern Ireland legislation does not allow for the designation of particular parking spaces for classes of person other than disabled persons.	21.4 21.5 21.8
NI.34	Traffic Signs Regulations (NI) 1979 (as amended).	21.9 41.3
NI.35	Powers of local authorities are limited to the removal of abandoned vehicles under Article 30 of the Pollution Controi and Local Government (NI) Order 1978.	21.11
NI.36	Article 50 of the Road Traffic (NI) Order 1981 and Motor Vehicles (Variation of Speed Limit) Regulations (NI) 1984.	22.2
NI.37	Pelican Pedestrian Crossing Regulations (NI) 1970 and Zebra Pedestrian Crossing Regulations (NI) 1974.	24.4
NI.38	Road Traffic (NI) Order 1981 Article 153.	25.2
NI.39	Road Traffic (NI) Order 1981 Article 142.	25.2
NI.40	Road Traffic (NI) Order 1981 Article 162.	25.2
NI.41	Road Traffic (NI) Order 1981 Article 161.	25.2
NI.42	The Department of the Environment for Northern Ireland is empowered to make traffic regulation orders to control the movement of heavy goods vehicles as a specified 'class of traffic' under the Road Traffic (NI) Order 1981.	27.4
NI.43	Section 15 of The Transport Act (NI) 1967.	27.7

Annotation No	Comment for Northern Ireland	Main Text Chapter Reference(s)
NI.44	The Road Transport (Qualifications of Operators) Regulations (NI) 1977 and The Road Transport (Qualifications of Operators) (Amendment) Regulations (NI) 1981.	27.7
NI.45	Fourteen days.	27.7
NI.46	Motor Vehicles (Construction and Use) Regulations (NI) 1976 (as amended).	27.8
NI.47	The Motor Vehicles (Authorisation of Special Types) Regulations (NI) 1968.	27.8
NI.48	In Northern Ireland it is desirable but not mandatory for the surface finish of a shared surface road to contrast with the surface of roads with footways.	31.6
NI.49	The dimensions for residential roads will be contained in the Department of the Environment's proposed publication 'Layout of Housing Roads Design Guide'.	31.9
NI.50	In Northern Ireland the Department of the Environment for Northern Ireland Roads Service is the sole authority dealing with roads. While procedures may follow the same basic principles outlined in the text the operation of these procedures is carried out under different legislation. The main items of legislation are given in Ref (NI.9). Further advice on highway matters may be obtained from: Department of the Environment for Northern Ireland Roads Service Commonwealth House 35 Castle Street BELFAST BT1 1GU	13.1 28.2 28.3 31.1 31.2 35.3 35.5 35.6
NI.51	Articles 122 to 128 of the Road Traffic (NI) Order 1981.	43.1
NI.52	In Northern Ireland the Land Acquisition and Compensation (NI) Order 1973 provides a statutory right to compensation for injurious affection to land caused by physical factors arising from the use of new or substantially altered public works which came into use on or after 17 October 1969. Compensation is only payable for depreciation in the value of the claimants' interest and does not extend to loss of profits. Compensation can be claimed (under Part II of the Order) by owners of property where its value is depreciated by noise and other specified physical factors arising from the use of a new or altered highway (the period during which claims can be made is 2 years starting one year after the first opening of the new or altered highway).	35.4
NI.53	There are no equivalent noise regulations in Northern Ireland.	35.4

45 Application in Scotland

45.1 Introduction

The principles and techniques described in this manual are generally, equally appropriate to the consideration of problems and the development and design of highway and traffic management schemes in Scotland. However, legislative powers and duties are set down under Scottish law which though often similar in principle to that which holds in England and Wales, may differ in detail or sometimes more substantially. Terminology may also be different.

In particular the term 'highway' is used throughout the manual. This term is not legally recognised in Scotland and such references should be read as 'road'.

The Scottish Development Department (SDD) have provided a detailed annotation to the text of the manual, indicating where differences for Scotland should be noted. These are shown in the form [SCO.1],

[SCO.2] etc. inserted into the text; and the equivalent information for use in Scotland is provided in 45.2 below.

Where more detailed information is required direct contact should be made with:

Chief Road Engineer
The Scottish Development Department
New St Andrew's House
Edinburgh
EH1 3SZ
Telephone: 031-244-4286

The SDD have also provided details of equivalent Scottish Circulars, Advice Notes and Design Standards and these are annotated in a similar way in the lists of references and sources of information provided at the end of each chapter.

45.2 List of Detailed References

Annotation No	Comment for Scotland	Main Text Chapter Reference
	PART 1	
	CHAPTER 1	
Sco.1	Policy for Scottish Roads: 1984, Scottish Development Department.	1.10
	CHAPTER 2	
Sco.2	General Register Office for Scotland (GRO(S)) and the Scottish Development Department have defined 'localities' in the 1981 Census. These are broadly contiguous built-up enumeration areas such that the population in the locality is more than 500 and a distance of more than 1 km separates them.	2.1
Sco.3	Technical Memorandum SH 9/86. 'Traffic Flows and Carriageway Width Assessment for Urban and Rural Roads; defines urban roads as roads in built up areas which are single carriageways with a speed limit of 40 mph, or dual carriageways with a speed limit of 60 mph or less.	2.1
Sco.4	The mode of travel to work and car ownership by locality is available from Census, Small Area Statistics (General Register Office for Scotland) and Car Ownership Statistics, published in 'Scottish Transport Statistics 1982' (Government Statistical Service).	2.3
Sco.5	Public transport statistics are published in 'Scottish Transport Statistics, 1985' (Government Statistical Service).	2.4
Sco.6	Freight figures are published in 'Scottish Transport Statistics, 1985' (Government Statistical Service).	2.5

Annotation No	Comment for Scotland	Main Text Chapter Reference
Sco.7	Road Accident figures are published annually in 'Road Accidents, Scotland' (Government Statistical Service). Various other statistical bulletins are published from time to time which cover particular topics in depth.	2.7 2.9
Sco.8	Road lengths and traffic volumes are published in 'Scottish Transport Statistics, 1985' (Government Statistical Service). Traffic figures are related to major roads only and are averaged over two years.	2.8
Sco.9	Scottish Development Department: Technical Memorandum SH 4/85, 'National Road Traffic Forecasts, 1984'.	2.9
Sco.10	Scottish Transport Statistics, published annually (Government Statistical Service).	2.10
Sco.11	Census 1981: Key Statistics for Urban Areas, Scotland: Localities General Register Office for Scotland, (HMSO).	2.10
	CHAPTER 3	
Sco.12	Local Government (Scotland) Act 1973 as amended.	3.2
Sco.13	Unitary Development Plans are not part of the statutory planning framework in Scotland.	3.2 3.3
Sco.14	Town and Country Planning (Scotland) Act 1972.	3.2
Sco.15	Roads (Scotland) Act 1984.	3.2
Sco.16	See Table Sco. 3.1 (page 395).	3.2
Sco.17	Structure and Local Plans were introduced by the Town and Country Planning (Scotland) Act 1969 (now consolidated in Part II of the Town and Country Planning (Scotland) Act 1972) to replace the old development plans established by the Town and Country Planning (Scotland) Act 1947.	3.3
Sco.18	Not applicable.	3.3
Sco.19	Detailed provision as to the form and content of Structure and Local Plans and the procedures for their preparation and approval or adoption is made by the Town and Country Planning (Structure and Local Plans) (Scotland) Regulations 1983. A commentary on the 1983 regulations is provided by SDD Circular 32/1983.	3.3
Sco.20	Scottish Planning Law and Procedure: Eric Young and Jeremy Rowan-Robinson (published by Hodge 1985).	3.3
Sco.21	Structure Plans are prepared by regional and general planning authorities and require ministerial approval.	3.3
Sco.22	There is no annual Roads White Paper for Scotland. The document 'Policy for Scottish Roads' is prepared from time to time and was last issued in 1984.	3.3

ACTS OF PARLIAMENT	MOST IMPORTANT ASPECTS IN RELATION TO ROADS AND TRAFFIC IN URBAN AREAS
ACQUISITION OF LAND (AUTHORISATION) (SCOTLAND) ACT 1947	Provides procedures for acquiring land and making CPOs for road purposes.
NEW TOWNS (SCOTLAND) ACT 1968	Empowers the appropriate Secretary of State to designate areas as New Towns and provides for the establishment of Development Corporations with wide powers to secure their layout and development.
ROAD TRAFFIC ACT 1972	Provides for the licensing of vehicles and drivers, the construction and use of vehicles and penalties for driving offences.
TOWN AND COUNTRY PLANNING (SCOTLAND) ACT 1978	Provides the basis for land use planning, the preparation of development plans and the system of development control whereby, with certain exceptions, no development of land should take place without the prior consent of the local authority.
LOCAL GOVERNMENT (SCOTLAND) ACT 1973, (as amended)	Establishes local authorities and the legal and administrative framework within which they must work and also nominates the authorities to be responsible for different functions.
LAND COMPENSATION (SCOTLAND) ACT 1973	Provides for the compensation of owner-occupiers of land adversely affected by public works including new or alterations to existing roads. Also provides for the making of regulations (currently the Noise Insulation (Scotland) Regulations 1975) for the soundproofing of buildings affected by such works.
ROAD TRAFFIC ACT 1974	Imposes a duty on local authorities to promote road safety, to carry out investigations into road accidents and to take remedial measures.
INNER URBAN AREAS ACT 1978	Gives additional powers and responsibilities (and provides for additional finance) to those authorities with problems of urban decay in inner cities.
LOCAL GOVERNMENT PLANNING AND LAND ACT 1980	Established Urban Development Corporations (to regenerate urban areas) and Enterprise Zones (with reduced planning controls on development).
THE ROAD TRAFFIC REGULATION ACT 1984	Provides for the regulation and control of the speed, movement and parking of vehicles.
ROADS (SCOTLAND) ACT 1984	Provides inter alia for roads authorities to construct, maintain and improve roads and for the stopping up of roads, interference with them, the making up of private roads and the acquisition of land.

ACTS OF PARLIAMENT	MOST IMPORTANT ASPECTS IN RELATION TO ROADS AND TRAFFIC IN URBAN AREAS
TRANSPORT ACT 1985	Significantly amended the regulations applying to bus operations by the abolition of road service licensing. Requires bus operators outside London to register a service with the Traffic Commissioners. Requires authorities to invite tenders for services they intend to subsidise.

REGULATIONS AND ORDERS	MOST IMPORTANT ASPECTS IN RELATION TO ROADS AND TRAFFIC IN URBAN AREAS
LOCAL AUTHORITIES TRAFFIC ORDERS (PROCEDURES) (SCOTLAND) REGULATIONS 1969 (SI 1969 No. 487)	Sets out the procedures to be followed by a local authority when making an order to control the speed, movement or parking of vehicles on the road.
TOWN AND COUNTRY PLANNING (USE CLASSES) (SCOTLAND) ORDER 1973 (SI 1973 No. 1165)	Specified the different classes of use of land or buildings and provides that changes of use within the same class do not require planning permission.
TOWN AND COUNTRY PLANNING (GENERAL DEVELOPMENT) (SCOTLAND) ORDER 1981 (SI 1981 No. 830 (S86))	Specified the types of development requiring planning permission, the procedures to be followed in determining a planning application (notably with regard to developments affecting existing and proposed highways) and the making of an appeal to the Secretary of State.
TRAFFIC SIGNS REGULATIONS AND GENERAL DIRECTIONS 1981 (SI 1981 No. 859)	Prescribes the traffic signs and the circumstances and conditions which apply to their use on the public road.

Table Sco. 3.1 [Sco.16] The more important Acts of Parliament, Regulations and Orders with considerations for Roads and Traffic in Urban Areas in Scotland (See also Table 3.1 for England & Wales).

Annotation No	Comment for Scotland	Main Text Chapter Reference
Sco.23	Local Plans are normally prepared and adopted by general and district planning authorities; only exceptionally will a Local Plan require to be approved by the Secretary of State for Scotland.	3.3
Sco.24	A similar, but not identical process, is followed in Scotland.	Figure 3.1 Figure 3.2
Sco.25	The regional and islands councils, as local roads authority for their areas, are asked to produce a comprehensive TPP document only once every 4 years. In each intervening year, authorities are asked to prepare a TPP supplement consisting of the expenditure programme for the following 5 years and a short supporting commentary explaining additions to and major changes in the programme. The expenditure programme element of the TPP assists the local authorities' financial planning process and Government consideration of capital expenditure and of Rate Support Grant.	3.4
Sco.26	Transport Supplementary Grant does not exist in Scotland.	3.4
Sco.27	Scottish Development Department Circular 12/1980, 'Transport Policies and Programmes: Submissions from 1980 Onwards', gives advice on the preparation of TPP's and integration with the planning system. In preparing their TPPs, authorities are asked to ensure proper coordination with the strategic policies contained in the Regional Report and the developing Structure Plans. It is intended that the TPP should be the vehicle for working out in more detail the policies laid down in the Structure Plan. The TPP should provide in its turn the framework for the roads and transport input to the local plans under preparation by the district authorities.	3.4
Sco.28	Scottish Development Department: Structure and Local Plans: Circular 32/1983.	3.7
	Scottish Development Department (1981): Planning Advice Note 27 Structure Planning.	3.7
	Scottish Development Department (1984). Planning Advice Note 30 Local Planning.	3.7
Sco.29	Scottish Planning Law and Procedure, Eric Young and Jeremy Rowan-Robinson, Hodge (1985).	3.7
Sco.30	Scottish Development Department: Transport Policies and Programmes: Submissions from 1980 onwards; Circular 12/1980.	3.8
Sco.31	Town and Country Planning (Structure and Local Plans) (Scotland) Regulations, HMSO (1983).	3.8
	CHAPTER 4	
Sco.32	See Table Sco. 4.1 (page 397).	Table 4.1

AUTHORITY	LAND USE PLANNING	ROADS AND TRAFFIC	PUBLIC TRANSPORT
CENTRAL GOVERNMENT			
SECRETARY OF STATE FOR SCOTLAND	1. Promote legislation and determine policy on national and regional issues. 2. Approve Structure Plans. 3. May "call-in" Local Plans. 4. Appoint Reporter to conduct public inquiries or determine planning appeals (SoS may retain the right to determine a planning appeal).	1. Promote legislation and determine policy on national and regional issues. 2. Roads Authority for Trunk Roads with reserve powers for all roads (and approval of speed limits on Principal Roads). 3. Issue of design standards for Trunk Road design and assessment to be used as guidance by other roads authorities. 4. Control of public expenditure provision for roads and transport and allocation of available provision to regional and islands councils.	1. Promote legislation and determine policies. 2. Administration of fuel duty rebate and transitional rural bus grant. 3. Rural transport innovation grants.
LOCAL GOVERNMENT			
REGIONAL COUNCILS	Strategic Planning Authority with responsibility for preparing the Structure plan. See Note * below re General Planning Authorities.	1. Roads Authority for all non-trunk roads in their area. 2. May act as agent of SoS for any of his functions as Roads Authority.	1. Determine level of subsidy. 2. Identify socially desirable services and enter into contracts with operators for provision. 3. Co-ordinate school transport services. 4. Administer concessionary fares schemes.
DISTRICT COUNCILS	Planning Authority with responsibilities for 1. Preparation of Local Plans. 2. Development control. See Note * below re General Planning Authorities.	Responsible for cleansing of all public roads (i.e. adopted roads) other than Special Roads (usually Motorways) and Trunk Roads. May provide roadside seats and, by agreement, may act as agent of SoS for cleansing Trunk Roads.	Taxi and private hire car licensing.
ISLANDS COUNCILS	As for Regional and District Councils above;* as do Borders, Dumfries and Galloway, and Highland Regional Councils as General Planning Authorities.	As for Regional and District Councils.	As for Regional and District Councils.

Table Sco. 4.1 [Sco. 32] Main powers and responsibilities of the agencies involved in Scotland (See also Table 4.1 for England and Wales)

397

Annotation No	Comment for Scotland	Main Text Chapter Reference
Sco.33	There is a uniform two tier system of Regional and District Councils throughout Scotland, except for Shetland, Orkney and the Western Isles where there are single tier Islands Councils. The division of responsibilities between Regional and District Councils is similar to that between County and District or Borough Councils in England outside the Metropolitan Areas. However, in the Regions of Borders, Dumfries and Galloway, and Highland both strategic and local planning matters are dealt with by the Regional Councils which are known as 'General Planning Authorities', as in the case with the three Islands areas. There are no parish councils in Scotland and community councils have no roads or traffic powers. Regional Councils may act as agents for the Secretary of State for Scotland in respect of any of his functions as roads authority. The Regional and Islands Councils are responsible for local roads, that is those roads that are not part of the trunk road network. These councils have a duty to formulate general policies on the transportation requirements for their respective areas.	4.1
Sco.34	There are no Urban Development Corporations in Scotland, although the Scottish Development Agency has similar wide powers to promote and influence development.	4.1
Sco.35	Capital Expenditure, Scotland.

For the purpose of their annual capital expenditure programmes, regional and island councils receive expenditure allocations in the form of formal consent to incur liability to meet capital expenses. Authorities can supplement allocations by the use of capital receipts generated. Procedural arrangements allow authorities to vary consents for individual programmes (eg. by carrying forward underspend from the previous year, by the anticipation of consent for the next year and by inter-programme transfer).

Local authority capital expenditure on roads is not generally assisted by specific grant. The authorities fund the expenditure by borrowing and the cost of servicing the borrowing then counts as relevant expenditure which scores in the calculation of Rate Support Grant. Rate Support Grant is the block grant given to local authorities annually to supplement their local tax income in the funding of current expenditure. In addition, those areas of the country which are assisted areas under the Government's regional policies qualify for support for capital expenditure programmes from the European Regional Development Fund. | 4.2 |
Sco.36	There is no Transport Supplementary Grant in Scotland.	4.2
Sco.37	Scottish Development Department (1979): Inner Urban Areas Act 1978, Circular 10/79.	4.2 4.4
Sco.38	Section 3 of the Roads (Scotland) Act 1984 gives the Secretary of State similar powers.	4.2
Sco.39	General Improvement Areas do not have an equivalent in Scotland. There are powers under the Housing (Scotland) Acts to make Housing Action Areas and carry out environmental improvements of residential areas. The powers enable local authorities in certain circumstances to close or divert roads and to assist in the provision of car parking for residents.	4.2

DEFINITION	ADDITIONAL INFORMATION
A Road means any way (other than a waterway) over which there is a public right of passage (by whatever means) and includes the road's verge and any bridge (whether permanent or temporary) over which, or tunnel through which, the road passes; and any reference to road includes a part thereof.	On some roads this right of passage may only be exercised on foot, on horseback or by specific classes of vehicles (as described by any order which may be applicable). Public roads, refers to those roads which are maintained at public expense (i.e. by the roads authority). Roads not maintainable at public expense are none the less roads.
A Carriageway is a road which includes a public right of passage by vehicles (other than pedal cycles only).	These rights may be restricted by the implementation of a traffic regulation, speed limit or other orders (see Table 5.2). The right of way for vehicles does not detract from the established right of pedestrians to cross the carriageway or to pass along it in the absence of a footway.
A Footway is a road associated with a carriageway over which there is a public right of passage on foot only.	——
A Footpath is a road not associated with a carriageway over which there is a public right of passage on foot only.	The essential difference between a footway and a footpath is that the former is adjacent to a carriageway. A way which is exclusively for passage on foot is a footpath. Some footpaths may also include a right of way on pedal cycle (Countryside (Scotland) Act 1967 section 47).
A Bridleway is a public right of way on foot and on horseback.	The right of way may also apply to leading horses or driving animals.
A Cycle Track is a road over which there is a public right of passage by pedal cycle or by pedal cycle and foot only.	——

Table Sco. 5.3 Statutory definitions for Scotland [Ref. Sco. 42]

Annotation No	Comment for Scotland	Main Text Chapter Reference
Sco.40	Current Expenditure, Scotland:— In addition to their capital expenditure on new road developments or major improvements to the network, local authorities incur substantial current expenditure each year in maintenance and repair. Financial assistance from central government for this expenditure is also provided through the Rate Support Grant. Local authority current expenditure levels are controlled by central government as part of its general overall control of public expenditure.	4.3
Sco.41	Scottish Development Department (1980): Transport Policies and Programmes: Submissions from 1980 onwards, Circular 12/1980.	4.5
	CHAPTER 5	
Sco.42	Table Sco.5.3 (above).	5.6 Table 5.3

Annotation No	Comment for Scotland	Main Text Chapter Reference
	CHAPTER 6 (Nil)	
	CHAPTER 7 (Nil)	
	PART 2 CHAPTER 8 (Nil)	
	CHAPTER 9	
Sco.43	Transport Supplementary Grant does not exist in Scotland.	9.5
	CHAPTER 10	
Sco.44	Scottish Development Department (1986): Scottish Traffic and Environmental Appraisal Manual (STEAM).	10.1 10.11 10.12
Sco.45	Computerised Highway Information and Planning System (CHIPS), Scottish Development Department.	10.3
Sco.46	Chief Road Engineer, Scottish Development Department. Volumetric and automatic classified counts (presently under development) are also held.	10.3
Sco.47	Regional Council.	10.4
Sco.48	The Scottish Development Department (Central Statistical Unit) maintains a data bank for Scotland as a whole.	10.4
Sco.49	Unitary plans are not part of the statutory planning framework in Scotland.	10.5
Sco.50	The Scottish Development Department also uses these procedures.	10.5
Sco.51	Completion of the second six year cycle should complete the traffic flow estimates for every link of the major road network in Scotland.	10.5
Sco.52	Chief Road Engineer, Scottish Development Department.	10.5
Sco.53	Scottish Development Department (1986): Network Evaluation from Surveys and Assignments: (NESA86).	10.7 10.12
Sco.54	Scottish Development Department (1975): Memorandum on the Noise Insulation (Scotland) Regulations 1975: Regulations 3 and 6, HMSO 1975.	10.11 10.12
Sco.55	Government Statistical Service: Road Accidents, Scotland 1985.	10.12 (Ref. deleted)
Sco.56	Scottish Development Department (1983): Traffic Surveys by Roadside Interview: Technical Memorandum SH6/83.	10.12
	CHAPTER 11	
Sco.57	Chapter 10 of STEAM	11.4
Sco.58	Chapter 8 of STEAM	11.13

Annotation No	Comment for Scotland	Main Text Chapter Reference
Sco.59	Chapter 9 of STEAM	11.13
Sco.60	Scottish Development Department (1985): Network Evaluation from Surveys and Assignments, 1986.	11.14
Sco.61	Scottish Development Department (1986): Scottish Traffic and Environmental Appraisal Manual (STEAM).	11.14
Sco.62	Scottish Development Department (1985): National Road Traffic Forecasts: Technical Memorandum SH4/85.	11.14
	CHAPTER 12	
Sco.63	Scottish Development Department (1983): Structure Plans and Local Plans: Circular 32/83.	12.1 12.9
Sco.64	Scottish Development Department (SDD).	12.3
Sco.65	The Scottish Development Department (1986), 'Scottish Traffic and Environmental Appraisal Manual (STEAM)', sets out the methodology and relates both to traffic and the environmental appraisal. The framework indicating the impacts on different groups is presented in a similar manner using similar tabulations. Distinction is made between those frameworks that are used at the Preliminary Report stage and the framework used at a Public Inquiry. The former is concerned with the routes from which a choice is to be made and with making a recommendation to the Secretary of State. At a Public Inquiry the Secretary of State has selected his Preferred Route and the framework will show the information on which the selection has been based and the traffic, economic and environmental effects of the choice.	12.3 12.9
Sco.66	Network Evaluation from Surveys and Assignments (NESA) SDD 1986, is used to provide the cost benefit effects.	12.3 12.6
Sco.67	The average accident costs and rates differ in Scotland. Tables Sco.12.2 and Sco.12.3 set out the values that are presently used in NESA86.	12.5
Sco.68	See Table Sco.12.2 (below).	Table 12.2
Sco.69	See Table Sco.12.3 (page 402).	Table 12.3

Table Sco 12.2 [Sco.68]

Description	Road type category	Accident rate (pers. injury/ million veh kms)	Hilliness rises/ falls and bend- iness category	Verge width (m)
Urban	1–10	1.84	–	–
Single carriageway 6 m	11	0.42	1	0.5
Single carriageway 7.3–10 m	12,13	0.42	1	2.0
Dual Carriageway 2–3 lane	14,15	0.28	1	–
Motorway	16–19	0.17	1	–

AVERAGE ACCIDENT RATES USED IN NESA 1986

Table Sco 12.3 [Sco.69]

Accident type	all purpose		motorway	all roads
	urban[1]	rural[2]		
Fatal	103,480	119,020	110,590	111,520
serious injury	5,590	7,620	6,960	6,260
slight injury	700	1,230	1,340	840
average injury	4,210	9,970	9,090	5,870
average damage only	330	390	470	340
average total cost of accidents per personal injury accident (including an allowance for damage only accidents)	6,310	11,790	11,330	7,890

[1]Urban roads are defined for this purpose as those roads (other than motorways) with speed limits of 40 mph or less.

[2]Rural roads are defined for this purpose as those roads (other than motorways) with speed limits of over 40 mph.

ACCIDENTS COSTS FOR DIFFERENT ACCIDENT AND ROAD TYPES (1979 Prices)
Source: SDD (1986) NESA

Annotation No	Comment for Scotland	Main Text Chapter Reference
	CHAPTER 13	
Sco.70	Scottish Development Department (1983): Structure and Local Plans: Circular 32/1983.	13.1 13.5
Sco.71	When an examination in public is required before a structure plan is approved by the Secretary of State or when a public inquiry is called to consider objections to the context of a proposed local plan.	13.4
Sco.72	Roads (Scotland) Act 1984.	13.4 13.5
Sco.73	Acquisition of Land (Authorisation Procedure) (Scotland) Act, 1947.	13.4 13.5
Sco.74	Town and Country Planning (Scotland) Act, 1972.	13.4 13.5
Sco.75	Reporter.	13.4
Sco.76	Scottish Development Department: Public Inquiry Procedures, Circular 14/75 and Memorandum.	13.4 13.5
Sco.77	Town and Country Planning (Inquiries Procedure) (Scotland) Rules 1980 (Statutory Instrument 1980 No 1676).	13.5
	PART 3	
	CHAPTER 14	
Sco.78	Roads (Scotland) Act 1984.	14.3
Sco.79	Town and Country Planning (Scotland) Act, 1972.	14.3

Annotation No	Comment for Scotland	Main Text Chapter Reference
	CHAPTER 15	
Sco.80	The Local Authorities' Traffic Orders (Procedure) (Scotland) Regulations 1969, Statutory Instrument No 1969/487.	15.2 15.14
Sco.81	The Secretary of State's Traffic Orders (Procedure) (Scotland) Regulations 1973, Statutory Instrument No 1973/1121.	15.2 15.14
Sco.82	A similar but not identical process is followed under the Local Authorities Traffic Orders (Procedure) (Scotland) Regulations 1969, with publication being required in the Edinburgh Gazette as well as local newspapers.	15.2
Sco.83	Edinburgh Gazette.	15.2
Sco.84	Section 201 of the Town and Country Planning (Scotland) Act 1972.	15.4 15.9
Sco.85	In Scotland bus stop clearway orders need not be restricted only to 7am to 7pm, other times can apply.	15.5
Sco.86	Scottish Development Department.	15.5
Sco.87	The Local Authorities Traffic Orders (Exemption for Disabled Persons) (Scotland) Regulations 1971, Statutory Instrument No 1971/1521.	15.6 15.14
Sco.88	No restriction in time is applied in Scotland.	15.6
Sco.89	Scottish Development Department (1982): Orange Badge Scheme of Parking Concessions for Disabled and Blind People: Circular No 38/82.	15.6
Sco.90	Section 68 of Roads (Scotland) Act 1984 provides for the roads authority to make an Order stopping up a road which it considers has become dangerous or has or will become unnecessary.	15.8
Sco.91	Section 198 of Town and Country (Planning) Scotland Act 1972.	15.8
Sco.92	It is more common for the Planning Authority in Scotland to make such an order if the road to be stopped up is not a Trunk Road or a Special Road under Section 198A of the Town and Country Planning (Scotland) Act 1972.	15.8
Sco.93	Section 205 of the Town and Country Planning (Scotland) Act 1972.	15.8
Sco.94	Section 199, subject to Section 206 of the Town and Country Planning (Scotland) Act 1972.	15.8
Sco.95	This would be the Planning authority in consultation with the Roads authority under the Town and Country (Planning) Scotland Act 1972, as amended by the Local Government (Miscellaneous Provisions) Scotland Act 1981.	15.9
Sco.96	Local roads authority.	15.10

Annotation No	Comment for Scotland	Main Text Chapter Reference
Sco.97	Under Section 19 of the Civic Government (Scotland) Act 1982, taxi licensing authorities (District and Islands Councils) may appoint and mark out stands for taxis on any road and may erect signs. Before doing so, the authority must consult the trade, give notice to the Chief Constable, and must obtain the consent of the roads authority. It is an offence for any person to cause or permit a vehicle other than a taxi to wait on an appointed taxi stand.	15.10
Sco.98	Cycling is permitted on footpaths and bridleways only if there is a right to do so. However, cycling on a footway is an offence under Section 129 of the Roads (Scotland) Act 1984 unless the footway in question is a cycle track. Statutory powers to convert a footway into a cycle track are contained in the Roads (Scotland) Act 1984.	15.11
Sco.99	A road is a restricted road if there is on it a system of street lighting by lamps not more than 185 metres apart and the road is either an unclassified or a Class C road, or if, by an order under Section 82 and 83 of the Road Traffic Regulation Act 1984, the status of restricted road is imposed.	15.12
Sco.100	185 metres.	15.12
Sco.101	Town and Country Planning (Scotland) Act 1972.	15.14
Sco.102	Scottish Development Department (1982): Orange Badge Scheme of Parking Concessions for Disabled and Blind People: Circular 38/82.	15.14
Sco.103	Roads (Scotland) Act 1984.	15.14
Sco.104	Scottish Development Department (1980): Speed Limits: Circular 18/80.	15.15
Sco.105	Scottish Development Department (1985): Speed Limits: Technical Guidance Letter 1985.	15.15
Sco.106	Scottish Development Department (1982): Illumination and Reflectorisation of Traffic Signs: Technical Memorandum SH4/82.	15.15
Sco.107	Scottish Development Department (1975): Orders for Residents' Parking Schemes: Circular R347.	15.15
Sco.108	Scottish Development Department (1975): Car Parking for the Medical Profession: Circular R348.	15.15
	CHAPTER 16 NIL	
	CHAPTER 17	
Sco.109	Until such time as Sections 36–40 of the Road (Scotland) Act 1984 are brought into operation by a commencement order, speed humps cannot be applied to roads in Scotland.	17.2

Annotation No	Comment for Scotland	Main Text Chapter Reference
	CHAPTER 18	
Sco.110	Scottish Development Department (1983): Road Safety during Installation and Maintenance of Permanent Traffic Signal and Related Equipment on All Purpose Roads: Technical Memorandum No SH5/83.	18.7
	CHAPTER 19	
Sco.111	Scottish Development Department (1986): Scottish Traffic and Environmental Approval Manual [see Sco.63].	19.2 19.6 19.8
Sco.112	Noise Insulation (Scotland) Regulations (1975).	19.5 19.8
	CHAPTER 20	
Sco.113	Scottish Development Department (1980): Type Approval of Traffic Control Equipment: Technical Memorandum SH4/80.	20.17
Sco.114	Scottish Development Department (1973): Criteria for Traffic Light Signals at Junctions: Technical Memorandum SH3/73.	20.17
Sco.115	Scottish Development Department (1970): Area Traffic Control Systems and Improvements of other signal linking systems: Circular R231.	20.17
	CHAPTER 21	
Sco.116	Local roads authority.	21.2
Sco.117	Scottish Development Department: Road Traffic Regulation (Parking) Act 1986: Letter of 29 August 1986.	21.4
Sco.118	Scottish Development Department (1975): Orders for Residents' Parking Schemes: Circular R347.	21.5 21.13
Sco.119	Scottish Development Department (1984): Orange Badge Scheme of Parking Concessions for Disabled and Blind People: Circular 30/84 and letter of 31 May 1984.	21.7 21.13
Sco.120	Scottish Development Department (1975): Car Parking for the Medical Profession: Circular R348.	21.8 21.13
Sco.121	Secretary of State for Scotland.	21.12
Sco.122	Scottish Development Department (1982): Orange Badge Scheme of Parking Concessions for Disabled and Blind People: Circular 38/82.	21.13
Sco.123	Scottish Development Department (1974): Parking Meters and Parking Control Equipment: General Approvals: Circular R325.	21.14
Sco.124	Scottish Development Department (1974): Signs and Traffic Regulation Orders for Restrictions on Lorries: Circular R310.	21.14

Annotation No	Comment for Scotland	Main Text Chapter Reference
Sco.125	Functions of Traffic Wardens (Scotland) Order 1971 (Statutory Instrument 1971 No 374) (S52).	21.14
Sco.126	The Road Traffic (Owner Liability) (Scotland) Regulations 1975 (Statutory Instrument 1975 No 706) (S119).	21.14
	CHAPTER 22	
Sco.127	Scottish Development Department (1980): Speed Limits: Circular 18/80 and Scottish Development Department (1985): Speed Limits: Technical Guidance Letter 1985.	22.2 22.6
Sco.128	Scottish Development Department (1978): Transverse Yellow Bar Markings at Roundabouts: Circular 76/78.	22.7
Sco.129	Speed humps cannot be applied until such time as Sections 36–40 of Road (Scotland) Act 1984 are brought into operation by a commencement order.	22.7
	CHAPTER 23 NIL	
	CHAPTER 24	
Sco.130	Scottish Development Department (1983): Junctions and Accesses: The Layout of Major/Minor Junctions: Technical Memorandum SH8/82.	24.3 24.17
Sco.131	Scottish Development Department (1987): The 'Pelican' Pedestrian Crossing Regulations and General Directions 1987: Circular 2/87. A Technical Memorandum will be issued following publication of TA51/87 and TD28/87 by the Department of Transport.	24.4 24.7 24.17
Sco.132	Scottish Development Department (1981): Design and Operation of Pelican and Zebra Crossings: Technical Memorandum SH5/81 applies at present. Scottish Development Department (1975): School Crossing Patrol Signs: Circular R358.	24.5 24.17
Sco.133	Scottish Development Department (1978): Traffic Signs General Circular 43/78.	24.5 24.17
Sco.134	Speed humps cannot be applied until such time as Sections 36–40 of Roads (Scotland) Act 1984 are brought into operation by a commencement order.	24.6
Sco.135	Scottish Development Department (1982): Pedestrian Facilities at Traffic Signal Installations: Technical Memorandum SH9/82.	24.9
Sco.136	Town and Country Planning (Scotland) Act 1972.	24.11 24.17
Sco.137	Scottish Development Department (1981): Pedestrian and Combined Pedestrian/Cycle Subways: Layout and Dimensions: Technical Memorandum SH7/81.	24.11 24.17

Annotation No	Comment for Scotland	Main Text Chapter Reference
	CHAPTER 25	
Sco.138	Section 129(5) of the Roads (Scotland) Act 1984.	25.2
Sco.139	Town and Country Planning (Scotland) Act 1972.	25.2
Sco.140	Roads (Scotland) Act 1984.	25.4 25.7
Sco.141	Scottish Development Department (1981): Pedestrian and Combined Pedestrian/Cycle Subways: Layout and Dimensions: Technical Memorandum SH7/81.	25.4 25.7
	CHAPTER 26	
Sco.142	Scottish Development Department (1985): Transport Act 1985: Circular 32/85.	26.1 26.9
Sco.143	Bus stop clearway orders need not be restricted only to 7am to 7pm, other time periods can apply.	26.2
Sco.144	Scottish Development Department (1977): Implementation of Bus Priorities: Circular SH5/77.	26.5 26.10
	CHAPTER 27	
Sco.145	Scottish Development Department (1982): Spillages of Hazardous Substances on the Highway: Letter effecting Department of Transport Circular 1/82.	27.9 27.10
Sco.146	Section 59 of Roads (Scotland) Act 1984.	27.9
Sco.147	Roads (Scotland) Act 1984.	27.10
Sco.148	Scottish Development Department (1978): Advisory Link Roads for Goods Vehicles: Circular R410.	27.11
Sco.149	Scottish Development Department (1976): Lorry Routes: Circular R374.	27.11
Sco.150	Scottish Development Department (1975): Traffic Regulation Orders for Restrictions on Lorries: Circular R355.	27.11
Sco.151	Scottish Development Department (1974): Heavy Lorries—Heavy Commercial Vehicles (Controls and Regulations) Act 1973: Circular R309.	27.11
Sco.152	Scottish Development Department (1974): Signs and Traffic Regulation Orders for Restrictions on Lorries: Circular R310.	27.11
	PART 4	
	CHAPTER 28	
Sco.153	District or General Planning Authority.	28.2
Sco.154	In all cases, all neighbours must be notified of a planning application.	28.2
Sco.155	Two months.	28.2

Annotation No	Comment for Scotland	Main Text Chapter Reference
Sco.156	Reporter from Scottish Office Inquiry Reporter Unit.	28.2
Sco.157	Reporter.	28.2
Sco.158	Court of Session.	28.2
Sco.159	Similar procedures do not apply. However, Regional Councils may implement call-in procedures for planning applications.	28.2
Sco.160	The Town and Country Planning (General Development) (Scotland) Order 1981 as amended by the Town and Country Planning General Development (Scotland) (Amendment) (No 2) Order 1985.	28.2
Sco.161	Similar powers exist for the Secretary of State for Scotland.	28.2
Sco.162	Similar consultations are required by the Town and Country Planning (General Development) (Scotland) Order 1981.	28.2
Sco.163	In Scotland similar agreements are provided for by: the Town and Country Planning (Scotland) Act 1972 Section 50; the Roads (Scotland) Act 1984 Section 18; and the Roads (Scotland) Act 1984 Section 48. However, any person (other than a roads authority) who proposes to build a new road or extend an existing road must apply to the local roads authority for 'construction consent' to build it (Section 21, Roads (Scotland) Act 1984). In addition, if the new road is to be associated with a new private housing development then a road bond is also required. If the local roads authority refuse construction consent or apply conditions which the applicant considers unreasonable, the applicant may appeal to the Secretary of State. The local roads authority must adopt a new road when asked to by the developer if it has been built in accordance with the construction consent.	28.3
Sco.164	Town and Country Planning (General Development) (Scotland) Order 1981, Statutory Instrument 1981 No 830 (S86).	28.4
Sco.165	Town and Country Planning (General Development) (Scotland) Amendment (No 2) Order 1985, Statutory Instrument 1985 No 2007.	28.4
Sco.166	Town and Country Planning (Scotland) Act 1972.	28.4
Sco.167	Roads (Scotland) Act 1984.	28.4
	CHAPTER 29 NIL	
	CHAPTER 30	
Sco.168	Scottish Development Department (1986): The Use of Conditions in Planning Permission: Circular 18/1986.	30.9
Sco.169	Scottish Development Department (1983): Structure and Local Plans: Circular 32/1983.	30.9

Annotation No	Comment for Scotland	Main Text Chapter Reference
	CHAPTER 31	
Sco.170	Scottish Development Department (1977): Scottish Housing Handbook No 3—Housing Development: Layout, Roads and Services.	31.1 31.10
Sco.171	Roads (Scotland) Act 1984, on completion of any new road in accordance with the Construction Consent, the local roads authority must adopt it if asked to by the developer (see Sco.160).	31.2
Sco.172	Roads (Scotland) Act 1984.	31.10
	CHAPTER 32	
Sco.173	Scottish Development Department (1983): Junctions and Accesses. The Layout of Major/Minor Junctions: Technical Memorandum SH8/82.	32.2 32.9
	CHAPTER 33 NIL	
	PART 5 CHAPTER 34	
Sco.174	Scottish Development Department.	34.1 34.5
Sco.175	Scottish Development Department (1986): Network Evaluation from Surveys and Assignments.	34.2
Sco.176	Scottish Development Department (1987): Current Technical Memoranda: Technical Memorandum SH 1/87, this lists priced and unpriced memoranda and is revised annually.	34.11
	Requests for copies of unpriced memoranda should be addressed to The Chief Road Engineer, Scottish Development Department, New St Andrew's House, Edinburgh EH1 2SZ—Telephone 031 244 4286 (SH series) or 031 244 4367 (SB series).	
	Requests for copies of priced memoranda should be addressed to The Scottish Office Library, Official Publications Section (Sales), Room 2/65, New St Andrew's House, Edinburgh EH1 3SZ—Telephone 031 244 4806— and should be accompanied by the appropriate remittance (cheques payable to The Scottish Office).	
	CHAPTER 35	
Sco.177	Scottish Development Department (1983): Structure and Local Plans: Circular R32/1983. Unitary Development Plans do not apply in Scotland. Planning Advice Note No 30 gives guidance on the handling of road proposals in Local Plans.	35.1 35.7
Sco.178	Scottish Development Department (1981): Development Control, Circular 24/81 (Partially replaced by Circular 6/84): Local Government and Planning (Scotland) Act 1982.	35.1 35.7

Annotation No	Comment for Scotland	Main Text Chapter Reference
Sco.179	Where the local roads authority is not the planning authority they must apply for planning permission in the normal manner and have their application considered by the district planning authority; this would be the case in Central, Fife, Grampian, Lothian, Strathclyde and Tayside. Where the local roads authority is also the planning authority, as in Borders, Dumfries and Galloway, or Highland Regions and Orkney, Shetland or Western Isles, they proceed under the Town and Country Planning (Development by Planning Authorities) (Scotland) Regulations 1981 and 1984 [Sco.191 and 192]. In these circumstances the local road authority give notice of their intention to construct a road and if there are no objections within the specified period then planning permission is deemed to be granted by the Secretary of State. If objections are received then the local roads authority must give notice to the Secretary of State of their intention to carry out the proposed development along with details of consultations they have carried out and the representations received. The Secretary of State can then require an application for planning permission to be made to him if he considers it necessary; if not, planning permission is deemed to have been granted by him at the expiry of a 28 day period.	35.1
Sco.180	There is no annual Roads White Paper for Scotland. 'Policy for Scottish Roads' which is prepared from time to time, and the current roads programme should be consulted.	35.2
Sco.181	Similar powers exist under the Town and Country Planning (General Development) (Scotland) Order 1981.	35.2
Sco.182	Planning authorities are required to consult with the Secretary of State (Article 13(1)(a) of the Town and Country Planning (General Development) (Scotland) Order 1981) before granting planning permission for a proposed development which lies within 67 metres of the middle of an existing or proposed trunk road or includes the formation, laying out or alteration of any means of access to such a road. Where the Secretary of State, on being consulted, has advised against the granting of planning permission and the authority is minded to grant consent; or he has recommended conditions which the planning authority do not propose to attach to the permission, then the Secretary of State must be notified. The applications will then be considered in all its aspects and a decision taken as to whether or not the application should be called in for the Secretary of State's decision (SDD Circular 24/1981).	35.2
Sco.183	Scottish Development Department on behalf of the Secretary of State for Scotland.	35.2
Sco.184	Town and Country Planning (Scotland) Act 1972.	35.2 35.7
Sco.185	Similar powers exist in the Roads (Scotland) Act 1984, Section 104, and Acquisition of Land (Authorisation Procedure) (Scotland) Act 1947.	35.3
Sco.186	Scottish Development Department (1976): Compulsory Purchase Procedures—Compulsory Purchase of Land (Scotland) Regulations 1976: Circular 42/1976.	35.3 35.7

Annotation No	Comment for Scotland	Main Text Chapter Reference
Sco.187	Secretary of State for Scotland under the Roads (Scotland) Act 1984.	35.6
Sco.188	A similar but not identical process is followed in Scotland (see also Sco.177 and 180).	35.6 Fig 35.1 Fig 35.2 Fig 35.3
Sco.189	The Town and Country Planning (General) (Scotland) Regulations 1976, Statutory Instrument 1976 No 2022.	35.7
Sco.190	The Town and Country Planning (General Development) (Scotland) Order 1981, Statutory Instrument 1981 No 830.	35.7
Sco.191	The Town and Country Planning (General Development) (Scotland) Amendment (No 2) Order 1985, Statutory Instrument 1985 No 2007.	35.7
Sco.192	Roads (Scotland) Act 1984; Part III: Sections 19 and 20: Construction of New Roads, Part IX: Sections 103–105: Land Acquisition Powers for construction and improvement of roads.	35.7
Sco.193	Land Compensation (Scotland) Act 1973.	35.7
Sco.194	The Town and Country Planning (Development by Planning Authorities) (Scotland) Regulations 1981 (Statutory Instrument 1981 No 829).	35.7
Sco.195	The Town and Country Planning (Development by Planning Authorities) (Scotland) (Amendment Regulations) 1984 (Statutory Intrument 1984 No 238).	35.7
Sco.196	Scottish Development Department Leaflets: Road Schemes Affecting Property (1975), Public Inquiries into Roads Proposals (1976). Scottish Office Leaflets: Road Compensation: your rights explained, Insulation against traffic noise (1976), Compensation: A guide for house owners and tenants (1979).	35.8
	CHAPTER 36	
Sco.197	Scottish Development Department (1985): Traffic Flows and Carriageway Width Assessment for Urban and Rural Roads: Technical Memorandum SH9/86.	36.1 Table 36.1 36.9 36.10
Sco.198	Scottish Development Department.	36.1
Sco.199	Scottish Development Department (1982): Design Standards for Road Layout and Geometry: Highway Link Design: Technical Memorandum SH3/82 and Amendment 1 (1985), Amendment 2 (1986) and Addendum 1 (1986).	36.1 36.10
Sco.200	Scottish Development Department (1986): Safety Fences and Barriers: Technical Memorandum SH3/86.	36.9

Annotation No	Comment for Scotland	Main Text Chapter Reference
Sco.201	Scottish Development Department (1986): Network Evaluation from Surveys and Assignments.	36.10
	CHAPTER 37	
Sco.202	Scottish Development Department (1982): Design Standards for Road Layout and Geometry: Highway Link Design: Technical Memorandum SH3/82 and Amendment 1 (1985), Amendment 2 (1986) and Addendum 1 (1986).	37.1, 37.2, 37.3, 37.5, 37.9
	CHAPTER 38	
Sco.203	Scottish Development Department (1977): Roundabout Design: Technical Memorandum SH9/77 and Addendum 1 (1979).	38.3 38.5
Sco.204	Scottish Development Department (1980): Design of Major/Minor Priority Road Junctions: Technical Memorandum SH2/80.	38.3 38.5
Sco.205	Scottish Development Department (1986): Network Evaluation from Surveys and Assignments.	38.4 38.5
Sco.206	Scottish Development Department (1983): Junctions and Accesses: The Layout of Major/Minor Junctions: Technical Memorandum SH8/82.	38.6
	CHAPTER 39	
Sco.207	Scottish Development Department (1983): Junctions and Accesses: The Layout of Major/Minor Junctions: Technical Memorandum SH8/82.	39.1 39.2 39.3 39.6
Sco.208	Scottish Development Department (1977): Roundabout Design Technical Memorandum SH9/77 and Addendum 1 (1979).	39.6
Sco.209	Scottish Development Department (1980): Design of Major/Minor Priority Road Junctions: Technical Memorandum SH2/80.	39.6
	CHAPTER 40	
Sco.210	Scottish Development Department (1977): Roundabout Design: Technical Memorandum SH9/77 and Addendum 1 (1979).	40.1 40.6
Sco.211	Scottish Development Department (1982): Design Standards for Road Layout and Geometry: Highway Link Design: Technical Memorandum SH3/82 and Amendment 1 (1985), Amendment 2 (1986), and Addendum 1 (1986).	40.7
	CHAPTER 41	
Sco.212	Scottish Development Department.	41.3, 41.5
Sco.213	Scottish Development Department (1973): Criteria for Traffic Light Signals at Junctions: Technical Memorandum SH6/73 and Scottish Development Department (1973): Criteria for Traffic Light Signals: Circular R287.	41.3 41.6 41.14

Annotation No	Comment for Scotland	Main Text Chapter Reference
Sco.214	Scottish Development Department (1982): Pedestrian Facilities at Traffic Signal Installations: Technical Memorandum SH9/82.	41.3 41.6 41.14
Sco.215	Scottish Development Department (1984): Traffic Signals on High Speed Roads: Technical Memorandum SH2/84.	41.3 41.14
Sco.216	Scottish Development Department (1974): Portable Traffic Signals for use at Roadworks: Circular R323 and Scottish Development Department (1976): Portable Traffic Signals for use at Roadworks: Circular R362.	41.3 41.8 41.14
Sco.217	Scottish Development Department (1980): Type Approval for Traffic Control Equipment: Circular SH4/80.	41.3 41.15
Sco.218	Scottish Development Department (1970): Area Traffic Control Systems and Improvements of Other Signal Linking Systems: Circular R231.	41.3 41.15
Sco.219	Scottish Development Department (1983): Road Safety During Installation and Maintenance of Permanent Traffic Signals and Related Equipment on All Purpose Roads: Technical Memorandum SH5/83.	41.3 41.15
Sco.220	Scottish Development Department (1986): Maintenance of Traffic Signals on All Purpose Trunk Roads: Technical Memorandum SH12/86.	41.3 41.15
	CHAPTER 42 NIL	
	CHAPTER 43	
Sco.221	Scottish Development Department Circulars, Letters and Technical Memoranda.	41.15 43.1
Sco.222	50,000 visitors, and in accordance with criteria set out in Scottish Development Department Circular 17/83 [Sco.227].	43.3
Sco.223	Brown background signs are not applied in Scotland. On motorways tourist attractions with over 50,000 visitors would be blue background, white border, symbol, legend and route number.	43.3
Sco.224	Tourist Attractions: Brown background signs are not applied. On roads, other than motorways, the signs have white background, blue border, symbol, legend and mileage. The thistle symbol is used to denote a tourist attraction. A limited number of other approved symbols are also permitted.	43.3
Sco.225	Scottish Development Department (1975); Size, Design and Mounting of Traffic Signs: Circular R332 (Joint Circular with Department of Transport).	43.1 43.7
Sco.226	Scottish Development Department (1984): Town and Country Planning (Control of Advertisements) (Scotland) Regulations 1984: Circular 10/84.	43.1 43.7
Sco.227	Scottish Development Department (1983): Signposting: Report of Scottish Tourist Boards Working Party: Circular 17/83.	43.1 43.7

Annotation No	Comment for Scotland	Main Text Chapter Reference
Sco.228	Scottish Development Department (1985): Signposting of Tourist Facilities and Tourist Attractions: Signposting of Historic Properties: Circular 29/85.	43.1 43.7
Sco.229	Scottish Development Department (1986): Signposting of Tourist Attractions and Facilities: Circular 29/86.	43.1 43.7
Sco.230	Scottish Development Department (1982): Illumination and Reflectorisation of Traffic Signs: Technical Memorandum SH4/82.	43.1 43.7
Sco.231	Scottish Development Department (1986): Reflecting Road Studs: Technical Memorandum SH5/86.	43.1 43.8
Sco.232	Scottish Development Department (1984): The Traffic Signs (Amendment) Regulations and General Directions: Circular 23/84.	43.1 43.8
Sco.233	Scottish Development Department (1983): The Traffic Signs (Amendment) Regulations and General Directions: Circular 2/83.	43.1 43.8
Sco.234	Scottish Development Department (1981): Revision of Traffic Signs Regulations and General Directions: Circular 26/81.	43.1 43.8
Sco.235	Scottish Development Department (1982): Traffic Signs and Safety Measures for Minor Works and Minor Roads: Technical Memorandum SH2/82.	43.1 43.8
Sco.236	Scottish Development Department (1986): Criteria for the Use of Gantries for Traffic Signals on Trunk Roads and Trunk Road Motorways: Technical Memorandum SH8/86.	43.1 43.8
Sco.237	Scottish Development Department (1972): Street Name Plates and House Numbering: Circular R254.	43.1 43.8

46 Application in Wales

46.1 Introduction

The general principles described in this manual and most of the legislative and procedural arrangements are applicable in Wales. However, it is the usual practice for the Welsh Office to issue its own, often equivalent, Circulars and there are in addition certain matters where practice or standards in Wales are different.

These points are indicated by the annotation [Wa.1] [Wa.2] etc. in the text and advice on practice for Wales is given in 46.2 below.

Inquiries for more detailed information should be addressed to:

Welsh Office
Highways Directorate
Phase 1
Government Buildings
Ty Glas Road
Llanishen
Cardiff
CF4 5PL
Telephone: 0222 753271

46.2 List of Detailed References

Annotation No.	Comment for Wales	Main Text Chapter Reference
Wa.1	In Wales TPPs are not required to be submitted to the Welsh Office Highways Directorate but many County Councils still prepare them and make them available. As there are only 8 local highway authorities in Wales, close liaison can be achieved in order to obtain necessary information.	3.4
Wa.2	WO Circular 193/73, Local Transport Grants.	3.4, 4.2
Wa.3	WO Circular 43/84, Memorandum on Structure and Local Plans.	3.7
Wa.4	WO Circular 104/73, Local Transport Grants.	3.7
Wa.5	Not applicable to Wales.	3.8
Wa.6	WO Circular 138/78. Inner Urban Areas Act 1978.	4.2
Wa.7	WO Circular 138/78, Inner Urban Areas Act 1978.	4.4
Wa.8	Not applicable to Wales.	4.5
Wa.9	WO Circular 4/84, Orange Badge Scheme of Parking Concessions for Disabled and Blind People.	15.6, 15.15
Wa.10	In Wales, District Councils may also make such Orders with the consent of the County Council.	15.10
Wa.11	WO Circular 49/82.	15.14
Wa.12	WO Circular 57/84 and WO Circular 63/84.	15.15
Wa.13	WO Circular 3/86, Cycle Tracks Act 1984.	15.14

Annotation No.	Comment for Wales	Main Text Chapter Reference
Wa.14	WO Circular 47/83, Speed Limits.	15.15
Wa.15	WO Circular 10/80, Local Speed Limits.	15.15
Wa.16	WO Circular 107/85, Car Parking for the Medical Profession.	15.15
Wa.17	WO Circular 214/74, Resident Parking Schemes.	15.15
Wa.18	'and the Welsh Office Highways Directorate'	18.5
Wa.19	WO Circular 80/75, Duty of Local Authorities to Promote Road Safety.	18.7
Wa.20	WO Circular 39/86, Road Traffic Regulation (Parking) Act.	21.13
Wa.21	WO Circular 214/74, Resident Parking Schemes.	21.13
Wa.22	WO Circular 4/84, Orange Badge Scheme of Parking Concessions for Disabled and Blind People.	21.13
Wa.23	WO Circular 57/84, Parking for Disabled People.	21.13
Wa.24	WO Circular 107/75, Car Parking for the Medical Profession.	21.13
Wa.25	WO Circular 27/85, Parking Meters: General Approval.	21.14
Wa.26	WO Circular 164/78.	21.14
Wa.27	WO Circular 140/74, Definition of Goods Vehicles in Parking Place Orders.	21.14
Wa.28	WO Circular 152/74, Parking Meters and Parking Control Equipment: General Approval.	21.14
Wa.29	WO Circular 245/72, Disc Parking.	21.14
Wa.30	WO Circular 10/80, Local Speed Limits.	22.6
Wa.31	WO Circular 47/83, Speed Limits.	22.6
Wa.32	WO Circular 52/86, Road Humps.	22.7
Wa.33	WO Circular 167/78, Transverse Yellow Bar Markings at Roundabouts.	22.7
Wa.34	WO Circular 179/75, School Crossing Patrol Signs.	24.17
Wa.35	WO Circular 132/78, Traffic Signs.	24.17
Wa.36	Only a letter of guidance issued in Wales, Nov 1986.	24.17
Wa.37	WO Circular 56/85, Transport Act 1985.	26.9
Wa.38	WO Circular 155/73, Bus Operation in Residential and Industrial Areas.	26.9
Wa.39	WO Circular 36/82, Spillages of Hazardous Substances on the Highway.	27.10

Annotation No.	Comment for Wales	Main Text Chapter Reference
Wa.40	WO Circular 24/82, Lorry Controls.	27.11
Wa.41	WO Circular 54/78, Advisory Link Roads for Goods Vehicles.	27.11
Wa.42	WO Circular 46/83, Town and Country Planning Act 1971—Planning Gain.	28.5
Wa.43	WO Circular 2/85, The use of Conditions in Planning Permission.	30.9
Wa.44	WO Circular 43/84, Memorandum on Structure and Local Plans.	30.9
Wa.45	WO Circular 46/83, Town and Country Planning Act 1971—Planning Gain.	30.9
Wa.46	WO Circular 155/73, Bus Operation in Residential and Industrial Areas.	32.9
Wa.47	Letter of Guidance issued in Wales.	33.7
Wa.48	WO Guidance 43/84, Memorandum on Structure and Local Plans.	35.7
Wa.49	WO Guidance 2/81, Development Plans Direction.	35.7
Wa.50	WO Circular 11/87, Compulsory Purchase Orders Procedures.	35.7
Wa.51	Issued by letter in Wales.	35.7
Wa.52	These two leaflets available with Welsh Translation.	35.8
Wa.53	Welsh Version of Traffic Signs Regulations 1985.	39.6
Wa.54	WO Circular 73/78, Conversion of Large Conventional Roundabouts to Small and Mini Layouts.	40.7
Wa.55	Issue of Specifications by Welsh Office, Highways Directorate.	41.3
Wa.56	WO Circular 64/73, Criteria for Traffic Signals at Junctions.	41.14
Wa.57	WO Circular 207/75, Portable Traffic Signals for Use at Roadworks.	41.14
Wa.58	Indication that joint Circulars are issued by DTp, SDD and WO.	43.1
Wa.59	The Traffic Signs (Welsh and English Language Provisions) Regulations and General Directions 1985 (Statutory Instrument 1985/713).	43.7
Wa.60	The Traffic Signs Manual is not solely produced by DTp, but jointly with SDD and WO.	43.7
Wa.61	WO Circular 54/75, Size, Design and Mounting of Traffic Signs.	43.7
Wa.62	WO Circular 18/84, Town and Country Planning (Control of Advertisements) Regulations 1984.	43.7
Wa.63	WO Circular 26/86, Tourist Attraction Signing.	43.7

Annotation No.	Comment for Wales	Main Text Chapter Reference
Wa.64	WO Circular 58/84, Reflecting Road Studs.	43.8
Wa.65	WO Circular 14/83, The Traffic Signs (Amendment) Regulations and General Directions.	43.8
Wa.66	WO Circular 38/84, The Traffic Signs (Amendment) Regulations and General Directions.	43.8
Wa.67	WO Circular 23/78, Street Name Plates and Numbering of Premises.	43.8

Printed in the United Kingdom for Her Majesty's Stationery Office
Dd240128 10/87 C100 G443 10170